THE OUTLINE OF KNOWLEDGE

EDITED BY

JAMES A. RICHARDS

CHEMISTRY
By William Allen Hamor—Introduction by Professor Charles Baskerville

PHYSICS
By George Matthew

ELECTRICITY
By Professor Wm. J. Moore

MEDICINE
By Dr. Theodore H. Allen

MATHEMATICS
By L. Leland Locke

VOLUME VIII

J. A. RICHARDS, INC.
NEW YORK

Copyright 1924
J. A. RICHARDS, INC.
MANUFACTURED IN U. S. A.

Typesetting, Paper, Printing, Binding and Cloth
By THE KINGSPORT PRESS
Kingsport, Tenn.

CONTENTS

PART ONE

CHEMISTRY

CHAPTER		PAGE
X	The Atomic Theory and the Work of Davy	1
XI	Berzelius and the Development of the Atomic Theory	15
XII	The Development of Organic Chemistry	28
XIII	Valence, the Constitution of Organic Compounds, and the Development of Stereo-Chemistry	41
XIV	Progress in Inorganic Chemistry during the Modern Period	51
XV	The Atomic Weights and the Periodic Law	63
XVI	The Development of Applied Chemistry	84

PART TWO

PHYSICS

I	An Analysis of Matter	99
II	Radio-Activity	107
III	The Properties of Matter	112
IV	Heat	129
V	The Sources of Light	139
VI	The Speed of Light	145
VII	Reflection and Refraction	152
VIII	The Nature of Light	163
IX	Sound	176

PART THREE

ELECTRICITY

I	The Nature of Electricity	191
II	Electrostatics—Atmospheric Electricity	200
III	Fundamental Discoveries	212
IV	Electro-Magneto Machinery	221

CONTENTS

CHAPTER		PAGE
V	The Development of Power Transmission	234
VI	The History of Electric Lighting	243
VII	The Development of Electro-Chemistry	257
VIII	The Telephone	265
IX	Electric Railways	277
X	The Electro-Magnetic Telegraph	286
XI	Wireless Telegraphy and Telephony	298

PART FOUR

MEDICINE

I	The Ancients	313
II	The Greeks	327
III	The Romans	339
IV	Byzantine and Arabian Schools	347
V	The Close of Medievalism	358
VI	The Century of Schools	369
VII	The Period of Systematization	386
VIII	The Contributions of the Practitioner	397
IX	Nineteenth-Century Theories	408
X	Modern Treatment of Disease	415
XI	Modern Physiology	424

PART FIVE

MATHEMATICS

	Introduction	439
I	Number	447
II	Calculation	468
III	Analytic Geometry	483

CHEMISTRY

CHAPTER X

(Continued from Volume VII)

THE ATOMIC THEORY AND THE WORK OF DAVY

The first of the observations of Dalton which furnished the experimental basis for the atomic theory consisted in the determination of the composition of two hybrides of carbon. Dalton writes: "It was in the summer of 1804 that I collected at various times and in various places the inflammable gas [marsh gas] obtained from ponds." He found that marsh gas, like olefiant gas (ethylene), contains nothing but carbon and hydrogen, and that these two substances, termed light and heavy carburetted hydrogen, respectively, showed a simple multiple ratio between the weights of the constituent elements, namely:

In carburetted hydrogen from stagnant water, 4.3 of carbon were combined with 2 of hydrogen.

In olefiant gas, 4.3 of carbon were combined with 1 of hydrogen.

This regularity induced him to investigate other compounds in the same direction; thus, in the case of carbonic oxide and carbonic acid he found that, for the same amount of carbon, the ratios of oxygen present in these were again respectively, as 1: 2. His conviction that there must be a law underlying these simple relations scarcely necessitated any further accretion after he had encountered similar simple numerical proportions in the results of his analysis of nitrous oxide, nitric oxide, nitrous acid and nitric acid—*i.e.*, the anhydrides of the two last—and the oxygen compounds of sulphur. He had, therefore, demonstrated that when different quantities of one element combined chemically with one and the same quantity of another, these amounts stood in a simple relation to one another—a relation which could be expressed by whole numbers. The "law of multiple proportions" was thus discovered; it had, indeed, been deduced from experiments which were of necessity not very exact, but this was to be expected from the condition of analytical chemistry at that time.

Dalton next sought an explanation of the numerical relations he had discovered, and this was afforded him by the atomic hypothesis. For instance, he had but to assume that in carbon monoxide one atom of carbon was combined with one of oxygen, and in carbonic acid one atom of carbon was united to two of oxygen. Upon this basis Dalton erected his Atomic Theory, which may be detailed from statements in his "New System of Chemical Philosophy" (1808-1810), as follows:

1. All bodies of sensible magnitude are constituted of a vast number of extremely small particles or atoms of matter bound together by a force of attraction, which, as it endeavors to prevent their separation, is called attraction of cohesion; but as it collects them from a dispersed state is called attraction of aggregation, or, more simply, affinity.

2. The ultimate particles of all homogeneous bodies are perfectly alike in weight, figure, etc. In other words, every particle of water is like every other particle of water, every particle of hydrogen is like every other particle of hydrogen, etc.

3. No new creation or destruction of matter is within the reach of chemical agency. All the elements we can produce consist in separating particles that are in a state of cohesion or combination and joining those that were previously at a distance.

4. The ultimate particles of all simple bodies are atoms incapable of further division. These atoms (at least viewed along with their atmospheres of heat) are all spheres, and are possessed of particular weights which may be denoted by number.

5. If there are two bodies which are disposed to combine, then their combination takes place by atoms.

6. In an elastic gas each particle occupies the center of a comparatively large sphere and supports its dignity by keeping all the rest, which by their gravity, or otherwise, are disposed to encroach upon it, at a respectful distance.

The method by which Dalton determined the relative atomic weights from the proportions by weight in which the elements unite to form compounds, falls next to be described.

To accomplish this the first thing necessary was to settle the number of atoms in a compound. According to Dalton, this number is to be sought for, in general, in the simplest possible ratios. In estimating it, he started from the following principles:

1. When only one compound of two elements is known, this is composed of an atom of the second order.

2. When two compounds are known, the one consists of an atom of the second and the other of an atom of the third order.

3. When three compounds are known, one atom of the second and two atoms of the third order must be assumed.

How did Dalton now proceed to the determination of the atomic weights—*i.e.*, the relative weights of the smallest particles? In the first place it was necessary to choose a unit for comparison. As unit he assumed hydrogen with the atomic weight = 1, and he referred all the other atomic weights to this. To fix the others, he then applied his first principle. At that time only one compound each of oxygen and of nitrogen with hydrogen was known, viz., water and ammonia, respectively; therefore, the atomic weights of oxygen and nitrogen can be determined directly from the composition of these compounds. In this way Dalton found them to be 7 and 5, respectively. He checked the numbers so obtained by the proportions of the oxygen and nitrogen in the oxygen compounds of nitrogen. He was acquainted with four of the latter. In nitric oxide he found 7 parts of oxygen for 5 of nitrogen; its atom was, therefore, the atom of the second order, derived from these elements. In nitric acid, according to his view, there were 14 parts of oxygen for 5 of nitrogen, or two atoms of the former gas for one of the latter. In nitrous oxide, 7 parts of oxygen were combined with 10 parts of nitrogen, and in this he therefore assumed two atoms of nitrogen and one of oxygen. Nitrous acid, however, is supposed to contain 10½ parts of oxygen for 5 of nitrogen, and in it he might have assumed two atoms of nitrogen and three of oxygen. He preferred, however, to regard this substance as a compound of nitric acid and nitric oxide.

Likewise, he found in ethylene 5.4 parts of carbon for 1 of hydrogen, and in marsh gas the same quantity of carbon for 2 of hydrogen. On this account he regarded ethylene as consisting of atoms of the second order, and assumed the atomic weight of carbon to be 5.4. Carbonic oxide likewise consisted of atoms of the second order, since he found in it 7 parts of oxygen for 5.4 of carbon, while carbonic anhydride had atoms of the third order, because it contains 14 parts of oxygen for 5.4 of carbon.

As the analytical methods Dalton employed were liable to many sources of error, it was out of the question that the results he obtained could be accurate. However, he it was who propounded the principle of the determination of the combining weights of the elements, and this work brought him everlasting fame.

Dalton's atomic theory, generally speaking, was favorably received by chemists. Thomas Thomson (1773-1852), who founded the first chemical laboratory for general instruction in Great Britain while professor in the University of Glasgow, became its devoted supporter, and his "System of Chemistry" (1807) made it known to the general public. In 1808, Thomson supplied an observation of his own in support of the law of multiple proportions.

To quote his own inference:

"It appears that there are two oxalates of strontian, the first obtained by saturating oxalic acid with strontian water, the second by mixing together oxalate of ammonia and muriate [chloride] of strontian. It is remarkable that the first contains just double the proportion of base contained in the second." He also investigated the potash salts of oxalic acid.

"Oxalate of potash readily crystallizes in flat rhomboids, commonly terminated by dihedral summits. The lateral edges of the prism are usually beveled. At the temperature of 60° it dissolves in thrice its weight of water. . . . The salt combines with an excess of acid and forms a super-oxalate, long known by the name of salt of sorrel. The acid contained in this salt is very nearly double of what is contained in oxalate of potash. Suppose 100 parts of potash; if the weight of acid necessary to convert this quantity into oxalate be x, then 2x will convert it into super-oxalate."

Similar research was done by W. H. Wollaston (1766-1828), who, by experiment, found that in the two compounds termed "subcarbonate of potash" and "carbonate of potash," the proportions of carbonic acid relatively to the same amount of potash were as 1:2. He also showed that "super-sulphate" (bisulphate) of potash contains "exactly twice as much acid as is necessary for the mere saturation of the alkali present." These contributions proved the applicability of the law for salts, and the importance of the relation thus made evident was, in general, realized by the chemists of the day.

Dalton's attempts at a graphic presentment of the ultimate particles of various substances must not be forgotten. The symbols he used to represent the atoms of the elements and to indicate the constitution of chemical compounds, as well as his relative weight values, are here given. This system of notation never came into general use owing to the introduction of a simpler system by Berzelius some time afterward.

Fig.	Rel. wt.	Fig.	Rel. wt.
1. Hydrogen	1	11. Strontites	46
2. Azote	5	12. Barytes	68
3. Carbone or Charcoal	5	13. Iron	38
4. Oxygen	7	14. Zinc	56
5. Phosphorus	9	15. Copper	56
6. Sulphur	13	16. Lead	95
7. Magnesia	20	17. Silver	100
8. Lime	23	18. Platina	100
9. Soda	28	19. Gold	140
10. Potash	42	20. Mercury	167

21. An atom of water or steam, composed of 1 of oxygen and 1 of hydrogen, retained in physical contact by a strong affinity, and supposed to be surrounded by a common atmosphere of heat 8
22. An atom of ammonia, composed of 1 of azote and 1 of hydrogen 6
23. An atom of nitrous gas, 1 azote + 1 oxygen 12

24. An atom of olefiant gas, 1 carbone + 1 hydrogen............ 6
25. An atom of carbonic oxide, 1 carbone + 1 oxygen........... 12
26. An atom of nitrous oxide, 2 azote + 1 oxygen............... 17
27. An atom of nitric acid, 1 azote + 2 oxygen................. 19
28. An atom of carbonic acid, 1 carbone + 2 oxygen............ 19
29. An atom of carburetted hydrogen, 1 carbone + 2 hydrogen... 16
30. An atom of oxynitric acid, 1 azote + 3 oxygen.............. 26
31. An atom of sulphuric acid, 1 sulphur + 3 oxygen............ 34
32. An atom of sulphuretted hydrogen, 1 sulphur + 3 hydrogen... 16
33. An atom of alcohol, 3 carbone + 1 hydrogen................. 16
34. An atom of nitrous acid, 1 nitric acid + 1 nitrous gas........ 31
35. An atom of acetous acid, 2 carbone + 2 water............... 26
36. An atom of nitrate of ammonia, 1 nitric acid + 1 ammonia + 1 water 33
37. An atom of sugar, 1 alcohol + 1 carbonic acid.............. 35

It is now necessary to discuss the position which Davy and Gay-Lussac, among others, held respecting Dalton's atomic theory, as well as to narrate their services to chemistry in general.

Humphry Davy, the son of an engraver, was born at Penzance in 1778. The family circumstances were somewhat impecunious, and at the age of seventeen he was apprenticed to a surgeon-apothecary in his native town. At the age of twenty he was placed in charge of the laboratory of the Pneumatic Institute at Bristol, founded by Beddoes for the application of gases to the treatment of diseases. Davy's environments here were most propitious for a successful career of scientific research. His laboratory was well furnished, and was supported by the subscriptions of scientific men. He had plenty of time at his disposal, and the age was one of discovery and rapid progress in the science. His experiments related chiefly to nitrogen monoxide, or nitrous oxide, and in a short time he published his "Researches Chemical and Philosophical, chiefly concerning Nitrous Oxide and its Respiration." His courage and his determination were well proved by these experiments. The effects of this gas, supposed to be poisonous, were tried upon himself. He discovered its anesthetic action. He then subjected himself similarly to the action of hydrogen, nitrogen, and carbonic acid. In 1801, Davy left Bristol to become a lecturer at the Royal Institution, and two years later was elected Fellow of the Royal Society. He was soon a necessary figure in the fashionable life of the day; his auditors at the Royal Institution were numbered by the thousand; his name was on everybody's lips. It was Coleridge who said, "I attend Davy's lectures to increase my stock of metaphors." He was knighted in 1811 and created baronet in 1812. A terrible mining disaster at Felling brought him an invitation from the governors

CHEMISTRY

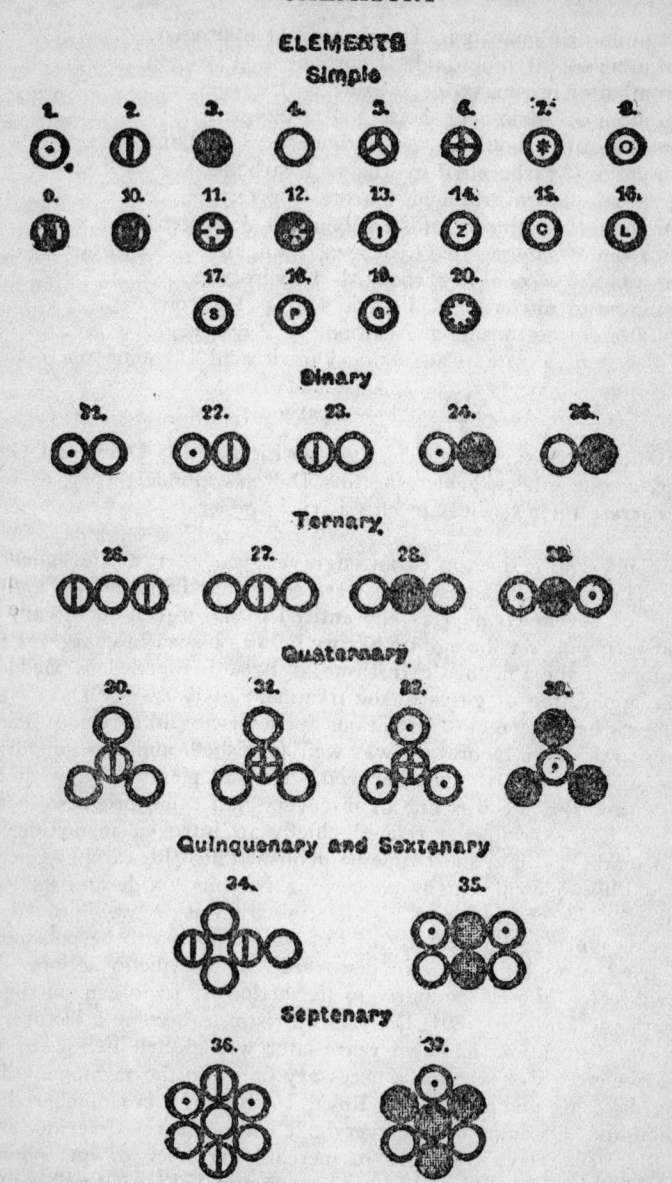

ELEMENTS

Simple

Binary

Ternary

Quaternary

Quinquenary and Sextenary

Septenary

Fig. 20 DALTON'S GRAPHIC PRESENTMENT OF THE ELEMENTS.

ATOMIC THEORY—WORK OF DAVY

of the mine to investigate the conditions of such occurrences, and after an extended investigation into the nature of marsh gas in its different admixtures with air, he projected his well-known safety lamp. This is but one instance out of many of his scientific insight being turned to material advantage. Davy was elected President of the Royal Society in 1820, and died at Geneva in 1829.

At the Royal Institution Davy had at his command an excellent electric battery, and, as he had for some time considered that the most-needed step in chemistry was the decomposition of some of the substances then regarded as elementary, he thought that this was the most promising means for the solution of the question.

In 1790 Galvani made his well-known experiment, and ten years later Volta invented his electric cell. These were important elements in the inquiry which went to correlate chemical and electrical phenomena, and the perception that a close relation existed between electrical force and chemical reaction spread rapidly at the beginning of the nineteenth century, after the decomposition of water into its constituents by the galvanic current had been proved by Nicholson and Carlisle in (1800), and that of salts into their bases and acids by Berzelius and Hisinger (in 1803). The most important of the many and varied observations on the deportment of chemical compounds when subjected to the action of the current, however, were made by Davy, and his discoveries entitle him to be regarded as the pioneer of electrochemistry, as well as one of the most brilliant chemists the world has ever seen.

Davy was among the first to investigate the question of the decomposition of water. This work was begun in 1800. In his Bakerian lecture delivered before the Royal Society in 1806, the subject of which was, "On Some Chemical Agencies of Electricity," is found an investigation concerning the products of the electrolysis of water. Besides hydrogen and oxygen there were also formed acid and alkali. Davy states this as a fact:

"The appearance of acid and alkaline matter in water acted on by a current of electricity at the opposite electrified metallic surfaces was observed in the first chemical experiments made with the column of Volta."

The problem requiring solution then was to ascertain whether the acid and alkali were derived from the water, and if not, whence they came. Davy therefore proceeded to carry out this electrolysis in vessels of various materials, and showed that the products mentioned, the acid and alkali, were due to the glass, or to the matter dissolved in the water, or to the air itself. If the water, distilled in silver, was electrolyzed in gold vessels, in an atmosphere of hydrogen, the acid and alkali did not appear. To give his own description:

"I repeated the experiment under more conclusive circumstances.

I arranged the apparatus as before [gold cones and water distilled in silver vessels]; I exhausted the receiver and filled it with hydrogen gas from a convenient air-holder; I made a second exhaustion and again introduced hydrogen that had been carefully prepared. The process was conducted for twenty-four hours, and at the end of this time neither of the portions of the water altered in the slightest degree the tint of litmus. It seems evident then that water chemically pure is decomposed by electricity into gaseous matter alone, into oxygen and hydrogen."

He next investigated the decomposition of salt solutions, and found confirmation of the statements of Berzelius and Hisinger. But he proceeded with still greater circumspection, and sought to follow up the phenomena more exactly. All the means were at his command, and he did not hesitate to avail himself of them.

Direct observation proved to Davy that hydrogen, the alkalies, the metals, etc., are separated by means of the current at the negative pole, and oxygen and the acids at the positive pole. From this he concluded that the former substances possess a positive, while oxygen and the acids possess a negative electrical energy; that in this case, as usual, the oppositely electrified bodies attract each other; and that, in consequence, the positive substances separate at the negative pole, and vice versa. In this assumption Davy had arrived at an explanation of the phenomena of decomposition observed in the galvanic circuit. But he proceeded a step further, and endeavored to refer all chemical combination and decomposition to similar causes.

According to him the heat observed in certain cases of decomposition were manifestations of electricity.

On November 19, 1807, Davy delivered an account to the Royal Society of his most recent work on the nature of the alkalies. He had made an attempt to decompose them by the electrolysis of their aqueous solutions, but without success; he had then passed a powerful current through solid potash fused over a flame, and had observed most intense light at the negative pole, due probably to the combustion of the element he was seeking. And his next experiment was decisive; to give his own description: "A small piece of pure potash, which had been exposed for a few seconds to the atmosphere, so as to give conducting power to the surface, was placed upon an insulated dish of platina, connected with the negative side of a powerful battery, . . . the positive pole was brought in contact with the upper surface of the alkali. On passing the current, the potash began to fuse at both its points of electric action. There was violent effervescence at the upper surface; at the lower or negative surface there was no liberation of elastic fluid, but small globules having a high metallic luster appeared." And he treated soda in the same manner with similar results. "It appears," he said, "that in these facts there is evidence for the decomposition of potash and soda into oxygen and two peculiar substances." To these two peculiar substances he gave the names potassium and sodium.

In 1808, Davy had decomposed hydrochloric acid by means of potassium, and in this way had obtained hydrogen and potassium chloride, the latter of which he had also prepared by burning potassium in chlorine. He proved, in 1809, that the chlorides (muriates) of the metals are not decomposed by heating them with calcium metaphosphate or with silicic anhydride, but that decomposition at once begins when aqueous vapor is conducted over the mixture. Davy considered that Henry's hypothesis furnished the explanation of these experiments, and that hydrochloric acid could only be separated as soon as the quantity of water necessary for its existence was supplied.

About the same time Gay-Lussac and Thénard showed that water is produced as well as silver chloride by the action of this acid upon silver oxide; and, as formerly, they assumed that this water was already present in the hydrochloric acid. They then effected the synthesis of the acid, by exposing a mixture of chlorine and hydrogen to sunlight. On this occasion, they advanced a complete theory regarding hydrochloric acid and chlorine, by means of which they were able to explain all their experiments. According to them, hydrochloric acid was a compound of an unknown radical, "muriaticum," with oxygen and water; chlorine, on the other hand, was anhydrous hydrochloric acid combined with more oxygen.

Davy next sought to find the oxygen which was assumed to be present in "oxymuriatic acid," but by no means whatever could he abstract the oxygen from this compound; a succession of electric sparks produced no effect, neither did strongly ignited carbon. If the gas were oxidized, muriatic acid, phosphorus and sulphur might be expected to combine with the oxygen and liberate the muriatic acid; no such result had been obtained, however, and the oily liquids which were produced only yielded muriatic acid on the addition of water. The "oxymuriatic acid," when passed over oxides of potassium, barium, and other metals, produced "muriates" with evolution of precisely that amount of oxygen contained in the oxides. Referring to this experiment, Davy remarks, "It is contrary to sound logic to say that the exact quantity of oxygen is given off from a body not known to be compound, when we are certain of its existence in another." He therefore explained these facts by regarding "oxidized muriatic acid" as an elementary substance, and muriatic acid as its compound with hydrogen; but chemists hesitated about accepting his views. Davy maintained that this element, to which he gave the name "chlorine," resembled oxygen in many respects, and, in a limited sense, was also to be regarded as an acidifier and supporter of combustion.

The work of Davy was clear and brought conviction, and by 1820 his theory of the nature of chlorine was generally accepted. But oxygen could no longer be regarded as the sole acid-making principle, and this necessitated a new theory of acids.

A French saltpeter manufacturer, Courtois, in 1811 discovered a peculiar substance in the soda obtained from sea plants; he related his observation to Clément, who showed the body in question to Davy. Davy soon demonstrated its elementary nature, and Gay-Lussác, after a complete investigation of iodine, as he termed it, and its compounds, succeeded in showing its marked likeness to chlorine. Bromine was discovered by Balard, in 1826, in the mother liquor of sea-water. Hydrofluoric acid resisted all attempts to isolate its radical, but Ampère's suggestion that it was constituted similarly to muriatic acid found general acceptance.

From his observation that iodic anhydride was devoid of acid properties, but acquired them after combination with water, Davy arrived at the conclusion that hydrogen and not oxygen was the acidifying principle in the latter compound; hydrogen, in his opinion, was an essential constituent of all acids. The assumption that hydrated acids and salts contained water or metallic oxides together with acid anhydrides, he held to be unproven and unnecessary.

The French chemist Dulong expressed himself in a like manner after an investigation of oxalic acid and its salts; the former he looked upon as a compound of hydrogen with carbonic acid, while in the latter he assumed an analogous combination of the metals with the elements of carbonic acid.

The principles of a new theory of acids was, therefore, included in the discussions of Davy and Dulong, but it is to be deplored that they did not follow them up sufficiently, as otherwise they might have prevented the distinction which now began to be drawn between acids containing oxygen and those which did not.

With regard to Davy's attitude to the atomic theory of Dalton, it should first be mentioned that he asserted in 1809 that William Higgins was the originator of this doctrine. The latter's "A Comparative View of the Phlogistic and Antiphlogistic Theories with Inductions" (1789), Davy maintained, contained views similar to those of Dalton; but later he recognized Dalton's service.

Davy regarded Dalton's atomic weights as simply the proportion numbers of the elements, and maintained that there was no positive basis upon which to proceed for the determination of the atomic weights. Two other investigators of this time—Wollaston and Gay-Lussac—also refused to admit that Dalton's atomic weights were really such. Previous to Davy, Wollaston had asserted that these were the chemical equivalents of the elements, while Gay-Lussac would only concede that the ratio of one element to another was fixed by analytical and

ATOMIC THEORY—WORK OF DAVY

synthetical determinations. His law of combining volumes had a definite bearing on the atomic theory, however, and this generalization, along with his work in analytical chemistry and numerous researches in inorganic chemistry, render further notice of him necessary.

Josephe Louis Gay-Lussac (1778-1850) was a student of Berthollet, and in 1809 became professor of chemistry at the Ecole Polytechnique, at the same time holding the chair of physics at the Sorbonne. In 1832, he accepted the chair of chemistry at the Jardin des Plantes. Gay-Lussac was a masterly investigator, capable of the most accurate analytical work and exact in observation, and enriched chemistry with many valuable researches. Of especial importance was his work on iodine and its compounds; on cyanogen, which he characterized as the first compound radical; on sulphur and its compounds; on the oxides of nitrogen; on the isolation of boron; and his conjoint investigations with L. J. Thénard on the alkali metals, and with Liebig on the fulminates. He also introduced improved methods of inorganic and organic analysis, and is to be regarded as having laid the foundations of volumetric analysis. His name is particularly associated, however, with his investigations on the combining volumes of gases.

In 1805, Gay-Lussac and Alexander von Humboldt published a memoir entitled "Experiments on the Ratio of the Constituents of the Atmosphere," in which they announced that they had found the volume ratio, hydrogen : oxygen :: 200 : 100. This led Gay-Lussac to extend his investigations to the volume relations of other gaseous substances which are compounds of gaseous constituents, and by the close of the year 1808 he was able to announce results which showed the existence of a simple and general law. He summarized his results as follows:

"I have shown in this memoir that the compounds of gaseous substances with each other are always formed in very simple ratios, so that representing one of the terms by unity, the other is one, or two, or at most three. These ratios by volume are not observed with solid or liquid substances, nor when we consider weights, and they form a new proof that it is only in the gaseous state that substances are in the same circumstances and obey regular laws. . . . The apparent contraction of volume suffered by gases on combination is also very simply related to the volume of one of them, and this property likewise is peculiar to gaseous substances."

This law of combining volumes is stated by Ostwald in his "Outlines of General Chemistry" as follows:

"If gaseous substances enter into chemical combination, their volumes are in simple rational proportions, and if a gaseous substance is formed by their union, its volume also is rationally related to the volumes of the original gases."

Gay-Lussac was himself inclined to conjoin his law of volumes with the atomic theory—indeed, he recognized in it a support for the latter. A similar molecular condition was essential, however, in order that all gases should deport themselves alike toward pressure and changes of temperature, and, besides, obey his law of volumes. In other words, equal volumes of gases must contain equal numbers of molecules. Gay-Lussac drew no distinction between these molecules and atoms, recognizing but one kind of final particles. Dalton opposed this reasoning, and stated that he held the same view as to combining volumes at one time, but finally saw that it was untenable. To quote from his "A New System of Chemical Philosophy":

"At the time I formed the theory of mixed gases I had a confused idea, as many have, I suppose, at this time, that the particles of elastic fluids are all of the same size; that a given volume of oxygenous gas contains just as many particles as the same volume of hydrogenous. But . . . I became convinced that different gases have not their particles of the same size; and that the following may be adopted as a maxim till some reason appears to the contrary, namely:

"That every species of pure elastic fluid has its particles globular and all of a size; but that no two species agree in the size of their particles, the pressure and temperature being the same."

He also maintained that gases do not combine exactly by volumes, but frequently by fractions of volumes. He said: "The truth is, I believe, that gases do not unite in equal or exact measures in any one instance; when they appear to do so, it is owing to the inaccuracy of our experiments. In no case, perhaps, is there a nearer approach to mathematical exactness than in that of one measure of oxygen to two of hydrogen; but here the most exact experiments I have ever made gave 1.97 hydrogen to 1 oxygen."

His argument may be illustrated as follows, taking hydrochloric acid as an example:

One atom of hydrogen chloride consists of one atom of hydrogen and one atom of chlorine. Then, if equal volumes of gases contain equal numbers of molecules, one volume of hydrogen and one volume of chlorine should produce one volume of hydrogen chloride, but they really form two. Consequently, each one of these can contain only half as many atoms as the original volumes of the constituents. Such ratiocination is manifestly conclusive so far as the theory of the volumes containing the same number of atoms is concerned, unless some different definition of atoms is assumed.

The connection between Gay-Lussac's law of volumes and Dalton's atomic theory was shown by the Italian physicist Amadeo Avogadro (1776-1856) in 1811.

Avogadro discarded Dalton's artificial distinction between the ultimate particles of a compound and those of an element, and made a distinction between what he termed "molecule integrants" and "molecules elementaires," or molecules and atoms, the former being compound particles made up of the indivisible atoms. The researches of Gay-Lussac indicate, then, that a molecule of water consists of one molecule of hydrogen and one-half molecule of oxygen. A molecule of hydrogen chloride consists of one-half molecule of hydrogen and one-half molecule of chlorine, and so the difficulty pointed out by Dalton was effaced from chemical literature.

Avogadro's assumption that "equal volumes of gases, elementary or compound, at the same temperature and pressure contain equal numbers of molecules," altho only a hypothesis, is generally referred to as "Avogadro's Law." It is of fundamental importance to chemistry. He also stated that the relative weights of gaseous molecules may be determined by measurement of the relative weights of equal volumes of the gaseous substances—that is, by comparison of gaseous densities; and that the number of gaseous volumes interacting indicates the relative number of molecules interacting, and similarly the volume of the compound gas formed when compared with that of the constituents gives the number, whole or fractional, or elementary molecules entering into the composition of one compound molecule.

Avogadro's conclusions produced practically no effect at the time they were promulgated, and fifty years passed by before they were received with due recognition. These conclusions of Avogadro are sometimes credited to the French mathematician Ampère (1775-1836), but the memoir of the latter did not appear until 1814, and is much less important than that of Avogadro.

While Davy and Gay-Lussac were conducting their valuable investigations, an important literary-chemical event, most impressive and attractive in nature, occurred when William Prout (1785-1850) advanced his hypothesis of the genesis of the elements.

In 1815, in a paper upon the relations between the specific gravities of bodies in the gaseous state and their atomic weights, Prout stated that he had often observed the close approximation to round numbers of many of the weights of the atoms. From the table at his command he further deduced that all elementary numbers, hydrogen being considered as 1, are divisible by 4, except carbon, nitrogen and barium, and these are divisible by 2, appearing, therefore, to indicate that they are modified by a higher number than unity or hydrogen. He considered the other number might be 16, or oxygen, and that possibly all substances were composed of these two elements.

A short time after, in 1816, he expressed the following views: "If the views we have ventured to advance be correct, we may almost consider the πρώτη ὕλη of the ancients to be realized in hydrogen, an opinion, by the by, not altogether new. If we actually consider this to be the case, and further consider the specific gravities of bodies in their gaseous states to represent the number of volumes condensed into one, or, in other words, the number of the absolute weights of a single volume of the first matter ($\pi\rho\omega\tau\eta$ $\ddot{\upsilon}\lambda\eta$) which they contain, which is extremely probable, multiples in weight must always indicate multiples in volume and *vice versa* and the specific gravities or absolute weights of all bodies in a gaseous state must be multiples of the specific gravity or absolute weight of the first matter, because all bodies in a gaseous state, which unite with one another, unite with reference to this volume."

Prout's conjecture was taken up by Thomas Thomson, who, being carried away by the attraction of simplicity, became the advocate of a philosophical speculation contrary to experimental facts, and even perceived in it a fundamental law of chemistry. Other chemists, too, showed a predilection for "Prout's Hypothesis," and, notwithstanding the fact that Berzelius and Turner demonstrated its untenability, some exact investigators as late as 1840 betrayed an inclination to some of Prout's views. In fact, some writers of the present day consider that there may be a kernel of truth concealed in it, and, altho it has suffered numerous reversals, it is still revived at intervals.

CHAPTER XI

BERZELIUS AND THE DEVELOPMENT OF THE ATOMIC THEORY

COMPLETE success had rewarded the exertions of Lavoisier, and, through the efforts of Proust, Richter, Dalton, Gay-Lussac, and Davy, the spirit of order was creeping in on all sides, but it was exceedingly fortunate for chemistry that an investigator with the sense of co-ordination that Berzelius possessed should have made his advent just at this time, when laws required confirmation and theories nourishment. The foundations of the new system required extension and generalization, and how opportune was the appearance of one who could illumine the whole domain of chemistry. Berzelius ruled as an autocrat for over a quarter of a century, and the modern chemist can hardly over-extol his obligation to him.

Jons Jakob Berzelius was born at Wäfversunda, in Ostergötland, Sweden, on August 20th, 1779. His father was a schoolmaster in Linköping, and died four years after the birth of his son, who for some time afterward had to endure many privations.

Berzelius studied medicine at Upsala, and subsequently practiced, but he had early acquired a devotion to chemistry and kept in close touch with it. He was but twenty when he undertook his first extensive chemical research—an investigation of the medicinal springs at Medevi, in the neighborhood of his birthplace. A short time after, in 1802, in conjunction with Hisinger, he commenced the examination of the action of the electric current on various salts, with the most far-reaching results for chemistry and for himself; for almost immediately the desire to keep so promising a student in Stockholm induced the authorities to create for him a new academic position, that of assistant professor of medicine, botany and pharmacy at the University of Stockholm.

In 1807, he was installed in the chair of medicine and pharmacy, and also taught chemistry at the Military College from the year 1806. In 1815, he accepted the chair of chemistry in the Chirurgico-Medical Institute of Stockholm, where he accomplished the researches which made him famous, and where his lectures enabled him to impress his views upon the rising generation of chemists. Among his pupils may be mentioned Heinrich and Gustav Rose, Mitscherlich, Wöhler,

Christian Gottlob Gmelin, Magnus, Mosander, Svanberg and Sefström.

From the year 1818, when he was nominated permanent secretary to the Stockholm Academy, of which he had been a member since 1808, and more particularly after 1832, when Mosander succeeded him in his chair, Berzelius devoted himself to literary work with a subservience which has hardly been equaled from a utilitarian standpoint by any chemist either before or after him. He died on the 7th of August, 1848.

Berzelius was an exceptional observer, and a most accurate and operose investigator, exhibiting very close attention to details. It is difficult to render an account of his achievements, as they extended over almost the entire field of chemistry and produced reforms of great importance.

And one must not forget that the laboratory in which Berzelius accomplished his famous researches was small and imperfectly equipped. To give Wöhler's description of his first visit to it:

"No water, no gas, no hoods, no oven, were to be seen; a couple of plain tables, a blowpipe, a few shelves with bottles, a little simple apparatus, and a large water-barrel whereat Anna, the ancient cook of the establishment, washed the laboratory dishes, completed the furnishings of this room, famous throughout Europe for the work which had been done in it. In the kitchen which adjoined, and where Anna cooked, was a small furnace and a sand-bath for heating purposes."

Berzelius introduced many improvements in analytical chemistry. It was he who first employed far smaller amounts of substances than the large quantities recommended by Klaproth, who introduced the spirit-lamp which bears his name, thereby rendering the incineration of filter-paper and the ignition of precipitates facile, and who worked out many new methods of analysis. Among the latter was his plan of decomposing silicates by the aid of chlorine. He enriched mineralogy by many analyses of minerals and mineral waters, and in a number of these—*e.g.*, those of platinum ores—he devised new methods of separation.

Berzelius was the first to characterize minerals as being in every respect "chemical compounds," and he classified them similarly to substances prepared artificially. He was also able to demonstrate that the doctrine of chemical proportions, and consequently the atomic theory, were applicable to minerals.

The close attention which Berzelius gave to details resulted in the discovery of selenium (1817), thoria (1828), and, in conjunction with Hisinger and independent of Klaproth, he discovered ceria (1803). He also discovered many new chemical compounds, among which were the compounds of selenium with hydrogen and oxygen, and some molybdenum compounds; isolated the elements silicon (1810), zirconium, and tantalum (1824); and extended the knowledge of the platinum metals.

Passages in the works of Berzelius indicate that he regarded the firm establishment of the doctrine of chemical proportions, and, in conjunction with this, the determination of the atomic weights of the elements and the constitution of chemical compounds, as his main task. To quote from his "Lehrbuch der Chemie," fifth edition:

"I resolved to make the analysis of a number of salts whereby that of others might become superfluous. . . . I soon convinced myself by new experiments that Dalton's numbers were wanting in that accuracy which was requisite for the practical application of his theory. . . . I recognized that if the newly arisen light was to spread, it would be necessary to ascertain with the utmost accuracy the atomic weights of all elementary substances, and particularly those of the more common ones. Without such work, no day would follow the dawn. This was therefore the most important object of chemical investigation at the time, and I devoted myself to it with unresting labor. . . . After work extending over ten years . . . I was able in 1818 to publish a table which contained the atomic weights, as calculated from my experiments, of about 2,000 simple and compound substances."

In the years 1812 to 1816, Berzelius investigated the stages of oxidation of most of the metals and metalloids then known, and, by determining the composition of these oxides, confirmed the law of multiple proportions. His analytical work greatly surpassed that of Dalton, and in the rules established for his guidance in deciding the number of atoms in a given compound or molecule, he exhibited a greater knowledge; still, his rules were, in some respects, arbitrary and unsatisfactory.

He took oxygen = 100 as his standard, giving as his reason for this preference the following:

"To refer the other atomic weights to that of hydrogen offers not only no advantages, but has, in fact, many inconveniences, seeing that hydrogen is very light and is seldom a constituent of inorganic compounds. Oxygen, on the other hand, unites all the advantages in itself. It is, so to speak, the center-point round which the whole of chemistry revolves." This view is, again, at the present time held by many chemists, who take 16 as the atomic weight of oxygen, and base the atomic weights of all the other elements upon this number.

Berzelius began his work at the time when Wollaston was attempting, by his use of the term equivalents, to eliminate the question of atoms. Thomson was employing the standard oxygen = 1, considering that this number would give more of the atomic weights as whole numbers, and failing to perceive that the law of volumes had any particular significance from the atomic standpoint.

Berzelius, however, perceived in the law of volumes a corroboration of the atomic theory, and allowed himself to be guided by it in his views upon the number of atoms in chemical compounds, and, consequently, upon the numerical values of the atomic weights. His "volume theory" contained the attempt to combine Gay-Lussac's law with the atomic theory. He set forth the atomistic view, which he had himself put into shape under the influence of the law of volumes, definitely and conclusively in two papers. He started with the assumption that in the case of every simple substance, when it was in the gaseous form, one volume corresponded with one atom, and, therefore, made use of the designation "volume atoms" for those smallest particles. Wherever it was practicable, he attempted to measure the volumes of the combining substances, and from these deduced the atomic numbers. The analysis of the compound, in which the volumes of the elementary constituents were known, led him to the true determination of the atomic weights of the latter. For example, from the fact that water consists of two volumes of hydrogen and one of oxygen, he deduced the atomic composition of water which holds at the present day, together with the relative atomic weights of oxygen and hydrogen; and from the mode of formation of carbonic oxide and carbonic acid he arrived at the true composition of these compounds, and at the atomic weight of carbon, and so forth.

Still, the use which Berzelius made of Gay-Lussac's law was too limited to free him from the necessity of employing rules for deciding the number of atoms in compounds.

In 1818, Berzelius gave a table of atomic weights which contained values which compare favorably with those of other observers. Nine years later he published another table which brought his atomic weights still closer to those now current.

The reason given by Berzelius for halving in 1826 many of the atomic weights assigned to the metals in 1818 was as follows:

"It is known that the oxide of chromium contains three atoms of oxygen. Chromic acid for the same number of chromium atoms contains twice as much oxygen, which would be six atoms; but in its neutral salts chromic acid neutralizes an amount of a base containing one-third as much oxygen as it contains itself, a relation found to hold in the case of all acids with three atoms of oxygen—*e.g.*, sulphuric acid and sulphates. In order to harmonize the multiple relation between the amount of oxygen in the oxide and in the acid, it is most probable that the acid contains three atoms of oxygen to one atom of chromium, and the oxide three atoms of oxygen to two of chromium. Isomorphous with the oxide of chromium are those of manganese, iron and aluminium; these also we know to contain three atoms of oxygen, and consequently must represent them as containing two atoms of the radicle. But if the ferric oxide consists of $2Fe + 3O$, the ferrous oxide is $Fe + O$, and the whole series of oxides isomorphous with it contains one atom of the radicle and one atom of oxygen."

Thus we see that E. Mitscherlich's law of isomorphism—that compounds of analogous composition and containing the same number of atoms crystallize in the same crystalline form—announced in 1819, and which Berzelius regarded as "the most important since the establishment of the doctrine of chemical proportions," was an aid in testing his atomic weight determinations, for, according to him, isomorphism indicated similarity in atomic constitution.

Berzelius further showed that with the exception of cobalt and silver the law of specific heat justified the change made in 1826. This law was advanced in 1819 by P. L. Dulong and T. A. Petit, who, in investigating the specific heats of the metals and other bodies, reached the important conclusion that these were very nearly inversely proportional to their atomic weights. Multiplied by their atomic weights, the specific heats gave a constant quantity. This resulted in the law as stated by them: the atoms of the different elements have the same capacity for heat. It is not difficult to perceive that by means of the specific heat one could readily approximate to the true atomic weight, and arrive at a decision as to which of two or more possible figures represented the true weight.

There were exceptions to the law which have been explained only in late years. However, the law was extended to simple chemical compounds, and proved of great assistance after it was more fully understood. Berzelius opposed the acceptance of it at first, in part, because it would necessitate a revision of his table of atomic weights, and might endanger the accepted views as to some of the atomic relations. He gradually gave up this position, however, when the law was confirmed by other workers, and more accurate determinations made than the first ones of Dulong and Petit.

Berzelius substituted for Dalton's geometrical symbols a more convenient system of chemical notation, which, to give his own words, "might facilitate the expression of chemical proportions, show briefly and clearly the number of elementary atoms in each compound, and after the determination of their relative weights, present the results of each analysis in a simple and easily retained manner." The atoms of each element was represented by the initial letter of its Latinized name, a second letter being added when two elements had names beginning with the same capital. An index number was added when more than one atom was present.

A compound was thus represented by placing the proper number of these symbols side by side. Thus, H is hydrogen, Cl is chlorine, and HCl is hydrogen chloride. Berzelius assumed the existence of certain double atoms (where two atoms of an element occur together). These were indicated by a mark across the symbol; thus H with a stroke through it, followed by O, was water, or as it is now written, H_2O. For convenience' sake, an atom of oxygen was often indicated by a point or dot, thus:

Carbon Dioxide, C̈; "Nitrous Acid," N̈̈; Potassium Nitrate, KN̈.

These symbols were a great advance over those suggested by Dalton, which were diagrammatic and quite unpractical. Dalton, however, criticized the system of notation of Berzelius, saying that "Berzelius' symbols are horrifying; a young student in chemistry might as soon learn Hebrew as make himself acquainted with them."

Berzelius adopted dualism as the basis of his chemical system. He extended the term atom so that it included what he regarded as compound atoms, which were built up of two parts, each of which might be a simple atom or several atoms, in which each of the two parts acted as a single simple atom. This was the dual structure, which dominated all of his views with regard to chemical phenomena, and for more than a decade held a preëminent position in chemistry. Berzelius seemed to have formed this idea of dualism from his observations upon the volumes of gases. For a certain number of these gases the equivalent is formed of two atoms. This was true not only of hydrogen, but of nitrogen, chlorine, and others, in the form of vapor. The atomic weights of these bodies represent also the specific gravities, or the weights of one volume compared with one volume of the standard; but since it requires two volumes of nitrogen, two volumes of chlorine, etc., to form the first stage of oxidation with oxygen, two volumes of nitrogen, etc., represent the equivalents of these bodies compared with oxygen. Berzelius considered that these atoms, therefore, were united two and two, and called them the double or compound atoms.

A uniform method of considering compounds dualistically became possible to a still greater degree in the light of electro-chemical phenomena, and Berzelius introduced this into chemistry and established it.

Davy had inclined to the assumption that electrical processes and the phenomena of chemical affinity arose from a common cause. His electro-chemical theory was characterized by the axiom that the small particles of substances which have an affinity for one another only become oppositely electrified upon contact. The researches of Berzelius, however, caused the abandonment of this principle, while otherwise many of Davy's original ideas were retained. Davy advanced ideas as to the manner in which he considered chemical and electrical phenomena to be related, but he never succeeded in producing a theory which might serve as the basis of a chemical system. This was accomplished by Berzelius, and therefore his views are of greater importance in the development of chemistry than those of Davy are. To quote from A. Ladenburg's "Lectures on the History of Chemistry":

"According to Berzelius, it is not only when two substances are brought into contact that electricity is generated, but it is a property of matter; and in every atom, two oppositely electrical poles are assumed. These poles do not, however, contain equal quantities of electricity. The atoms are unipolar, the electricity of the one pole predominating over that of the other; and thus every atom (and therefore every element) appears to be either positively or negatively electrical. In this respect it is possible to arrange the elementary substances into a series, so that each member is always more electro-negative, while the other substances are only relatively positive or negative according as they are compared with elements which come before them or after them in the electrical series. This series does not constitute a table of affinities in the Geoffroy-Bergman sense; and it does not express the affinity of the individual substances for oxygen, for example. Berzelius has not forgotten Berthollet's teaching, that affinity is not of a constant character and independent of the physical conditions, as he supposes this unipolarity to be; and he is also well aware that oxygen can be removed from metallic oxides by carbon or sulphur—that is to say, by other electro-negative substances. With him, affinity depends principally upon the intensity of the polarity—*i.e.*, upon the quantity of electricity which is contained in the two poles." This is variable, however, especially with changes of temperature, and, generally speaking, is increased by furnishing more heat, which explained why certain combinations only occurred at a high temperature.

Chemical combinations of the elements or compounds consisted, according to Berzelius, in the attraction of the dissimilar poles of the small particles and in the consequent neutralization of the different electricities. When positive electricity predominated in the original substance, then an electro-positive compound resulted, and vice versa. If the electricities neutralized one another, then an electrically indifferent product was the result. Oxygen, as the most electro-negative element, served Berzelius here as the standard by which to determine the kind of polarity of the various elements. Those elements which yielded basic compounds with oxygen, even altho only their lowest oxides were basic, were classed as electro-positive, and those whose oxides were acids as electro-negative. Following this principle he arranged the simple substances in a series, in which oxygen as the first member was followed by the other metalloids, while hydrogen formed the bridge between the latter and the metals, the whole ending with sodium and potassium.

Such conceptions formed the substance of his electro-chemical theory, which constituted the basis of the dualistic theory of chemical composition. Berzelius established it as follows:

"If the electro-chemical views are accurate, it follows that every chemical combination depends wholly and solely upon two opposite forces, namely, the positive and the negative electricities, and that every compound must be composed of two parts, united by the effects of their electro-chemical reactions, since there is not any third force. From this it follows that every compound substance, whatever the number of its constituents may be, can be divided into two parts, of which the one is positively and the other is negatively electrical. Thus, for example, sulphate of soda is not composed of sulphur, oxygen, and sodium, but of sulphuric acid and soda, each of which can in turn, be separately divided into an electro-positive and an electro-negative constituent. In the same way, also, alum cannot be regarded as immediately composed of its elementary constituents, but is to be looked upon as the product of the reaction of sulphate of alumina, as negative element, with sulphate of potash, as positive element; and thus the electro-chemical view justifies what I have said with respect to compound atoms of the first, second, third, etc., orders."

In the year 1819, when Berzelius contributed a complete exposition of his electro-chemical theory, he was convinced that all acids contained oxygen. In his view water assumed in hydrated acids the rôle of a weak electro-positive constituent, and in metallic hydroxides that of a weak electro-negative one; the hydrates of sulphuric acid and of cupric oxide, therefore, received the formulæ—

$$\overset{+}{H_2O}.\overset{-}{SO_3} \qquad \overset{+}{CuO}.\overset{-}{H_2O}.$$

The binary conception, which had already been applied by Lavoisier to acids and bases, and even by Rouelle to salts, thus received the strongest support from the electro-chemical theory, and was materially developed as a result.

Finally, however, the theory of the oxygen acids, based on the tenet established by Lavoisier, was abandoned by chemists during the second decade of the nineteenth century, as a knowledge of facts in opposition to it augmented, and at last Berzelius convinced himself of the existence of acids free from oxygen, at which time the unadaptable system of dualism began to decline in favor. It had explained, however, the mysterious chemical force, even tho the identification of chemical affinity with electrical polarity was one not justified by the facts at hand, and dominated chemistry for two decades.

As a result of the efforts of Berzelius, chemistry was now in the possession of a comprehensive theory of chemical reaction, a rational and systematic nomenclature, and a large quantity of experimental data. He was responsible for a solid basis in the laws of constant proportions and multiples, and the table of atomic weights which he published in 1827 was remarkably accurate, the determinations approaching the more exact work of the present time. These contributions equipped chemistry for the period of remarkable extension in the accumulation of data and in the formulation of theory which the past eighty years have witnessed.

Mention has been made of the law of Dulong and Petit and of the law of Mitscherlich. The exceptions to the former, exhibited by many of the non-metals in a greater or less diminution of the atomic heats, have only in some measure been explained in recent years by the proof that the specific heats of such elements vary greatly with the temperature. In the case of simple chemical compounds, a relation was soon found between their specific heats and atomic weights by Neumann in 1831, who said:

"I find that for compound substances a simple relation exists between the specific heat and the stoichiometric quantities; and I call stoichiometric quantities the amounts of substances which, as for instance in the case of the anhydrous carbonates, contain the same amount of oxygen, while in the case of sulphur compounds the amount of sulphur is the measure of the stoichiometric quantity. For chemically similar substances the specific heats are inversely proportional to the stoichiometric quantities; or what comes to the same thing, the stoichiometric quantities of chemically similar substances have the same heat capacity. The investigation of the carbonates first led me to the discovery of this law."

Regnault, who extended the empirical basis of the law of constant atomic heat in 1840, while engaged in investigations on the specific heats of compounds corroborated Neumann's result, but it was reserved for Kopp in 1865 to definitely prove that the connection between the specific heat and the composition of a compound holds in the perfectly simple and general manner enunciated by Petit and Dulong, and that heat capacity is of the nature of an additive property.

The law of Mitscherlich was the outgrowth of coördinating physical form with chemical composition, a question which, until the time of Eilhard Mitscherlich (1794-1863), had been attacked entirely from the crystallographic side.

In 1801, Abbé Haüy (1743-1822), the founder of the science of crystallography, produced a system of mineral classification based first on their crystalline character, and secondly on their chemical composition. His guiding principle was that every difference in the fundamental form of a crystal implied difference in its chemical composition.

This supposed law was supported by numerous facts, but there were also on record well-defined and undoubted exceptions. As far back as 1772, Romé de l'Isle had observed that copper sulphate and ferrous sulphate crystallize from a mixed solution in the form of the latter, and in 1788 Klaproth established the chemical identity of rhombohedral calcite and rhombic aragonite.

Mitscherlich was the first to recognize definitely the relation between crystalline form and chemical constitution. He explained the occurrence of isomorphous crystals in substances of different nature by demonstrating that they possessed a similar chemical composition. For instance, he found, on examining the salts of phosphoric and arsenic acids, that only those of analogous composition and containing equal amounts of water of crystallization were isomorphous. His subsequent investigations of selenates and sulphates, of the isomorphism of magnesium and zinc oxides, and of iron, chromium and aluminium salts, confirmed the intimate connection existing between crystalline form and chemical composition. Primarily, after making those observations, Mitscherlich was of opinion that isomorphism depended chiefly on the number of the elementary particles, but he soon became convinced that the chemical nature of these had also to do with it.

The importance of Mitscherlich's work met with immediate recognition, and data in support of the law were quickly accumulated. With regard to its deductive application, it is employed for purposes of classifying the elements and of atomic weight determination. From the isomorphism of the salts of an acid of selenium with sulphates and chromates, Mitscherlich was led to the discovery of that acid (selenic acid); and his recognition of the isomorphism with potassium sulphate of the green potassium salt of a manganese acid, and of the isomorphism with potassium perchlorate of the red potassium salt of another manganese acid, has revealed the true composition of these two acids.

It has been mentioned how the isomorphism of sulphates and chromates induced Berzelius to modify the formula of basic chromic oxide and to a subsequent halving of the atomic weights of most of the metals. He still adhered to the idea that the amounts of the elements contained in equal gaseous volumes were proportional to their atomic weights. However, this assumption was soon invalidated by the remarkable results of an investigation which exercised such a marked influence on the views of many chemists that it must be described at this point.

This was the work of Jean Baptiste André Dumas (1800-1884) on the atomic weights. In 1827, Dumas published a paper entitled "Memoir on some points of the atomistic theory," in which he stated that "The object of these researches is to replace by definite conceptions the arbitrary data on which nearly the whole of the atomic theory is based."

Dumas showed that the conception of the equivalent cannot be employed as the basis of a system, because it loses its significance when it is extended further than to acids, to bases, and to other substances which closely resemble each other (oxides and sulphides); and, particularly, that it becomes quite obscure when the attempt is made to identify the equivalent with the combining weight, since very many substances can combine in several proportions. For example, 8 parts of copper are combined with 1 part of oxygen in cuprous oxide, while for 8 parts of copper, 2 parts of oxygen are contained in cupric oxide. Calculated from these numbers, the equivalent of copper, referred to that of oxygen as unity, is 8 or 4.

In order to confirm his ideas, Dumas adopted Avogadro's hypothesis as a basis, and devised in 1827 an admirable method for the determination of vapor densities.

He considered that the determination of the density of vapors and gases, elementary as well as compound, was necessary to elucidate the question of the composition of the elementary molecule. But his practice did not agree with his theory; he and his contemporaries argued from the premise that the vapor densities of elements are proportional not only to their molecular weights, but also to their atomic weights, which of course involved the unwarranted assumption that all elementary gaseous molecules are composed of the same number of atoms —*i.e.*, of two.

He was successful in elaborating a method for conducting determinations of this kind at high temperatures, and used it for ascertaining the relative densities of the vapors of iodine, phosphorus, sulphur, mercury, etc. His results, from which he anticipated confirmation of his views, induced him to abandon them. He found the density of phosphorus vapor to be twice as great, and that of sulphur vapor to be three times as great as he had previously assumed, while that of mercury vapor was only one-half of what he had supposed. In view of these facts he began to doubt; in fact, he declared that even the simple gases do not contain, in the same volume, the same number of chemical atoms. According to him, the assumption could still be made that there is the same number of molecular or atomic groups present in equal volumes of all gases; but that this is only a hypothesis, which cannot be of service. Dumas was obliged to admit that Gay-Lussac's law, when applied in the way he had applied it to the determination of atomic weights, furnished erroneous results. Hence he believed that it could not be employed for this purpose, and he abandoned Avogadro's hypothesis.

Berzelius also was able no longer to maintain the law of volumes so far as its application in atomic weight determinations was concerned, and confined his proposition to the permanent gases.

The reform which Dumas had aimed at was, therefore, without result, and, if anything, he had merely introduced obscurity into the atomic system of Berzelius. As a result, chemists regarded Avogadro's law with indifference. The law of Dulong and Petit was shown also to have some unexplained exceptions, and Mitscherlich, by his further discovery of dimorphism, had thrown much doubt upon his law of isomorphism. Consequently, at the close of the thirtieth year of this century the atomic theory was regarded by many chemists as either disproved or excluded to a very hypothetical position.

Even Gay-Lussac and Liebig doubted whether it was possible to determine the relative weights of the atoms with certitude, and would have left the atomic weights out of consideration, substituting the establishment of equivalents. Leopold Gmelin, however, was at the head of the movement to supplant the system of Berzelius by the equivalents of Wollaston.

According to Gmelin, there was no strict distinction between mixtures and compounds, and this demonstrates that he did not believe in the real existence of atoms. Two substances, especially when they possess only a weak affinity for each other, can combine, according to him, in an infinite number of proportions; but the greater the affinity, the greater is their tendency to combine in few proportions only. These proportions then stand to each other in simple relations. "There can, therefore, be assigned to every substance a certain weight in which it combines with definite weights of other elements. This weight is the stoichiometric number, the chemical equivalent, the mixture weight or atomic weight, and so on. Compounds are composed in such proportions that one mixture weight of one substance is united to $\frac{1}{4}$, $\frac{1}{3}$, $\frac{1}{2}$, $\frac{2}{3}$, $\frac{3}{4}$, 1, $1\frac{1}{2}$, 2, $2\frac{1}{2}$, 3, 4, 5, 6, 7, or more mixture weights of the other." According to Gmelin Gay-Lussac's law runs as follows: "One measure of an elastic fluid substance combines with 1, $1\frac{1}{3}$, 2, $2\frac{1}{2}$, 3, $3\frac{1}{2}$, and 4 measures of the other."

Gmelin's table of equivalents is well known. It ran: $H=1$, $O=8$, $S=16$, $C=6$, etc. Water was written HO, and in formulæ generally the attempt was made to replace by simplicity what they had lost in conception and in purpose. As Ladenburg observes, "Chemistry was to become a science of confined observation—indeed almost to description alone. Skill in manipulation was all that was required; speculation was banished as dangerous.

"It had come to this, then: Inorganic chemistry, in connection with physics, had not been able to maintain the conception of the atom."

By the assistance of the growing science of organic chemistry, however, the theories of chemistry were rescued and advanced, and the atomic theory was reintroduced. But reference must be made to the status of the atomic theory in England at this time.

In England in the 1833 edition of Edward Turner's "Elements of Chemistry" the atomic theory is referred to as follows:

"In consequence of the satisfactory explanation which the laws of chemical union receive by means of the atomic theory it has become customary to employ the term atom in the same sense as combining proportion or equivalent."

A discovery of great importance was made in 1834, when Michael Faraday (1794-1867), professor in the Royal Institution of London, who had been engaged in studying quantitatively some changes produced by the passage of a current of electricity, detected the connection which existed with the combining numbers of the elements, and thereby deduced his law of electrical equivalents.

Faraday made the observation that the same galvanic current decomposed electrolytes—*e.g.*, water, hydrochloric acid and metallic chlorides—in such a manner that equivalent amounts of hydrogen or metal were separated at the negative pole, and the corresponding quantities of oxygen or chlorine at the positive. He classified those facts together under the title of "The Law of definite Electrolytic Action." In the determination of electro-chemical equivalents he perceived a sure auxiliary means for adjusting chemical atomic weights in doubtful cases.

CHAPTER XII

THE DEVELOPMENT OF ORGANIC CHEMISTRY

LAVOISIER showed that organic substances were composed principally of carbon, hydrogen, and oxygen, together with nitrogen, and sometimes sulphur and phosphorus. He had observed that an element was capable of forming more than one oxide, and from this he concluded that organic radicals deported themselves similarly. He consequently regarded sugar as the neutral oxide "d'un radical hydrocarboneux," and oxalic acid as its higher oxide. He even hazarded the conjecture that the fatty oils, which he considered to be hydrocarbons, might actually constitute organic radicals in the free state, and might, by oxidation, be converted into neutral oxides and vegetable acids.

Among Lavoisier's other investigations in organic chemistry, his research on the process of vinous fermentation is worthy of mention. He expressed the results in the form of the equation—

3 oz. 7 gros of water + 2 lbs. 8 oz. sugar produce, on fermentation, 1 lb. 7 oz. 5 gros 18 grains of alcohol + 1 lb. of carbonic acid.

"In this equation," says he, "there is only sugar whose constitutional parts are unknown to me. I know the composition of water, of alcohol, and of carbonic acid, and nothing is easier than to substitute these values in the equation established and then deduce the constituent parts of sugar."

However, Lavoisier did not regard organic chemistry as a separate division of the science. He classed all acids together, and, like Lemery (1675), subdivided them into mineral, vegetable, and animal acids. With a few exceptions, the immediate followers of Lavoisier followed the same plan, and the division of chemistry into inorganic and organic chemistry was not generally adopted until it became clear that several compounds occur both in the vegetable and animal kingdom, and therefore that no difference existed between vegetable and animal chemistry. In this connection the work of M. E. Chevreul (1786-1889) should be emphasized, as it was his investigations which demonstrated that many of the fats and acids and other substances, occurring in both kingdoms, were identical.

However, for some time subsequently considerable doubt prevailed as to the boundary of inorganic and organic chemistry. One reason

DEVELOPMENT OF ORGANIC CHEMISTRY

for this was that inorganic substances, as well as some which had to be considered as organic, gave on analysis numbers which demonstrated that their composition was in accordance with the laws of constant and multiple proportions. As Berzelius stated in 1811, the majority of organic substances, however, appeared not to obey these laws, and consequently he undertook to decide this question by the analysis of a large number of them. After years of labor, and after improving the appliances and methods of organic analysis, he finally obtained results which proved that altho most organic compounds possessed a much more complicated composition than the mineral compounds, yet they obeyed the laws of constant and multiple proportions. He adopted the views of Lavoisier, and said (Schorlemmer):

"After we have got a clearer insight into the difference existing between the products of organic and inorganic nature, and the different manner in which their ultimate components are united with each other, we find this difference consists really in the fact that in inorganic nature all oxidized bodies contain a "simple radical," while all organic substances are "oxides of compound radicals." The radicals of vegetable substances consist generally of carbon and hydrogen, and those of animal substances of carbon, hydrogen, and nitrogen."

In his ideas as to these radicals he was especially influenced by the research of Gay-Lussac upon cyanogen, in which he showed that this radical played the rôle of an element. Attempts were multiplied to discover the various organic substances having complex groupings of atoms which performed as elements. Thus, Gay-Lussac regarded alcohol as ethylene and water. Döbereiner considered oxalic acid as carbonic acid and carbon monoxide. As Berzelius pointed out, this was opposed to the electro-chemical theory, and there was danger of confusion and error.

The search for the proximate constituents in organic substances induced a rapid development of the science, leading especially to many efforts at definitely determining the chemical constitution of these bodies. One of the most important of the discoveries in the third decade was that of isomerism. This was viewed as an error by chemists at first, so little prepared were they to believe that bodies similarly composed could be chemically and physically different. It was in the year 1823 that Liebig announced that his analysis of silver fulminate yielded the same results as Wöhler had found in the preceding year for his silver cyanate. He was confident that his figures were correct, and believed that Wöhler must have made a mistake. A careful repetition of the analyses showed him that both were correct, and so it was proved that two bodies, totally unlike, could and did have the same composition. Gay-Lussac saw that the only explanation of this lay in the different mode in which the elements were combined. In 1826, Berzelius reported on Liebig's fulminate of silver as follows:

"This substance has been made the subject of a new joint investigation by Gay-Lussac and Liebig, and the result is of the utmost interest. Fulminate of silver dried at 100° loses all its water, and in 3 experiments they found between 16.87% and 17.38% cyanogen, the mean being 17.16%. The silver oxide was separated by hydrochloric acid, and was found to be 77.528% of the weight of the salt. These quantities add up to 94.688%. The deficiency is only 5.312%, a quantity absolutely equal to that of the oxygen in the silver oxide. Hence the salt was composed of 77.528% of silver oxide and 22.472% of cyanic acid; but this result is identical with that obtained by Wöhler in his analysis of silver cyanate, in spite of which agreement between the analytical results the two substances have not the same properties. The chief difference is that Wöhler's cyanate of silver, when heated by itself, does not explode, but only burns with moderate intensity; and further, that when decomposed by acids it is completely changed into carbonic acid and ammonia . . . while fulminic acid has explosive properties, and gives ammonia and prussic acid when its salts are decomposed by oxyacids. These facts point unquestionably to a difference in composition." ("Jahresbericht," 1826).

In 1825, Michael Faraday announced the results of his work on the hydrocarbons from oil-gas, when he demonstrated the existence of butylene, an isomer of ethylene. In 1827, Berzelius commented on this discovery in part as follows:

"The two gases are of like constitution, but . . . a given volume of the one contains twice as many simple atoms as does the other, and this produces a certain dissimilarity in physical and chemical character. . . . Definite knowledge concerning this phenomenon would be of such significance in the doctrine of the composition of vegetable and animal bodies, and would have so important a bearing on organic chemistry, that it must not be accepted as demonstrated until its truth has been subjected to the most severe proof. It is not my intention to dispute the possibility or the actuality of such a fact, but I maintain that before accepting it with confidence the relation observed by Faraday must be found in a number of other cases."

In 1832 and 1833, Berzelius formally adopted the addition to the doctrine of chemical composition rendered necessary by these observations, and suggested his classical classification of the new phenomena, concluding as follows:

"But since it is requisite that we should be able to express our conceptions by definite and appropriately chosen terms, I have proposed to call substances of the same composition and of different properties 'isomeric,' from the Greek ἰσομερης (composed of equal parts)."

The general designation isomerism has since then been retained. Berzelius soon saw himself necessitated to define more strictly the meaning to be attached to this word, and therefore he distinguished between polymerism and metamerism, as special cases of isomerism.

The ideas of Berzelius with regard to the probable cause of isomerism in organic compounds are clearly shown in many of his statements; in his view isomeric compounds are those in which the atoms of the elementary constituents have grouped themselves differently into compound radicals. "The isomerism of compounds in itself presupposes that the positions of the atoms in them must be different." And it appears that he considered it possible to determine the mutual relations of the atoms in their compounds.

At the period that is now reached, to quote Carl Schorlemmer, "we find Berzelius laying stress again on a difference between organic and inorganic substances, first pointed out by Gmelin (1817), and according to which the latter, but not the former, could be prepared artificially. Berzelius was of opinion that within the sphere of living nature the elements obeyed laws totally different from those ruling in inanimate nature. It was then commonly supposed that the compounds found in plants and animals were produced by the action of a so-called 'vital force,' and that altho they might be changed into other compounds none of them could be prepared artificially from their elements. Thus, grape-sugar, a compound widely distributed in the vegetable kingdom, by fermentation yielded alcohol, which could be converted into ether, acetic acid, and many other compounds; and all these were considered to be organic, as none of them could be prepared synthetically."

It was Friedrich Wöhler's synthesis of urea which finally removed this obstacle to the growth of organic chemistry. In 1828, Wöhler made the discovery that cyanate of ammonia, which was regarded as an inorganic compound, could be converted into urea, a substance hitherto known only as a product of animal metabolism. This was the first synthesis of an organic compound, and is generally referred to as marking the beginning of scientific organic chemistry. Yet it remained an isolated fact for a long time and failed to shake the belief in a "vital force," a belief which was maintained during the lapse of many years.

In 1830-1831, Liebig perfected and simplified the operations for the ultimate analysis of organic compounds, and this to such a degree that his processes have not required any essential alterations to fit them to modern requirements. These perfected methods enabled Liebig to carry out his famous researches in Giessen, work which renders a brief biographical mention of this master fitting.

Justus Liebig was born at Darmstadt on May 12, 1803. The fact of his father being a dealer in dye-stuffs brought him early into contact with laboratory problems. At fifteen years he was sent to a neighboring town to learn the business of apothecary. But pharmacy was not chemistry, as Liebig was beginning to understand it, so he entered the University of Bonn. Here was certainly change, much "ingenious contemplation," but no chemistry. He traveled to Erlangen, where he heard lectures, read books, and at nineteen obtained a degree. Then his chance came. His ability being made known to the Grand Duke of Hesse-Darmstadt, he was provided with the means of studying in Paris. There worked those giants, Gay-Lussac, Chevreul, Vauquelin, and Dulong; nor was it long before Liebig was received into the laboratory of Gay-Lussac. Liebig had meanwhile won the appreciation of Humboldt; his was a personality that inspired immediate and warm friendships. "Of slender form was he, a friendly earnestness in his regular features, great brown eyes with shady eyebrows which attracted one instantly." It was Humboldt who, in 1824, brought him as extraordinary professor of chemistry to Giessen. Two years later he was elected to the ordinary professorship, which office he held for the next twenty-six years. The dull little town of Giessen became famous; the fires of Liebig's laboratory acted as a beacon light, attracting chastened spirits from the four quarters of the civilized world. For it was not long before the master had roused the Darmstadt Government to build a laboratory where all might come and seek and find. And the movement spread. Liebig, through his pupils, tinctured the world; there were other governments than that of Darmstadt, and soon there were other public laboratories than that of Giessen. In 1845 Liebig was created Baron. In 1852 he accepted a call of the Bavarian Government to the Munich professorship of chemistry. Warmly appreciated by the Bavarian court, entering into the social and philosophical life of the university town, courted by all the scientific circles of Europe, yet continually fighting weakening health, Liebig passed the remainder of his life in Munich. He died in 1873.

Liebig devoted his full powers of mind to organic chemistry, but did not neglect inorganic chemistry, as his work on the compounds of silicic acid, alumina and antimony clearly shows. His work in physiological and agricultural chemistry rendered him a general benefactor of mankind, and, to quote A. W. von Hofmann, "If we sum up in our minds all that Liebig did for the good of mankind, in industries, in agriculture, and in the laws of health, we may confidently assert that no other man of learning, in his course through the world, has ever left a more valuable legacy behind him."

Writing in 1810, Gay-Lussac and Thénard gave, as a reason for the slow progress of animal and vegetable chemistry, the inadequacy of the methods of organic analysis. In their "Recherches physico-chimiques," which appeared in 1811, they gave an exhaustive description of a new method of organic analysis, the results of analyses of sugar, starch, gum arabic, milk sugar, wood, and mucic, oxalic, tartaric and acetic acids, as well as of oils, resins and waxes, and the following generalizations made from the results of their work:

1. A vegetable substance is always acid when it contains more oxygen than will form water with the hydrogen.

2. It will be always resinous, oily, or alcoholic when it contains less oxygen than suffices the hydrogen.

3. The body will be neither acid nor resinous, but analogous to sugar or ligneous fiber, when the oxygen and hydrogen are present in just the proportions to form water.

This classification was, of course, of little service, but it was suggestive, and altho no proper classification was possible at this time, the interpretation of Gay-Lussac and Thénard gave a stimulus to the study of the constituents of organic compounds.

Berzelius explained in 1819 that his electrochemical theory could not be extended to organic chemistry, because under the influence of the vital force the elements there possessed entirely different electro-chemical properties. In decay, putrefaction, fermentation, etc., he observes phenomena which he regards as demonstrating the tendency of the elements to return to their normal condition. He did not, at that time, as yet consider it possible to regard all organic substances as binary groups. Dualism was, indeed, extended as far as possible; the oxygen compounds were looked upon as "oxides of compound radicals, which, however, do not exist free, but are wholly hypothetical," a mode of regarding the matter which was especially applicable to the acids.

In 1838, Liebig defined a compound radical, enunciating three characteristics and making use of cyanogen as an instance: "We term cyanogen a radical because (1) it is the unchanging constituent of a series of compounds; (2) because it is capable of replacement in these by simple substances; and (3) because in these cases where it is combined with one element this latter can be exchanged for its equivalent of another element." At least two of the conditions here adduced had to be fulfilled in order that an atomic complex might be stamped as a radical. The existence of these conditions, moreover, could only be established by the most minute investigation of the chemical behavior of organic bodies. That is to say, the nature of the radicals assumed in the latter could only be arrived at from the study of their reaction- and decomposition-products.

This radical theory aroused considerable interest, and chemists of eminence were attracted to the task of investigating the constituents of compounds related to one another. Thus, the research of Bunsen upon the cacodyl compounds, which formed one of the strongest supports of the theory, may be mentioned.

Robert Wilhelm Bunsen (1811-1899) enriched every branch of

chemistry by his valuable researches. He created the gas analysis method of to-day, with Kirchhoff he developed spectrum analysis into one of the great branches of to-day, and in his investigations in analytical and inorganic chemistry and in geochemistry he showed himself a pioneer in the science.

Bunsen's researches on the cacodyl compounds resulted in the proof that the so-called "alkarsin," the product of the distillation of acetate of potash with arsenious acid, contained the oxide of an arsenuretted radical $As_2C_4H_{12}$ ($H = 1$, $C = 12$, $As = 75$), this radical remaining unchanged in a long series of reactions of that oxide, and being even itself capable of isolation. This "compound element" containing arsenic (an unusual constituent of organic bodies) was thus shown to be a true radical.

Inasmuch as the radical was supposed to be constituted of atoms held together by stronger forces than those which united the group to other atoms, it attained a real significance in the minds of chemists; and as the dualistic theory and the theory of compound radicals became more solidly intrenched in chemistry, they rendered the atomic theory, on which, of course, they were founded, an essentiality, and even after dualism was discredited the only changes were in the ideas as to the nature of the ultimate particles, or atoms.

About this time, however, facts became known which could not be brought into accord with the radical theory, and as a result doubts were expressed as to the theory of dualism; but was the discovery of the principle of substitution which actually caused this theory to succumb, and paved the way for the so-termed unitary theory.

The conception of equivalence might have led to that of replacement or substitution, since the quantities of two acids were equivalent when they saturated the same quantity of a base. The acid in a neutral salt could thus be replaced by its equivalent without the neutrality being interfered with. The word "replacement" received further justification after Mitscherlich had studied the phenomena of isomorphism. It could then be said that certain elements in a crystal might be replaced by others without alteration of the crystalline form. Such substitutions possessed the peculiarity, however, that they were not connected with any proportions by weight, and it may thus appear all the more remarkable that they should render important assistance in the determination of atomic weights. The hypothesis underlying the phenomena of isomorphism was that one atom could only be replaced by one other; that is to say, that the numbers of the atoms in isomorphous compounds must be identical. Since chemically similar substances had alone been compared, an extension of the prevailing views, based on the phenomena of isomorphism, would have been quite possible; but this class of phenomena had never led to any attack upon the system.

In the bleaching of wax by means of chlorine, Gay-Lussac had observed that for every volume of hydrogen eliminated, an equal volume of chlorine was taken up. He had also found the same thing in the action of chlorine on hydrocyanic acid. In the course of their investigation of the benzoyl compounds, previously referred to, Wöhler and Liebig, when acting with chlorine upon bitter almond oil, had discovered benzoyl chloride; and they expressly remark that this substance is produced from the bitter-almond oil by two atoms of chlorine taking the place of two of hydrogen.

In the year 1834 Dumas à propos of an investigation on the mutual action between chlorine and oil of turpentine, but more especially of his work upon the production of chloral from alcohol, condensed into two empirical rules the facts with regard to substitution, for which he proposed the designation metalepsy (*i.e.*, exchange, μετάληψις). These were not intended to comprise a theory of substitution, as his first utterances on the subject show, but only to give expression to the facts. They were as follows:

"When a compound containing hydrogen is exposed to the dehydrogenizing action of chlorine, bromine, or iodine, it takes up an equal volume of chlorine, bromine, etc., for each atom of hydrogen that it loses.

"If the compound contains water, it loses the hydrogen of this without replacement."

The second of these rules was deduced from the transformation of alcohol into chloral, and was thus intended to explain the mode of formation of the latter and at the same time to support Dumas' view of the constitution of alcohol, the latter being regarded by him as a compound of ethylene and water.

By means of various examples, Dumas further endeavored to prove the general validity of the laws which he advanced. In establishing the correct composition of the Dutch oil he pointed out that the chloride of carbon obtained from it by means of chlorine, and examined by Faraday, supplied a new argument in favor of the accuracy of his views. He also found similar support in the action of chlorine on hydrocyanic acid, on bitter almond oil, etc.

However, he was unsatisfied with this, and extended his statement to one of greater significance, regarding oxidations as cases of substitution, as, for instance, the conversion of alcohol into acetic acid.

While Dumas limited himself at this time (1835) to condensing the known facts into the above laws, Auguste Laurent (1807-1853), a pupil of Dumas, went further, and considered the nature of the compounds resulting from substitution and made a comparison of them with the original ones. He was thereby induced to enunciate the proposition that the structure and chemical nature of organic compounds are not materially changed by the entrance of chlorine and the separation of hydrogen. This law is the core of the substitution theory proper, of which Laurent was the propounder.

Laurent endeavored to give expression to the observed facts, and to the hypotheses based upon them, in the so-called nucleus theory. This theory is of importance in the science (altho it never obtained any general recognition in it) because chemists have adopted, if in another form, many of the ideas embraced by it, and also because it was adopted by Gmelin as the basis of the organic portion of his excellent handbook. On this account the chief points of Laurent's doctrines will be stated.

According to Laurent, all organic substances contain certain nuclei, which he calls either fundamental ("radicaux fondamentaux") or derived. The former are compounds of carbon with hydrogen, in which the mutual proportion of the number of the atoms is a simple one (1 to 2, 3, 4, etc., 2 to 3, etc.). For any definite proportion, several nuclei exist which are polymeric among themselves. Besides, these fundamental radicals are so chosen that the hydrogen and carbon atoms contained in them occur in pairs.

The derived nuclei ("radicaux dérivés") were produced from the original nuclei, either through the substitution of hydrogen by other elements or by the addition of other atoms.

This theory manifestly sprang from the old radical theory, but with an important change, namely: the radical here is not an unchanging group of atoms, but it is a combination which can be changed through the substitution of equivalents. It is but a step in the evolution of the modern theory, as seen in the benzene nucleus.

The nucleus theory was regarded as unscientific by Liebig, and Berzelius opposed it, but the latter was moved before long by Malaguti's investigation of the simple and compound ethers—in which he demonstrated that the chlorine atoms again played the part just as the hyrodgen atoms they had displaced—and, as Armitage observes in his "History of Chemistry," he saw "that here was the thin edge of a most potent wedge, which, unless immediately removed, might break down the whole fabric of that chemical theory he had spent so much on building."

Before Laurent, in conjunction with Gerhardt, had again brought forward his ideas in a more perfect form, Dumas entered the lists to do battle against the radical theory, and, with this, against the dualistic idea in general. His beautiful discovery of "chloracetic acid" afforded him the immediate occasion for this, and he now gave in his adhesion to Laurent's opinions, which formerly he would have nothing to do with.

By the action of chlorine, in sunlight, upon acetic acid, Dumas had obtained a crystalline substance whose composition could be expressed by the formula $C_4Cl_6H_2O_4$, and which could, therefore, be regarded as acetic acid, $C_4H_8O_4$, in which six atoms or volumes of hydrogen were replaced by six atoms of chlorine. The interesting and important part of this reaction lay in the properties of the new compound, which Dumas called chloracetic acid. This acid had the same saturating capacity as acetic acid, so that Dumas was able to assert that by the entrance of chlorine in place of the hydrogen, the chief character of the compound was not altered; or, as he expresses himself, "that in organic chemistry there are certain types which persist even when an equal volume of chlorine, bromine, or iodine is introduced into them in place of the hydrogen which they contain."

He was thus led to the same view which had already been taken up by Laurent, but his theory of types (1839) was hardly a mere application of the views of Laurent. The principal propositions of this theory were as follows:

1. The elements of a compound body can, in many cases, be replaced by equivalents of other elements or of compound bodies which play the part of simple ones.

2. If such a substitution occurs equivalent for equivalent, the compound in which the replacement has taken place retains its "chemical type," and the element or group which has been taken up plays in it the same part as the element which has gone out.

The term "chemical type" failed to satisfy Dumas, however, and he permitted it to merge into that of "mechanical type," which included all compounds which might be supposed to be formed from one another by substitution, even tho they differed in properties.

Berzelius could not accept these views, and when Dumas characterized his electrochemical theory as erroneous, an embittered discussion ensued which lasted for years. The proposition of Dumas that every chemical compound forms a complete whole and cannot therefore consist of two parts, that its chemical character is dependent primarily upon the arrangement and number of the atoms, and in a lesser degree upon their chemical nature, proclaimed a decided unitarism, and was therefore violently opposed by Berzelius.

Berzelius sought to get over the difficulties which the substitution of hydrogen by chlorine and other elements involved, by arguing that compounds formed in this manner must have a constitution different from that of the original ones. But here he entered upon dangerous ground, and was thereby led, prudent investigator as he was, into the most utter contradictions of the principles which he had formerly held to be inviolable.

Facts now increased which went to demonstrate the correctness of the theory of substitution, and in 1842 Melsens found that by the action of potassium amalgam on a water solution of trichloracetic acid, its chlorine was completely replaced by hydrogen, acetic acid being reproduced. This way a discovery of the greatest import, as it showed inverse substitution was possible, yet it did not shake Berzelius's faith. He merely decided to look upon acetic acid in the same way as its chlorine derivative—*i.e.*, as a copulated oxalic acid with copula methyl, C_2H_3, formulating the two compounds thus:

$C_2H_3 + C_2O_3HO$ .... Acetic acid.
$C_2Cl_3 + C_2O_3HO$ .... Chloracetic acid.

This was practically giving up the fight, as by it he acknowledged that the "Paarling," or copula, could undergo substitution, and that its exact nature did not have a predominating influence in determining the nature of the compound into which it entered. Yet Berzelius remained an opponent of the theory of types until his death in 1848, and his adherents experienced great difficulty in reconstructing radicals anew from his copulæ after his death.

In 1845, A. W. Hofmann discovered the substituted anilines, and observed that it appeared without doubt that chlorine or bromine could assume the rôle of hydrogen in organic compounds, taking their electro-negative character with them into the new compounds. Liebig commented on Hofmann's report as follows: "The author appears to have definitely proved that the chemical nature of a compound does not in any way depend upon the nature of the elements contained in it as is assumed by the electro-chemical theory, but entirely on their arrangement." Liebig now turned to the unitary theory and opposed Berzelius's attempted explanations. Other prominent chemists, too, became his opponents, and yet, in spite of the slight regard in which the radical theory was held in many quarters, it soon became evident that, for the investigation of chemical constitution, the assumption of radicals, which had been displaced by the theory of types, was indispensable.

In the fifth decade a fusion of the radical theory with the doctrine of types occurred on the Unitary side, and as a result of the work of Auguste Laurent and Charles Gerhardt (1816-1856) the older theory of types was transformed into the new theory.

In 1839, Gerhardt published his views on the process which occurs when an element is replaced by a group of atoms. In his opinion it was not a substitution, but a union of two residues to a unitary whole and not an articulated binary compound. He termed these groups of atoms "le reste" or "le restant," and later developed his theory of residues, according to which a residue could have the composition of a compound radical but was not present as such in a compound. His conception of radicals soon replaced the older views, and its introduction into the theory of types induced a fusion of both theories.

The first advance in this direction was made in 1849, when C. A. Wurtz (1817-1884) discovered the compound ammonias. Hofmann found another method of preparing the bases discovered by Wurtz, and the "typical" view of these bases was first arrived at by means of his investigations. He showed that in the amine bases, as well as in aniline, the two hydrogen atoms of the amide could be replaced by alcohol radicals. A. W. Williamson (1824-1904) then demonstrated that in a similar manner the alcohols and their ethers could be referred to the type water. He also pointed out that acetic acid must have a constitution similar to that of alcohol, and proposed to call the radical C_2H_3O, obtained from ethyl by oxygen substitution, othyl. Gerhardt, employing a reaction similar to that by which Williamson had prepared the ethers, discovered the anhydrous acids; and chemists began to attempt to find among the more simple inorganic compounds other types for organic compounds, thereby giving rise to Gerhardt's theory of types. According to this theory, the organic compounds of known constitution can be classified under four types, namely, hydrogen, hydrochloric acid, water, and ammonia; for example, the hydrocarbons, aldehydes, and the acetones or ketones were classed in the first type; the halides (chlorides, bromides, iodides, and fluorides) in the second; the alcohols, ethers, monobasic acids, and sulphides and hydrosulphides in the third; and the amines were placed in the fourth type.

The general arrangement and the comprehensive character of Gerhardt's system leave nothing to be desired. Even altho views have been considerably changed and cleared up since that time, and altho one is compelled, from the modern standpoint, to look upon the types as insufficient, still Gerhardt's services to chemistry can never be questioned. Unfortunately he did not live to witness the reception which was extended by many chemists to the views laid down by him in the fourth volume of his "Lehrbuch der Organischen Chemie." The type theory was particularly extended by the assumption of "mixed types," which was intended to render clear the relations of many organic compounds to two or more types. This was particularly applied by August Kekulé.

It was also in the fifth decade that Hermann Kolbe (1818-1884) revived the much-ridiculed copulæ. He and Sir Edward Frankland (1825-1899) were followers of Berzelius, and held similar views to Gerhardt, but as they did not accept at that time either the new atomic weights or the existence of radicals containing oxygen, they made use of other formulæ.

Kolbe united the conclusions deduced from his researches with the declining theory of Berzelius; he induced the latter with new life by casting aside whatever of it was dead and replacing this by vigorous principles. From his own and other investigations he came to the conclusion that the unalterability of radicals, as taught by Berzelius, could no longer be maintained, since the facts of substitution had to be taken into account. He did, indeed, adopt Berzelius' hypothesis of copulæ, but attached another meaning to these, since he allowed that they exercised a not inconsiderable influence upon the compounds with which they were copulated.

He endeavored to make this theory have a deeper bearing upon the constitution of organic compounds, and, as a result of the influence of several important researches, his ideas regarding copulæ and conjugated compounds were altered several times. His theoretical views and, with them, the revived radical theory reached their completed form in a contribution published in 1859.

The principal result of Kolbe's speculations is given as follows: "Organic compounds are all derivatives of inorganic, or result from the latter—in some cases directly—by wonderfully simple substitution-processes." This idea runs through the 1859 contribution and is illustrated by numerous examples from the wide field of organic chemistry.

CHAPTER XIII

VALENCE, THE CONSTITUTION OF ORGANIC COMPOUNDS, AND THE DEVELOPMENT OF STEREO-CHEMISTRY

In the preceding chapter mention has been made of the influence exerted by Frankland on the views developed by Kolbe respecting the constitution of organic compounds. It was Frankland who, in his now classical paper—"A New Series of Organic Compounds containing Metals"—demonstrated that the pairing of the radicals with the elements was to be explained on the ground of some characteristic property of the atoms, and thus he expelled the useless part of the radical theory (1852).

Frankland observed that "When the formulæ of inorganic chemical compounds are considered, even a superficial observer is struck with the general symmetry of their constitution; the compounds of nitrogen, phosphorus, antimony and arsenic especially exhibit the tendency of these elements to form compounds containing 3 or 5 equivalents of other elements, and it is in these proportions that their affinities are best satisfied; thus in the ternal group we have NO_3, NH_3, NI_3, NS_3, PO_3, PH_3, PCl_3, SbO_3, SbH_3, $SbCl_3$, AsO_3, AsH_3, $AsCl_3$, etc.; and in the five atom group NO_5, NH_4O, NH_4I, PO_5, PH_4I, etc. Without offering any hypothesis regarding the cause of this symmetrical grouping of atoms, it is sufficiently evident, from the examples just given, that such a tendency or law prevails, and that, no matter what the character of the uniting atoms may be, the combining power of the attracting element, if I may be allowed the term, is always satisfied by the same number of these atoms."

He then proceeded to represent the organo-metallic compounds obtained by formulæ which brought out the analogy with the inorganic types, from which they were thought to have been derived.

From his work on the organo-metallic compounds, Frankland developed the doctrine of the valence of the elements, the germ of which may be recognized in much that has gone before, particularly in the law of multiple proportions, which stated that the elements show different yet definite stages in their combinations.

The so-called doctrine of the polybasic acids contributed materially to the development of ideas upon the subject of the saturation capacity of the atoms. Gay-Lussac, Gmelin, and others inclined to the assumption that the atoms of the various metallic oxides contained one atom of oxygen united to one atom of metal, and that these oxides combined with one atom of acid to form neutral salts. Berzelius also, after 1826, considered that this combining proportion was the rule. However, by Thomas Graham's famous investigation of the phosphoric acids (1833), it was shown that a view so simple as this, according to which almost every acid was looked upon as monobasic, was untenable. Graham proved that in the ortho-, pyro-, and metaphosphoric acids, for each "atom" of phosphorus pentoxide there were three, two and one "atoms" of "basic water," these latter being replaced by equivalent amounts of metallic oxides.

The saturation capacities of these acids were in this way shown to be dependent upon the amounts of "basic water" which entered into their constitution. Liebig extended this to many other acids and distinguished between mono-, di-, and tri-basic acids, and the property was referred to as the "basicity" of the atoms, a term which, with the ideas inherent in it, clung for some time to the theory of valence. In 1857, for example, the terms "basicity," "valency," and "atomicity" were used as synonymous, and as the measure of the number of hydrogen atoms that could be replaced or held in combination.

The idea of "basicity" was soon extended to the compound organic radicals. In 1855, C. A. Wurtz (1817-1884), a pupil of Liebig and Dumas, showed that glycerine ($C_3H_8O_3$) may be regarded as the hydrate of the radical C_3H_5. Four years previous A. W. Williamson (1824-1904) had expressed the view that a large number of compounds may be referred to the type of water, the mono-basic acids to one molecule, and the polybasic acids, which are of greater molecular complexity, to a condensed water type. He wrote

$$\begin{matrix}C_2H_3O\\H\end{matrix} O = \text{acetic acid}\dots\dots\dots \begin{matrix}SO_2\\H_2\end{matrix} O_2 = \text{sulphuric acid.}$$

Wurtz now showed that the composition of glycerine could be represented by the formula

$$\begin{matrix}C_3H_5'''\\\\H_3\end{matrix} O_3,$$ which was similar to the formula by which, in accordance with the ideas of Williamson, ordinary phosphoric acid $$\begin{matrix}(PO)'''\\\\H_3\end{matrix} O_3$$ was represented.

Gerhardt in his "Traité de Chimie Organique" stated that "In order to compare the radicles among themselves, I propose to refer them all to the radicle of hydrogen, and consequently I name them monatomic, diatomic, triatomic according to the quantity of hydrogen which they are capable of replacing in the type H_2O—*i.e.*, according to whether they are equivalent to 1, 2, or 3 atoms of hydrogen—so for instance in alcohol and in ether:

$$\begin{array}{cc} C_2H_5 & C_2H_5 \\ O & O \\ H & C_2H_5 \end{array}$$

C_2H_5, the radicle ethyl, is monatomic because it replaces H (one atom of hydrogen) in the type water."

The terms "monatomic" and "polyatomic" had been employed much earlier, but in a different sense. Thus, in 1827, Berzelius called fluorine, chlorine, etc., "polyatomic," because several atoms of these halogens unite with a single atom of another element. In 1833, Gaudin de Saintes used the same terms to express the number of atoms in a molecule, in which sense they were used by Gmelin, Clausius, and Odling. Williamson attached the idea of capacity for saturation or atomicity of the radical to the number of hydrogen atoms capable of substitution, and the notion of atomicity was soon extended to the known compound radicals and played an important part in the theories of types, etc., which obtained in organic chemistry.

Frankland's speculations concerning the substitution value of radicals compared with that of elementary atoms were of great importance, yet they did not meet with immediate approval.

By 1858, however, the valence theory had made rapid progress. In this year August Kekulé first deduced the valence of carbon from its simplest compounds, declaring it to be tetravalent. This had already been recognized by Kolbe and Frankland, if not expressly stated by them. But Kekulé rendered further and much greater service by inquiring into the manner in which two or more of these tetravalent carbons were united with one another. The doctrine of atomic chains, open and closed, sprang from this, and the domination of the structural idea in chemistry became complete.

In the same year and independently of Kekulé, M. S. Couper arrived at conclusions almost identical with those of Kekulé.

Both Kekulé and Couper expressed with absolute definiteness the axiom that the "atomicity of the elements" was to be made use of for arriving at the constitution of chemical compounds. The idea of the term "atomicity" had without any doubt been introduced by Frankland six years previous to this. The further development of the above axiom and its utilization in the theory of the linking of atoms was carried out mainly by Kekulé, and in the succeeding years also by Butlerow and Erlenmeyer.

While the radical and type theories were attempts at securing an idea of the structure of chemical compounds, it was the valence theory which rendered it possible to furnish a lucid answer to the question as to the composition of such bodies; and, especially after the year 1870, the determination of the constitution of complex molecules became the higher aim of chemistry.

Some rudiments of systematic classification had before this been introduced into organic chemistry, and these classificatory beginnings were of great assistance in the erection of structural chemistry. In 1836, Laurent, when he brought forward his nucleus series, arranged organic compounds in series, and it was in 1841 that Gerhardt entered on a research to discover some general law which might suggest an all-sufficing system of classification, and the following year he was ready with his "ladder of combustion"—with its highest rung cerebral matter, its lowest carbonic acid, water and ammonia—to enfold the whole science of organic chemistry. He soon found, however, that this arrangement, according to mere complexity of composition, was no sufficient classification, so he betook himself to another line of inquiry. A note of triumph seems to ring through the following lines from the preface to his "Précis de Chimie Organique," published in 1844: "I have succeeded in establishing homologous series. . . . These have indicated to me the means of classifying organic substances in natural families, and of disposing them on a kind of combustion ladder." As a matter of fact, it was only the word "homology" that Gerhardt could claim as his own. Two years earlier J. Schiel had shown that a very simple relation existed between the alcohols then known, that their radicals might all be represented by the general expression $nR + H$, R suggesting the group C_2H_2 ($C = 6$); moreover, in the same year Dumas had demonstrated the existence of a similar relation between the several members of the fatty acids known to him. Yet Gerhardt generalized from this fact of homology and proved the possibility of predicting the existence of terms unknown in his series.

Many systems of classification were suggested during the sixth decade, the classification by series as that of Schiel and Dumas, that of series depending upon formulæ, series depending upon chemical behavior, and many other systems. The lack of agreement among chemists, however, as to the formulæ belonging to the different compounds, as to the relative weights of the molecules, the atomic weights, and even the number of atoms, prevented a general acceptance of any of the classifications proposed until Kekulé established the fact of the tetravalence of the carbon atom, showed the difference between saturated and unsaturated compounds, and deduced his chain formulæ.

About 1860 Frankland's views regarding a saturation capacity peculiar to the elements were accepted either delitescently or expressly by most chemists, but it was considered that this saturation capacity, under certain circumstances, might be a varying one. In 1856, Gerhardt had stated that nitrogen was sometimes triatomic and sometimes pentatomic. This view was also held by Frankland, Wurtz, Williamson and Couper, and the latter three considered that the valence was also variable in the cases of many other elements. Kolbe thought it must be assumed that a constant valency was characteristic of a few elements and a varying one characteristic of many more, since he perceived in it another expression for the law of multiple proportions and nothing was known concerning the cause of valence. As early as 1854, Kolbe had concluded that each element possessed a maximum saturation capacity, but that lower stages of saturation might exist along with this; and toward the beginning of the sixties, several chemists who took an active part in developing the structure theory expressed the same opinion in a more definite manner. Erlenmeyer, in particular, maintained in various papers, and afterward in his "Lehrbuch der organischen Chemie," that each element possesses a maximum valency, or that each is furnished with a definite number of "Affinivalenten" or affinity-points ("Affinitätspunkten"), only part of these, however, being in many cases combined with the affinity-points of other elements.

Kekulé's theory of the constant valence of the elements could not withstand the critical examinations to which it was subjected, however, and in the course of the last forty years the majority of chemists have adopted the view that the atoms of most of the elements possess a varying saturation capacity, varying according to the conditions.

Altho the structure theory was unable to accomplish the extreme expectations which aimed at a knowledge of the spacial arrangement of the atoms, it possessed none the less great practical value. The development of organic chemistry since the middle of the sixth decade shows in fact that, through the aid of the structural hypothesis, the discovery of new modes of formation and decomposition of compounds, the recognition of the relations existing between various classes of bodies, and, especially, the interpretation of the constitution of numerous organic substances became possible. Kekulé's theory of the aromatic compounds forms the most striking proof of this.

In 1865-1866, taking the quadrivalence of carbon as his principle, Kekulé called attention to the fact that in the fatty compounds the carbon atoms are linked together by one valence of each. In the case of benzene, the next simplest assumption was made, in accordance with which the carbon atoms are linked together by one and two valencies alternately, so as to form a closed chain or ring. Of the twenty-four affinities of the six carbon atoms, eighteen are employed in linking carbon to carbon, thus:

$$\frac{6}{2}.4 + \frac{6}{2}.2 = 18$$

Six valencies then remain which are satisfied by the six hydrogen atoms of the benzene. Hence, according to Kekulé, benzene may be represented by means of a regular hexagon whose sides are composed of single and of double lines alternately, the CH groups occupying the corners, thus:

$$\begin{array}{c} H \\ C \\ \diagup \diagdown\!\!\!\!\diagdown \\ HC \quad CH \\ \| \quad\; | \\ HC \quad CH \\ \diagdown \;\;\; \diagup\!\!\!\!\diagup \\ C \\ H \end{array}$$

Kekulé and his pupils, together with many other chemists who had busied themselves with the derivatives of benzene after this view had been published, now directed their efforts to comparing all the known and rapidly increasing observations bearing upon this class of bodies with the deductions drawn from the above formula, and therewith to proving by actual experiment the admissibility of the assumptions on which the formula was based. The result was that Kekulé's anticipations were realized and his hypothesis substantiated.

In 1866, Kekulé had stated that "What is wanted is that the largest possible number of substitution products of benzene should be prepared by the most diverse methods; that they should be most carefully compared with regard to isomerism; that the modifications so found should be counted. . . ."

And in the 1867 edition of his text-book, he called attention to a number of cases of isomerism which at that time had received no explanation. Among these we find that of ethylene chloride with ethylidene chloride; of acetal with diethyl glycol; for maleic and fumaric, for mucic and saccharic acids, the last effort of his philosophy had only found him the two formulæ $\left.\begin{array}{l}C_4H_2''O_2\\H_2\end{array}\right\}O_2$ and $\left.\begin{array}{l}C_6H_8''O_6\\H_2\end{array}\right\}O_2$ respectively. Kekulé instanced, too, those bodies which only differed in their effect on polarized light, the tartaric, the malic and camphoric acids, and the amyl alcohols.

It was owing to these cases of isomerism that structural formulæ could not be assigned. In some cases a greater number of isomeric bodies were known than could possibly be accounted for by an arrangement of the atoms in formulæ upon a plane surface, retaining, of course, the accepted views as to valence, etc., and since these isomers differed principally in certain physical properties, they were at first termed "physical isomers." The study of these resulted in the consideration of the arrangement of atoms in space—the chemistry of space, or Stereochemistry, in which branch of the science an extended view of atomic grouping was essayed.

Modern stereochemistry was anticipated by Emmanuel Swedenborg in 1721, when he made an attempt to explain the phenomena of chemistry and physics on geometrical principles in his "Prodromous Principiorum rerum Naturalium sive Novorum Tentaminum Chymiam et Physicam Experimentalem Geometrice Explicandi," and similar beginnings were made by Johann Barchusen ten years earlier.

In 1865 Carius, who first used the term "physical isomerism," explained it as follows:

"I have tentatively expressed a view as to the cause of what I call 'physical isomerism.' Substances [which exhibit this property] yield, under the same or nearly the same conditions, products which are either identical or physically isomeric. According to our present views, I think it improbable that such substances should have their atoms differently arranged—*i.e.*, that they should be metameric. But it is quite conceivable that in the formation of physical isomers differences of condition may cause the production of substances with the same arrangement of the atoms within the molecule, but with a different aggregation of these molecules; and that thereon depends the difference in their properties. . . . Thus we must consider as certainly only physically isomeric a large number of the substances distinguished by the difference of their action on polarized light, such as the two modifications of amyl alcohol, the tartaric acids, the malic acids, etc."

This explanation was inadequate, and in 1873 Johannes Wislicenus (1835-1902), who succeeded Kolbe as professor of chemistry at Leipzig in 1885, suggested the substitution of the term "geometrical isomerism" for "physical isomerism." He had been engaged in an investigation of the various modifications of lactic acid, and has found that the ethylene lactic acid, or hydracrylic acid, prepared by Beilstein by treating β-iodo-propionic acid with silver oxide, possessed properties different from those of the ethylene lactic acid obtained from ethylene cyanhydrin. This difference was so marked that he thought it might be explained by assigning the two acids different structural formulæ. The first was optically inactive, while the second (paralactic acid) was dextro-rotary. This one point of difference appeared hardly sufficient to "make it necessary to assign to paralactic acid a structural formula other than that of the fermentation lactic acid." It seemed much more likely that here, at any rate, were cases of what Carius had called "physical," but what Wislicenus now proposed to call "geometrical isomerism." He said, "My conclusion for the present is to declare paralactic acid and the fermentation lactic acid as most probably only geometrically isomeric. Their great similarity, even identity in all chemical properties, the ease of transformation, on heating, of the first into the second, and their differences, particularly in optical behavior, may all alike be explained on this basis.

"Concerning the special 'how' of this explanation, I am engaged in experimental investigations."

The next year J. H. Van't Hoff furnished an answer to this. However, before giving his exposition, mention must be made of Louis Pasteur's (1822-1895) pioneer work in this field. Pasteur studied the various tartrates crystallographically, and showed that there are four isomeric tartaric acids, viz.: racemic acid, inactive tartaric acid, and right and left rotating tartaric acids. He showed, moreover, that the two latter acids crystallize in similar, but in oppositely built-up (enantiomorph) forms; that they both rotate a ray of polarized light through equal angles, but in opposite senses; and that when mixed in equal quantities they yield optically inactive racemic acid. Further, he succeeded in decomposing racemic acid again into the two optically active tartaric acids by three different methods.

Pasteur established the correlation of molecular disymmetry and rotary power in these investigations, and it remained to discover under what conditions the dissymmetry could obtain in two molecules structurally identical. This was undertaken in 1874 by J. H. Van't Hoff in Holland and J. A. Le Bel in France, who in papers published that year offered an explanation practically the same for cases of isomerism which could not be included under the theories of the time.

Van't Hoff states that in general Le Bel's original paper and his were in accord, but that while Pasteur's researches formed Le Bel's starting point, he took for his own "Kekulé's law of the tetravalence of carbon, [to which he] added the hypothesis that the four valencies are directed toward the corners of the tetrahedron in the center of which is the carbon atom." To quote from Freund's "Study of Chemical Composition," "Van't Hoff introduced no fundamental change in, or addition to, the original valency hypothesis; a two-dimensional representation of molecular structure could not at any time have been considered as really true to the actual occurrence, but it was legitimate to use it, because of its greater simplicity, as long as it proved adequate to the purpose. And with this recognition and restriction we continue to use plane structural formulæ in the majority of cases."

Van't Hoff, following up the suggestion that may be found implied in Pasteur's paper, and that was implicitly stated by Wislicenus, introduces into the science the consideration of the arrangement of atoms in space:

"Stereochemistry [from στερεός, solid], in their restricted sense of the word, comprises chemical phenomena which demands a consideration of the grouping of atoms in space."

Carbon compounds only were considered at first, but the scope of the phenomena dealt with has been extended and now includes compounds of trivalent and pentavalent nitrogen, of tin, and of sulphur.

Van't Hoff's theory of the asymmetric carbon atom, however, met with difficulties on its enunciation. To quote from F. P. Armitage's "History of Chemistry":

"When Van't Hoff enunciated his theory of the asymmetric carbon atom, he was able to say, with much show of truth, that all optically active substances did contain certainly one such atom. Soon, however, were heard dissentient voices. What of propyl alcohol, asked one; and of styrolene, demanded another. The propyl alcohol owes its activity to traces of amyl alcohol, answered Henniger; the styrolene is impure, said Van't Hoff; and their evidence was irrefutable. But Van't Hoff could not, in 1874, maintain that the presence of one asymmetric carbon atom necessarily implied optical activity; for secondary amyl alcohol and its derivatives, also propylene alcohol, were certainly inactive, yet all contained an asymmetric carbon atom. The problem set the stereochemists was somewhat similar to that of the relation between tartaric and racemic acid, so happily solved years before by Pasteur. His methods were recalled; and Le Bel soon showed that these inactive bodies were in reality mixtures of two optically opposite isomers, and, others helping, that indeed every substance with but one asymmetric carbon atom was equally capable of "mesotomism." The four varieties of tartaric acid had offered no difficulty; with two asymmetric carbon atoms similarly habited there was necessarily neutralization or duplication of optical activity. But where two or more carbon atoms occurred, asymmetric by union with different radicals, as in the sugars and their derivatives, many more cases of physical isomerism suggested themselves, and have since been verified. Without doubt the asymmetric carbon atom has made a triumphant progress, winning for Le Bel the Jecker prize in 1881, for Van't Hoff a dominant voice in the scientific councils of the world; it will rank with the phlogiston of Stahl, the oxygen of Lavoisier, the atom of Dalton, and the dualism of Berzelius."

Among the most noted workers in the field of stereochemistry have been A. von Baeyer, Wallach, Victor Meyer, Riecke, Bischoff, Werner, Hantzsch, Auwers and Overton. Even now the subject is in its infancy, and stereochemical theories are as yet insufficiently advanced to present a clear view of the question of geometrical isomerism, yet, as Ladenburg has said, "It is beyond doubt that the founding and development of stereochemistry (a name which originated with Victor Meyer) is the most important thing that was accomplished in organic chemistry during the last two decades of the nineteenth century. Stereochemistry possesses a significance for this period similar to that which the foundation and introduction of the theory of aromatic compounds possessed for the twenty years preceding."

CHAPTER XIV

PROGRESS IN INORGANIC CHEMISTRY DURING THE MODERN PERIOD

A RAPID growth in inorganic chemistry ensued after the introduction of the New Chemistry by Lavoisier. A mass of information concerning the nature of the elements and their compounds was accumulated, and many new bodies were discovered. However, even now, after the accurate study of the chemical behavior of mineral substances by many careful investigators, we are still far from a definite knowledge of the nature of all the elements and their compounds, and new bodies are from time to time added to the extensive series already known. In the case of the elements, for example, Lavoisier in his "Traité de Chimie" mentioned twenty-six, while eighty-one are at the the present time accepted. An endeavor to sketch the important advances in inorganic chemistry since the time of Davy and Gay-Lussac will be made in this chapter.

Cadmium was discovered by Stromeyer in 1817 and about the same time by Hermann. It was named by Stromeyer "cadmia fornicum" (furnace zinc), because it was found in the zinc furnace, cadmia being the original name for zinc.

In the same year lithium was discovered by Arfvedson in petalite and spodumene. The metal was first obtained by Bunsen and Matthiessen in 1855. The name is Greek and means stony, and the metal was so called because it was then supposed to be found only in rocks, and not in the plant and animal bodies.

Silicon was first isolated in 1810 by Berzelius by fusing together iron, carbon and quartz, and Wöhler showed that it exists in the crystalline form as well as in the amorphous state.

In 1827, Wöhler isolated aluminium by the action of potassium upon its chloride, and eighteen years later St. Claire Deville prepared the metal on a large scale by using sodium, while Bunsen effected its preparation by electrolytic means. Aluminium is now prepared in quantity by the electrolytic decomposition of the oxide, alumina, dissolved in cryolite. Beryllium, or glucinum, was also obtained by Wöhler, who effected its isolation in 1828 by the action of potassium upon the chloride. Bromine was isolated by Balard in 1826 from the mother liquor by sea-salt, and was further investigated three years later by Löwig; along with iodine, which was discovered by Courtois in 1811 in the ashes of sea plants, and chlorine, it constituted the group of halogen elements of Berzelius, since fluorine was then unknown. The latter was first isolated in 1886 by Moissan by the electrolysis of hydrogen fluoride in the presence of potassium fluoride.

Tellurium, which had been discovered by Müller von Reichenstein in 1782, was thoroly investigated by Berzelius, who discovered an element chemically analogous to it—selenium—in 1817.

The isolation of the metals comprising the cerium and yttrium groups has presented numerous difficulties. Altho the discovery of yttria—impure, it is true, from admixture with other earths—was accomplished by Gadolin in 1794, and investigators have busied themselves with the question, the chemistry of the cerium metals is not even yet completely elucidated, and may possibly remain unsolved for a considerable time to come. After Klaproth and Berzelius had independently prepared cerium sesquioxide from cerite, and the latter had identified this as the oxide of a metal, Mosander discovered two new oxides in crude yttria, the metals of which—lanthanum (1834) and didymium (1841)—he isolated. Two years later (1843) he added to these two others, erbium and terbium, whose existence and nature is not yet, however, definitely settled, in spite of the admirable work which has been done on the subject. This has given us a better knowledge of yttrium, while yttria, which was formerly held to be a homogeneous substance, has proved itself a mixture of the oxides of various metals, of which, however, only one or two have as yet been isolated; for example, the discovery of scandium by Nilson and Cleve in 1879, and of ytterbium by Marignac. The most recent additions to the knowledge of chemistry of this group of elements and their compounds have been made by Welsbach, Drossbach, Krüss, Winkler, Crookes, Brauner, Baskerville, Urbain and others. Welsbach separated didymium into praseo- and neodymium. An analytical method has been elaborated for the separation of the various constituents of the cerium, ytterbium and thorium earths, which has been of help in the manufacture of mantles for incandescent light burners. Quite recently Urbain has separated ytterbium into two other elements—neoytterbium and lutecium. In spectrum analysis, chemistry now possesses an exceedingly valuable instrument for investigating rare metals and earths, and its use in the last five decades has been extensive.

Spectrum analysis has grown out of some apparently insignificant and disconnected observations made by Marggraf, Scheele, Herschel and others upon the light emitted by flames colored by certain salts. The spectra of such flames were investigated by various scientists, among whom Talbot, Miller, Alter and Swan deserve first mention; but it was only after Kirchhoff (in 1860) proved the definite statement—that every glowing vapor emits rays of the same degree of refrangibility that it absorbs—that spectrum analysis became developed by Bunsen and himself into one of the great branches of our science. Its importance for analytical chemistry, especially in the discovery of new elements, is almost beyond mention, and it opened up a new era in chemistry.

Roscoe once said, "The spectroscope, next to the balance, is the most useful and important instrument which the chemist possesses." Crookes has remarked, "If I name the spectroscope as the most important scientific invention of the latter half of this century, I shall not fear to be accused of exaggeration." The very importance of the subject prevents an entrance into any long discussion of it here. It has come to form a distinct branch of chemical science. In the hands of men like Bunsen and Crookes it has explored the recesses of the rocks for minute traces of hidden treasures, while with it workers like Miller, Huggins and Lockyer have fathomed the abysses of space and determined the constitution of the stars.

Among the elements discovered by the use of the spectroscope were rubidium and cæsium in lepidolite and in the Durkheim mineral water by Bunsen and Kirchhoff; indium by Reich and Richter, in 1863, as a constituent of Freiberg zinc blende; gallium in 1875 by Lecoq de Boisbaudran; and thallium by Crookes in 1861. The chemical nature of the last-mentioned metal was established by Lamy in the same year.

The knowledge of the metals discovered in the preceding era was greatly enlarged by investigations conducted during this period. The analogues of nitrogen—phosphorus, arsenic, antimony and bismuth—were carefully examined, and the atomic weight which Berzelius determined for phosphorus was confirmed by Dumas, while his atomic weight for arsenic was corroborated by Pélouze and Dumas. The metals of the alkaline earths—barium, strontium, calcium and magnesium, which were isolated by Davy—were investigated by Berzelius, Marignac and Dumas, who determined their atomic weights. Recently Winkler found that magnesium is an excellent reducing agent for metallic oxides. Cobalt and nickel have been the subject of researches of an important nature, mainly because of the remarkable compounds they form—*e.g.*, nickel tetra-carbonyl and the ammonio-cobaltic compounds. Nickel is now extensively used in metallurgy, especially in the production of nickel steel.

The rarer metals have, of course, received considerable attention. Uranium, which was discovered by Klaproth in 1798, was investigated further by Péligot, Roscoe, and, lately, by Zimmermann, Molybdenum and tungsten, isolated respectively by Hjelm and d'Elhujar, have become better known, and the acids and the complicated salts of these have been studied by Scheibler, Marignac, Friedheim and Gibbs. Uranium, and, particularly, tungsten and molybdenum are now employed extensively as steel-hardening materials. Uranium compounds are also used in dyeing and ceramics.

Titanium, zirconium and thorium have now become, in the form of various compounds, particularly the oxide, of practical importance. Thorium was discovered by Berzelius in 1828; its oxide, thoria, is applied in the manufacture of Welsbach gas mantles, which consist essentially of a web of 99 per cent. thoria and 1 per cent. cerium oxide. Titanium is employed for the manufacture of special alloys, and zirconium, as zirconia, is made use of both in gas and electric illumination. Germanium, an element which resembles these in some respects, was discovered by Winkler in 1886 in a Freiberg silver ore.

The element vanadium, which was discovered by Del Rio in 1801, was isolated by Roscoe in 1867. He also investigated its compounds carefully, determining its different stages of combination with oxygen and chlorine. This metal, which is widely distributed, is utilized in the production of sheet and tool steel and armor plates. Tantalum, a related metal, which, along with columbium, or niobium, was examined exhaustively by Blomstrand and Marignac, is used in alloys to make small springs and anvils, and in the metallic form to make special incandescent electric light filaments.

The metals of the platinum group—platinum, palladium (Wollaston, 1803), rhodium (Wollaston, 1804), iridium (Tennant, 1803), osmium (Tennant, 1803), and ruthenium (Claus, 1844)—have been given careful consideration by chemists. Platinum is used extensively in making chemical apparatus, especially crucibles and stills; and osmium and iridium have recently come into use as filaments for incandescent lamps.

About fifteen years ago the number of the chemical elements was enlarged by two gases of great theoretical interest—argon and helium.

As early as 1785, Cavendish had noticed that a residue of about 0.6

per cent. remained when the nitrogen and oxygen were removed from air, and in 1894 Rayleigh discovered that nitrogen from the atmosphere was 0.5 per cent. heavier than nitrogen prepared chemically. Rayleigh and Ramsay then prepared large quantities of this atmospheric residue and found it to be a gas different from nitrogen. They called it "argon" from the Greek "argos," lazy.

Helium was discovered by Ramsay in 1895 in the mineral cleveite. It had already been found to exist in the chromosphere of the sun by Janssen in 1868, and his observations were confirmed by Frankland and Lockyer. Helium, primarily obtained by heating cleveite with sulphuric acid, and since found in small quantity—often together with argon—in the mineral uraninite, malacone, etc., as well as in the gases from some mineral water springs, is, like argon, inert and indifferent. Up to now, in spite of persistent effort, no compound of either argon or helium has been prepared. And further, altho many diffusion experiments with both gases have been carried out, with the object of seeing whether they were really elementary, the densities of both have remained unaltered—*i.e.*, it has been found impossible to subdivide them by diffusion into two or more components. From the ratio of the specific heats at constant volume and constant pressure, it follows that the molecule and atom are identical in both argon and helium—*i.e.*, that the gases are monatomic; and this applies also to the other more recently discovered gases of the air—krypton, neon and xenon.

These were separated from liquid air in 1898 by Ramsay and Travers. The atomic weights of these gases and the proportions in which they are present in the air are as follows:

	Atomic Weight.	One Part by Volume in Air.
Helium	4	2,450 volumes
Neon	20	808 "
Argon	39.9	105 "
Krypton	81.8	746,000 "
Xenon	128	3,846,000 "

Since the interest attached to these gases has been recently augmented by the discovery of Ramsay and Soddy that radium emanation eventually changes, at least in part, into helium, and since Ramsay has shown that when the radium emanation decays in the presence of water neon is produced, and that argon results when the decay takes place in the presence of water containing a copper salt in solution, the radioactive elements may be conveniently referred to here.

Henri Becquerel found in 1896 that compounds of uranium spontaneously and continuously emit some radiation which, among other properties, has that of making air a conductor of electricity. This effect, the quantity of which can be determined with great accuracy, was used by Mme. Sklodowska Curie to measure the amount of radiation produced by various compounds of uranium and of thorium, which latter had been found by Schmidt to emit the same kind of radiation.

She subsequently tested a large number of rocks and minerals, and found that certain minerals which contained uranium and thorium—*e.g.*, pitchblende (oxide of uranium), chalcolite (double phosphate of copper and uranium)—possess radio-activity much greater than that "theoretically" due to the amount of uranium present.

Mme. Curie therefore inferred that, "It appeared probable that if pitchblende, chalcolite, etc., possess so great a degree of activity, these substances contain a small quantity of a strongly radio-active body, differing from uranium and thorium and the simple bodies actually known. I thought that if this were indeed the case, I might hope to extract this substance from the ore by the ordinary methods of chemical analysis."

The investigation was consequently pursued, and, with the assistance of her husband, Pierre Curie, and Gustave Bémont, Mme. Curie commenced the laborious treatment of the residue remaining after the extraction of the uranium from pitchblende, a large quantity of which had been placed at her disposal by the Austrian Government, and finally separated the salts of radium in 1898. While endeavoring to isolate radium, Mme. Curie discovered polonium, and other investigators—Debierne, Giesel, Marckwald and Hofmann—have given the names of actinium, emanium, radio-tellurium and radio-lead to similar substances, the two last being possibly products of the spontaneous change in radium. Among those who have worked with success upon the problem of radio-activity, Elster and Geitel, Rutherford, Soddy and Ramsay may be mentioned here.

Radium maintains a temperature one or more degrees above that of the atmosphere, injures the eyes, and disorganizes the flesh when kept long in contact with it. Its peculiar properties have been explained in various ways. The most plausible suggestion is that atoms of high atomic weight slowly disintegrate into ultimate corpuscles or particles, and that this decomposition is attended with the development of great energy.

The successive disintegration of the radium atoms as exemplified by the disintegration products is shown in the following table, which represents, according to Ernest Rutherford, the complete radium series as at present known:

Element.	Radiation emitted.	Period.	Range of α particles in air at normal pressure.
Radium	α particles	2000 years[1]	3·5 cms.
↓ Emanation	α particles	3·8 days	4·2 cms.
↓ Ra. A	α particles	3 minutes	4·8 cms.
↓ Ra. B	β particles	26 minutes	—
↓ Ra. C	α and β particles, γ rays	19 minutes	7·06 cms
↓ Ra. D	?	40 years	—
↓ Ra. E	?	6 days	—
↓ Ra. F	β particles	4·5 days	—
↓ Ra. G	α particles	140 days	3·86 cms.
↓ ?			

(Ra. A through Ra. C: Rapid change; Ra. D through Ra. G: Slow change)

It appears that uranium is the source of radium, and Boltwood has recently announced that the immediate parent of radium, "ionium." Radium resembles barium chemically and, according to Mme. Curie and Thorpe, it has an atomic weight of 226.5. Several observers have demonstrated that it possesses a characteristic spectrum, and consequently, notwithstanding its disintegration and peculiar conduct, radium is regarded as a chemical element, owing to an affidation among chemists to recognize a body as a chemical element when, under proper conditions, it possesses a definite atomic weight and exhibits a spectrum containing characteristic and novel lines.

In 1823, Mitscherlich discovered the existence of sulphur in two different crystalline varieties—rhombic and oblique, and a third variety, the plastic form, was also known. Frankenheim learned that by heating and cooling, these varieties could at definite temperatures be converted into one another, and in describing these phenomena the term isomerism was employed, to which, however, Berzelius published

VIII

an objection in 1841. To quote from his "Jahresbericht" for that year:

"I feel compelled to call attention to the fact that the word isomerism, which is applied to different substances composed of an equal number of atoms of the same elements, is not compatible with the view as to the cause of the different properties exhibited by the various modifications of sulphur, carbon, silicon, etc. . . . While the term still lends itself to the expression of the relation between ethylformate and methylacetate, it is no longer suitable in the case of simple substances which assume different properties, and it might be desirable to substitute for it a better chosen term—*e.g.*, allotropy, or allotropic modifications. In accordance with these views there can be more than one cause for that which we call isomerism, namely:

(1) Allotropy, in which case . . . the difference between the sulphides of iron is due to the fact that they contain different modifications of sulphur.

(2) Differences in the relative position of the atoms in the compound, of which the two kinds of ether (ethylformate and methylacetate) are so striking a proof.

(3) A combination of (1) and (2)."

Since then the term allotropy has been in constant use, and numerous allotropic phenomena have been observed, particularly among the non-metals. The allotropism of carbon was the first observed example (1773), and its modification exhibit marked points of difference; for instance, comparing diamond and graphite:

		Crystallographic System	Optical Properties	Chemical and Physical Properties	Specific Gravity	Hardness
Carbon	Diamond	Cubic	Colorless, transparent; high refractive index, $\mu = 2.417$	Non-conductor of heat and electricity; not attacked by oxidizing agents; ignition temperature 760° to 875°	3.52	10
	Graphite	Hexagonal? Oblique?	Opaque	Good conductor of heat and electricity; oxidized to graphitic acid; ignition temperature 575° and above	2.25	1

When amorphous carbon (coal, peat, lampblack, etc.) and diamond are heated, they pass into the graphitic variety, and graphite is now produced in large amounts by heating carbon to a high temperature

(4,000° C.) by an alternating electric current. Henri Moissan (1852-1907), an eminent French chemist, succeeded in preparing synthetic diamonds by dissolving pure sugar charcoal in molten pure iron and suddenly cooling the mass by plunging it into water; and three English chemists, Sir F. A. Abel, W. H. Noble and Sir William Crookes, obtained diamonds by exploding some of the high explosives in steel bombs, the liquid carbon produced crystallizing as it cooled. However, no diamonds have thus far been produced of commercial size or amount.

The most peculiar, as well as noteworthy, example of allotropism is afforded by the conversion of oxygen into ozone. Ozone was first noticed by Van Marum in 1785 in electrified air. In 1840, C. F. Schönbein called attention again to this substance, discovering its oxidizing action, and showed that it was produced in the electrolysis of water and in the slow combustion of phosphorus and sulphur. He gave it the name "ozone," which means a smell. The investigations of Marignac, De la Rive, Becquerel, Tait, Fremy, Andrews and Brodie have proved it to be modified oxygen. Its density was determined by Soret in 1860. The latter, and before him Andrews, proved that the ozone molecule contains three atoms of oxygen, while a molecule of the latter is made up of two atoms. Ozone is now used in the sterilization of water.

Among other allotropic modifications those of selenium and phosphorus are of interest. Berzelius investigated the allotropes of selenium, and those of phosphorus were studied by Berzelius, Schrötter, Hittorf and Schenck. Schrötter discovered the red variety in 1845, and Hittorf found that it could be transformed into a metallic modification. Several additional allotropes of sulphur have been discovered in late years, and the fact that many metals can also exist in allotropic forms has been clearly demonstrated—*e.g.*, colloidal gold, silver, platinum and mercury.

The list of the compounds of the elements was greatly extended from the time of Lavoisier, particularly with the discovery of new acids and the growing knowledge of the different basicity of the various acids. It is important to mention some of the discoveries of moment.

In 1818, one of the most interesting of inorganic compounds was discovered by Thénard. He proved that water was not the sole oxide of hydrogen, but that another—peroxide of hydrogen, but which he termed "oxygenated water"—may be prepared. This compound plays a prominent rôle in many processes of nature, and is now prepared in quantities, by treating barium dioxide with sulphuric acid, for disinfecting and bleaching purposes.

The list of the halogen acids was completed prior to 1820. Gay-

Lussac and Balard studied hydriodic and hydrobromic acids; the former, Davy and Faraday investigated hydrochloric acid; while Thénard, Gay-Lussac and Berzelius contributed greatly to an intimate knowledge of hydrofluoric acid. In 1869, Gore and Nicklés continued the investigation of anhydrous hydrofluoric acid, and the latter lost his life through its action. Gore and Frémy established its composition, but, as before mentioned, the element fluorine was not isolated until 1886.

The oxygen compounds of chlorine, iodine and bromine have been given much attention since the commencement of the nineteenth century. The work of Gay-Lussac on chloric acid, Balard on hypochlorous acid, Millon on chlorous acid, and Davy and Stadion on chlorine peroxide, was exceedingly valuable and led to researches which firmly established the composition of these bodies. The oxygen compounds of iodine received careful attention in the hands of Davy and Magnus, and the latter discovered iodic acid, the principal compound of that halogen.

Following Gay-Lussac's discovery of "hyposulphurous acid" in 1813 and dithonic acid in 1819, little attention was given to the compounds of sulphur and oxygen until the fourth decade, when the thio-acids, which contain more sulphur and are more closely related to sulphuric acid, were recognized. More recently the early known oxides of sulphur—sulphur dioxide and sulphur trioxide—have received several additions in sulphur sesquioxide, sulphur tetroxide and sulphur heptoxide. Sulphuric acid, the most important of all chemicals, is used in enormous quantities in the industries, and its manufacture has been immensely developed. Over two million tons were used in the United States in 1908.

The very poisonous compounds of hydrogen with phosphorus, arsenic and antimony—phosphine, arsine and stibine—were given considerable attention during the first and second decades of the modern period. Phosphine, or hydrogen phosphide, was discovered in 1873, by Genbembre, and its composition was studied by Davy. Rose continued its investigation at a later date. Arsine was prepared in a pure state by Soubeiran; Gehlen fell a victim to its toxic action in 1815.

Phosphorous and phosphoric acids were known to Lavoisier, but their constitution was not established until a much later period. It was upon the relations which Gay-Lussac, Stromeyer and Graham found existing between the ortho-, pyro- and meta-phosphoric acids, that Liebig founded his theory of polybasic acids, which marked such an important step forward in chemistry.

The important compound hydroxylamine, which may be regarded as ammonia in which a hydrogen atom has been replaced by hydroxyl (OH), was discovered by Lossen in 1865. It has led to a knowledge of many remarkable organic compounds. Similarly, the analogous compound, hydrazine, which was first prepared by Curtius in 1887, has entered into the preparation of a series of interesting compounds; for example, the hydrazones and hydrazides. It is an exceedingly powerful reducing agent.

Of the simple carbon compounds, the greater number were discovered in the first decade. Carbon disulphide, which was accidentally discovered by Lampadius in 1796 while heating pyrites with coal, was accurately examined by Vauquelin in 1812. It is now prepared in an electric furnace, by conducting sulphur vapor over heated carbon, and finds extensive use as a solvent. Carbonyl chloride, or "phosgene gas," was discovered by Davy in 1811, and carbon oxysulphide by von Than quite recently. The compounds of carbon with certain metals—carbides—are now of great technical importance. In 1808, Davy discovered potassium carbide, the first described in chemical literature, and in 1862 Wöhler prepared calcium carbide, now one of the most important on account of its use in the generation of acetylene and in the manufacture of calcium cyanamide, a new constituent of fertilizers. Calcium carbide has, since 1894, been prepared by fusing limestone and carbon together in an electric furnace.

Before closing this brief resumé of some of the advances made in the knowledge of chemical compounds mention must be made of the metallic peroxides, hydrides and nitrides.

Sodium peroxide, which was discovered by Gay-Lussac, is now used extensively under the name "ozone" as a bleaching and oxidizing agent, and calcium peroxide, discovered by Gay-Lussac and Thénard, is used in dentistry. The discovery of the hydrides belongs to the present day; among the most important of these is calcium hydride, which is used for generating hydrogen. The metallic nitrides, as magnesium, calcium, boron and lithium nitrides, have only lately been investigated carefully, but may become of great importance.

Numerous important chemical and physical facts were learned concerning the gaseous bodies, especially during the second, third and seventh decades, and the experiments which were conducted with a view of liquefying gases are of the highest import, more particularly with regard to the production of liquid air and its application to researches at low temperatures.

The experiments of Davy and Faraday, in which the gases were generated in curved closed glass tubes and cooled to about —20° C. in a freezing mixture, resulted in the liquefaction of all the common gases, with the exception of hydrogen, nitrogen, oxygen, methane, carbonic oxide and nitric oxide. In 1834, Thilorier liquefied carbon dioxide in considerable quantities and obtained the solid; he was the first to operate on a large scale, and subsequent investigators made use of many of his observations. Between the years 1844 and 1855, Natterer studied the relationship of pressure and volume over wide ranges of pressure, and in 1852 he exposed hydrogen to a pressure of 2,790 atmospheres, but he was unable to effect its liquefaction.

It was only in 1877 that Raoul Pictet and Lewis Cailletet succeeded, almost simultaneously, in liquefying the majority of the so-called permanent gases. Their success was due to a recognition of the fact that reduction of temperature was necessary as well as pressure, but it was not possible by the aid of the methods and appliances which they employed, to obtain the liquids in large amounts and to determine their physical constants. This was accomplished by Wroblewsky, a chemist in Cracow, and he and Olszewsky first obtained quantities of oxygen and nitrogen in the liquid state, and described many of their properties. These two investigators share with Dewar, an English chemist, the honor of having first devised practical methods for the production of liquid air in quantity; and in 1896 C. Linde in Germany and W. Hampson in England constructed technically efficient forms of apparatus for producing liquid air.

Liquid air has not as yet, however, found any technical application upon a large scale. Nearly pure oxygen is obtained from it very cheaply, and the attempt has been made to apply it in the manufacture of explosives, but, so far, liquid air has achieved the most important results in chemical research.

In the first place, it must be mentioned that Dewar, by its aid, has succeeded in liquefying hydrogen, and in obtaining air, oxygen and hydrogen in the solid state; and that in doing so he has achieved almost everything that can be done in this direction. However, he is at present attempting to reach the so-called absolute zero.

The results that have been obtained by means of this agency with respect to the discovery of the "noble gases" are of greater importance. Since these have been described, it only remains to be stated that Onnes, in his cryogenic laboratory in Leyden, has recently announced that he has liquefied helium and that it boils at —268.5° C.

CHAPTER XV

THE ATOMIC WEIGHTS AND THE PERIODIC LAW

In a preceding chapter an attempt was made to trace the early development of the atomic theory, and later it was shown how this theory became a necessity for the development of organic chemistry.

It has fallen into disfavor because of the difficulties encountered by Berzelius and others in distinguishing between atoms and molecules; but much light was thrown upon this and other matters as the chemistry of the compounds of carbon was better understood; and the fact that the dominant doctrine of the new chemistry quietly assumed the truth of Dalton's theory in all its important particulars was reflected upon the older chemistry, so that this great theory became the basis for it all.

The old confusion between atoms and equivalents was not entirely done away with until after Frankland's investigations of the organometallic bodies, yet in 1846 Laurent had clearly distinguished between atom, molecule and equivalent, and his definitions are still current. He stated that "the atom of M. Gerhardt represents the smallest quantity of a simple body which can exist in a combination; my molecule represents the smallest quantity of a simple body which must be employed to perform a chemical reaction."

This definition of a molecule was employed until quite lately in general, but in 1888 Lothar Meyer pointed out that it was insufficient. Gerhardt defined "equivalent" as follows:

"According to our views, the conception of equivalent implies that of similarity of function; it is known that the same element can play the part of one or other of several very different elements, and it may happen that to each of these different functions corresponds a different weight of the first element."

Seven years previously, in 1842, when he had not arrived at a clear distinction between "equivalent" and "atomic weight," Gerhardt had doubled the equivalents of carbonic acid and of water, and in 1843 he followed this up by doubling the values of the symbol weights used by French chemists ($H = 0.5$, $O = 8$, $C = 6$, etc.), rendering them thereby identical with Berzelius' atomic weights. The reasons for this change were derived from the study of chemical reactions. He found that the amounts of water, carbonic acid, ammonia and sulphurous acid evolved in the interactions between the quantities of organic compounds represented by the formulæ assigned to them on chemical grounds, were always two (or multiples of two) equivalent weights of H_2O, CO_2 SO_2, when $H = 0.5$, $O = 8$, $C = 6$, $S = 16$.

Both Gerhardt and Laurent expressed sound views on the selection of atomic weights. They recommended the choice of such of these as were in agreement with the requirements of the law of isomorphism, the law of Avogadro and the law of heat capacity, and which above everything are chemically adequate. However, apparently the chemical public was not yet ready for the change. In his great text-book on organic chemistry, the publication of which was begun in 1853, Gerhardt retained Gmelin's equivalent-weight notation. He is reported to have said in private conversation that unless he had done so no one would have bought the work; in the introduction of the book the matter is put more formally:

"I have even sacrificed my notation, retaining the old formulæ the better to show by example how irritational they are, and leaving to time the consummation of a reform which chemists have not yet adopted."

Confusion continued to reign for some time longer. The terms equivalent, atomic weight, molecular weight were used and abused in every conceivable sense; sometimes even employed as synonymous.

About the middle of the century two units or standard elements were in use for the determination of combining weights. Dalton had suggested hydrogen as unity, and this standard was adopted by Gmelin and many others. Wollaston and Berzelius took oxygen as the standard, Wollaston giving it the value 10, and Berzelius using it as 100; Thomson had given it the value 1. The standard of Berzelius was the accepted one for a long time, but about 1842 a return was made to the standard of Dalton. It was in this year that Dumas, whose atomic weight determinations are classical, redetermined the ratio oxygen: hydrogen from the composition of water, and had ascertained it to be 15.96: 2, and had expressed his belief that the true value was probably 16: 2. His number, which in the same year was confirmed by the results of Erdmann and Marchand, was for a long time considered as extremely exact.

However, the work of Jean Servais Stas (1813-1891) soon after furnished numbers for the combining weights of a large number of elements which had all been determined by direct reference to 16 of oxygen, and the accuracy of which was far superior to that of the ratio oxygen: hydrogen. Indirectly he had obtained for hydrogen in terms of oxygen $= 16.00$, the value 2.02. Though not attaching special importance to this result, Stas asserted that the composition of water was not known with sufficient accuracy for hydrogen to be a suitable standard, and he expressed himself in favor of 16 of oxygen.

ATOMIC WEIGHTS AND PERIODIC LAW

Since, however, 16.00 was then generally accepted as the exact combining weight of oxygen in terms of the hydrogen standard, Stas' recommendation involved no recalculation; that is, no change in practice, only a change in theory desirable from the point of view of future possibilities. The adoption of the oxygen standard advocated would have meant that if a redetermination of the composition of water should lead to a change in the value of the ratio oxygen : hydrogen, the effect of this would only be an alteration of the value used for the combining weight of hydrogen, and not the necessity of a recalculation and a consequent change of all the combining weight values determined directly in terms of oxygen. Stas' suggestion, which it must be admitted was not pressed strongly, did not receive much support.

All the work of Stas was monumental in the care taken to secure accuracy. The determinations of atomic weights by him of importance were those of silver, potassium, sodium, lithium, lead, chlorine, bromine, iodine, sulphur, nitrogen and oxygen.

Much of this work was carried out to prove or disprove the correctness of Prout's hypothesis, and Stas concluded as follows: "I have arrived at the absolute conviction, the complete certainty, as far as it is possible for a human being to attain a certainty in such a matter, that the law of Prout, together with M. Dumas' modifications, is nothing but an illusion, a mere speculation definitely contradicted by experience."

In 1860, J. C. Marignac (1817-1894), who had determined the atomic weights of a number of elements, published a paper in support of what he termed Prout's "law." He observed that " . . . the differences between the results obtained by M. Stas and those required by the law of Prout are certainly very small, but they are considerably greater . . . than the greatest differences between the results obtained in each set of experiments."

The results referred to, as well as those of Marignac himself, are appended:

	Stas (1860).	Marignac.	Prout.
Silver	107.943	107.921	108
Chlorine	35.46	35.46	35.5
Potassium	39.13	39.115	39
Sodium	23.05	....	23
Ammonium	18.06	....	18
Nitrogen	14.041	14.02	14
Sulphur	16.037	....	16
Lead (synthesis of sulphate)	103.453	....	103.5
Lead (synthesis of nitrate)	103.460	....	103.5

Marignac reasoned from Stas' results that Prout's hypothesis was substantiated rather than disproved. He employed the two arguments of the Proutians, that Stas' numbers were very close approximations to whole numbers and hence could be considered as such, and that those approximations were too numerous to be accidental. This fatal error of rounding off fractions into whole numbers was the very thing which misled Prout at the beginning and with him there was far more excuse for it. Marignac further said that should future determinations of other elements give similar approximations he would feel assured of the existence of some fundamental cause which brought about the multiple relation of the atomic weights and subordinate causes which modified it. He thought that Prout's Law deserved to rank with that of Gay-Lussac or of Mariotte.

In another place Marignac referred to Prout's Law as one of those not absolute but only approximate laws, like many other natural laws.

From 1888 onward, there appeared in quick succession redeterminations of the ratio oxygen : hydrogen, all demonstrating that Dumas' experimental number 15.96 was too high; but in the meantime Lothar Meyer and Seubert, strong champions of the hydrogen standard, has made this value the basis of very popular atomic weight tables. The new data did not provide a sufficiently reliable number to make recalculations of all the other values desirable, and the obvious way out of the difficulty, the use of the tables of Ostwald in which the 16,000 oxygen standard was used, was not generally accepted. As a result two tables of atomic weights, one based on $O = 16$ and the other on $O = 15.96$, were in use until quite recently.

From the year 1896 onward, K. Seubert exerted himself to effect a general agreement with regard to the basis upon which all atomic weight should be founded, and in 1900 an International Atomic Weights Commission was appointed for the purpose of settling the question. The result of their deliberations has been to make oxygen ($O = 16$) the "official" basis instead of hydrogen ($H = 1$); the hydrogen unit is, however, often preferred still, both in practical work and in teaching. The main ground for the Commission's taking oxygen as the foundation is the fact—originally brought forward by Berzelius—that by far the greater number of the atomic weights have been derived from compounds of oxygen and not from compounds of hydrogen.

Among the chemists other than those mentioned whose efforts were directed to improving the methods of determining atomic weights may be mentioned Turner, Penny, Marchand, Pélouze De Ville, and Scheerer. Recently Morley and Richards have done noteworthy work.

The most recent table of International Atomic Weights is as follows:

ATOMIC WEIGHTS AND PERIODIC LAW.

Element	Symbol	O=16	Element	Symbol	O=16
Aluminium	Al	27.1	Molybdenum	Mo	96.0
Antimony	Sb	120.2	Neodymium	Nd	144.3
Argon	A	39.9	Neon	Ne	20.0
Arsenic	As	74.96	Nickel	Ni	58.68
Barium	Ba	137.37	Nitrogen	N	14.01
Bismuth	Bi	208.0	Osmium	Os	190.9
Boron	B	11.0	Oxygen	O	16.00
Bromine	Br	79.92	Palladium	Pd	106.7
Cadmium	Cd	112.40	Phosphorus	P	31.0
Cæsium	Cs	132.81	Platinum	Pt	195.0
Calcium	Ca	40.09	Potassium	K	39.10
Carbon	C	12.00	Praseodym'm	Pr	140.6
Cerium	Ce	140.25	Radium	Ra	226.4
Chlorine	Cl	35.46	Rhodium	Rh	102.9
Chromium	Cr	52.0	Rubidium	Rb	85.45
Cobalt	Co	58.97	Ruthenium	Ru	101.7
Columbium	Cb	93.5	Samarium	Sa	150.4
Copper	Cu	63.57	Scandium	Sc	44.1
Dysprosium	Dy	162.5	Selenium	Se	79.2
Erbium	Er	167.4	Silicon	Si	28.3
Europium	Eu	152.0	Silver	Ag	107.88
Fluorine	F	19.0	Sodium	Na	23.00
Gadolinium	Gd	157.3	Strontium	Sr	87.62
Gallium	Ga	69.9	Sulphur	S	32.07
Germanium	Ge	72.5	Tantalum	Ta	181.0
Glucinum	Gl	9.1	Tellurium	Te	127.5
Gold	Au	197.2	Terbium	Tb	159.2
Helium	He	4.0	Thallium	Tl	204.0
Hydrogen	H	1.008	Thorium	Th	232.42
Indium	In	114.8	Thulium	Tm	168.5
Iodine	I	126.92	Tin	Sn	119.0
Iridium	Ir	193.1	Titanium	Ti	48.1
Iron	Fe	55.85	Tungsten	W	184.0
Krypton	Kr	83.0	Uranium	U	238.5
Lanthanum	La	139.0	Vanadium	V	51.2
Lead	Pb	207.10	Xenon	Xe	130.7
Lithium	Li	7.00	Ytterbium (Neoytterbium)	Yb	172.0
Lutecium	Lu	174.0			
Magnesium	Mg	24.32	Yttrium	Y	89.0
Manganese	Mn	54.93	Zinc	Zn	65.37
Mercury	Hg	200.0	Zirconium	Zr	90.6

Reverting to the middle of the past century, one finds that much of the credit of removing the difficulties attending the determination of the atomic weights, and of transferring them to a more substantial foundation than had hitherto been in use, is due to Stanislao Cannizzaro (1826———). It was he who, by his criticism in a paper entitled "Sunto di un Corso de Filisofia Chimica" ("Outlines of a Course of Chemical Philosophy") (1858), elucidated the methods employed for arriving at the relative atomic weights of the elements. He recognized, as especially reliable, the deduction of these values from the vapor densities of chemical compounds—a method now in universal use.

Cannizzarro's paper began as follows (Freund):

"It seems to me that the progress of chemistry within the last year has served to confirm the hypothesis of Avogadro, Ampère and Dumas concerning the similar constitution of gaseous substances; namely, the assumption that equal volumes of gases, whether elementary or compound, contain an equal number of molecules. But they by no means contain an equal number of atoms, the reason for this being that the molecules of different substances, or even of the same substance in the different states which it can assume . . . may consist of a different number of atoms of the same or of different kinds. In order to bring my pupils to this same conviction I have let them follow the same path that had led me to it; namely, that of the historical examination of chemical theories.

"I begin by showing how from a consideration of the physical properties of gases, together with Gay-Lussac's law concerning the relation between the volume of a compound and that of its constituents, there has arisen, as it were, of itself that hypothesis which was first enunciated by Avogadro and shortly afterward by Ampère. While expounding in detail the line of argument followed by these two physicists I proceed to prove that it is not in contradiction to a single known fact, provided only that we do as they did: (1) Distinguish between the molecules and the atoms; (2) avoid confounding the criteria for comparing the weights and numbers of molecules with those employed for ascertaining the weights of atoms; (3) abandon the erroneous view that while the molecules of a compound may consist of any number of atoms, those of the different elements must consist of one atom only, or at any rate of an identical number of atoms."

He then discussed molecular weight determinations and showed that the hypothesis of Avogadro was a guide in such work. His argument in favor of making the weight of half the hydrogen molecule the standard met with favor and acceptance. Turning from the molecule to the atom, Cannizzaro showed that the law of Dulong and Petit, and Avogadro's hypothesis were a guide in the determination of the atomic weights. To quote further from his paper:

ATOMIC WEIGHTS AND PERIODIC LAW

"We next proceed to the investigation of the composition of the molecules. Whenever the substance cannot be decomposed, it must be assumed that the whole weight of its molecules is composed of one kind of matter only; but if the substance is a compound we analyze it and thereby determine the invariable ratio by weight of its constituents, and we then proceed to divide the molecular weight into parts proportional to those of the relative weights of the constituents and thus obtain the quantities of the elements contained in a molecular weight of a compound, all of them referred to the same unit in terms of which all molecular weights are expressed. According to this method I compile the table of molecular composition which follows:

Name of the substance	Weight of one volume, or molecular weight referred to the weight of a half hydrogen molecule = 1	Weights of the constituents of one volume or of one molecule, all referred to the weight of a half hydrogen molecule = 1					
Hydrogen	2	2	Hydrogen				
Oxygen	32	32	Oxygen				
Electrified oxygen	128	128	Oxygen				
Sulphur under 1,000°	192	192	Sulphur				
Sulphur above 1,000°	64	64	Sulphur				
Phosphorus	124	124	Phosphorus				
Chlorine	71	71	Chlorine				
Bromine	160	160	Bromine				
Iodine	254	254	Iodine				
Nitrogen	28	28	Nitrogen				
Arsenic	300	300	Arsenic				
Mercury	200	200	Mercury				
Hydrochloric acid	36.5	35.5	Chlorine	1	Hydrogen		
Hydrobromic acid	81	80	Bromine	1	Hydrogen		
Hydriodic acid	128	127	Iodine	1	Hydrogen		
Water	18	16	Oxygen	2	Hydrogen		
Ammonia	17	14	Nitrogen	3	Hydrogen		
Arsenine	78	75	Arsenic	3	Hydrogen		
Phosphine	35	32	Phosphorus	3	Hydrogen		
Mercurous chloride	235.5	35.5	Chlorine	200	Mercury		
Mercuric chloride	271	71	Chlorine	200	Mercury		
Arsenic chloride	181.5	106.5	Chlorine	75	Arsenic		
Phosphorous chloride	138.5	106.5	Chlorine	32	Phosphorus		
Ferric chloride	325	213	Chlorine	112	Iron		
Nitrous oxide	44	16	Oxygen	28	Nitrogen		
Nitric oxide	30	16	Oxygen	14	Nitrogen		
Carbonic oxide	28	16	Oxygen	12	Carbon		
Carbonic acid	44	32	Oxygen	12	Carbon		
Ethylene	28	4	Hydrogen	24	Carbon		
Propylene	42	6	Hydrogen	36	Carbon		
Acetic acid	60	4	Hydrogen	32	Oxygen	24	Carbon
Acetic anhydride	102	6	Hydrogen	48	Oxygen	48	Carbon
Alcohol	46	6	Hydrogen	16	Oxygen	24	Carbon
Ether	74	10	Hydrogen	16	Oxygen	48	Carbon

"From this it follows that all the different quantities of hydrogen contained in the molecules of the different substances are whole multiples of the quantity contained in the hydrochloric acid molecule."

He defined the atomic weight as the weight of one atom of the element referred to the weight of the hydrogen atom taken = 1.00 (or oxygen = 16.00), and stated that it is determined by finding the least amount of the element present in the molecular weight of any of its compounds, which if these are volatile is the least amount present in 2 volumes of any of these compounds in the gaseous state.

It is unnecessary that the molecular weight of the element be known, only the molecular weights of as many volatile compounds as possible, together with the composition of these compounds expressed as parts of the molecular weights.

Chemists were thus taught to rely on Avogadro's hypothesis, all inferences drawn from which, Cannizzaro showed, "are in complete agreement with all the physical and chemical laws so far discovered." He gave as an application of Dulong and Petit's law the following:

"The specific heat of copper in the free state . . . confirms the atomistic conception of its chlorides based on analogies with the corresponding chlorides of mercury. Their composition leads us to the inference that they have the formulæ CuCl and CuCl$_2$, and that the atomic weight of copper is 63, a fact made apparent by the following relations:

	Ratio between the components expressed by numbers whose sum is = 100	Ratio between the components expressed by the atomic weights
	Chlorine Copper	
Cuprous chloride	36.04 : 63.96	35.5 : 63 = Cl : Cu
Cupric chloride	52.98 : 47.02	71 : 63 = Cl$_2$: Cu

"But the number 63 for the atomic weight, when multiplied by the specific heat of copper, gives a product nearly equal to that of the atomic weight of mercury or of iodine multiplied by their respective heats. We get:

$$\underset{\text{At. wt. of copper}}{63} \times \underset{\text{Spec. heat of copper.}}{0.09515} = 6$$

By the use of this law and Avogadro's hypothesis an approximation to a correct table of atomic weights was obtained, and the road for the inception of the great natural law underlying them was opened up.

ATOMIC WEIGHTS AND PERIODIC LAW

Before the atomic theory was formulated, numerical relations were proposed by Richter, the founder of Stoichiometry, between the equivalents obtained by him for the various bases and acids. This mathematical work served but little purpose beyond bringing the whole subject of his equivalents into some disrepute. Only a few years passed after the publication of the first tables of atomic weights before their inter-relation became a subject of speculation and research. In 1815 we have Prout pointing out the strange fact of their close approximation to whole numbers and boldly rounding them off into such. If they were integral multiples of hydrogen, he reasoned, then this might be the primal matter and all elements made up of it. The "Multiplen-fieber" quickly took possession of the chemical world, even of conservative, level-headed workers such as Berzelius. Enthusiastic support was given it by the English chemists especially and, when Berzelius afterward became its great antagonist, Thomson and others busied themselves in its defense. The newly organized British Association devoted its fresh energies to an examination into the conditions of the various sciences and, among other inquiries, set on foot one as to the grounds for believing in what was then called and has been often so called since, Prout's Law. The result of this inquiry was adverse to the "law" and it would have been dropped, in all probability, had it not been taken up by Marignac, Dumas and the French chemists, with certain modifications rendered necessary by the more perfect knowledge of the atomic weights.

Meanwhile, a different style of numerical regularity had been brought to the notice of chemists. In 1817, Döbereiner first noticed a strange grouping of analogous elements into threes, or triads as they soon came to be called. He said, according to Venable:

"Noteworthy relations are revealed when one examines the stoichiometrical values of the chemical elements and compounds arranged in series.

"1. Those most often found in plants have the smallest values and are the most abundant. The highest values are less widely distributed.

"2. Those corresponding in many physical and chemical properties, as iron, cobalt and nickel, have almost the same stoichiometrical value.

"3. Compounds which have like equivalent numbers are almost alike in chemical constitution."

For a long period following this paper there was no further attention given to this question, but in 1829 Döbereiner published another paper which appears to have been a result of the atomic weight determinations of Berzelius in 1825. He indicated that the atomic weight of bromine approximates the arithmetical mean of the atomic weights of chlorine and iodine, namely:

$$\frac{35.470 + 126.470}{2} = 80.970, \text{ considering } H = 1.$$

Of this mean he stated that tho somewhat greater than 78.383, the number actually found by Berzelius, it so closely approximates to it as to justify the hope that repeated accurate determinations of all the atomic weights involved will lead to a disappearance of any difference. He found similar relations for the alkaline earths, the alkalies, and for the group comprising sulphur, selenium, and tellurium, as shown by the equations:

$$\frac{356.019 \,(= Ca) + 956.880 \,(= Ba)}{2} = 656.449 \,(= Sr),$$

but experiment gave for strontium, regarding $O = 100$, 647.285.

$$\frac{195.310 \,(= Na) + 589.916 \,(= K)}{2} = 392.613 \,(= Li),$$

but experiment gave for lithium, regarding $O = 100$, 390.897.

$$\frac{32.239 \,(= S) + 129.243 \,(= Te)}{2} = 80.741 \,(= Se),$$

but experiment gave for selenium, considering $H = 1$, 79.263.

For more than twenty years little was added to the work of Döbereiner and no new ideas were advanced. This was in part due to imperfections in the determinations of the atomic weights and ignorance as to whether they should be written as had been done by Berzelius or many of them doubled as was done by Gerhardt.

Further, the whole question of atomic weights was in much doubt and numerical speculations concerning them would have had little significance during this period.

The first to continue the consideration of such "triads" was Dumas, who in 1851 called attention to the triads of Döbereiner, and suggested that in a series of bodies, providing the extremes are known, the intermediate bodies might be discovered, and state that a suspicion arose as to the possibility of the intermediate bodies being composed of the extremes of the series and thus processes of transmutation might be hoped for.

The next year P. Kremers pointed out the existence of certain regularly ascending series among the elements, and in 1858 he followed up the old idea of triads, arranging the elements in the form of "conjugated triads," thus:

Li = 7,	Na = 23,	K = 39.
Mg = 24,	Zn = 40,	Cd = 112.
Ca = 40,	Sr = 87.5,	Ba = 137.

In these triads we have the following proportions: Li : Na : K as 7 : 23 : 39 as Li : Mg : Ca.

Such close agreement was not found in every case, however, and in 1863 Kremers gave up the doctrine of triads.

In 1853, J. H. Gladstone announced that he found the numerical relations between the elements to be of three varieties, namely:

1. The atomic weights of analogous elements are the same.

2. The atomic weights of analogous elements are in multiple proportions.

3. The atomic weights of analogous elements may differ by certain regular increments.

He considered the doctrines of triads as partly a natural law.

The following year J. P. Cooke published a study of these numerical relations. He stated that the triads broke up natural groups of elements—a fatal blow to the doctrine—and classified the elements into six series, in each of which the number whose multiples form the differences is different and may be said to characterize the series. In the first it is nine, in the second eight, in the third six, in the fourth five, in the fifth four and in the last three. The elements were further arranged in series according to the strength of their electro-negative properties, or in other words, as their affinities for oxygen, chlorine, sulphur, etc., increased, while those for hydrogen decrease as we descend.

Cooke laid stress on the fact that his grouping demonstrated that the elements may be clasified in a few series similar to the homologous series of organic chemistry. In 1858, John Mercer carried out this comparison with the organic radicals more fully, basing his work partly on that of Max von Pettenkofer, who, while engaged on the subject of the regularities in the atomic weights, made the following comparison:

1. The equivalents of the inorganic elements, which form natural groups, show among themselves such constant differences as the equivalents of organic compound radicals which belong to natural groups.

2. The simple inorganic elements can therefore be regarded from the standpoint of the compound organic radicals.

Pettenkofer also criticized the doctrine of triads.

Lennsen and Odling were about the last chemists to attempt to develop the doctrine of the triads. The former gave twenty triads, grouping the elements according to their chemical and physical characteristics, but this classification was unsatisfactory and he suggested a division in diads, the third member forming a binding member; for example, the triads K, Na and Li became diad K, Na, and binding member Li.

The consideration of the numerical regularities of the atomic weights from the point of view of the homologous organic series, of which the ideas of Pettenkofer form a good illustration, was also taken up by Dumas, who later published his view of double parallelism. He made this comparison:

$$N = 14 \quad P = 31 \quad As = 75 \quad Sb = 122$$
$$F = 19 \quad Cl = 35.5 \quad Br = 80 \quad I = 127$$

On adding 108 to the number for nitrogen we obtain that for Sb, and on adding it to F we get I, and so the addition of 61 gives us respectively As and Br. These facts teach the propriety, he says, of arranging the metals in series that shall show a double parallelism, for such a classification brings to view the various analogies existing between these elements.

None of these considerations materially advanced the subject of triads from the state in which it had been left by Döbereiner. But, to quote from Freund's "Study of Chemical Composition," "When stress had once been laid on the approximate constancy of the differences in the atomic weights of elements forming a group, the ever-dominant desire for simplicity in numerical relations asserted itself. This led to unjustifiable attempts to alter the experimental values in order to make them agree with preconceived ideas. We know how variable and arbitrary were the criteria (prior to 1860) used in the determination of equivalent and atomic weights in general; but in the special cases of groups of elements there was more uniformity, hence the numbers obtained were comparable, and since the above considerations concerning classification applied only to groups of elements, it was possible to bring out within this compass a relation between atomic weight and properties. The extension to the case of elements in general soon followed. This was done in a set of short papers published from 1863 onward by Newlands, the forerunner of Lothar Meyer and Mendeleeff."

The work of Newland followed immediately upon that of de Chancourtois, who was the first to devise a symmetrical arrangement of the elements in his theory of the "Telluric Screw." His first paper (1863) considered some numerical relations between the atomic weights. To quote from Venable's "Periodic Law": "These relations were in part along the line of the old triads. Thus zinc was pointed out as the mean between magnesium and cadmium, copper between

ATOMIC WEIGHTS AND PERIODIC LAW

cobalt and zinc. In the group of the alkalies, one of lithium and one of potassium made two of sodium; one of lithium and two of potassium made one of rubidium, etc. Similar relations were observed for other groups. He also endeavored to show a certain kind of symmetry when the lowest member of a group was subtracted from the next higher member and when the lowest member of a triad was deducted from the highest."

In a paper published in 1864, Newlands furnished a table containing the elements arranged in the order of their atomic weights. In a side column the differences between these weights were given, each being deducted from the one next higher in the scale. The next year Newlands announced his "law of octaves," which he deduced from his arrangement of the elements. He said in part that, "If the elements are arranged in the order of their equivalents with a few slight transpositions, as in the accompanying table, it will be observed that elements belonging to the same group usually appear on the same horizontal line.

	No.		No.		No.		No.			No.		No.			No.			No.
H	1	F	8	Cl	15	Co Ni	22	Br		29	Pd	36		I	42	Pt	Ir	50
Li	2	Na	9	K	16	Cu	23	Rb		30	Ag	37		Cs	44	Tl		53
G	3	Mg	10	Ca	17	Zn	25	Sr		31	Cd	38	V	Ba	45	Pb		54
Bo	4	Al	11	Cr	19	Y	24	Ce	La	33	U	40		Ta	46	Th		56
C	5	Si	12	Ti	18	In	26	Zr		32	Sn	39		W	37	Hg		52
N	6	P	13	Mn	20	As	27	Di	Mo	34	Sb	41		Nb	48	Bi		55
O	7	S	14	Fe	21	Se	28	Ro	Ru	35	Te	43		Au	49	Os		51

"It will also be seen that the numbers of analogous elements generally differ either by 7 or by some multiple of 7; in other words, members of the same group stand to each other in the same relation as the extremities of one or more octaves in music."

The same year he gave as an explanation of the existence of triads the fact that "in conformity with the Law of Octaves, elements belonging to the same group generally have numbers differing by seven or by some multiple of seven. That is to say, if we begin with the lowest member of a group, calling it 1, the succeeding members will have the numbers 8, 15, 22, 29, etc., respectively. But 8 is the mean between 1 and 15; 15 is the mean between 8 and 22, etc., and therefore as an arithmetical result of the Law of Octaves the number of an element is often the exact mean of those of two others belonging to the same group and consequently its equivalent also approximates to the mean of their equivalents."

Two years before the presentation of Newland's paper before the London Chemical Society, containing the "Law of Octaves," Lothar Meyer (1830-1895), published the first edition of his "Die Modernen Theorien der Chemie," in which he gave a table of the elements arranged horizontally according to their atomic weights, so that analogous elements stood under one another and the change of valence, along with that of atomic weight, could be easily observed.

This was Meyer's first attempt, and his table exhibited less evidence of periodicity than that of Newlands, but it caused Meyer to give the question of the relationship of the atomic weights more serious consideration and his mind continued working on the atomic relationship. His first table had been in the following form:

Meyer's First Table. 1864.

	4 val.	3 val.	2 val.	1 val.	1 val.	2 val.
	....	....	....	....	Li 7.03	(Be 9.3)
Diff.					16.02	(14.7)
	C 12.0	N 14.4	O 16.00	F 19.0	Na 23.5	Mg 24.0
Diff.	16.5	16.96	16.07	16.46	16.08	16.0
	Si 28.5	P 31.0	S 32.0	Cl 35.46	K 39.13	Ca 40.0
Diff.	$\frac{89}{2}$·1 44.45	44.0	46.7	44.51	46.3	47.0
	....	As 75.0	Se 78.8	Br 79.97	Rb 85.4	Sr 87.0
Diff.	$\frac{89}{2}$·1 44.55	45.6	49.5	46.8	47.6	49.0
	Sn 117.6	Sb 120.6	Te 128.3	I 126.8	Cs 133.0	
Diff.	$\frac{89}{2}$·4 44.7	$\frac{87}{2}$·1 43.7	....	....	35.5	
	Pb 207.0	Bi 208.0	....	....	(Tl 204.0?)	Ba 137.1
	4 val.	4 val.	4 val.	2 val.	1 val.	
	{ Mn 55.1	Ni 58.7	Co 58.7	Zn 65.0	Cu 63.5	
	{ Fe 56.0					
Diff. {	49.2	45.6	47.3	46.9	44.4	
	48.3					
	Ru 104.3	Rh 104.3	Pd 106.0	Cd 111.9	Ag 107.94	
Diff.	$\frac{93}{2}$·8 46.0	$\frac{93}{2}$·8 46.5	$\frac{93}{2}$ 46.5	$\frac{83}{2}$·3 44.5	$\frac{89}{2}$·2 44.4	
	Pt 197.1	Ir 197.1	Os 199.0	Hg 200.2	Au 196.7	

On leaving Eberswald in 1868, he left with his successor the elaborate table on the following page, according to Seubert.

The following year Dmitri Mendeléeff (1834-1907), a Russian chemist, published his first paper embracing the important principles of the Periodic Law. He states that he was led to the consideration of the question in this way:

"When I undertook to write the text-book, entitled 'The Foundations of Chemistry.' I had to decide for some one system, lest in the classification of the elements, I should have allowed myself to be guided by accidental, and, so to speak, instinctive reasons rather than by an accurate and definite principle."

Mendeléeff then showed that the principles hitherto used in classification had not been of a quantitative nature, and he laid stress on the superiority of a system which is based on numerical relations and therefore leaves no scope for arbitrary interpretation. Consideration of the numerical data available in the case of the elements led him to the rejection of the optical, electrical and magnetic properties, because these vary with the conditions; and of the vapor density, because this is not known for many elements, and is different for the allotropic modifications.

He next emphasized the unalterability of the atomic weight, stating that, "For this reason I have tried to take as basis for my system

SUGGESTION FOR A SYSTEM OF ELEMENTS BY LOTHAR MEYER, SUMMER 1868

1	2	3	4	5	6	7	8
Cr = 52.6	Mn = 55.1 49.2 Ru = 104.3 92.8 = 2.46.4 Pt = 197.1	Al = 27.3 28.7/2 = 14.8 Fe = 56.0 48.9 Rh = 103.4 92.8 = 2.46.4 Ir = 197.1	Al = 27.3 Co = 58.7 47.8 Pd = 106.0 93 = 2.465 Os = 199	Ni = 58.7	Cu = 63.5 44.4 Ag = 107.9 88.8 = 2.44.4 Au = 196.7	Zn = 65.0 46.9 Cd = 111.9 83.3 = 2.44.5 Hg = 200.2	C = 12.00 16.5 Si = 28.5 89.1/2 = 44.5 89.1/2 = 44.5 Sn = 117.6 89.41 = 2,441.7 Pb = 207.0

9	10	11	12	13	14	15	
N = 14.4 16.96 P = 31.0 44.0 As = 75.0 45.6 Sb = 120.6 87.4 = 243.7 Bi = 208.0	O = 16.00 16.07 S = 32.07 46.7 Se = 78.8 49.5 Te = 128.3	F = 19.0 16.46 Cl = 35.46 44.5 Br = 79.9 46.8 I = 126.8	Li = 7.03 16.02 Na = 23.05 16.08 K = 39.13 46.3 Rb = 85.4 47.6 Cs = 133.0 71 = 2,35.5 Te = 204.0	Be = 9.3 14.7 Mg = 24.0 16.0 Ca = 40.0 47.6 Sr = 87.6 49.5 Ba = 137.1	Ti = 48 42.0 Zr = 90.0 47.6 Ta = 137.6	Mo = 92.0 45.0 Vd = 137.0 47.0 W = 184.0	

of classification the value of the atomic weight. ... Beginning with the one of smallest atomic weight, I arranged the elements according to the magnitude of their atomic weights, when it became evident that there exists a kind of periodicity in the properties of the simple substance. ...

"Hence in this system of classification the atomic weight of an element determines the place to be assigned to it, ... and all the comparative investigations that I have made lead me to the conclusion that the magnitude of its atomic weight determines the character of an element in the same measure, as the molecular weight determines the properties and many of the reactions of a compound.

"I designate by the name of 'Periodic Law' the mutual relations between the properties of the elements and their atomic weights, relations which are applicable to all the elements, and which are of the nature of a periodic function."

Mendeléeff's first table was very imperfect, and the scheme of arrangement he followed was not entirely according to the size of the atomic weights. It was according to this arrangement:

MENDELÉEFF'S TABLE.   1869.

				Ti	50	Zr	90	?	180
				V	51	Nb	94	Ta	182
				Cr	52	Mo	96	W	186
				Mn	55	Rh	104.4	Pt	197.4
				Fe	56	Ru	104.4	Ir	198
				Ni,Co	59	Pd	106.6	Os	199
H	1			Cu	63.4	Ag	108	Hg	200
	Be	9.4	Mg	24	Zn	65.2	Cd	112	
	B	11	Al	27.4	?	68	Ur	116	Au	197
	C	12	Si	28	?	70	Sn	118	
	N	14	P	31	As	75	Sb	122	Bi	210
	O	16	S	32	Se	79.4	Te	128?	
	F	19	Cl	35.5	Br	80	I	127	
	Na	23	K	39	Rb	85.4	Cs	133	Tl	204
			Ca	40	Sr	87.6	Ba	137	Pb	207
			?	45	Ce	92			
			?Er	56	La	94			
			?Y	60	Di	95			
			?In	75.6	Th	118			

He made use of other arrangements also, but the tables which he gave in 1871 contain the plan resorted to in its final and perfected form. One of these tables gave the horizontal and the other the vertical method of arrangement. (See opposite page.)

These tables contain the Periodic Law as it is known to us. They have not been very materially altered, tho they have been corrected in minor points. The work since has been mainly one of elaboration, and, as Venable observes, "The credit for the expansion and filling out of the Periodic Law, its extension to the other properties of the elements and the bringing of the various compounds of these elements into consideration also, has been almost entirely due to the skill and knowledge of Mendeléeff."

MENDELÉEFF'S TABLE I.

Series	Group I R_2O	Group II RO	Group III R_2O_3	Group IV RH_4 RO_2	Group V RH_3 R_2O_5	Group VI RH_2 RO_3	Group VII RH R_2O_7	Group VIII RO_4
1	$H = 1$							
2	$Li = 7$	$Be = 9.4$	$B = 11$	$C = 12$	$N = 14$	$O = 16$	$F = 19$	
3	$Na = 23$	$Mg = 24$	$Al = 27.3$	$Si = 28$	$P = 31$	$S = 32$	$Cl = 35.5$	
4	$K = 39$	$Ca = 40$	$— = 44$	$Ti = 48$	$V = 51$	$Cr = 52$	$Mn = 55$	$Fe = 56, Co = 59,$ $Ni = 59, Cu = 63$
5	$(Cu = 63)$	$Zn = 65$	$— = 68$	$— = 72$	$As = 75$	$Se = 78$	$Br = 80$	
6	$Rb = 85$	$Sr = 87$	$?Yt = 88$	$Zr = 90$	$Nb = 94$	$Mo = 96$	$— = 100$	$Ru = 104, Rh = 104,$ $Pd = 106, Ag = 108$
7	$(Ag = 108)$	$Cd = 112$	$In = 113$	$Sn = 118$	$Sb = 122$	$Te = 125$	$I = 127$	
8	$Cs = 133$	$Ba = 137$	$?Di = 138$	$? Ce = 140$				
9	(—)							
10			$? Er = 178$	$La = 180$	$Ta = 182$	$W = 184$		$Os = 195, Ir = 197,$ $Pt = 198, Au = 199$
11	$(Au = 199)$	$Hg = 200$	$Tl = 204$	$Pb = 207$	$Bi = 208$			
12				$Th = 231$		$U = 240$		

MENDELÉEFF'S TABLE II.

Gr. Ser.	2	2.	4.	6.	8.	10	12.
I.		Li 7	K 39	Rb 85	Ce 133	10	....
II.		Be 9.2	Ca 40	Sr 87	Ba 137	....	....
III.		B 11	?Sc	Yt 89?	Di 139?	Er 175?	....
IV.		C 12	Ti 48	Zr 90	Ce 141	La 180?	Ur 240
V.		N 14	V 51	Nb 94	?2	Ta 182	....
VI.		O 16	Cr 52.5	Mo 96	?	W 184	Th 231
VII.		F 19	Mn 55	....	..		....
VIII.			Fe 56	Ru 103	..	Os 194	....
			Co 58.6	Rh 104	..	Ir 195	....
			Ni 58.6	Pd 106	..	Pt 197	....
I.	H 1	Na 23	Cu 63.5	Ag 108	..	Au 197	....
II.		Mg 24	Zn 65	Cd 112	3	Hg 200	....
III.		Al 27.3	Ga 69	In 113	..	Tl 204	....
IV.		Si 28	???	Sn 118	..	Pb 204	....
V.		P 31	As 75	Sb 120	..	Bi 208	....
VI.		S 32	Se 79	Te 125?	..	....	....
VII.		Cl 35.5	Br 80	I 127	..	....	

In 1870, Meyer offered a full table representing the nature of the elements as a function of their atomic weights which was so similar to Mendeléeff's that many accused him of plagiarism, but his claims to the authorship of the authorship of the Periodic Law are based on his 1864 and 1868 tables, and his 1870 system appears to have been an expansion of his earlier tables. It is generally considered that Mendeléeff and Meyer worked out the Periodic Law independently.

The Periodic Law soon attracted merited attention, but for several years its importance was not generally recognized, and it was not until the discovery of some new chemical elements, thereby fulfilling certain predictions of Mendeléeff, that it became accepted.

Mendeléeff had obtained the atomic weights of elements not fully investigated by taking the mean of the weights of what he termed the "atom-analogues." For instance, the atom-analogues of selenium were arsenic and bromine on the one hand, sulphur and tellurium on the other; its atomic weight should be $\left\{\dfrac{75+80+32+125}{4}\right\} = 78.$

He had also applied the Periodic Law to the determination of the properties of unknown elements. This was accomplished by estimating the physical and chemical character from those of the atom-analogues, since he had established that all properties were functions of atomic weight. He described the properties of three undiscovered elements, and the following values he predicted will show why the the Periodic Law was finally gladly accepted:

EKA-ALUMINIUM
Suggested by Mendeléeff
Atomic weight, 68.
Specific weight, 6.0.
Atomic volume, 11.5.

GALLIUM
Discovered in 1875 by Lecoq de Boisbaudran
Atomic weight, 69.9.
Specific weight, 5.96.
Atomic volume, 11.7.

LOTHAR MEYER'S TABLE REPRESENTING THE NATURE OF THE ELEMENTS AS A FUNCTION OF THEIR ATOMIC WEIGHTS

I	II	III	IV	V	VI	VII	VIII	IX
	B = 11.0	Al = 27.3	—	—	—			
	C = 11.97	Si = 28	Ti = 48					
	N = 14.01	P = 30.9	V = 51.2	As = 74.9	Zr = 89.7	? In = 113.4		Tl = 202.7
	O = 15.96	S = 31.98	Cr = 52.4	Se = 78	Nb = 93.7	Sn = 117.8		Pb = 206.4
	F = 19.1	Cl = 35.38		Br = 79.75	Mo = 95.6	Sb = 122.4	Ta = 182.2	Bi = 207.5
			Mn = 54.8			Te = 128 ?	W = 183.5	
			Fe = 55.9		Ru = 103.5	I = 126.5		
			Co, Ni = 58.6		Rh = 104.1		Os = 198.6 ?	—
					Pd = 106.2		Ir = 196.7	—
Li = 7.01	Na = 22.99	K = 39.04	Cu = 63.3	Rb = 85.2	Ag = 107.66	Cs = 132.7	Pt = 196.7	
? Be = 9.3	Mg = 23.9	Ca = 39.9	Zn = 64.9	Sr = 87.0	Cd = 111.6	Ba = 136.8	Au = 196.2	
							Hg = 199.8	

Difference from I to II and from II to III about = 16.
Difference from III to V, IV to VI, V to VII fluctuating about 46.
Difference from VI to VIII, from VII to IX = 88 to 92.

EKA-BORON	SCANDIUM
Suggested by Mendeléeff	Discovered in 1879 by Nilson
Atomic weight, 44.	Atomic weight, 43.97.
Oxide, Eb_2O_3; Sp. Gr., 3.5.	Oxide, Sc_2O_3; Sp. Gr., 3.864.
Sulphate, $Eb_2(SO_4)_3$.	Sulphate, $Sc_2(SO_4)_3$.
Double sulphate not isomorphous with alum.	Double sulphate, $3K_2SO_4.Sc_2(SO_4)_3$.
	Crystallizes in fine columns.

The other, eka-silicon ($Es = 72$), was discovered by Winkler in 1886. It is now called germanium ($Ge = 72$).

At the present time all chemists recognize the dependence of the properties of the elements upon the atomic weights and the perodic law has become the central idea in the classification and study of the elements and their compounds. This law is the greatest discovery in chemistry since the announcement of Dalton's atomic theory, and has been much more rapidly accepted. It promises to lead up to results of the utmost importance.

The close and mystifying relationship existing between the chemical elements which was revealed by the Periodic Law, naturally has attracted the minds of scientists to thoughts similar to the conception of one primordial matter as expressed by the Ionian philosophers, and later by Bacon, Descartes and Boyle. To quote Freund:

"Within the last two decades experimental evidence, physical and chemical, has been accumulating in support of these speculations, and the last few years' contributions have been such as to make the complexity of the atoms as much of an established fact as that of the molecular and atomic structure of the masses of matter that we perceive. Moreover, the empirical results which, taken in their entirety, can almost be said to have proved this point, have also supplied evidence which justifies the course hitherto followed by chemists in assigning to the atoms a very special place in the scale of the complexity of different kinds of matter. It seems that the diversity of matter begins only with the atom: that while the component parts of a molecule A are not the same as those of another kind of a molecule B, or C, or D, etc., the constituents of an atom M are identical with those of any other different atom P, or Q, or R, etc.; that all atoms are compounded of the same one kind of primordial matter."

The most important papers which have been published on the unity of matter and on the composite character of the elements are those of Sir William Crookes, Anton Grunwald, Gustav Wendt, Henry Wilde, Eduard Meusel, W. Preyer, C. T. Blanshard and Sir Norman Lockyer.

Of these speculations and views, the most important is the

hypothesis of Crookes. According to him, the chemical elements have resulted by gradual condensation from a primary material which he terms "protyle." He arrived at this view in 1886 from observations on the phosphorescence spectra of the yttrium earths. When he advanced this hypothesis, "provisionally," Crookes had to assume the complexity of the elementary atoms, but since then experimental and theoretical knowledge on this point has become more definite, as is shown by J. J. Thomson's investigations on the structure of the atom. Thomson started from the hypothesis that the atom is an aggregation of a number of simpler systems, and that these are formed by "corpuscles" associated with equal charges of positive electricity. He then traced the analogies between atomic structures and atomic properties, and furnished an explanation for the empirical relations between atomic weight and atomic properties embodied in the Periodic Law. As Freund remarks, "In a section of the community usually referred to as the 'general public' there seems to be an impression that the recognition of the divisibility of the atom has dealt a deathblow to that atomic theory which was founded by Dalton just a hundred years ago. No misconception could be more complete. While nothing has had to be given up, nothing to be modified, there has been deepening of the fundations, extension of scope, correlation with other sciences. Except that some of the anticipations expressed have since been realized, the situation to-day is what it was when Kekulé "stated that while from a philosophical standpoint he did not believe in the actual existence of atoms, yet as a chemist he regarded the assumption of atoms, "not only as advisable, but as absolutely necessary in chemistry."

CHAPTER XVI

THE DEVELOPMENT OF APPLIED CHEMISTRY

ANALYTICAL chemistry—that division of chemistry which treats of the methods of ascertaining the chemical composition of substances and mixtures both as to kind (qualitative analysis) and quantity (quantitative analysis)—has been an indispensable aid to all branches of chemistry, pure and applied, during their modern development, and has itself undergone considerable elaboration and perfection. In particular, analytical methods, both qualitative and quantitative, have been and are being continuously improved.

The services of Boyle, Hoffmann, Marggraf, Scheele and Bergman in qualitative analysis have been mentioned, and it will be remembered that Bergman was the first to publish a system of qualitative analysis in the wet way. He laid a firm foundation for the methodical employment of reagents, and the methods of qualitative analysis now in use have been developed from his analytical course of procedure. Wilhelm August Lampadius and Johann Göttling contributed materially to the systematic arrangement of the analytical methods in use during the first decade. The former published in 1801 his "Handbuch der Chemischen Analyse der Mineralkörper," and the latter his "Praktische Anleitung zur Prüfenden und Zerlegenden Chemie" in 1802. Other works followed these, and analytical methods became known and improved.

Qualitative analysis in the dry way has been perfected by the use of the blowpipe, an instrument which was originally employed for soldering metals, and which was first employed for testing minerals by Cronstedt and Engestroem. Bergman and Gahn studied thoroly the deportment of various substances and reagents under the flame of the blowpipe, and their treatise on this important branch of chemical analysis was published in 1779. Berzelius, Hausmann and Wollaston later became interested in this field, and Berzelius, who was notably instrumental in introducing the blowpipe into chemistry, published a treatise on the application of this instrument in 1820. More recently the art of dry assay ("docimacy") was considerably advanced by the important flame-reactions of Bunsen. His treatise, "Flammen-Reactionen," was published in 1880.

After the preparatory investigations of Bergman, Klaproth, Vauquelin and Proust, it was Berzelius who worked out new methods of quantitative analysis, thereby promoting the systematic development of this branch. He had shown great ingenuity and inspired his pupils, more especially Heinrich Rose and Friedrich Wöhler, with like powers. Rose and Wöhler extended the observations of Berzelius, and made analytical methods generally known by the publication of their treatises. The "Handbuch der Analytischen Chemie" of the former first appeared in 1829, and passed through six German editions and three French editions; while the "Practische Uebungen in der Chemichen Analyse" of Wöhler which was published in 1853, was translated into Russian, French and English.

The chief exponent and great master of analytical chemistry, however, was C. Remigius Fresenius (1818-1897), who for over half a century devoted his life and labors to its extension. He collated and examined all methods formerly in use, and devised many new ones; but his greatest services were the establishment of the "Zeitschrift für Analytische Chemie" in 1862, and the publication of his "Anleitung zur Quantitativen Chemischen Analyse" in 1841 and his "Anleitung zur Quantitativen Chemischen Analyse" in 1846. These works have been published in numerous editions and translations since.

Other chemists who have aided in the discovery of new tests, improved methods of separation and determination, and in the designing of suitable chemical apparatus for analytical operations are Liebig, Stromeyer, Bunsen, Fremy, Turner, Schreerer, Rammelsberg, Gibbs, Blomstrand, Marignac and Winkler. Classen's services in electroanalysis are noteworthy.

Volumetric analysis—that process in which the reagents are employed in solutions of known strength—has been greatly developed during the last seventy years, and volumetric methods are much used in technical analysis, owing to the fact that no weighing is necessary after the standard solutions are once made up, thus saving considerable time.

The quantitative analysis of gases was greatly perfected by Bunsen, whose researches in this direction began in 1838. Bunsen published methods of estimating various gases by absorption and combustion, which have required only slight modifications since, but the qualitative analysis of gases has only lately been developed in a scientific manner. The work of Winkler in this connection has been important, and he and Hempel have improved the apparatus for gasometry and gas analysis and have generalized methods.

The quantitative analysis of organic compounds has gradually developed from the observation that carbonic acid and water are products of their combustion. Lavoisier indicated the right path here, and his process was improved upon by Gay-Lussac and Thénard, Berzelius, Liebig, and more recently by Dennstedt, Collie and Hempel.

The exact determination of nitrogen only became possible after 1830, when Dumas had devised his method. Other methods of determining nitrogen have been worked out by Will and Varrentrapp, and by Kjeldahl, whose method is extensively used in agricultural-chemical analysis for estimating protein. Many methods for determining the halogens, sulphur, phosphorus, and other elements which occur less frequently in organic bodies, have been worked out, and these have found extended application in forensic chemistry, hygiene and agricultural chemistry.

The beginnings of phytochemistry, the chemistry of plant-life, can be traced back to investigations made at the close of the eighteenth century.

Priestley, Senebier, de Saussure, and others were familiar with the fact that green plants under the influence of sunlight will remove carbonic acid gas from the atmosphere and decompose it. They were also aware of the fact that ammonia salts are of value in stimulating the growth of plants, Nicholas Leblanc having pointed this out at the end of the eighteenth century.

Altho the problems of plant-life, the mode and manner of plant-nourishment and growth, had engaged the labors of many trained observers for many years, yet even during the first three decades of this century the belief was almost universal that plants, like animals, derive their nourishment directly from organic matter.

This assumption found its chief advocates in Germany and France in Albrecht Thaer and Mathieu de Dombasle respectively. In their opinion inorganic salts, the importance of which could not be absolutely denied, acted merely as stimulants and not as if they were essential to the growth of the plant. Indeed, Thaer held that the creation of earths in plants through their vital forces was possible. In this assumption he followed the opinion of Schrader who so early as the year 1800 imagined that he had proved by actual experiments the generation of the ash-constituents of plants by the vital forces.

J. G. Wallerius, a Stockholm chemist, had sought to lay a much more rational foundation for agricultural chemistry in 1761 in his "Akerbrukets Chemiska Grunder," when he made a comparison between the plant constituents and the constituents of the soil on which they grew.

It was Justus von Liebig who demonstrated the falsity of the views of Thaer and Dombasle, and who entirely disproved the humus-doctrine, as the theory held at that time was called. It was in 1840, after exhaustive investigations on the weathering of rocks, on the formation of oils, and on the effects of rain and the gases which rain holds in solution, that Liebig published his classic work on the application of chemistry to agriculture and physiology.

In this Liebig completely undermined the foundations of the humus

DEVELOPMENT OF APPLIED CHEMISTRY

theory and enunciated the following foundation principles of modern agricultural chemistry:

1. Inorganic substances form the nutritive material for all plants.

2. Plants live upon carbonic acid, ammonia (nitric acid), water, phosphorus acid, sulphuric acid, silicic acid, lime, magnesia, potash and iron; many need common salt.

3. Manure, the dung of animals, acts not through the organic elements directly upon plant-life, but indirectly through the products of the decay and fermentative processes; thus carbon becomes carbonic acid and nitrogen becomes ammonia or nitric acid. The organic manures, which consist of parts of remains of plants and animals, can be substituted by the inorganic constituents into which they would be resolved in the soil.

Practical field trials, carried out by governments and large landowners, proved the correctness of Liebig's deductions from his laboratory experiments, and the many investigators in this line since have come either directly or indirectly from Liebig's school. Liebig's conclusion that one must restore to the soil that which the removal of the crop had withdrawn, if one would prevent its exhaustion, is the basis of successful agricultural practice to-day.

A French chemist, J. B. Boussingault, worked independently along similar lines to Liebig, and the services which he rendered in carrying out researches on the nutrition of plants by new methods were of great importance.

Mention may be made here about nitrification in soils and the assimilation of free nitrogen by plants, the most important discoveries in agricultural chemistry of recent years. In 1849, Georges Ville, then director of the Agricultural Experiment Station at Vincennes, proved by actual experiment that certain plants assimilate free atmospheric nitrogen, but his conclusions were strongly disputed, being directly opposed to those of Boussingault and Liebig, and also to subsequent investigations by Lawes, Gilbert and Pugh in 1857. An important experiment bearing on the point and extending over many years was begun in 1855 by Herr Schultz, of Lupitz, in Altmark, Germany. He grew lupines on very poor soil with the addition of non-nitrogenous manures only and found that, notwithstanding this, the soil became richer in nitrogen year by year. The next step toward the solution of the question was the discovery in 1877 of the now well-known process of "nitrification" in soils by Schloesing and Müntz, this nitrification being the work of definite microbes, some of which have been isolated, while more recent work has proved that the direct assimilation of atmospheric nitrogen by leguminous plants is brought about by the agency of certain micro-organisms (tubercle bacteria) originally present in the soil. Cultures of these specific bacteria are now prepared on a manufacturing scale, under the name of "nitragins," for application to soils naturally deficient in them.

It only remains to mention as a factor in the present and future growth of agricultural chemistry the experiment stations and laboratories established now by the governments of every civilized country. In the United States, for example, there are at present sixty-one agricultural experiment stations, all in charge of efficient specialists, and many intricate problems of national importance have been solved.

The large chemical industries and, in fact, all branches of chemical technology have been immensely developed during the nineteenth and twentieth centuries, and the achievements of chemistry in the arts and industries have been stupendous and varied.

During the Modern Chemical Period pure chemistry and applied chemistry have been constantly interactive, and the latter has profited immensely by the extension of the former, while pure chemistry (theoretical, inorganic, organic and practical chemistry) has in turn been greatly benefited by the opportunities offered by the industries. The advancement of technical chemistry has been especially aided, however, by the development of analytical chemistry, which has allowed of a keen insight into the composition of the various industrial products, thereby leading to the introduction of many technological innovations. Then, too, industrial research has been and is being constantly fostered by chemical manufacturers, and this has led to the accruement of important novelties and improvements.

The literature of technical chemistry is very extensive, but the standard treatises of Rudolf von Wagner ("Handbuch der Chemischen Technologie"), Karl Karmarsch ("Geschichte der Technologie seit der Mitte des achtzehnten Jahrhunderts"), T. E. Thorpe ("A Dictionary of Applied Chemistry") and Ernst von Meyer ("A History of Chemistry," translated by McGowan) contain accounts of the development of the important industries.

The manufactures of sulphuric acid and soda, which may be looked upon as the basis of all the other chemical industries and which are naturally followed by those of hydrochloric acid, bleaching powder, chlorate of potash, and other salts of potassium, nitric acid, etc., only attained to their full vigor after the various processes involved had been explained by chemical investigation and after the most favorable conditions for those processes had been worked out.

Important practical improvements were made in the manufacture of sulphuric acid so early as the beginning of the nineteenth century— *e.g.*, the amount of steam required was regulated and the process was made continuous (the latter by Holker). The first attempt to explain this remarkable chemical process of the formation of sulphuric acid from sulphurous acid, air, water and nitrous gas was made by Clément and Désormes, who recognized the important part played by the nitric oxide. How essential for the manufacture the careful observations on the chemical behavior of nitrous acid to sulphurous and sulphuric have been is sufficiently evidenced by the introduction of the Gay-Lussac and Glover towers to which they gave rise and which have made the process into one complete whole.

In 1831, Peregrine Phillips discovered the "contact process" by bringing about the combination of sulphur dioxide and oxygen in presence of platinum, but it was only forty to fifty years later that Clemens Winkler converted this experiment into a technical manufacture. The contact process, in many modifications, has developed and improved so rapidly that many think it will eventually supplant the old chamber process altogether.

Common salt forms the foundation of the soda industry, whose history commences with the beginning of the modern chemical period. Nicholas Leblanc was the first to succeed in converting salt into soda, with sodic sulphate as an intermediate product, Malherbe and de la Metherie having some time previously attempted to utilize the latter substance in the same way, but without material success. It was in 1791 that Leblanc commenced the actual manufacture of soda, and in the year 1823 Muspratt began the erection of his alkali works at Liverpool; his name deserves a foremost place in connection with the development of the soda industry. The formation of soda from the sulphate, by fusing the latter with coal and limestone, was ultimately so far explained by exact chemical experiments as to allow of a tenable theory of this fusion process being advanced.

Scientific researches have also given rise to numerous important improvements in the soda manufacture—*e.g.*, to the beautiful process of Hargreaves and Robinson, by which sulphate of soda is prepared directly without the previous production of sulphuric acid, to the introduction of revolving soda furnaces, and to many processes for utilizing and rendering harmless the unpleasant alkali waste. But the greatest advance of all this direction is the comparatively recent and exceedingly simple process of Chance, by which nearly all the sulphur in alkali waste can be recovered at a very cheap rate.

Purely chemical observations have also led to what was, until quite recently, the most important of all the innovations in the soda industry, viz., the conversion of common salt into carbonate of soda without the intermediate formation of sulphate at all, by the ammonia-soda process. The manufacture of "ammonia soda" and of artificial manures has grown so enormously of late years that the demand for salts of ammonia has increased proportionately, but this requirement has in its turn been met by the introduction of improved apparatus for the working up of gas liquor and by the successful attempts to extract the nitrogen of fuel in the form of ammonia, at the same time that the heat from the fuel or the residual coke is itself being utilized.

Berthollet's experiments upon the bleaching action of chlorine and the chlorides of the alkalies led to the manufacture of the bleach liquor known under the name of "Eau de Javelle." Chloride of lime was first produced by Messrs. Tennant & Co. in Glasgow in the year 1779. Weldon's process for the recovery of the manganese dioxide, required in the preparation of chlorine, from the otherwise worthless chlorine waste has been in practical working since 1867. Deacon's method of producing chlorine directly from hydrochloric acid has never been very widely used.

The manufacture of bromine and iodine is based upon the original work of Gay-Lussac and Balard. Laboratory experiments have also led to the production of iodine from mother liquors which were formerly looked upon as valueless—*e.g.*, those from Chili saltpeter and from phosphorite after its treatment with acid. To A. Frank is due the merit of having made bromine available for technical purposes by preparing it from the mother liquor of the Stassfurt waste salts.

Nitric acid plays an important part in chemical industries, especially since the development of the manufacture of explosives on a large scale. Potassium nitrate, which has been known and valued for so long, is still an indispensable ingredient of black gunpowder. Since the introduction of the nitrate of soda from the Chili deposits, nitric acid has been prepared from it (instead of from the more expensive nitrate of potash) by the old process of distillation with sulphuric acid, the latest advance here being the distillation of the nitric acid in a vacuum.

The explosives, whose preparation now forms a great industry, have all been made available for practical use by chemical investigations. The epoch-making discovery of gun-cotton by Schönbein and Böttger (independently) in 1846 must be recalled here. Nitro-glycerine had been known as a chemical preparation, discovered by Sobrero, for fifteen years before it began to find extended application in 1862, as the result of Nobel's researches.

The match industry owes its enormous development to the increased knowledge of chemical preparations and processes. There is a marked contrast between the "chemical tinder" of 1807—*i.e.*, matches containing a mixture of chlorate of potash and sulphur, which were ignited by dipping them into sulphuric acid—and the present friction matches! Those prepared with ordinary yellow phosphorus were most probably first introduced in 1833 by Irinyi of Pesth, and subsequently by Romer of Vienna and Moldenhauer of Darmstadt; they have since undergone many improvements, the most important of these being subsequent to the discovery of amorphous (non-poisonous) phosphorus, which has been used since the year 1848. Phosphorus has been manufactured on the large scale for about fifty years. Scheele's process for its preparation was improved upon by Nicolas so far back as 1778, and has been materially modified in recent years.

Closely connected also with the soda industry are the manufactures of ultramarine and of glass. The former substance was discovered in 1828 by Chr. Gmelin and at about the same time by Guimet; a little later it was also discovered, independently, by Köttig of Meissen, who was the first to prepare it on a technical scale.

The production of glass reached a high state of development in olden times through pure empiricism, but has been greatly benefited by chemical research. The manufacture of glass with sulphate of soda, and the improvements in flint and crystal glasses belong to the last century, while progress has also been made in silvering (by Liebig), and in glass painting through the discovery of new mineral colors.

Water glass, which was known to Agricola and Glauber, was made available for technical purposes by Fuchs in 1818, and has since then been used for a great number of different purposes—*e.g.*, for impregnating wood and preparing cements.

The attempts to utilize raw vegetable products, particularly wood and straw, for the production of paper were first carried out in the year 1846. In caustic soda a reagent was found by means of which cellulose could be prepared from these materials, while of late years a solution of calcium sulphite in sulphurous acid has shown itself especially well adapted for this purpose. The above process for the production of sulphite cellulose resulted from the chemical investigations of Tilgham. Cross and Bevan's discovery that cellulose can be dissolved by carbon disulphide and soda, and thus be converted into a soluble cellulose xanthate has enormously extended the uses to which the plastic material can be put. Objects of all kinds, from "artificial silk" to billiard balls, can now be made of pure cellulose.

The beet-sugar industry has developed into an enormous manufacture from experiments carried out by chemists on a small scale. Marggraf's discovery, in 1747, that sugar was present in the juice of beet, was not at that time capable of being applied commercially. Achard, a pupil of Marggraf, and others again took up at the end of the eighteenth century the problem of obtaining sugar from beet on the large scale, and they devised a process which was carried out in factories during the years of the Napoleonic wars. However, this process was unable to exist, being a very imperfect one and giving but a small yield of sugar, and it is from the year 1825 that the real rise of the beet-sugar industry dates, various factors entering into its growth, not the least of which was the practical application of chemical knowledge. Scheibler's strontia process for obtaining the crystallizable sugar from molasses is based upon a knowledge of the various saccharates of strontia. The filtration of the refined juice through bone charcoal was first recommended by Figuier in 1811 and then by Derosne in 1812, and has since become an essential part of the process. The use of vacuum pans for evaporating the syrup was introduced by Howard in 1813, since which time many improvements have been made in them. Osmosis, which was first applied on the large scale by Dubrunfaut in 1863 for extracting the crystallizable sugar from molasses, was developed by researches in physical chemistry.

The development of the fermentation industries has been immensely extended by chemical investigation, while at the same time the nature of the processes themselves has been explained. The latest work of E. Buchner and his pupils has resulted in showing that fermentation is brought about by an enzyme ("zymase") produced from the yeast.

Among the more important observations in this branch during recent years are those of Effront upon the favorable effect of a minute quantity of hydrofluoric acid on the fermentation process, and of others upon the advantages gained by ventilation and by the use of pure yeast cultures.

A knowledge of the normal composition of wine and beer has led to rational suggestions for the improvement of those liquors. It would be impossible to attempt even a bare enumeration of the more important innovations in this branch, many of which are due to Pasteur—*e.g.*, the Pasteurization of beer.

In no other section of technical chemistry have there been so many discoveries made by systematic investigation as in that of artificial dyes.

The first aniline dye which was produced upon a technical scale was the mauve prepared by W. H. Perkin in 1856, by acting upon aniline with bichromate of potash and sulphuric acid, and it is to him that the introduction of the color industry is due. A. W. Hofmann observed in 1858 the formation of aniline red (magenta), which was shortly afterward manufactured by another method by Verguin of Lyons and introduced into commerce under the name of fuchsine. This was followed by the discovery of aniline blue, aniline violet and aniline green, all of which were first prepared by Hofmann himself, while he proved that all of them were derivatives of fuchsine. The discovery of methyl violet by Lauth in 1861 and that of aniline black by Lightfoot in 1863 were of great practical importance. In addition to this new and important methods for the production of rosaniline dyes have been discovered and developed—*e.g.*, oxalic acid, formic aldehyde and carbonyl chloride are now used for the synthesis of diphenylamine blue, the new magenta, methyl violet, and allied compounds.

The valuable dye alizarine was formerly prepared entirely from the madder root, but is now obtained from coal-tar, this revolution having been brought about by Graebe and Liebermann's successful synthesis (in 1869) of alizarine from anthracene, a constituent of coal-tar. Following alizarine, other derivatives of anthracene were prepared from the year 1880 onward.

An immense industry—that of so-called chemical preparations—has gradually been developed on scientific lines from apparently insignificant beginnings which had their origin in the work of the apothcary; such "preparations" belong partly to inorganic and partly to organic chemistry. As instances of this one may take the great increase in the production of silver salts, bromine and iodine for photographic and other purposes, and the manufacture of numberless other metallic salts—*e.g.*, thiosulphates, hydrosulphites, borates and silicates, not to speak of newly introduced compounds like the peroxides of hydrogen and sodium, sodium persulphate and other per-salts and compounds of lithium, rubidium, vanadium, etc. The already imposing list of inorganic preparations is being continually added to.

The manufacture of organic preparations is still more extensive. The various alcohols themselves, their ethers and esters, chloroform, chloral, iodoform, aldehyde, etc., are now all essential to chemical manufactures and to medicine. The processes by which these compounds are manufactured are the result of scientific researches, old and new.

From what has been said it is seen that coal-tar is the raw material from which many organic preparations are obtained, the technical importance of which it is difficult to estimate. Formerly a troublesome waste material, it is now of at least equal value with the other products from the distillation of coal. The manufacture of ammonia and salts of ammonia from gas liquor is now a thoroly rational one, thanks to the careful chemical examination of the latter, and it forms a large and important branch of industry.

The manufacture of coal gas was at first developed quite empirically, and it was only in the second half of the nineteenth century that improvements were introduced which were based upon the scientific investigation of the relations existing between the composition of the gas and the mode in which the distillation of the coal was conducted, and this also applies to improved methods of purifying the crude gas. The present distillation process was introduced about the year 1880, after it was seen that by raising the temperature of decomposition the yield of gas from pit coal was nearly doubled. In order to achieve the necessary white heat, gas retorts are now made from the most refractory fireclay (instead of iron), and they are heated by regenerator gas.

About fifteen years ago acetylene began to come into prominence as an important illuminant; indeed, enthusiasts on the subject prophesied that the brilliant light which it gave would prove to be "the light of the future." Produced from calcium carbide, a product of electrochemistry, it looked for a time as if acetylene were destined to become a formidable competitor of the electric light.

The first impulse toward the use of furnace gas as a heating agent was given by the experiments of Faber de Faur and of Bunsen, experiments made with the object of utilizing the gases issuing from the mouth of iron blast furnaces, which are rich in carbon monoxide. These, as well as the gases from coking ovens, were for long allowed to escape, and still are to some extent, but for the most part they now constitute important sources of heat. Lowe introduced "water gas" into technical use in 1875, preparing it by passing steam over red-hot coal; it is now much used for heating and illuminating purposes and will undoubtedly become even more employed in time.

The above résumé of the development of industrial chemistry during the Modern Period will indicate how it has been elevated by a continuous infusion of scientific spirit, and manufacturing, once a matter of empirical judgment and individual skill, is more and more becoming a system of scientific processes. Quantitative measurements are replacing guesswork, and thus waste is diminished and economy of production insured. In the United States several decades ago few industrial establishments furnished regular employment to chemists, but now American manufacturers are becoming more and more appreciative of scientific research, and the results so far obtained have resulted in far-reaching improvements. In the production of a metal from its ores, or of indigo from coal-tar, it is chemistry that points the way, and the more complex the problem the greater the dependence. In devising new processes and in the discovery of new and useful products, chemistry is again the pathfinder. The community is apt to overlook the extent and diversity of the services rendered by the chemist, because of the quiet and unobtrusive way in which the work is carried out.

The measure of a country's appreciation of the value of chemistry in its material development and the extent to which it utilizes this science in its industries, generally measure quite accurately the industrial progress and prosperity of that country. In no other country in the world has the value of chemistry to industry been so thoroly understood and appreciated as in Germany, and in no other country of similar size and natural endowment have such remarkable advances in industrial development been recorded, and this too, with steadily increasing economy in the utilization of the natural resources.

Ex-President Roosevelt has well said, "The life of the nation depends absolutely on the material resources which have already made the nation great," and M. T. Bogert recently has eloquently indicated how the chemist can and will be of service in that great problem, the conservation of natural resources. This work is not entirely that of the engineer, and, with the awakening of the producer and manufacturer to the value of science in industry, the outcome of the conversation movement can only be a successful one through the assistance of the chemist.

PHYSICS

PHYSICS

CHAPTER I

AN ANALYSIS OF MATTER

When a child first opens his eyes on the world about him a confusing array of experiences thrust themselves upon his notice. The clothes in which he is wrapped, the incomprehensible voice-sounds that come to his ears, the ever-changing personalities of his environment—everything is wonderful, strange and fearsome because of its strangeness. So must the world of nature have seemed strange to early man, strange and terrifying. The sights and sounds of the forest, the wind rushing through the trees or lashing the rivers into foam, thunder and clouds and lightning, clear sun and quiet stars—all spoke to man in his earlier development in personal voices. Each new object of sense constituted for him an object for suspicious investigation or superstitious fear. Familiarity may or may not breed contempt, but that it does induce a form of indifference is certain.

When a leaf rustles in the forest to-day, the rational explanation of a breath of wind takes the place of the old-time fear of a wood-demon; when a tidal wave rushes up a river, the modern knowledge of tides releases man from a blind terror. And this goes even farther, for when a lightning-flash strikes, the law of the association of ideas will lead the mind to correlate the incident with Benjamin Franklin and with the harnessing of the lightning to many everyday uses. Having passed the stage of superstitious wonder, man at once attempts to classify the phenomena of nature among those experiences of whose character already he feels himself sure.

The earliest recorded beginnings of physical science were made, so far as history can testify, by the Chaldean astrologers. Their study of the stars, however, directed as it was rather to the prediction of individual and national destinies than to determining the real nature of the material universe, laid the ground-work for further study, but bequeathed little of practical importance in physics.

No great names in science have been bequeathed to the world by Assyria or Chaldea. They may have furnished material for the imaginative genius of the Greeks, but the latter alone were capable of formulating into a system the vague wisdom of the Orient. As John Lord remarks, "The East never gave valuable knowledge to the West; it gave the tendency to Egyptian mysticism, which in its turn tended to superstition. Instead of astronomy, it gave astrology; instead of science, it gave magic, incantations and dreams."

The Chaldean and Assyrian civilizations which gave birth to the astrology of the Magi flourished and declined in the fertile valleys of the Tigris and Euphrates. Nearly a thousand years before them, however, there had been developing in the fecund region of the Nile the people who produced the first of those marvelous pyramids which remain to-day the greatest monuments of history. Some considerable knowledge of physics and the elementary application of machines the Egyptians must have possessed, or at least the builders of the pyramids, whoever they were. The stones are much larger than those used in architecture to-day. The columns of the Egyptian temples still standing in ruins are immense. Travelers look with astonishment and admiration at the gigantic structures whose walls, lintels, columns and entablatures are formed of material cut in extraordinary dimensions. No scientific works remain to show how the ancient builders of Egypt managed to carry and put in place such large blocks of stone. Mural paintings, sculptures and incriptions are the only means of conveying such slight information as has been handed down to the present generation.

It has been held by some students of antiquity that the pyramids were designed as institutions to embody cosmic discoveries; for example, that certain specific measurements of the structure bear a definite ratio to such matters as the exact length of the earth's circumference and diameter, the length of an arc of meridian and standard units of measure. Other theorists, with far more probability in their favor, believe the pyramids to have been constructed as the tombs of the great kings whose names are graven in the interior and whose sarcophagi (with their mummies) are often found in the central chamber. Still others have declared that the pyramids were used for astronomical study.

Whatever other purpose the pyramids may have served, they seem to have been little adapted for observatories. It is a matter of common knowledge that an object viewed through a roll of paper is better seen in detail than when looked at without such aid. Place a lens in either end of the roll, adjust the focus of the lenses and a telescope is made. The eye takes in a great deal more than the mind perceives. In gazing at an object, especially at a distance, the detail of the object is obscured by the light reflected from hundreds of other objects in the neighborhood. The simple roll of paper overcomes this difficulty in exactly the same way that the ventilating passages, the so-called "telescopes" of the pyramids, might do. A star is visible in broad daylight when viewed through such a long, narrow passage as were these nine-inch "telescopes" of the pyramids. A fatal defect in this telescope thesis, however, is the fact that the earth revolves, and a star visible for a few seconds at the aperture of the passage would be lost almost immediately from the field of vision.

In their astronomical observations and in their arithmetical calculations the Egyptians were inferior to the Chaldeans. They were familiar with the true meridian and the length of the sidereal year. They did not know the signs of the zodiac, however, nor are there any inscriptions of Egyptian origin such as are found on the Assyrian bricks, wherein appear the square and cubic multiplication tables and the three hundred and sixty degrees of the circle. The Egyptian "zodiac" of the temple at Derderah is now known to be a production comparatively modern in origin, even showing Greek influence.

The Hellenic philosophers made the first definite classification of elements, asserting that earth, air, fire and water were the four indivisible substances out of which the whole world was made up. They knew a god of the water, Poseidon (Neptune); a god of earth, Anteus; a god of fire, Pluto, while each of the four winds was a deity. However simple and clear such a division might seem, modern science has proved that each of these supposed elements is divisible into several elementary substances. Thus ordinary water, for instance, is known to be compounded of oxygen and hydrogen; air is a mixture of nitrogen, oxygen, carbonic acid gas and a number of other elements more recently isolated, among which helium is of especial interest; and so numerous are the component parts of earth that it seems most strange how it ever could have been conceived as an element at all. Despite all errors in explaining the phenomena of nature, however, Greece must be credited with having made the first real beginning of that "classified knowledge" out of which has developed the natural science of modern times.

Thales, the founder of the Ionic school of philosophers, is reported to have determined the course of the sun from solstice to solstice and to have calculated eclipses. He attributed an eclipse of the moon to the interposition of the earth between the sun and moon, and an eclipse of the sun to the interposition of the moon between the sun and earth, and thus taught the rotundity of the earth, sun and moon. He also held that water is the principle of all things—a somewhat egregious error from the modern point of view. As early as two hundred and eighty years before the present era Aristarchus, Hippocrates and Galen made many scientific advances, but Physics was not yet strongly differentiated from its attendant sciences.

The mantle of the Greek philosophers was caught up by Pliny, who perished in the eruption of Vesuvius in 23 A.D. His Natural History in thirty-seven books treats of everything in the natural world—of the heavenly bodies, of the elements, of thunder and lightning, of the winds and seasons. Like nearly all the Greek and Roman philosophers, however, and many great theorists of later date, Pliny contented himself with theorizing.

In mathematics, metaphysics, literature and art the Greeks displayed wonderful creative genius, but in natural science they achieved comparatively little. "It would not be correct to say that they possessed little or no aptitude for observing natural phenomena," says Florian Cajori in his "History of Physics," "but it is true that, as a rule, they were ignorant of the art of experimentation and that many of their physical speculations were vague, trifling and worthless. As compared with the vast amount of theoretical deduction about nature, the number of experiments known to have been performed by the Greeks is surprisingly small. Little or no attempt was made to verify speculation by experimental evidence. As a conspicuous example of misty philosophizing we give Aristotle's proof that the world is perfect: 'The bodies of which the world is composed are solids, and therefore have three dimensions. Now, three is the most perfect number—it is the first of numbers, for of one we do not speak as a number, of two we say both, but three is the first number of which we say all. Moreover, it has a beginning, a middle and an end.'"

Mechanical subjects are treated in the writings of Aristotle. The great peripatetic had grasped the notion of the parallelogram of forces for the special case of the rectangle. He attempted the theory of the lever, stating that a force at a greater distance from the fulcrum moves a weight more easily because it describes a greater circle.

Aristotle's views of falling bodies are very far from the truth. Nevertheless they demand attention, for the reason that, during the Middle Ages and Renaissance, his authority was so great that they play an important rôle in scientific thought. He says: "That body is heavier than another which, in an equal bulk, moves downward quicker." In another place he teaches that bodies fall quicker in exact proportion to their weight. No statement could be further from the truth.

A modern writer endeavors to exonerate Aristotle as a physicist. "If he could have had any modern instrument of observation—such as the telescope or microscope, or even the thermometer or barometer—placed in his hands, how swiftly would he have used such an advantage!" But in the case of falling bodies, the experiment was within his reach. If it had only occurred to him, while walking up and down the paths near his school in Athens, to pick up two stones of unequal weight and drop them together, he could easily have seen that the one of, say, ten times the weight did not descend ten times faster.

Immeasurably superior to Aristotle as a student of mechanics is Archimedes (287-212 B.C.). He is the true originator of mechanics as a science. To him belongs the honor of enunciating the theory of the center of gravity (centroid) and of the lever. In his "Equiponderance of Planes" he starts with the axiom that equal weights acting at equal distances on opposite sides of a pivot are in equilibrium, and then endeavors to establish the principle that "in the lever unequal weights are in equilibrium only when they are inversely proportional to the arms from which they are suspended." His appreciation of its efficiency is echoed in the exclamation attributed to him: "Give me where I may stand and I will move the world."

While the "Equiponderance" treats of solids or the equilibrium of solids, the book on "Floating Bodies" treats of hydrostatics. The attention of Archimedes was first drawn to the subject of specific gravity when King Hieron asked him to test whether a crown, professed by the maker to be pure gold, was not alloyed with silver. The story goes that the philosopher was in a bath when the true method of solution flashed on his mind. He immediately leapt from the bath and ran home, shouting, "I have found it!" To solve the problem, he took a piece of gold and a piece of silver, each weighing the same as the crown, the piece of silver being almost twice the size of the gold. He then determined the volume of water displaced by the gold, the silver and the crown respectively, and from that calculated the amount of gold and silver in the crown. The proportion of greater displacement in the crown above the piece of pure gold showed the extent of the alloy.

In his "Floating Bodies" Archimedes established the important principle, known by his name, that the loss of weight of a body submerged in water is equal to the weight of the water displaced and that a floating body displaces its own weight of water. Since the days of Archimedes able minds have drawn erroneous conclusions on liquid pressure. The expression "hydrostatic paradox" indicates the slippery nature of the subject. All the more must we admire the clearness of conception and almost perfect logical rigor which characterize the investigations of Archimedes.

Archimedes is said to have shown wonderful inventive genius in various mechanical inventions. It is reported that he astonished the court of Hieron by moving heavy ships by aid of a collection of pulleys. To him is ascribed the invention of war engines and the endless screw ("screw of Archimedes") which was used to drain the holds of ships. This genius, "the greatest scientist before Galileo," perished in the siege of Syracuse by the Romans (212 B.C.).

About a century after Archimedes there flourished Ctesibius and his pupil Heron, both of Alexandria. They contributed little to the advancement of theoretical investigation, but displayed wonderful mechanical ingenuity. The force-pump is probably the invention of Ctesibius. The suction pump is older and was known in the time of Aristotle. According to Vitruvius, Ctesibius designed the ancient fire-engine, consisting of the combination of two force-pumps, spraying alternately. The machine had no air-chamber, and therefore could not produce a steady stream. Heron describes the fire-engine in his "Pneumatica." During the Middle Ages the fire-engine was unknown. It is said to have been first used in Augsburg in 1518.

Ctesibius is credited with the invention of the hydraulic organ, the water-clock and the catapult. Heron showed the earliest application of steam as a motive power in his toy, called the "eolipile." It was the forerunner of Barker's water-mill and the modern turbine. Heron wrote an important book on geodesy, called "Dioptra."

The Greeks invented the hydrometer, probably in the fourth century A.D. There appears to be no good evidence for attributing its origin to Archimedes. The hydrometer, a device in common use today for measuring the densities of water, milk and acids, is described in full by Bishop Synesius in a letter to Hypatia. It consisted of a hollow, graduated tin cylinder, weighted below. Immersed in a liquid, the depth to which it sank constituted a measure of the relative weight or density of that liquid. It was first used in medicine, to determine the quality of drinking-water, hard water being at that time considered unwholesome. According to Desaguliers, it was used for this purpose as late as the eighteenth century.

Since in such distant days, and with theories so diverse from those of modern times, the study of matter and of its properties began, the question arises whether the initial problem has yet been solved. Theories have been multiplied, modified, rejected, confirmed. Through centuries the evidence of experiment has accumulated; much has been learned of the nature and behavior of matter under varying conditions, but the complexity of the problem has become more evident the further it is studied and the complete answer is not yet. The world is rife to-day with stores of knowledge undreamed of a few centuries ago, but since every addition to the sum of information brings with it a new series of problems, human reason halts before the attainment of a conclusive knowledge as to the real essence of that which it calls Matter.

The Greek-Roman Asclepiades conceived matter to consist of extremely small, but still divisible and fragile, formless and mutable collections of atoms, cognizable indeed by the understanding, but not by the senses. These atoms originally moved about uncontrolled in a general vacuum and burst in pieces through accidental collisions. By union of the finest fragments thus engendered, the "Leptomeres," originate the visible bodies, whose differences of form and varying peculiarities have their foundation in the different association of the leptomeres into different bodies.

In a quaint series of inquiries by John Abercrombie, "The Investigation of Truth," published in Edinburgh three-fourths of a century ago, Matter is defined as "a name which we apply to a certain combination of properties or to certain substances which are solid, extended and divisible and which are known to us only by these properties."

Francis Bacon, "the wisest, brightest, meanest of mankind," as Pope styled him, conceived of matter as made up of two "tribes of things," the "sulphureous" and "mercurial," which, he says, "seem vastly extensive, so as to enter and occupy the whole material world."

Sir Isaac Newton regarded matter as "the coexistence of the smallest particles which are themslves extended and material" and which, through a power whose nature he did not further analyze, hang together. Newton, therefore, adhered to the atomistic school, of which the Greek Democritus of Abdera was the great classic expositor. He did not believe in the infinite sub-divisibility of matter.

In his "Treatise on Light" the great philosopher concludes that "it seems extremely probable that the Creator so formed Matter that its primary particles, out of which all possible bodies afterward arose, was firm, hard, impenetrable and movable." These particles therefore could not through any known force be divided, hence all bodies composed of these minute granules possessed interstices, because otherwise their parts could not be separated from one another, and matter was therefore divisible only until its atoms were reached. Moreover, these primary particles possessed not only a power which subjected them to certain immutable laws of motion, but also the capacity of being set in motion through other influencing causes, for example gravity, fermentation and cohesion.

In accordance with these premises, Newton justly combated the theory of his great contemporary, Cartesius, that matter occupied all space. His excellent development of the idea of the resistance of a medium led to conclusions which inevitably contradicted Cartesius' theory of filled space. In such a compact mass as the latter theory assumed, a mass which would be absolutely impenetrable, all motion must find an unlimited resistance. Cartesius assumed, it is true, that this subtle material was so finely divided as scarcely to exist at all, but Newton showed that this was only empty assertion. He based his opposition to the theory on the ground that the smallest subdividing of matter would not appreciably diminish the resistance which "filled space" would present to a moving body, especially since the body in motion would enforcedly have a density not greatly dissimilar to the resisting medium. Therefore, he argued, a medium wherein bodies move without perceptible retardation must be immensely more attenuated than the bodies themselves. On the other hand, a cannon-ball projected into the "filled space" of Cartesius, be that medium ever so finely divided, would lose more than half its motion before it had moved a distance of thrice its diameter. It would be impossible on this supposition for a man to move from a given spot, much less the heavenly bodies, whose courses show no perceptible retardation, as would inevitably be the case were they to be advancing through an absolutely dense medium.

The belief in "filled space" did not originate with Cartesius. It is rather remarkable that the two thinkers who of all men in history most powerfully have swayed philosophic thought, Aristotle and Kant, were both exponents of the doctrine that space is continuously filled.

The great ancient expositor of the atomic theory was Democritus of Abdera. He taught that the world consists of empty space and an infinite number of indivisible, invisibly small atoms. Bodies appear and disappear only by the union and separation of atoms. Even the phenomena of sensation and thought he affirmed to be the result of their combination.

Newton's belief in the granular, or atomic, nature of matter has been abundantly upheld by the evidence of modern research. It is true that the chemical atom is no longer considered the ultimate unit of material structure.

It has been remarked above that Newton did not attempt to describe the nature of force; he merely assumed its existence as evidenced by the behavior of matter. This was natural, for reason must commence with an assumption and arrived at conclusions based simply upon the evidence of the physical senses. While force is genrally conceived rather as an object of thought than of sense, yet it should not be forgotten that force has as real an existence as matter.

CHAPTER II

RADIO-ACTIVITY

The physical world may be comprehended within the limits of two notions—Force and Matter. Force is that which acts upon Matter, Matter is that by which man apprehends Force.

Force is by no means such a vague and various thing as is sometimes supposed. There is to-day a general tendency to reduce all force to a single underlying principle, and every further division of the atom conduces to this end. The establishment of the theory of the Conservation of Energy; the ready transmutation of various forms of Force, such as the conversion of sound into electricity and the latter into heat, light, motion or chemical energy; the advances in the study of radio-activity and the general acceptance of the kinetic theory of gases clearly show that Matter is one.

Gravity alone seems incapable of classification with other forces, and this is due to its independence of any quality but mass. Temperature will affect the conductivity of an electric wire, solution is greatly influenced by pressure, light has a determinative effect upon physical life as upon many chemical reactions, but gravity is not affected by these conditions of temperature or of the intervening medium. Its nature is utterly unknown.

Electricity has long been held to be a form of force. It acts upon matter to change its condition; it is not an object of sense in a current-laying wire or a charged Leyden jar. It seems to be typical of what is popularly understood by the name force. Yet the study of the cathode rays by Sir William Crookes and his great co-workers in this field of research—Roentgen, Hertz, Rutherford and others whose names are perhaps even more familiar—has made it apparent that something closely resembling material particles are actually discharged from the cathode or negative pole of an electric conductor when the current passes. So strong indeed is the accepted belief that the nature of electricity is material rather than dynamic that Professor Remsen recently formulated the thesis that electricity is one of the elements.

To obtain a clear understanding of the most modern theories with regard to the nature of matter, a brief description of the apparatus used by investigators is indispensable. Imagine an electric bulb or oval vessel of glass. In this are placed two electrodes, which may be either metallic points or bulbs, or, in short, any poles separated by smaller or greater intervals and charged with electricity. Their electrification will be maintained, for example, by placing them in connection with the terminals of an electric current of high voltage. A short tube provided with a stop-cock allows the bulb to be exhausted of air. When the electric tension passes a certain limit a current is established.

If the vacuum is maintained at something less than a thousandth of an atmosphere this current appears as a soft rose-colored glow passing within the bulb from the positive to the negative pole. Sir William Crookes pushed the exhaustion of air in his experiments to a prodigious degree, the pressure being only one millionth of an atmosphere. Concerning Crookes' experiments, M. A. Dastre writes: "The English scientist claimed that when exhausted to this point the residue no longer has the properties of ordinary gases. According to him it is a hyper-gas as different from the true gaseous state as the latter is from the liquid state and forming a fourth condition of matter, following the solid, the liquid and the gas proper; this he called radiant matter. Crookes desired to determine the nature of this fourth state of matter. In reality, the gas, rarefied to the millionth of an atmosphere, has not acquired, by this fact alone, an entirely new character; but it has acquired it most certainly when electrification is added to the rarefaction, and it is then that it constitutes the emanation or the cathode ray."

The vacuum must not be pushed too far; if one goes beyond the millionth part of an atmosphere—and the perfection of mechanism allows going much further than that—the gaseous residue cannot be electrified; electricity will not pass through; there is no longer a current. The electric force is incapable of penetrating absolute vacuum. The importance of this principle is very great from the theoretical point of view; it furnishes, in fact, a new test for matter.

But in Crookes' tube, in which the vacuum has been pushed to one millionth, the current behaves itself rather differently from what it does in the tubes where the rarefaction is less. The path of the current has lost much of its brilliancy; it no longer appears as an uncertain glow, wavering, striated, of a hue intermediate between rose and violet. All the remainder of the interior of the bulb now remains dark. The electricity passes as before between the positive electrode and the cathode or negative pole. The principal flow has been joined by a secondary one; from all points of the tube the positive currents are directed toward the cathode and go to reinforce the principal current. These positive charges which descend from all points of the exterior form the counterpart of the negative charges, which can be seen fixed on the cathode rays. Their existence, their development, their circulation result in consequence from the existence, the development and the inverse circulation of the negative electricity that carries with it the cathode ray.

Such is the cathode afflux; it is composed of the current directed toward the positive electrode and of secondary currents directed from all parts of the recipient toward the cathode. This cathode afflux has, besides, the character and the properties that physicists and chemists attribute to the electric current. It touches directly the cathode.

The afflux, however, is in fact perfectly distinct in every respect from the cathode radiation which follows it. The latter is formed of a pencil of rays perpendicular to the surface of the cathode. It traverses the tube in a perfectly straight line without being disturbed by the rays flowing toward the cathode in an opposite direction, of which we have just been speaking; it passes by them and through them unchecked.

This new pencil implanted perpendicularly on the cathode is not luminous. It is not directly visible; it forms a dark spot in the Crookes tube. It would entirely escape observation if it did not excite a peculiar fluorescence opposite to the cathode at the points where it meets the sides of the tube. The material of the glass becomes illuminated at these points and presents a luminous brilliant spot of a green color.

Crookes conceived the idea of arranging in the interior of the tube, in the path of the pencil of rays between the cathode and the wall, a cross of aluminum. He then saw outlined against the clear fluorescent background the exact silhouette of the cross.

If the cathode is a mirror with spherical concave surface the perpendicular lines at the surface form a conic pencil and converge toward a focus. The effects peculiar to cathode rays are magnified by this concentration, in the same manner that the effects of luminous rays are increased in the focus of a lens. In this manner Crookes was able to show the heating action of his supposed radiant matter; that is to say, of cathode rays. He succeeded in fusing, at one of these foci, not only glass but a wire of iridium-platinum, an operation which requires a temperature of more than 2,000°.

When the cathode rays are reflected from a sheet of platinum within the tube the marvelous phenomena of X-rays, or Roentgen rays, are produced. These rays are different in character from the cathode rays in that they pass readily through wood, flesh, cardboard and even thin sheets of metal. Their serviceability in locating and determining the nature of a fracture in a bone is too well known to need comment.

The cathode projectile does not depend upon the nature of the cathode. It has been proved to be composed of hydrogen. It has its origin necessarily in the breaking up of an atom of hydrogen. (Villard showed that the cathode rays exhibit the spectrum of hydrogen, and if every trace of this gas is removed the cathode emission is suddenly suppressed.)

"Hydrogen," observes M. Dastre in the article quoted above, "instead of being the final expression of simplicity and of lightness, as chemists believe, appears to be a quite complex edifice and rather heavy, since the current of the Crookes tube removes from the stones which represent it but the thousandth part of its mass. These stones are the fragments of atoms, or the atomic corpuscles of J. J. Thompson. The atom is no longer indivisible."

The infinitesimal mass of an atom is a fact sometimes lost sight of in discussing the constitution of matter. It has been estimated from experimentation with colored solutions of a known concentration that the weight of an atom of hydrogen is less than 0.000000000-0019008 oz., and its diameter is less than 0.000000002 in.

Following this line of inquiry as to the ultimate constitution of matter, there has recently appeared an article by Dr. W. D. Horne, which reads in part as follows:

"From considerations based (partly) on very elaborate mathematical calculations it is now maintained that matter is composed of electricity and nothing else. Electricity here is not considered as a form of energy any more than water is a form of energy, but as a vehicle of energy which can be moved from place to place, and whose energy must be in the form of motion or of strain. In motion it constitutes current and magnetism; under strain it constitutes charge, and in vibration it constitutes light."

Continuing, the same writer says: "Sir Oliver Lodge describes the atom of matter as constituted of an individualized mass of positive electricity diffused uniformly over a space the size of an atom, perhaps spherical in shape and about one two hundred millionth of an inch in diameter. Throughout this small spherical shape some eight hundred minute particles of negative electricity, all exactly alike, are supposed to be scattered, flying vigorously about, each repelling every other, and yet all contained within their orbits by the mass of positive electricity. The positive electricity is very much attenuated, and constitutes perhaps only about one per cent. of the mass of the atom, while the negative electrons are correspondingly dense, and so inconceivably small that the eight hundred are crowded in their atom than are the planets in the solar system. Atoms of different kinds of matter are supposed to be constructed in the same general manner and of the same kind of electrons, but the number of electrons in an atom are proportional to the atomic weight of the element. Thus, oxygen would have sixteen times as many electrons in its atom as hydrogen. When the crowding becomes excessive, as in the very heavy atoms of uranium (the heaviest substance known), thorium and radium, having atomic weights well over two hundred, the atoms become radio-active, probably due to numerous collisions between the electrons, some of which are being constantly shot away."

Radium is a bright, shining metal, similar in appearance to such metals as silver and platinum, except that it tarnishes instantly on exposure to air, while the salts of radium are white, crystalline substances, scarcely distinguishable at a casual glance from ordinary salt. This distinguishing property of radium, whose discovery has led to the foundation of the new science of radio-activity, is the continual production of what are known as radiations or rays. There are three types of these rays: The first consists of particles of matter carrying an electric charge, the second of electric corpuscles, and the third type of radiation seems to consist of ethereal waves, strongly resembling the well-known Röntgen Rays.

In a discussion of modern views on matter, Sir Oliver Lodge observed that the facts recorded in connection with the study of radio-activity constituted a phenomena quite new in the history of the world. "No one," he says, "hitherto has observed the transition from one form of matter to another, tho throughout the Middle Ages such a transmutation was looked for. The evolution of matter likewise has been suspected by a few chemists of genius. It was perceived on the strength of Mendeleeff's law (the periodic law), that the elements form a kind of family or related series, and it was surmised that possibly the barriers between one species and the next were not absolutely infrangible, but that temporary transitional forms might occur. All this was speculation, but here in radio-active matter the process appears to be going on before our eyes."

The properties of radium are traceable to the action of the radiations, and one of the important results of various experiments has been the discovery of various beneficial therapeutic actions.

In 1913, Zimmern, Cottenot and Dariaux reported remarkable results in the treatment of neuralgia and neuritis with the X-ray. They applied the rays directly over the nerve roots. In thirty-one cases treated, many of them severe and rebellious to other forms of therapy, prompt relief and cure were the rule. Dr. Robert Abbe, who was a pioneer in the application of radium to disease in this country, reported many cures of epithelial cancer made by the use of radium. In 1914, the difficulties attending the use of X-rays for the treatment of deep cancers were gradually solved. Friedlander added to the general enthusiasm by the discovery that vaccine could be sterilized in thirty minutes, without impairing its potency, by exposure to the violet rays, and this led him to believe that bacteria in the mouth could be killed and human beings thereby cured of throat affections.

CHAPTER III

THE PROPERTIES OF MATTER

The foregoing brief inquiry into the essence of matter leads naturally to a consideration of its properties. Of these properties, the first and foremost is that of weight. The term "ponderable matter" has long been used to distinguish matter in the mass, whereby is plainly indicated the most fundamental property of matter as such. Even in ancient times it was realized that any consideration of matter would deal primarily with questions bearing a definite relation to weight, and the development of the knowledge of the laws concerning the attraction of bodies for each other is closely allied to the inner history of Physics.

In that renascence of learning and thought which succeeded the gloom of the Dark Ages in Europe arose many great lights of science. Copernicus outlined the system which subsequently became known by his name. Kepler grappled with the problem of determining the paths of the planets. Galileo laid the foundation of experimental science. The belief in the earth as the center of the universe was then overthrown. Copernicus taught that the earth was not flat, but spherical; that it rotated on its axis and revolved around the sun; that seasons are due to the inclination of the earth's axis. He defined gravity as "nothing other than a certain natural appetite innate in the parts of matter by the divine providence of the Artificer of the universe, so that they assemble themselves in an exact unity, combining in the form of globes." The marvelous mathematical insight of Kepler proved the accuracy of the Copernican theory, and he demonstrated that the elliptical orbit of Mars would accord exactly with this theory and with no other.

The famous experiments of Galileo with falling bodies constituted as clear a proof of a principle as ever man has made. The young investigator was the first actually to try out the assertion of Aristotle that falling bodies would descend with a velocity proportionate to their weight—a stone weighing ten pounds would fall ten times as fast as a stone weighing but one pound. Galileo did not believe this, and having found from experimentation that it was not so, openly proclaimed his conviction that Aristotle was wrong. His opinions were hotly opposed by the learned professors of the University of

Pisa. By agreement the case was put to the test, and from the top of the leaning tower of Pisa Galileo allowed a small cannon ball and a large bomb to drop together. "The multitude saw the balls start together, fall together, and heard them strike the ground together. Some were convinced, others returned to their rooms, consulted Aristotle, and, distrusting the evidence of their senses, declared continued allegiance to his doctrine."

Galileo then experimented with a polished brass ball rolling down a smooth incline, in order to establish the ratio between the distance traversed and the time of falling. Clocks did not exist in his day, and he resorted to a very interesting and ingenious device for measuring the time elapsing during the progress of this experiment. Attaching a small spigot to the bottom of a water pail, he caught the escaping water, and measured its weight, comparing the increase of weight with the distance traversed by the ball. From these experiments he found the distance to increase very closely as the square of the time.

Galileo's reflections had brought him to the confident belief that Copernicus' theory of the solar system was as true as that of Aristotle was false. He taught and wrote much in support of this doctrine and by his sarcastic raillery against the narrow prejudice of his contemporaries incurred the enmity of many. As an old man of nearly seventy he published a brilliant defence of the Copernican system which aroused such fierce antagonism that he was forced publicly to abjure and curse his "detestable heresy"—viz., that the earth moves round the sun. His "E pur si muove" (But it does move!), uttered as he came forth from his trial, has become historic.

The extraordinarily active mind of this investigator seemed ever to be discovering new and interesting phenomena. It is said of Galileo that while he was praying in the cathedral at Pisa his attention was drawn to the lamps which had been lighted and left irregularly swinging above the altar. His mind at once set off on the question as to whether the period of a pendulum would vary exactly with the amplitude (width) of its vibration. He timed one of the swinging lamps by his pulse and found that the period of vibration was exactly the same, no matter whether the pendulum was swinging violently or dying down to rest.

Later experiments confirmed this conclusion and led likewise to the discovery that the length only of a pendulum affected the time of its oscillation. A slender wire, with a small steel ball for a bob, swings to and fro in exactly the same period as a heavy iron bar whose center of gravity is at an equal distance from the point of suspension. Galileo found out that the swing of a pendulum varied as the square root of its length. Thus a pendulum four feet long will vibrate half as fast as a pendulum a foot long.

The pendulum is used to-day in experimenting upon the attraction due to gravity in different parts of the earth, and by its help the flattening toward the poles of the curved surface of the earth can be exactly determined. The attraction due to gravity varies inversely as the square of the distance from the center of the earth. Thus a pendulum which possesses at New York a length of 39.1 inches will vibrate once every second at that point of the earth's surface. As it moves toward the poles the pendulum vibrates more rapidly. If the change of location is made in the direction of the equator the vibration is slower; this for the reason that the pull of the earth is less, since at the equator the pendulum is farther from the center of gravity of the earth.

Of the same character was the famous Foucault experiment to show the rotation of the earth. On this experiment it was shown that a pendulum at rest, if of sufficient length, would oscillate owing to the motion of the earth, the various factors operating throughout the pendulum, each point of which was at a varying distance from the center of the earth.

The discovery that a pendulum of fixed length always vibrated in the same period lead naturally to the invention of the pendulum clock. For this invention credit has been ascribed to several unknown men, but it is probable that the honor should be divided between Galileo and his famous Dutch contemporary, Christian Huygens. The significance of this invention in the history of physical science is great indeed, when account is taken of the innumerable forms of experimentation which have been reduced by its aid to exact sciences.

While Galileo, Kepler and Copernicus had completely overthrown the ancient theory of Aristotle that the earth is the center of the universe, and had mathematically proved that the solar system revolves about the sun as a center, they did show the "why" of these new and startling discoveries. The puzzle stared philosophers in the face, What is it that causes the planets to move in their orbits? To this question Descartes proposed the novel and striking explanation of a series of whirls or vortices. All space, he argued, was filled with a fluid, the parts of which, acting on each other, caused circular motion. Thus the fluid was formed into a multitude of vortices of various density and size. A huge vortex round the sun carries with it the earth and all the other planets. Each planet, in the same way, is the center of a vortex of its own, and draws bodies to itself in much the same way that a log of wood is drawn into the center of a whirlpool. Cohesion between the different parts of a body he explained in the same manner as the result of infinitesimally small vortices.

Unsatisfactory as this vortex theory seemed, and quite out of accord with the laws which Kepler's intellect had formulated, yet the weight of authority lent to it by the great name of Descartes resulted in its persistence as a generally accepted theory until the middle of the eighteenth century.

Greatest of all natural scientists of this or any time, and first to formulate completely and finally the laws of matter, was the great English mathematician and physicist, "prince of philosophers," Sir Isaac Newton. It was reserved for his genius to show why the apple which falls from a tree falls down to earth and not up to the clouds; how the earth, this infinitesimal point in space, does not rush headlong into the sun, or fly off at a tangent into the void beyond the solar system; why the wave rebounds from the cliff, and why the pendulum swings to and fro. Newton's Law of Universal Gravitation is the catechism of astronomy; his Three Laws of Motion have become the basis of physics and the bed-rock of the science of mechanics. That which is known as Newton's Law of Universal Gravitation is in brief as follows:

Any two bodies in the universe attract each other with a force which is directly proportional to the product of the masses and inversely proportional to the square of the distance between them.

The term mass, as used here and generally in a physical discussion, refers to a constant quality of weight in a body. As a pendulum varies in its swing at different points upon the earth's surface, so a pound of iron at the equator will weigh less than a pound in Greenland. The influence of the earth acts upon all bodies exactly as tho its whole mass were concentrated at the center. Hence a pound weight at the surface of the earth, 4,000 miles from its center, would weigh, according to Newton's law of gravitation, heavier and heavier as it approached the center. Similarly, if the weight were carried away to a distance of say 4,000 miles from the surface of the earth, it would weigh only one-fourth as much as it did at the surface, since it is twice as far away from the earth's center. Or again, a body which would weigh 1,000 ounces at sea level would weigh about 998 ounces at the top of a mountain four miles high. Nevertheless, the mass of the body—*i.e.*, its power to attract other bodies—would remain the same.

An athlete who weighs 150 pounds can leap at the surface of the earth over a bar six feet high. Carry him to the moon, and the same muscular effort would carry him at a bound over an obstacle forty feet high, and his descent on the other side would be comparatively slow. The mass of the moon being about one-seventh that of the earth, the same effort would accomplish seven times as much work, since the resistance to be overcome would be the mass of the man multiplied by the mass of the moon.

If it be true that the earth attracts the moon, it is equally true that the moon attracts the earth, as is shown by the tidal wave which follows the moon in its apparent revolution around the earth, and this attraction is equal to the product of the masses of the moon and the earth. Were the moon brought to a point one-fourth as distant as its present path around the earth, its speed of revolution would be enormously increased, and its influence on the water surface of the earth would raise resistless mountain tides, sweeping the land from east to west as the earth revolved. Newton's famous apple, detached from the tree, leaps to meet the earth; but it is equally true that the earth leaps up to meet the apple. The relatively great disturbance in the position of the apple is due only to the vastly greater mass of the earth.

Newton's great Laws of Motion were stated thus:

(1) Every body continues in its state of rest or uniform motion in a straight line unless impelled by external force to change that state.

Standing on a moving car, the passenger is thrown violently forward when the car comes to a sudden stop and backward when the car starts; he tends in each case to continue in the previous state, whether that were one of rest or motion. Water flies from a whirling grindstone, mud from the spinning wheels of a rapidly driven motor car. At each instant the world is rushing forward in a straight line through space, but at the same instant the prodigious mass of the sun is acting upon it to pull the earth into itself. Between these two forces the earth is impelled in an almost circular orbit around the sun—the centrifugal force is exactly balanced by the centripetal force which acts upon the earth exactly as two bits of floating wood in a quiet pond will come together or as a vessel drifts to meet an iceberg. The resultant of the two forces acting upon the earth may be apparent from the following diagram:

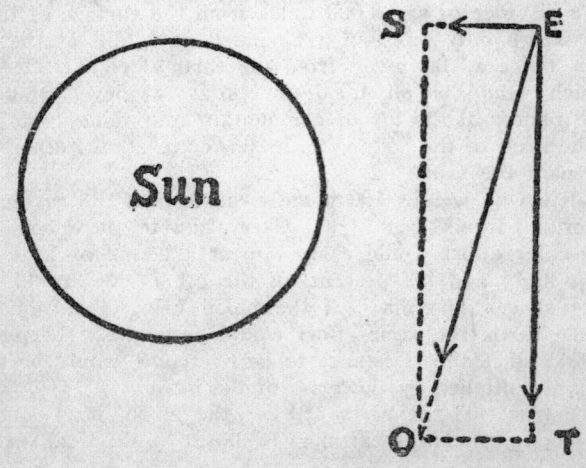

Suppose the short side of the oblong, ES, represents the direction and extent of the sun's attraction for the earth; then if ET, the long side, represents the tendency to fly off at a tangent, the resultant motion will evidently be between these two. Aristotle knew that if two such forces were acting at right angles on a body the resultant motion would be represented by the diagonal of a rectangle of which the forces were sides. The line EO, representing a part of the earth's path around the sun, appears as a straight line only because it is taken as a very small arc of an enormous circumference.

(2) Rate of change of momentum is proportional to the force acting and takes places in the direction in which the force acts.

On a steep slope gravity impels a body more than on a gentle incline. A sled will gather headway faster on an abrupt descent. A car will gain speed faster with a greater current through the motor. Other things being equal, a steamer with two propellers making 500 revolutions per minute would travel twice as fast as the same steamer under one propeller. Here, however, the resistance of the water at the bows (which increases for high speeds very nearly as the cube of the speed) and the whirl of water astern, which reduces the perfect efficiency of the screw, would have to be taken account of.

(3) Newton stated his third law thus: To every action there is an equal and opposite reaction.

This does not mean that a bouncing ball will go on bouncing forever. Every one knows that it will not. It does not mean that the "kick" of a gun is exactly equal to the force with which a bullet leaves the muzzle or that a pendulum will swing up on one side exactly as far as it swung down on the other. In all these cases the energy expended is equal to the work accomplished, but in each case part of the energy is expended in overcoming resistance and doing work which cannot be seen. A tennis ball dropped to the floor will rebound about three-fourths as high as the point from which it fell. Part of the energy of compression was expended in the flattening of the cover of the ball and part in overcoming the resistance of the air. The kick of the gun is taken up by a padding of clothes; the pendulum is retarded by friction.

The most elastic solid in the world is steel. To the majority of people it would appear that some such resilient material as rubber or ivory is the most elastic. This is not the case. Within a low range of strains it is true that rubber has very great elasticity; the tendency of its molecules to resume their former positions after being distended is very great. Beyond the limit of this tension, however, the rubber stiffens, the molecules fall asunder and the band breaks. A steel piano wire, on the other hand, will carry strains varying from one or two pounds to many hundreds of pounds, will stretch regularly under the tension and will always resume its original length. Many hundreds of stretchings will not measureably increase the length of the wire. If the elastic limit is reached, however, the molecules will not resume quite their former positions. As before observed, the elastic limits for steel are very wide indeed.

A plastic substance such as lead, on the other hand, possesses almost no elasticity. Its reaction to molecular displacement appears in the form of heat generated among the molecules. A very little hammering will soon make a piece of lead too hot to touch, while the same work done upon a piece of iron of the same weight does not appreciably warm it, for the reaction comes mainly in the rebound of the hammer from the iron. Steel is more elastic than iron and iron more than any other metal.

The extreme elasticity of steel may be gathered from the results of experimental evidence, whereby it has been shown that a drawn steel wire one millimeter (1/20 inch) in diameter returns completely to its original length so long as the stretching force is less than 32 kilograms (70 pounds). Within this limit, therefore, steel is said to possess perfect elasticity. A drawn copper wire of the same diameter shows perfect elasticity only until the stretching force has reached 12 kilograms (about 26½ pounds).

Robert Hooke, a contemporary and friend of Newton, formulated about the end of the seventeenth century what is known as Hooke's Law, which states:

"Within the limits of perfect elasticity elastic deformations of any sort, be they twists or bends or stretches, are directly proportional to the forces producing them."

This means simply that a rubber ball, a steel ball, an ivory ball or almost any sort of solid body will, if compressed, resume its former shape as soon as the pressure is removed, provided that the compression has not been too great. The greater the strain necessary to produce a small deformation, the greater is said to be the elasticity of the body. Gases alone possess perfect elasticity for all degrees of pressure. All gases under pressure tend to expand indefinitely upon the release of the pressure. By sufficient pressure and extreme cold all gases may be so far reduced in volume that they become liquid. The liquefaction of gases was first successfully accomplished by Michael Faraday about 1823. Other experimenters followed, but no great advance in this direction was made until 1877, when Cailletet and Pictet, working independently, succeeded in liquefying oxygen. Their process consisted in compressing the gas into a small tube, cooling it and then suddenly allowing it to expand by removal of the pressure. The principle is essentially the same as that in use to-day, and there exists no gas which has not been examined in the liquid state. Most gases as such are colorless; oxygen gas has no color, but liquid oxygen is milky white; hydrogen gas as such is colorless, but liquid hydrogen is steel blue.

As before observed, sufficient pressure will reduce most gases to the liquid state. It is a remarkable fact, however, that a temperature has been determined for every common gas above which no amount of pressure, however great, will succeed in making it liquid. This critical temperature varies for different gases. Liquid air cannot be produced at a temperature higher than 200° (Fahrenheit) below zero. Hydrogen must be cooled to a temperature of more than 400° below zero before it can be liquified. The terms "frigid" and "icy" are hopelessly inapplicable to these terrific degrees of cold, for ordinary ice, as is well known, is so warm that a vessel of liquid air placed upon a block of ice will boil violently, while the temperature of liquid hydrogen is nearly as far below that of liquid air as the latter is below the freezing point of water.

It might be interesting to note, in passing, that hydrogen, which for a long time resisted all efforts at liquefaction, was finally produced by James Dewar in 1902, not merely as a liquid but as a solid. This he accomplished by expanding liquid hydrogen into a space continually exhausted by an air pump, reaching thereby the incredibly low temperature of 430.6° Fahr. below zero. The record of extreme cold has been carried even farther back than this. In July, 1909, Prof. H. Kamerling Omnes, of Leyden, by evaporating liquid helium into an exhausted tube obtained a temperature which nearly reached 3° "absolute." This would equal 270° Centigrade, or 454° Fahrenheit, below zero.

Galileo had proved that air has weight by weighing a glass globe, forcing more air into it and weighing it again. The increase of weight he rightly attributed to the added air. It did not occur to him, however, that the weight of air had anything to do with nature's horror of a vacuum. He was amazed when informed that a lift pump had been constructed with a tube about forty feet long and that no amount of pumping would cause the water to rise higher than about thirty-three feet. He observed that Nature's horror of a vacuum was an instinct which she did not always display. Above the water was a vacuum, but the water refused to fill it. So, said he, Nature's dislike of a vacuum might be measured by the height of the column of water which it would support.

Galileo's friend and pupil, Torricelli, musing over this suggestion, came to the conclusion that the weight of the water in the suction pipe was supported by the weight of air upon the cistern outside. Torricelli knew that mercury was about thirteen times as heavy as water; he reasoned that the air ought to support a column of mercury one-thirteenth as high as the column of water in the suction pump. He had a glass tube made about 33 inches long, closed at one end and completely filled with mercury. Closing the open end of the tube with his finger, he inverted it in a dish of mercury. The mercury sank a little way in the tube and came to rest with its surface 30 inches above the free surface of the mercury in the vessel below. Torricelli had constructed the first barometer.

The name Pascal is indissolubly associated with the hydraulic press. He was interested, however, in Torricelli's novel experiment and, having tried it, concluded that "the vacuum is not impossible in Nature and she does not shun it with so great horror as many imagine." Pascal reasoned that if one were to ascend a mountain, the pressure of the air at the greater elevation should be less, because there would be less air overlying the mountain top than there was overlying an equal area of the plain. Accordingly he wrote to his brother-in-law, who lived near the Puy de Dome, an ancient volcano in the Auvergne, France, asking him to ascend the mountain with a Torricellian tube and observe whether the mercury column would not fall because of the diminished atmospheric pressure. The experiment was made and it was found that the mercury column became three inches shorter during the ascent, but gradually resumed its previous length during the descent to the plain.

Pascal also repeated Torricelli's experiment with wine instead of mercury, and he found, as he had inferred, that, since wine is less dense than water, the atmosphere balanced a column of it which was longer than the water column, for of course it would take a longer column of the lighter fluid to make the same weight.

The hypothesis of Torricelli and Pascal as to the pressure of the atmosphere was thus placed upon a firm experimental basis and was now competent to explain the phenomena of pumps, but it required the evidence of many more experiments to secure its general acceptance.

The most remarkable man of this period, however, in view of the multitude and the ingenuity of his experiments, was Otto von Guericke, who later became mayor of the city of Magdeburg. The Magdeburg Hemispheres have become a familiar word owing to his famous experiment made in 1654 at Regensburg before the Reichstag and the German Emperor, Ferdinand III. Two hollow hemispheres of steel, about 1.2 feet in diameter, were cast for his remarkable experiment. They were fitted at either end with heavy iron rings and provided with a tube and stop cock. The edges were made broad, smoothed and polished to a perfect plane so that they might fit exactly together. Then the air was pumped out of the interior, the stop cock turned off and twelve horses, six at each end, were hitched to the rings in the hemispheres. Their combined efforts failed to overcome the pressure on the outside of the spheres. Another team of horses was attached, and yet another, and the spheres were finally pulled apart.

THE PROPERTIES OF MATTER

A simple calculation will show that this result was inevitable, the average horse, it is estimated, being able to exert a pull equal to about 600 or 650 pounds horizontally. According to the known formula for the surface of a sphere of 1.2 feet diameter, these hemispheres would have about 652 square inches area. Reckoning the atmospheric pressure upon the outside of the two hemispheres at 15 pounds to the square inch, and assuming that the internal pressure has been reduced to a negligible quantity, it is apparent that the pressure to be overcome would equal, roughly, 9,780 pounds. According to von Guericke's calculations, a force of 2,686 pounds would overcome the atmospheric pressure upon the exterior of the spheres. Here must be some error!

There is extant a quaint old engraving showing the horses endeavoring to separate the exhausted hemispheres. On the occasion of this experiment von Guericke asserted that if you were to blow your breath into a large exhausted receiver, you would that moment breathe your last. The truth of this being doubted, he illustrated the power of "suction" by a new experiment. "A cylinder of a large pump had a rope attached to its piston, which led over a pulley and was divided into branches on which twenty or thirty men could pull. As soon as the cylinder was connected with an exhausted receiver the piston was suddenly pushed down by the atmospheric pressure and the men at the ropes were thrown forward."

The air pump used by the distinguished mayor of Magdeburg was his own invention. A better pump was made by Boyle and Hooke in England some six years later.

It was not long after these remarkable experiments of von Guericke that Robert Boyle published his "New Experiments Touching the Spring of the Air" and stated the law which has since borne his name:

Under like conditions of temperature and pressure the volume of a gas varies inversely as the pressure upon it.

"We took then a long glass tube," he writes, "which by a dexterous hand and the help of a lamp was in such a manner crooked at the bottom that the part turned up was almost parallel to the rest of the tube and, the orifice of this shorter leg being hermetically sealed, the length of it was divided into inches (each of which was divided into eight parts) by a straight list of paper, which containing those divisions, was carefully pasted all along it. (A similar strip of paper was pasted on the longer leg.) Then as much quicksilver as served to fill the arch or bended part of the siphon was poured in so as to be at the same height in both legs. This done, we began pouring quicksilver into the longer leg till the air in the shorter leg was by condensation reduced to take up but half the space it possessed.

We cast our eyes upon the longer leg of the glass and we observed, not without delight and satisfaction, that the quicksilver in that longer part of the tube was 29 inches higher than the other."

Experimentation in measuring the weight of the air was naturally followed by efforts at more exact estimation of temperature. The air thermometer of Galileo was an exquisitely sensitive instrument, but having an exposed liquid surface was subject to barometric influences as well as those of heat and cold. Fahrenheit, toward the end of this century, devised the thermometer which bears his name. He selected his zero at the lowest temperature which he knew how to obtain and took the highest fixed point at the temperature of the human body. He divided this space into twenty-four equal parts and then, finding these degrees too large, subdivided each into four parts, thus making the temperature of the body 96°. On this basis of division the freezing point of water happened to come at 32° and the boiling point of water at 212°. And there they stay to this day, despite the fact that all modern physicists measure temperature on the excellent Centigrade scale of Celsius, whereon the freezing point of water is zero and the boiling point 100°.

Nearly a century after the invention of Fahrenheit's thermometer and fifty years later than that of the Swedish astronomer Celsius, need was found for a third type of thermometer. The experiments of Charles, Dalton, Gay-Lussac and others had determined the fact that for every degree of Centigrade of increase in temperature above zero the volume of a gas increased by 1/273 of itself. Similarly a decrease of 1° below zero meant a decrease of 1/273 in volume of the gas. A decrease of 2° meant a reduction in volume of 2/273. Hence a fall of 273° would mean a reduction of 273/273, or, in other words, the volume of the gas would be reduced to zero. This was absurd, for the law of the indestructibility of matter would not allow that something could become nothing. The explanation, however, soon was found in the fact that all gases become liquid before reaching this point, and it is a matter of common knowledge that liquids are practically non-compressible. The temperature of 273° Centigrade then was taken as the zero of the absolute scale, because it was believed (and there is yet no evidence to disprove it) that a that temperature the molecular motions of all bodies would entirely cease, the molecules would be perfectly at rest.

With this thermometer in mind, the state of the law of gases, called Charles' Law, or Gay-Lussac's Law, is simple. It was:

The volume of a gas varies directly as the absolute temperature.

Brief mention herein has been made of the remarkable experiment of William Crookes upon the so-called cathode rays in the highly exhausted tubes which have since borne his name. In the course of his investigations upon the properties of the newly discovered ele ment, thallium, he attempted to carry out the necessary delicate weighings in a vacuum, in order to avoid the effect of the buoyancy of the air. Irregularities in the weighings which he was quite unable to explain led him to the invention of his famous radiometer, an instrument now common enough in the windows of opticians' stores.

It consists of a delicate paddle wheel with four metallic vanes, polished on one side and blackened on the other, mounted so as to revolve in a partially exhausted tube. Light falling upon the dark surfaces is absorbed, and the temperature of the residual gas next these surfaces is therefore raised in accordance with the well-known fact that "black is a warmer color than white." Higher temperature means greater molecular activity (as will appear in the chapter on Heat). Hence the vanes are pushed backward into the region of comparative quiet on the polished side. When light is withdrawn the revolution ceases and the brighter the light the faster the revolution. At first Crookes believed the rotation of the vanes to be due to ether waves, but by exhausting the bulb to an extremely high vacuum he found the wheels did not revolve. He therefore fell back upon the modern Kinetic Theory of Gases, attributing the motion to the bombardment of the vanes by the molecules of gas left in the tube.

The examination of the properties of gases began naturally with the study of air. Similarly the inquiries of the human mind into the characteristics of liquids began with an investigation of the properties of water. The story of Archimedes and the crown problem is probably the earliest historic record of the study of hydrostatics, tho Pliny makes mention of a Phenician who devised a highly ingenious scheme for transporting along the Nile two great columns of an Egyptian temple. The columns were rolled in huge cylindrical boxes, drawn by oxen to the bank of the Nile. There the bank was dug away from under them until they rested on their ends, when two large scows full of sand were floated underneath them. The sand was then thrown out, the boats rose and the pillars took the place of the sand.

No systematic study of displacement and pressure in liquids, however, was made before the time of Blaise Pascal. In 1653 there appeared his "Traité de l'équilibre des Liqueurs," in which he enunciated the law known by his name—to wit:

Pressure applied anywhere to a body of confined liquid is transmitted by the liquid so as to act with undiminished force on every part of the containing vessel.

"Whereby," he said, "it follows that a vessel full of water is a new principle of mechanics and a new machine for multiplying forces to any degree we choose."

The hydraulic press is the direct outcome of Pascal's principle of transmitted pressure. The mechanical advantage of this machine depends simply upon the relative size of the surfaces at which the force is applied and the power produced. If, for instance, the piston of the pump has an area of 10 square inches and the press itself has contact with the water over a surface of 1,000 square inches, the result will evidently be a power 100 times as great as the force. The press will move, however, only 1/100 as far as the pump piston, for force is indestructible.

The particles of a liquid being constantly in motion, it follows that, altho every molecule attracts every other molecule in a vessel of water, yet some of the molecules constantly will be acquiring as a result of collision or temperature a speed which will carry them beyond the attraction of the other molecules. That is what is meant by evaporation. The larger the exposed surface of the liquid the greater the possible number of escaping molecules. This explains why water evaporates so much faster when boiling than when cool, for the free surface of the liquid is enormously increased by the presence of the bubbles. When a vessel of water is heated, bubbles of gas are first seen to collect around the sides and on the bottom of the vessel. These are bubbles of dissolved air, of which all water contains a certain proportion. As the temperature rises the particles of air, owing to their increased molecular velocities, are forced out of solution, combining to form bubbles. When all the air has been driven out the water at the bottom of the vessel, owing to excessive heating, is vaporized bodily and the phenomenon of boiling appears. The air dissolved in water gets into it in exactly the same way that the water gets into the air—viz., by evaporation. Similarly liquids dissolve in each other, as chlorine or alcohol in water.

Pressure upon the surface of a liquid makes boiling more difficult. The movement of molecules in the liquid and the gas (air) above it will readily explain this fact, for as Robert Boyle showed in the case of gases, that under pressure they have a smaller volume, since the same number of molecules must still be there present, the molecules of gas above the liquid will be closer together and will leave less room for the molecules of the liquid to jump away from the surface. Following this reasoning, it is to be expected that if a vacuum exists above the free surface of a liquid the latter will evaporate more rapidly. Such is indeed the fact, and a very pretty demonstration of it may be made thus: If a watch glass with a little ether in it be placed upon a drop of water under the receiver of an air pump and the latter exhausted of air it will be found at the end of a couple of minutes that the watch glass is frozen fast to the floor of the receiver. The ether evaporates so rapidly under these conditions that the temperature of the water is reduced to freezing. Otto von Guericke remarked that when he had connected a large exhausted receiver to the air space above a cask of wine there followed "a loud boiling noise," which continued for some time. He did not know how to explain this sound, but to-day, with the aid of the experimenters of nearly three centuries, it would be accounted for by saying that the exhaustion of the air which rushed into the receiver caused such a rapid evaporation of wine in the cask as to produce the phenomenon of boiling. Exactly similar results may be produced by half filling a thin bottle or flask with boiling water. If the flask be now tightly corked and inverted the application of any cool substance, such as a wet cloth or the pouring of cold water over the bottom, will cause a contraction of the vapor-laden air within. This contraction, by relieving the pressure upon the surface of the water, will cause the latter to boil again. The operation may be repeated many times without reheating.

A question naturally suggests itself in this connection, Why is evaporation a cooling process? An answer may readily be found in that extremely serviceable Kinetic Theory of Gases. If the molecules of a gas are traveling, as has been pointed out, in open parabolic paths, these curving orbits are likely to intersect more frequently when the molecules are crowded and jostled together than when left comparatively free and untrammeled. A man walking along a country road feels far less conflict with the surrounding objects of nature than with the busy throng which hustles him and the cares that crowd upon him in the swarming city streets. His mental state is more placid, cooler. So is it with those entities called molecules, and the greater the expansion the more marked will be the fall in temperature.

The question may even be asked as to why a gas expands into a vacuum. For the present an answer must be found in the equilibrium of forces and the fact that particles of matter, like the charged corpuscles of an electric current, or the drops of water in a flowing stream, follow the path of least resistance and move in that direction determined by the sum of the forces acting upon them. On this basis may also be explained the familiar phenomena of capillarity and osmose or diffusion in liquids—the fact that a lump of sugar, if allowed to stand for a while, will sweeten a whole glass of water without stirring.

Evaporation is but an instance of the adjustment of forces to an equilibrium. When the air above a dish of water is confined by a cover, evaporation will proceed only until the vapor is saturated with the particles of water which have jumped out of the dish. When the point of saturation is reached there will be as many molecules leaping back to enter the liquid as those which free themselves from its surface. Evaporation therefore will cease.

In the same way solids whose particles are evaporating from the surface may saturate the air around. If the air is confined, evaporation will cease at saturation. Camphor which is carefully protected from air will act for many months or even years as a deterrent to moths, but if left exposed the rapidity of its evaporation is shown by the fact that a piece of camphor brought into a room may be detected from any part of the room in a few minutes. The exquisite odor of a bunch of roses will quickly perfume a large room, and the perfume of flowers consists of the particles of matter being thrown off by evaporation.

Not greatly unlike the phenomenon of crystallization in the fixation of its molecular particles is magnetism, one of the oldest observed physical phenomena. Pliny says the word "magnet" is derived from the name of the Greek shepherd Magnes, who on the top of Mount Ida observed the attraction of a large stone for his iron crook. It was also known to the ancients that artificial magnets may be made by striking pieces of steel with natural magnets, but it was not until about the twelfth century that the discovery was made that a suspended magnet will assume a north and south position. The compass, said to have been introduced into Europe from China, appeared first about 1190. The incalculable value to the world of this discovery is patent. It meant scientific navigation, exploration and the discovery of the New World.

With Galileo in Italy, "the originator of modern physics," may well be placed William Gilbert, "the father of the magnetic philosophy." Gilbert was appointed by Queen Elizabeth her physician-in-ordinary, and she settled upon him an annual pension for the purpose of aiding him in the prosecution of his philosophical studies. His first investigations were in chemistry, but later, for eighteen years or more, he experimented on electricity and magnetism. In 1600 he published his famous treatise, "De Magnete," in which he showed as the result of careful experimentation that the compass points to the north, not because of some mysterious influence of the stars but because the earth is itself a great magnet.

In reading over the six books of this great work, one cannot fail to be struck by the variety of the author's accomplishments. He writes in Latin and intersperses his pages with frequent Greek quotations; he is familiar with poets, historians and philosophers and discusses with clearness and fullness all the chemical and physical knowledge of previous ages. The work is truly monumental. It also contains Gilbert's own numerous valuable and costly contributions to magnetic science. First among these is his grand generalization, "the new and till now unheard of view," that the earth is a great magnet; and he is not afraid to say that this novel view "will stand as firm as aught that ever was produced in philosophy, backed by ingenious argumentation or buttressed by mathematical demonstration."

Gilbert's contempt for the methods of the schoolmen crops out everywhere. "Why should I," he writes, "submit this noble and this new philosophy to men who have taken oath to follow the opinions of others, to the most senseless corrupters of the arts, to lettered clowns, gramatists, sophists, spouters and the wrong-headed rabble, to be denounced, torn to tatters, and heaped with contumely? To you alone, true philosophers, ingenuous minds, who not only in books but in things themselves look for knowledge, have I dedicated these foundations of magnetic science—a new style of philosophizing."

Gilbert did not explain, nor has any satisfactory explanation yet been offered, as to why certain substances, notably iron and steel, exhibit marked magnetic properties. Nickel and cobalt are appreciably attracted by a strong magnet, but the other metals, copper, zinc, tin, lead, etc., show complete indifference to magnetic influence, while bismuth and antimony are actually repelled by it. Yet an alloy of copper, aluminum and manganese possesses magnetic qualities comparable to those of iron. In this unique restriction of its application, magnetism as a force stands alone. It is generally held to be due to a molecular adjustment. The facts that magnetic iron heated red hot and beaten loses its magnetism, that a magnet hung north and south and beaten likewise loses its magnetism, suggest that magnetism is due to the arrangement of the molecules of the magnetized body.

The expansive tendency of the molecules of a gas under ordinary conditions of temperature and pressure is quite different from the behavior under like conditions of the molecules of a liquid or a solid. There is every reason to suppose that the molecules of an unconfined gas would expand indefinitely into space. In accordance with current belief the molecules of every substance are in motion.

"In the solid state," writes a prominent American physicist of today, "it is probable that the molecules oscillate with great rapidity about certain fixed points, always being held by the attractions of their neighbors—*i.e.*, by the cohesive forces—in practically the same position with reference to other molecules in the body. In rare instances, however, as the facts of diffusion show, a molecule breaks away from its restraints.

"In liquids, on the other hand, while the molecules are in general as close together as in solids, they slip about with perfect ease over one another and thus have no fixed positions. This assumption is necessitated by the fact that liquids adjust themselves readily to the shape of the containing vessel. In gases the molecules are comparatively far apart, as is evident from the fact that a cubic centimeter of water occupies about 1,600 cc. when it is transformed into steam, and furthermore, they exert practically no cohesive force upon one another, as is shown by the indefinite expansibility of gases."

A highly illuminating discussion of the actual motions of molecules in these three fundamental states of matter has recently been given by J. W. Richards (president of the American Electro-Chemical Society) in an article entitled "Kinetic Molecular Energy." Dr. Richards writes: "The conditions of molecular motion is chiefly determined by velocity. According to the velocity of the molecules we have solids, liquids and gases. Within the lowest range of molecular velocity the movement of the molecules is oscillatory; we have a fixed relative position; the body has a size or shape; it is a solid. Within the next higher ranges of molecular velocity the velocity is able to carry the molecules just beyond the reach of opposing forces; the molecules move in closed elliptic orbits (like the planets around the sun); the body loses its form and shape, but retains its volume; it is a liquid. When the molecular velocity is raised still farther the molecules move in open parabolic paths; the body not only has no shape or form, but actually tends to increase its volume; it is a gas."

If attraction is exerted between the molecules of a substance it must be conveyed by some medium other than matter. This conclusion is involved in the hypothesis of the granular nature of matter, for force acting at a vacuous distance is unthinkable or at best incomprehensible. The cohesion of the molecules of a substance thus resembles gravity, which reaches across the enormous interplanetary spaces to grasp the masses of the planets and hold them in their courses round the sun; like gravity also the cohesive force which renders substances elastic does not seem to consist of material vibration or ether disturbances. Cohesion acts through infinitesimal spaces upon bodies infinitesimally small; gravity spans distances immeasurable to guide a myriad of suns and systems. Yet both these forces are conveyed through a medium at once infinitely rigid, since it is non-compressible, and infinitely fine, since it is frictionless. The distinguished author of the electromagnetic theory of light, speaking of the characteristics of the ether, writes:

"The vast interplanetary and interstellar regions will no longer be regarded as waste places in the universe, which the Creator has not seen fit to fill with the symbols of the manifold order of His kingdom. We shall find them to be already full of this wonderful medium; so full that no human power can remove it from the smallest portion of space or produce the slightest flaw in its infinite continuity. It extends unbroken from star to star, and when a molecule of hydrogen vibrates in the dog star, the medium receives the impulses of these vibrations, and after carrying them in its immense bosom for several years, delivers them, in due course, regular order and full tale, into the spectroscope."

CHAPTER IV

HEAT

It has been said that the history of man begins with the discovery of fire. How many conveniences of modern life are dependent in the last analysis upon the use of fire, it would be hopeless to attempt to enumerate. The survival of the human race with its primitive undeveloped physique, helpless for defense or attack except by virtue of superior cunning, would never have been possible without the aid of fire. It is, indeed, a well-known fact that life in any form is directly dependent for its development upon conditions of temperature. The myriad forms of physical life that are hourly born upon the surface of the globe owe their existence to the heat radiated from a gaseous ball, some 93,000,000 miles away.

All the heat in the world—excepting the negligible quantity reflected from the moon or transmitted from the stars—must be traced originally either to falling meteorites or to the sun. The warmth of the air, the rocks and the water is derived from these sources. Even the heat of a coal or wood fire is but an expression of solar energy, for it was the sun's heat which, through the growth of vegetable tissue, yesterday, or a million years ago, transformed the incombustible soil into a form apt for the burning.

The heat received by the earth from meteors would be nearly the same in amount as that which it receives from the sun by radiation, but for the probable circumstance that these meteors, reaching the earth's atmosphere at an exceedingly low temperature, radiate most of the heat engendered in their approach into outer space. For practical purposes, then, the sun may be considered as the original source of all terrestrial heat. No material body, it is true, is quite devoid of heat, for as long as its molecules are in vibration, matter must radiate into the space surrounding this vibratory energy. Heat as a physical phenomenon, then, is the vibration energy of molecules of matter—solid, liquid, or gaseous. Here must be noticed the difference between "radiant heat," so-called, and molecular heat. In the form of radiant heat, energy is transmitted by the sun to the earth. It is converted from radiant heat into molecular vibration upon contact with the matter of the earth, and the material bodies, so incited, afford the phenomenon commonly known as heat.

Anything like an exact study of heat was never possible before the dissociation of the ideas of the vibratory phenomenon of heat and the sensation of it. By the use of his sense of touch mainly, man has learned to decide in a general way whether a body is hot or cold, and whether it is gaining heat or losing it. Conclusions based on this sense of temperature, however, are likely to be very inexact, or even wholly false. The sensation of heat may often be mistaken for that of cold, and vice versa. If one hand is put into ice-cold water and the other into water as hot as it can endure, and after a minute or two both hands are thrust into water at blood-heat (98° F.), this same water will feel cold to one hand and warm to the other. Evidently the temperature sense is a relative matter. Heat as a sensation must be relegated to the domain of medicine or psychology; heat as a form of vibration, however, is a legitimate object of physical investigation.

Previous to the nineteenth century physicists generally considered heat as an invisible weightless fluid, which by passing into or out of a body caused it to become hot or cold. This view accorded readily enough with the facts observed in the heating of a body held in a flame, or near another hot body. It did not account for the heat produced by friction. In 1798 Benjamin Thompson, Count Rumford, an American by birth, brought forward the molecular theory of heat, according to which the increase in the temperature of a body means simply an increase in the average velocity of its molecules. This theory, tried out and carefully tested by the great English physicist, James Prescott Joule, in an exhaustive series of experiments, has proved thus far the best working hypothesis of the nature of heat.

"The earliest traces of the theory that heat is matter," writes Florian Cajori, "are found in ancient Greece among Democritus and Epicurus. In modern times it was advocated by Pierre Gassendi and Georg Ernst Stahl, author of that erroneous theory of combustion, according to which a burning body gave off a substance called 'phlogiston.' One such agent paved the way for the other. In 1738 the French Academy of Sciences offered a prize question on the nature of heat. The winners of the prize favored the materialistic theory. At first the only properties postulated for this material agent, called heat, were that it was highly elastic and that its particles repelled each other. By this repulsion the fact that hot bodies give off heat could be explained. Later it was assumed that the heat particles attracted ordinary matter, and that this heat was distributed among bodies in quantities proportional to their mutual attractions (or their capacities for heat). By the close of the eighteenth century this theory met with almost universal acceptance." Marat, afterward famous as a leader in the French Revolution, gave in 1780 an exposition of this theory by starting from Newton's corpuscular theory of light.

Professor Clerk Maxwell, in his "Theory of Heat," says: "We

must therefore admit that at every part of the surface of a hot body there is radiation of heat, and therefore a state of motion on the superficial parts of the body. Now, motion is certainly invisible to us by any direct mode of observation, and therefore the mere fact of a body appearing to be at rest cannot be taken as a demonstration that its parts may be in a state of motion. Hence, part at least of the energy of a hot body must be energy arriving from the motion of its parts. Every hot body is, therefore, in motion, the movements of the parts being too small to be observed separately."

Tyndall defined heat as "a mode of motion." It might more accurately be defined as "a mode of motion of the particles of a mass"; the greater the heat, the greater will be the motion of the particles. In accordance with the molecular theory discussed in the chapter on the Properties of Matter, any increase in temperature means simply this, and nothing more—an increased velocity of the molecules of the heated substances.

The researches that have been conducted recently in the domain of low temperatures, many experiments approximately absolute zero, have given some remarkable results. Solid mercury became superconductive at between 4.21° A. and 4.19° A. With tin the superconducting state was reached at about 3.8° A., while in the case of lead it occurred between 14° A. and 4.3° A. Up to these given points these metals followed the ordinary laws of change, but at the given temperatures their resistance was less than four ten million-millionths of its resistance at 0° C., and at 2.45° A. the resistance was less than half this amount. With the attainment of the "absolute zero," still more notable changes result.

The measurement of heat may be considered in any one of three ways. It is possible first to measure the degree of heat in a body, as did Galileo with his air thermometer as early as 1592. Measurements of this kind made with solids, liquids and gases have resulted in the establishment of extremely valuable physical data, more especially in the field of meteorology. Secondly, the actual amount of heat in a body may be measured. It is evident that a red-hot needle possesses a smaller amount of heat than a stove which is only moderately hot. The determination of the amount of heat possessed by a body constitutes the science of calorimetry.

The calorie, or heat unit, is defined as the amount of heat necessary to raise one cubic centimeter of water through one degree Centigrade.

Joule reasoned that if the heat of friction were merely mechanical energy which had been transferred to the molecules of a heated body, then the same number of calories must always be produced by the expenditure of a given amount of mechanical energy. His investigations in calorimetry, whereby he determined the mechanical power corresponding to a given amount of heat, first proved experimentally the identity of various forms of energy. In a series of experiments lasting over nearly 30 years, he caused mechanical energy to disappear in as many ways as possible, and measuring the amount of heat developed, found it to be for a given amount of energy in each case the same. Thus was established the principle of the Mechanical Equivalent of Heat.

The English physicist found that the equivalent of the calorie in work was equal to 426.4 kilogram meters (=3,081 ft. lbs.), that is to say, the amount of heat necessary to raise 1 cubic centimeter of water 1 degree Centigrade would, if all converted into work, be sufficient to raise 3,081 lbs. through 1 foot of height, or what is the same thing, to raise 1 pound through 3,081 feet. The mechanical equivalent of heat is such an important constant in nature that several physicists since Joule have thought it desirable to redetermine it. One of the most accurate determinations was made in 1879 by Henry A. Rowland of Baltimore. He obtained 427 gram meters as the mechanical equivalent of the calorie.

A third method of measuring the heat of a body is a relative one. Specific heat is a term used in comparing the relative amounts of heat necessary to increase equally the temperature of equal weights of different substances, for example, glass and water. It has been found that more heat is required to raise the temperature of a pound of water, say 10 degrees, than to increase to the same extent the temperature of an equal weight of almost any other substance. Therefore, water is taken as a standard of specific heat, and when the heat necessary to raise the temperature of glass 10 degrees is found to be five times as great as that necessary to raise the temperature of an equal amount of water 10 degrees, the specific heat of glass is determined at one-fifth or .2. The value to the physicist and chemist of determining specific heats of substances is great, for fixed relation has been found to exist between the specific heats of solids and their atomic weights. For this significant discovery, science is indebted to the researches of Berzelius, Regnault, Dulong and Petit.

Matter is variously affected by heat. In general, it increases the volume of a body; but just as magnetism has sometimes the contrary effect (as, for instance, its contractile influence upon nickel), so heat has sometimes the effect of reducing a body. Water, for example, is denser at 40° Fahrenheit than at freezing, which is proven by the fact that ice floats, having about one-tenth of its volume out of water. Were it denser than water, this could not be. Again, type metal contains a small proportion of antimony, since antimony expands on solidifying, making the perfectly sharp outline indispensable to good type. With the exceptions noted, however, the law is general that bodies contract with cold, and expand with heat. Railway rails are always laid with a slight space between them to allow for the expansion in the hot days of summer. Iron bridges frequently have a roller at one end to provide for the difference of length. The steel suspension cables of a bridge a mile long will vary in length nearly four feet between summer heat and winter cold. If the heat applied to a substance is strong and continuous, the result is a change of state; solid ice becomes water, water becomes a vapor. A great deal of energy is absorbed in this transformation of state. It takes nearly as much heat to change a pound of ice into a pound of ice water as to heat the same water to boiling. It takes more than five times as much heat to change the water into steam as to raise its temperature from freezing to boiling. Conversely a great amount of energy is liberated by the condensation of steam—a fact well illustrated in the immense power of the steam engine; and no small amount of heat is set free when water freezes. The country in the neighborhood of large lakes is thus appreciably warmed by the congelation of the water. For exactly the same reason the farmer often places tubs of water in his cellar that the freezing of the water may sufficiently warm the air to keep his vegetables from freezing.

More remarkable than the effect of the freezing of water upon the surrounding air, is that of evaporation. As the freezing of water in winter warms the air, so the evaporation of water in the open seasons of the year will cool it. The amount of evaporated water which can exist in the air depends upon the temperature. If the air has absorbed all the water vapor which it is capable of holding, it is evident that a fall in temperature will succeed in condensing a part of the suspended water-vapor which then falls as rain, or settles as mist. If the air is not completely saturated, it is evident that considerable cooling may take place before the "dew-point" is reached and condensation of water begins. In the hot days of the summer months the air is capable of taking up and holding in suspension a large amount of moisture. On such days the oppressiveness of the heat is greatly augmented by the "muggy" condition of the atmosphere. The excessive moisture of the human body cannot escape into the air, for the latter is already surcharged with moisture, or nearly so. The grateful effect of a breeze is thus made clear, for the excess of moisture which evaporates from the body has no opportunity to saturate the air immediately around, before a fresh supply of air appears to take up the exhalation from the skin. It was formerly held by scientific inquirers that the dew fell from the upper regions of the atmosphere. That idea has been quite swept away within recent times, and it is now known that the formation of dew is due to the condensation of water-vapor in the air close to the ground. A heavy dew is said to be the forerunner of fine weather. It actually indicates an unusual fall in temperature from the heat of the day—nothing more.

The formation of condensed particles of water-vapor in the upper regions of the atmosphere is generally conceded to be due to the impalpable dust particles which float everywhere in the terrestrial atmosphere rising to considerable heights. As water vanishes so strangely into the thin vapors of the air, so solid bodies have been observed by every one to disappear and dissolve in liquids.

There are probably few persons, if any, who have not noticed that sugar dissolves more readily in hot water than in cold, while salt is about equally soluble in both. In general, the solutions of solids in water or any other solvent are made easier by the application of heat. So also with solutions of liquids, for the viscosity of most liquids is reduced by the application of heat, they become less dense, and therefore mix more readily with the molecules of the liquid in which they are dissolved. Solution is such a familiar, everyday phenomenon that the complete disappearance of solid material in a liquid is taken as a matter of course. Yet it is truly a wonderful thing that a lump of sugar or a teaspoonful of salt dissolved in a glass of water will not raise the level of the water, and so soon as solution is complete will leave absolutely no visible trace of its presence. As the temperature is raised more of the solid may be made to disappear. Even boiling water, however, will take up but a limited quantity of a solute, and on cooling this may readily be seen by dropping in a crystal of the dissolved material or otherwise disturbing the mixture, causing it to exhibit the beautiful and fascinating phenomenon of crystallization.

A strange contrast to this condition of things is found in the fact of the solution of gases in liquids. Here the effect of temperature is quite the reverse of what has just been observed. The cooler the liquid, the greater the quantity of gas which may be dissolved in it. The quantity of gas which may be dissolved by a single pint of water is amazing, in some instances almost incredible. Hydrogen chloride, for example, is soluble to the extent of over 300 pints in a single liter of water; and the same quantity of water will dissolve without artificial pressure 1,148 pints of ammonia gas.

The effect of heat on a liquid—or indeed on any body—being recognized as an increase of its molecular velocities, the question arises as to how this increase of velocity is transferred from one part of matter to another. The most direct way for this to take place is by the transference of energy from one molecule to the next. In general this is accomplished most readily by the molecules of a solid, especially solids of exceptional density such as metals. For example, a short copper or iron wire held for a moment in a hot flame soon becomes too hot at the other end to hold. A silver wire will conduct the heat of the flame to the hand even more quickly. A stone feels colder to the hand than a piece of wood at exactly the same temperature, for the obvious reason that the stone, being a better conductor, carries off the heat of the body more rapidly. The tongue will freeze fast in winter to the blade of an ax, a fact well known in cold countries where the bit of a horse's bridle cannot be put directly in his mouth if it has been out in the frosty air. The same ax blade lying in the summer sun will feel hotter than any other part of the ax.

Liquids, however, are poor conductors, as has been shown by the fact that burning alcohol on the surface of water will register no perceptible heat in an instrument so sensitive as the air thermometer whose bulb is placed but half an inch below the surface of the water. Gases are almost non-conducting. "Dry air," writes a physicist of to-day, "is a practical vacuum as regards the rays of heat."

Liquids and gases, however, may carry considerable heat by the motions of comparatively large masses of themselves in a heated condition. This transference of heat by the movement of masses of a liquid or gas is termed "convection." The term thus describes the manner in which temperature is adjusted by winds in the atmosphere and currents in bodies of water.

Yet another method of the conveyance of heat is that by which most heat in the universe is carried—viz., radiation. The heat which is received from an open fire is not carried by conduction or convection. Not by convection, for the movement of masses of air is all toward the fire, not away from it; not by conduction, for gases have been shown to be very poor conductors. The only other possible explanation of the passage of the heat rays must then be found in a nonmaterial form of energy. To this form of heat transference the term "radiation" has been applied. Radiation thus explains the sensation of heat felt from a burning house, even when the house is at a considerable distance and the wind is blowing toward the fire. The method by which the heat of the sun is conveyed to the earth will likewise readily be seen to be the method of radiation. There could evidently be no mass movements nor yet molecular movements where is neither mass nor molecule. This radiant property must then be a function of the ether, not of matter in the mass. According to recent scholars, radiant heat must now be classed with light under the head of electricity.

The three forms of heat transference—conduction, convection, radiation—are all to be seen in the consideration of the common steam or water radiator. Convection brings masses of hot water or steam from the furnace to the radiator. Conduction transfers the heat to the outside of the radiator. Radiation carries the heat to every part of the room to be heated.

The application of heat to mechanical purposes has been astonishingly slow of development. From the time of the invention of Heron's eolipile there elapsed 1,000 years before the idea of heat as a source of motive power was turned to practical account. Steam fountains were designed in the seventeenth century, but they were merely modifications of the eolipile and applied for ornamental purposes only.

The first successful attempt to combine the principles and forms of mechanism then known into an economical and convenient machine was made by Thomas Newcomen, a blacksmith of Dartmouth, England. Assisted by John Calley, Newcomen constructed an engine—an "atmospheric steam engine." In 1711 such a machine was set up at Wolverhampton for the raising of water. Steam passing from the boiler into the cylinder held the piston up against the external atmospheric pressure until the passage between the cylinder and boiler was closed by a cock. Then the steam in the cylinder was condensed by a jet of water. A partial vacuum was formed and the air above pressed the piston down. This piston was suspended from one end of an overhead beam, the other end carrying the pump-rod. The fly-wheel was introduced in 1736 by Jonathan Hulls.

The next great improvements were introduced by James Watt in Scotland. Becoming interested in the steam engine and its history, he began to experiment in a scientific manner. He took up the study of chemistry under the guidance of Joseph Black, the originator of the doctrine of "latent heat." Observing the great loss of heat in the Newcomen engine, due to the cooling of the cylinder by the jet of water at every stroke, he began to ponder on the possibility of keeping the cylinder "always as hot as the steam that entered it." He himself tells how there flashed through his mind the happy thought of how this could be done. "I had gone to take a walk," he says, "on a fine Sabbath afternoon. I had entered the Green by the gate at the foot of Charlotte Street and had passed the old washing-house. I was thinking upon the engine at the time, and had gone as far as the herd's house when the idea came into my mind that, as steam was an elastic body, it would rush into a vacuum, and if a communication were made between the cylinder and an exhausted vessel, it would rush into it and might be there condensed without cooling the cylinder."

This improvement it is by right of which James Watt may justly be called the "inventor" of the steam engine. The steam engine as such has practically reached its maximum of efficiency. Only about 22 per cent. of the heat energy furnished by the coal consumed is actually converted into work, even in the best triple expansion engines. The efficiency of the locomotive is even lower, being about 17 per cent.

The steam turbine, the latest development of the steam engine, is in principle very much like the common wind-mill, the steam being driven at an angle against a multitude of little blades set into a revolving cylinder of steel—the shaft. In large sea-going vessels this engine is rapidly replacing the old-fashioned "reciprocating" machine, for its efficiency is higher, it occupies less than one-tenth the floor space and it runs without jarring the ship. The highest speeds ever attained by the vessels at sea—namely, about forty miles per hour—has been made with the aid of steam turbines. The construction of a turbine is an exceedingly difficult operation, for each of the little blades must be set singly into the shaft at exactly the right angle. Skilled workmanship and much time are required in this operation, and in view of the mechanical difficulties of constructing a turbine, it does not seem so remarkable that this engine, of which the extremely simple principle was familiar to Hero of Alexandria (120 B.C.), should have waited over 2,000 years to see perfection.

The efficiency of the steam engine is measured by the fall in temperature which the steam undergoes in passing from the boiler through the cylinder (thus driving the pistons) to the condenser. It is evident that as this heat is made to disappear, work must be produced. The greater the fall in temperature, then, the higher the efficiency of the engine. Unfortunately the steam engine is limited in this regard, for the highest temperature that can safely be maintained in the boiler is about 200° Centigrade, the steam being under a pressure of 15 atmospheres, or 225 pounds upon every square inch of surface. The lowest practicable limit of temperature in the condenser is about 30°. Hence the loss of heat and the resulting efficiency will be measured by a fall of 170° (200°—30°). A perfect steam engine should render about 36 per cent. of its heat energy into work, but owing to friction and other causes no steam engine approaches this degree of efficiency.

The gas engine has a considerably larger range of temperature fall possible in its mechanism. The explosion of the gases takes place at a very high temperature. The gas cylinder engine and turbine engine are supplanting the corresponding types of steam-driven machines. The improved Diesel engines are revolutionizing certain industries.

In conclusion, then, heat must not be considered as a weightless fluid, for the interchange of heat and mechanical energy is not consistent with this belief. Nor is heat "latent" any more than the lifting power of a steam crane is latent. All the evidence of to-day points to the conclusion that heat is only one of the many forms of vibration.

The effect of heat upon any material body is an increased rate of vibration of its molecules. The heat that reaches the earth from the sun, however, traverses the intervening space without heating it, as the intense cold of the upper regions of the atmosphere clearly indicates. It is therefore a property of the ether that it transmits vibrations without being itself affected by them. In matter, on the other hand, all parts of a conductor must become hot when heat is transferred from one end of it to the other. Convection cannot be considered as a form of vibration at all, since it does not represent the transmission of energy from particle to particle of a mass so much as the change of location of a relatively large amount of heat. It cannot proceed, however, without the aid of either conduction or radiation, inasmuch as the heat given by one mass to another can be received only through the medium of matter or ether. As before observed, ether-borne heat energy is now regarded as correlated with the mighty forces of the atom.

CHAPTER V

THE SOURCES OF LIGHT

RISING from underneath the world, and flooding all nature with the growing splendor of its Light, the morning sun has ever been to man a symbol of the power of goodness. The unparalleled poetic imagination of the Greeks clothed this symbolic object with personal attributes, and formulated the fiery chariot and flying steeds of the Sun God Apollo, the Baldur of the Norsemen, the Christ of early German legend. A growing Christianity synchronized with the effacement of the personal and divine attributes of Light. The third century in Europe saw the development of an established Church—Christian, and an established Science—Greek. The properties of Matter, Light, Sound, Heat, as defined by Aristotle, became the accepted creed of Europe.

A science not less dogmatic than theology ruled the thoughts of men until near the end of the sixteenth century, until Roger Bacon and Bruno and Galileo, with other less illustrious but not less courageous investigators, had suffered contempt and persecution, and even languished in prison for the splendid heresy of Experimental Truth. The conception of Force—intangible, irresistible, indestructible—was long in making its way into any system of popular philosophy; the world, as a cosmos of Substance possessed of varying Qualities, was all-sufficient explanation for medieval thought of the phenomena of Sense and the fabrications of Reason.

Light, like other things now conceded to be forms of force, was deemed a substance or a quality of substance. Generally it was held to be a substance, possessed, like other substances, of such qualities as elasticity (reflection) and solubility (absorption). The law of the angle of incidence and reflection was known to the Egyptians and the Greeks; the Assyrians were familiar with the lens; the Arabs imitated from Greece and developed a system of optics involving a knowledge of mirrors, plane and spherical lenses and prisms, the straight-line propagation of light, shadows and semishadows, or penumbræ.

That light travels in straight lines was one of the articles of faith of the Platonic school. Not all the Greek philosophers, however, maintained this view, and the variance of their opinions foreshadowed the uncertainty concerning light which has characterized all subsequent discussion of its exact nature. Aristotle wrote more voluminously than any of the Greeks upon this question, but his conclusions are dubious and obscure. Through his influence the Scholastics were led to regard light as something immaterial, rather a quality of bodies than a substance, and they sought to find in the bodies themselves something analogous with the color sensation of the eye. Both Euclid and Plato, however, conceived of light as a something projected from the eye upon an illuminated body, causing sight as soon as it met another substance which emanated from the body. Pythagoras and Democritus held that visible bodies projected something into the eye whereby they became visible.

The Greeks knew something of spherical and parabolic mirrors. The story is told of Archimedes that when the Romans were besieging his native city, Syracuse, he defended it by the use of mirrors reflecting the sun's rays, which focused upon the ships of the Romans as they came near, setting them on fire. The terrific heat developed in a modern solar engine makes this tale not so impossible as might at first sight appear, altho it is likely that the men, rather than the ships of the Romans, were the sufferers under the fierce reflection from the mirrors of the Greeks.

That the latter had gathered much other evidence with regard to the phenomena of light is unquestioned, for in a fragment of a Greek document discovered in Egypt mention is made of various familiar optical illusions. They had observed, for example, that a ring on the bottom of an empty vessel, just hidden by the edge, becomes visible when water is poured into the vessel, and Cleomides observed that in the same way the sun may be visible when it has actually sunk below the horizon. The Greeks had noticed, also, that the sun appears larger when rising or setting than when high in the heavens; they were familiar with the fact that light glances off from a mirror at the same angle as that at which it strikes.

Among the Romans no investigators of natural phenomena appeared to add anything of moment to the discoveries of the Greeks. Lucretius made some interesting comments on magnetism; Seneca observed and taught the identity of the colors in the edge of a piece of glass with those of the rainbow; he did not explain why they were identical; he remarked that a globular glass vessel, full of water, magnifies objects, from which he was led to conclude that there is nothing so deceptive as sight, an inference not particularly ingenious nor highly illuminating as an explanation.

Abû 'Ali al Hasan ibn al Hasan ibn Al Haitam rose into favor under one of the Caliphs of Egypt as a result of a plan (which he never carried out) to regulate the flow of the Nile for purposes of irrigation. He made a study of plane and spherical mirrors, and understood, also, the principle of parabolic reflectors, such as are used to-day in searchlights or the headlights of locomotives, in which all the rays leave the mirror in parallel lines. He knew that a ray of light is flashed back from the surface of water at the same angle as that at which it strikes; he knew, also, that a beam of light entering water is bent from its course—refracted, to use the modern term. He was aware of the fact of the apparent enlargement of the sun's diameter on approaching the horizon, and correctly explained it as due to the fact that the sun's diameter is then estimated by the size of less distant terrestrial objects, a view admitted by most scientists to-day. Al Hazen (as he is more briefly known) also first described the human eye with exactitude of detail, and originated the famous and difficult problem in optics known as Al Hazen's problem: "Given the position of a luminous point and of the eye, to find the spot at which reflection takes place on a spherical, cylindrical or conical mirror."

Earlier even than the mirror appears the record of the lens. Among the ruins of Nineveh is reported to have been found a lens of rock crystal. Burning-glasses were manufactured at an early date in Greece. In Aristophanes' comedy of The Clouds is found mention of "a fine transparent stone with which fires are kindled," and by which, standing in the sun, one can, "tho at a distance, melt all the writing" on a waxen tablet of the times.

From the millennium of the beginning of this era European thought for 500 years plodded blindly along the road that Grecian philosophy had pointed. Roger Bacon, the one great man in all his time who dared to make a place for original thought and experimental science, was crushed to silence by ten years' imprisonment for heresy. Petrus Ramus in Paris was forbidden, on pain of corporal punishment, to teach or write against the great Aristotle. With Petrus Ramus must likewise be mentioned Franciscus Patritius, a learned Italian, fiercely persecuted by the Aristotelians on account of his heretical theory that Light and Darkness together produce Warmth and Cold.

From the various theories of the philosophers of Greece it is evident that the Nature of Light, even in those early times, was a much-mooted question. Previous to the time of Newton opinions as to its exact constitution were divided; some held it to be a real substance, others, especially the followers of Aristotle, considered it a property or quality of matter. Early in the seventeenth century Descartes formulated a new hypothesis as to the nature of light. He held that it is neither material nor a property of matter, but a vibration of that something of which matter is composed, its "second element." He assumed that the whole universe is filled with minute spheres of this elemental substance. Through the constant motion of the particles of luminous bodies these little spheres are jarred, and since there is no empty space in the universe beside them, one sphere immediately touching another, this jar or disturbance is immediately distributed in straight lines. As an explanation of this thesis he compares the propagation of light with the motion imparted to the whole length of a stick when one end of it is pushed. A similar disturbance, in his opinion, may be caused by the eye, from which he explains how cats and other animals whose eyes glitter can see in the dark. Against this Cartesian hypothesis it has been urged that through these rows of spheres light would be propagated, not in straight lines alone, but in every direction, as pressure is transmitted in all directions by water. Descartes, however, had a large following for a time in his belief as to the nature of light.

Later appeared two main theories of light, viz., the Corpuscular Theory and the Undulatory Theory. The former theory was essentially that of the Greeks, altho they adorned it with various fanciful hypotheses. The great exponent of this theory in more recent times was Sir Isaac Newton, who based his acceptance of it on the conviction that the rectilinear propagation of light was explainable only on this basis. Sound waves, he argued, may be heard around corners; water waves swing round a jutting point of land. Since light travels in straight lines, the great philosopher concluded that it must be due to the projection from luminous bodies of extremely minute particles or corpuscles at a tremendous speed.

A contrary view was advocated by Christian Huygens about the end of the seventeenth century. The famous Dutch physicist regarded light, like sound, as a form of wave motion. A very serious difficulty confronted this theory at the outset. Sound, as is well known, cannot traverse a vacuum. Von Guericke, the Madgeburg Magician, had shown, some years previously, that a clock cannot be heard to strike in a receiver exhausted of air. Light, however, can be seen through such a vacuum without difficulty, and travels without perceptible retardation through the enormous interstellar spaces—possibly vacua —infinitely better than can be gotten by the best means artificially. Some medium, Huygens reasoned, must be there to transmit these vibrations. He boldly assumed such a medium, and called it the Luminiferous or Light-bearing Ether. The fact that other forms of undulatory motion, such as sound waves and water waves, can sweep around corners, he did not explain.

At first sight, the corpuscular theory of light would seem to be by far the simpler and more obvious explanation of the two, and for more than a hundred years the weight of Newton's authority threw the balance in favor of this theory. So many facts opposed to this theory have appeared, however, in modern experimentation that the corpuscular theory is to-day practically abandoned. Light is admittedly a form of vibration.

Light, it has been said, is a form of vibration, but it is evidently not the same vibration as that which takes place in the molecules of a heated conductor; nor is it the same as the series of condensations and rarefactions of the air that is called sound. These latter are vibrations of matter, and light is evidently a vibration of a different nature, for no amount of light applied to one side of an iron door will shine through to the other side. Heat, on the contrary, or sound, will very quickly be transferred by conduction to the farther side of the door. Light, as it reaches the earth from the sun, must be considered as something closely analogous to radiant heat, if not identical with it. Recent study of the effects of radiation show that light and radiant heat are actually the same. Modern theory regards light as a form of radiant heat whose wave lengths are such that they directly affect the optic nerve.

The great source of light on the earth—far transcending all others—is the sun. It is by no means the only source. The moon, tho intermittent in the amount of its light, and shining in full radiance for only a few nights each month, must, nevertheless, be reckoned as a valuable adjunct illuminant to the sun. The light from stars and planets, too, is considerable. Walter Hough, in his "Development of Illumination," says: "Under the clear night sky of the Arizona deserts the atmosphere seems charged with star mist; eminences miles away may be outlined, the dial of a watch may be read, and a trial followed with little difficulty. These are the conditions under which night journeys are made to avoid the burning sun." The planet Venus, he continues, at certain times sheds light sufficient for the traveler over open country.

"There are at times nights of remarkable luminescence. Clouds become phosphorescent, and often under certain states of electric stress, during high winds, glimmer with a faint light not amounting to a discharge of the electric fluid. Frequently successive flashes of 'heat lightning' aid the traveler in finding his way. It is possible, also, that the soil over certain regions may become phosphorescent under the light of the sun and retain the property during the night, as certain gems are phosphorescent after being submitted to sunlight. Snow has this property. Gaseous emanations of a phosphorescent character are occasionally abundant enough to produce temporary illumination, and the phosphorescent light of tropical seas has drawn forth many remarks on its beauty."

Most of the work in the cities of to-day is done by diffused light. The direct rays of the sun are found, in almost all cases, too powerful for purposes of reading or writing, but the diffused light reflected in a thousand different directions from all surfaces not perfectly black or smooth supplies an abundance of light, soft, yet bright enough for use. Since the introduction of artificial illuminants it has ever been the aim of inventors to produce a light resembling this diffused daylight. The old sperm oil lamps and tallow dips of Europe which came over with the colonists to America were there superseded by petroleum lamps. The addition of the argand chimney of glass—the invention of which dates back only to about 1780—facilitated the development of the first really practical artificial illuminant. Even to-day this old type of chimney and burner may be seen in the "student lamp," so popular for reading purposes. The invention of the argand lamp, with the brilliantly luminous kerosene, soon made night reading a general practice. Everybody could now read—even the poor—and everybody did. It is an interesting coincidence that is brought out by a recent writer on illumination, Dr. David T. Day, that the progress of the countries of the civilized world to-day is in nearly every case directly proportional to their consumption of kerosene.

The arc lamp and incandescent light of Edison marked a step forward toward the production of an ideal artificial light. But the arc light is not constant, and even when surrounded with a large globe not sufficiently diffused for reading purposes; the incandescent bulb, notwithstanding the improved tantalum, tungsten and osmium filaments, gives a glare too concentrated for ease in working. The nearest approach to diffused daylight has been made in the Hewitt mercury vapor lamp, where a small quantity of mercury in a long vacuum tube is first vaporized and then rendered luminous under the influence of the electric current. This lamp, however, is open to objection on the ground of its color. The nitrogen light, a description of which will be found in the chapter on electric lighting, is the first great positive advance in many years.

The significance of all these forms of electric light is that they do not inhere from the sun as do gas or animal and vegetable oils. They fit in with the atom's energy of matter and the force which gives rise to the illumination is a transformation of atomic force.

CHAPTER VI

THE SPEED OF LIGHT

AMONG all the properties of light none is more striking than its speed. Previous to the seventeenth century this had always been supposed to be infinite, and the discovery of the gradual propagation of light is one of the most wonderful achievements of that wonderful period in the history of physics—the Renaissance. The first attempt to measure the speed of light was made by Galileo. He ascertained the time for one person to signal with a lamp to another and receive back the signal. The experiment was tried at night, when the two observers were close together and again when they were nearly a mile apart. If a difference in time could be detected, then light would travel with finite velocity. Galileo was not able from his experiments to settle the question.

About thirty years later a young Dane, Alaf Römer, was observing the eclipses of Jupiter's moons.

It was noticed that the times of revolution of these moons in their orbits were not the same at all periods of the year, and were greater than the average when the apparent size of Jupiter was diminishing. Considering it in the highest degree improbable that the actual motions should be affected with any inequality of this sort, Römer became convinced that the observed irregularities must be explained on the supposition that the velocity of light is finite. He said that the discrepancy could be accounted for by assuming that it took time for light to come from Jupiter to the earth. On November 9, 1676, an eclipse took place at 5 h. 35 m. 45 s., while by computation it should have been at 5 h. 25 m. 45s. On November 22 he explained his theory to the French Academy more fully, and said that it required light 22 minutes to cross the earth's orbit. (The more correct value is now known to be 16 minutes and 36 seconds.) Like the news of so many other great discoveries, Römer's announcement fell upon deaf ears. It was fifty years before the scientific world recognized the truth and the value of his contribution to knowledge.

Römer computed the velocity of light to be 309,000 kilometers (about 186,000 miles) per second. Subsequent determinations made by astronomers and physicists have corrected this computation but little. The most accurate estimates of this figure are those made by Jean Léon Foucault, inventor of the gyroscope and originator of the Foucault pendulum, in France, and Albert R. Michelson, of the United States Navy, in America. The speed found by Michelson as the result of more than a hundred trials, lasting over some two months of daily experimentation, averaged 299,740 kilometers, or 186,300 miles per second. The speed of light in a vacuum is estimated as but slightly greater than in air.

The velocity of light in water was a pregnant question in determining the true nature of light. The discussion of this problem belongs to very recent times. It shows what remarkable influence the opinions of Isaac Newton exercised, and illustrates how easy it is even for scientific men to "take sides" in a discussion where only truth is sought. According to the adherents of the Newtonian school the speed of light in water—a denser medium than air—should be greater than its speed in air, just as the speed of sound in iron is greater than in wood. But if light be a vibrational phenomenon the speed should be less in water than in air. This was the fact which the exponents of the undulatory theory—of whom Thomas Young in England and Fresnel, Malus and Foucault in France were the leading lights—were called upon to demonstrate if the Newtonian theory was to be refuted. Foucault took up the idea, constructed a sort of "light siren" which made more than 1,000 revolutions per second, and reflecting a beam of light showed a deviation of the ray upon a mirror at a distance. This deviation he found to be greater when the ray of light was passed through water, and his experiment gave conclusive proof that the Newtonian theory of light was false. The speed of light in water was found to be just about three-fourths of the speed in air. That light in passing from air through a dense medium, such as water or glass, suffers a retardation, was a natural inference.

That a distant light gives less illumination than one which is near was early a fact of common observation. The exact extent to which distance would affect the amount of light received, however, is not so generally known. The earth receives a certain amount of light from the sun, an amount varying with the latitude and the seasons. At first blush it might seem as if this light would increase in direct proporion to the nearness to the sun, as if, supposing the earth were half as far away, the light would be twice as great, and the heat received on the earth would only be doubled. That such is not the case is now known to every student of the elements of physics.

It has been estimated, indeed, that if the earth were moved half way from its present position toward the sun, the whole face of nature would be changed. Life as it now exists would be impossible— no trees, grass, or any verdure would cover the face of the earth; water would be unknown, existing only as a prodigious enveloping veil of vapor through which the sun's rays would pass with considerable loss of energy. Enough would be transmitted, however, so that metals such as tin and lead and even zinc would be liquids, mercury a gas, sulphur a boiling fluid mass. An intense glare would illuminate the glowing rocks and naked soil—a light the like of which cannot be conceived by aid of any comparison with the physical world of to-day. And yet the sun would then be distant more than forty millions of miles from the surface of the earth. How bright must be the illumination which the sun casts upon the little planet Mercury, so much nearer to him than the Earth, it is utterly impossible to imagine. There is no standard of comparison. Yet Mercury is distant 37,000,000 miles from the sun.

The sense of perspective is a universal faculty. A ship grows continually smaller in approaching the horizon; a near-by fly crossing the path of vision looks larger than an eagle; a penny held close to the eye will obscure the world. Light, as before observed, travels in straight lines from every illuminated point. From a lighted candle rays of light radiate in every direction straight away from the flame. The artist familiarly represents the light of a candle by an illuminated circle around it, which rapidly shades from white to dark gray or black shadow. This illuminated circle represents in reality a hollow sphere or shell of light, and each radiant vibration coming from the source of light is spread over the surface of the sphere. It is a well-known fact that if the radius of such a sphere be made to increase, the area of the sphere will also increase, but much faster than the radius—in fact, as the square of the latter. The surface of a two-inch ball is four times as great as that of an inch ball; the surface of a three-inch ball is nine times as great as that of an inch ball. Similarly the light which from a point within would reach the surface of a hollow sphere one foot in diameter would be spread over nine times the same area if the radius of the sphere were three feet. Hence each point on the surface of the larger sphere would receive only one-ninth as much light.

The amount or intensity of light, then, varies not exactly as the inverse of the distance, but inversely as the square of the distance from the source of light. In general, as any light wave advances its energy is being distributed over a surface which increases directly as the square of the distance the wave has traveled. It must be noted, however, that this law of intensity applies only to the direct light from a luminous body; for the total illumination on a given surface is usually very much increased by the light reflected from near-by non-luminous bodies. Hence it is that white walls and furnishings add so much to the total amount of light in a room. The law of the Intensity of Light is evidently analogous to that of gravity, where it was seen that a pound weight at the surface of the earth (4,000 miles from its center) would weigh only ¼ lb. at the distance of 4,000 miles from the surface (8,000 miles from its center, or twice as far away as at the surface). It is this strangely persistent law of inverse squares which, more than any other fact of physics, points to the ultimate unification of all Force under one head. The law holds true for gravity, electric and magnetic attraction and repulsion, light, sound, heat and so-called "radiant heat," together with numerous other less fundamental physical relationships.

An ingenious yet extremely simple instrument for measuring the amount of light received from a given source was invented about the end of the eighteenth century by an American, Benjamin Thompson, afterward Count Rumford. In front of a ground glass screen be fixed an opaque rod, placing a bright lamp and a candle at such distances from the rod that the shadows thrown by each light upon the screen appeared equally bright. Measuring the distance of each light from the shadows cast, he found the lamp to be four times as far away as the candle, from which, by the law of inverse squares, he perceived that the lamp was twice as bright as the candle.

Some fifty years later another light-measuring instrument was produced by the famous chemist Robert Wilhelm Bunsen. This admirably simple device consisted of a sheet of white paper with a grease spot on it. The experiment may easily be made by any one. If the paper is equally illuminated from both sides the grease spot will be hardly visible, but if the light upon one side is made ever so little brighter than upon the other, the spot will at once appear on the darker side brighter (and on the brighter side darker) than the rest of the paper. The obvious reason of this is that the matt surface of the white paper reflects back more and transmits less of the light which falls upon it than does the part covered with a film of grease. If now a standard light be placed on one side of this paper, any other light whose "candle-power" is to be determined may be shifted back on the other side until the grease spot is no longer visible, when by measuring the distances of the two lights from the paper screen the relative intensity may easily be determined.

Incandescent electric lamps, arc lights and in fact all common illuminants are measured in candle power. One British standard candle power is the rate at which light is emitted by the flame of a sperm candle weighing ⅙ of a pound and burning 120 grains per hour. The amount of light from such a source, however, has been shown to vary as much as 20 per cent., hence the standard is somewhat unsatisfactory. Ordinary electric glow lamps are equivalent to 16 standard candles and are therefore called 16 c.p. (candle-power) lamps. Other varieties of photometer ("light-measurers") have subsequently been invented, one of which, Wheatstone's, produces very beautiful luminous effects.

THE SPEED OF LIGHT

Similar in many ways to the measurement of the light of the sun is the accurate estimation of solar heat. In 1883 Samuel Pierpont Langley invented the bolometer, briefly described as an exquisitely delicate thermopile. Langley's invention was a part of his careful and elaborate preparation for that remarkable trip to the (then almost unknown) summit of Mount Whitney, in southern California, where the summits of the Sierra Nevada, rising precipitously in the dry air to a height of nearly fifteen thousand feet over the Mojave Desert to the eastward, furnished a suitable location for the study of the influence of the earth's atmosphere upon the radiations from the sun. "I spent nearly a year," says Langley, "before ascending the mountain in inventing and perfecting the new instrument which I have called the 'bolometer,' or 'ray-measurer.' The principle on which it is founded is the same as that employed by my late lamented friend, Sir William Siemens, for measuring temperatures at the bottom of the sea, which is that a smaller electric current flows through a warm wire than a cold one.

"One great difficulty was to make the conducting wire very thin and yet continuous, and for this purpose almost endless experiments were made, among other substances pure gold having been obtained by chemical means in a plate so thin that it transmitted a sea-green light through the solid substance of the metal. This proving unsuitable, I learned that iron had been rolled of extraordinary thinness in a contest of skill between some English and American ironmasters; and, procuring some, I found that fifteen thousand of the iron plates they had rolled, laid one on the other, would make but one English inch. Out of this the first bolometers were made. The iron is now replaced by platinum, in wires, or rather tapes, from a two-thousandth to a twenty-thousandth of an inch thick, all but invisible, being far finer than a human hair. This thread acts as tho sensitive, like a nerve laid bare to every indication of heat and cold. It is, then, a sort of sentient thing; what the eye sees as light it feels as heat, and what the eye sees as a narrow band of darkness (the Frauenhofer line) this feels as a narrow belt of cold; so that, when moved parallel to itself and the Frauenhofer lines down the spectrum, it registers their presence."

Langley's fascinating story of his experimental trip to Mount Whitney, told in the records of the Royal Institution, is full of thrilling imaginative touches. A few lines may serve to show something of the immense difficulties which he had to overcome in getting his results. He writes: "We commenced our slow toil northward with a thermometer at 110° in the shade, if any shade there be in the shadeless desert, which seems to be chiefly inhabited by rattlesnakes of an ashen gray color and a peculiarly venomous bite. There is no water, save at the rarest intervals, and the soil at a distance seems as tho strewed with sheets of salt, which aids the delusive show of the mirage.

"At last, after a seemingly interminable journey, we pitched our tents and fell to work (for you remember we must have two stations, a low and a high one, to compare the results); and here we labored three weeks in almost intolerable heat, the instruments having to be constantly swept clear of the red desert dust which the hot wind brought. Close by these tents a thermometer covered by a single sheet of glass and surrounded by wool rose to 237° in the sun, and sometimes in the tent, which was darkened for the study of separate rays, the heat was absoltuely beyond human endurance.

"Finally our apparatus was taken apart and packed in small pieces on the backs of mules, who were to carry it by a ten days' journey through the mountains to the other side of the rocky wall, which, tho only ten or twelve miles distant, arose miles above our heads; and, leaving these mule-trains to go with the escort by this longer route, I started with a guide by a nearer way to those white gleams in the upper skies that had daily tantalized us below in the desert with suggestions of delicious, unattainable cold. That desert sun had tanned our faces to a leather-like brown, and the change to the cooler air as we ascended was at first delightful. But the colder it grew the more the sun burnt the skin—quite literally burnt, I may say; so that by the end of the third day my face and hands, casehardened, as I thought, in the desert, began to look as if they had been seared with red-hot irons, here in the cold, where the thermometer had fallen to freezing at night; and still, as we ascended, the paradoxical effect increased. The colder it grew about us the hotter the sun blazed above. It almost seemed as tho sunbeams up here were different things, and contained something which the air filters out before they reach us in our customary abodes. Radiation here is increased by the absence of water-vapor, too; and, on the whole, this intimate personal experience fell in almost too well with our anticipations that the air is an even more elaborate trap to catch the sunbeams than had been surmised, and that this effect of selective absorption and radiation was intimately connected with that change of the primal energies and primal color of the sun which we had climbed toward it to study.

"We suffered from cold (the ice forming three inches deep in the tents at night) and from mountain sickness, but we were too busy to pay much attention to bodily comfort and worked with desperate energy to utilize the remaining autumn days, which were all too short. Here, as below, the sunlight entered a darkened tent and was spread into a spectrum, which was explored throughout by the bolometer, measuring on the same separate rays which we had studied

THE SPEED OF LIGHT

below in the desert, all of which were different up here, all having grown stronger, but in very different proportions."

The delicately constructed bolometer of Langley has been brought in comparatively recent years to very high perfection so as to record a change of temperature of .0000001 of a degree Centigrade. Prof. C. B. Boys in 1888 constructed a similar instrument capable of indicating so minute quantities of radiant heat that in the absence of atmospheric absorption the heat radiated from a candle two miles away would be distinctly registered. A still more perfect instrument lately completed in America similar to the radiometer of Dr. Crookes reached a marvelous degree of sensitiveness to radiant energy.

Experiments were made on the heat of a candle situated 2,000 feet from the concave mirror which focused its rays upon the instrument. The feeble radiations of the candle at this great distance sufficed to turn the indicator through nearly a hundred scale divisions, and even the face of an observer when placed in the position before occupied by the candle produced a deflection of 25 scale divisions. As a tenth of a single scale division could readily be observed, it will be seen, to speak figuratively, that with this radiometer one might note the approach of a friend while yet some miles distant, merely by the glow of his countenance.

CHAPTER VII

REFLECTION AND REFRACTION

A STRANGE phenomenon of light which long puzzled the scientific world was that of polarization, or two-sidedness. A crystal of tourmaline held between the eye and a light source will appear transparent. A second crystal placed in front of it will also allow the light to pass as long as the two crystals are held lengthwise. If one of them be turned at a right angle to the other the light is cut off. The explanation of this was a hard nut for Young to crack. He cracked it thus: "It is possible," he wrote in a letter to a friend, "to explain in this (undulatory) theory a transverse vibration propagated in the direction of the radius and with equal velocity, the motions of the particles being in a certain constant direction with respect to that radius transverse to the ray; and this is Polarization."

Thus Young explained that what happened in the progress of a light ray is the same thing as that which happens in the progress of a water wave; a stick of wood may be seen to rise and fall with the waves, but it does not advance with them, for the vibration is transverse to the direction of propagation. The apparent motion of the water in a wave is a forward motion; the actual motion is up and down. So is it with light. The analogy may be carried further, for when the wave approaches the shore, the lower part of it is arrested and the upper part is still carried forward by the impulse from behind. The result is that the wave now takes a downward as well as a forward motion, and this effect becoming more and more pronounced the top of the wave curls completely over the water below and crashes as a breaker on the shore.

In light this change of direction also takes place whenever the light wave passes from air to a denser medium, such as water. If a ray of light strike the water at an angle, the lower part of the wave being arrested at the surface of the water, the ray bends downward into the water. A "normal" or perpendicular to the surface of the water would therefore form a larger angle with the ray in the air than in the water. The ray is said to be bent toward the normal in passing from a rare to a denser medium. Imagine the same ray to be shot back again, and it will obviously be bent from the normal as it leaves the water. It is evident from the water-wave analogy that the more the wave is

REFLECTION AND REFRACTION

stopped at the surface of the new medium the greater will be the bending.

In a substance like diamond, where the light travels less than half as fast as in air, the bending is very great, and the colors of which the white light is composed are much scattered and broken. Hence appear the magnificent lights in the diamonds. In crown glass, where the wave travels two-thirds as fast as in air, there is less stoppage and consequently less refraction of the ray. In water, as has been remarked, the speed is three-fourths of the speed in air, hence the bending is still less.

Owing to this bending downward of a ray of light as it enters the water, it is evident that an observant trout will sight a fisherman some seconds before the latter sees the trout, and in the same way the setting sun will be visible to a fish in the water as shining apparently some degrees above the horizon. The effects of refraction are interesting, sometimes startling. It has been noted above that a ray of light passing from water into air suffers a bending away from the normal to the surface. That is, it tends to lie down and run along the surface. This tendency is more marked as the angle of incidence increases. When the ray of light strikes the under surface of the water at a long angle it does not pass into the air, but runs along the surface of the water. Increase the angle ever so slightly, and the ray is actually bent down again through the water, affording the striking phenomenon of total reflection.

A familiar example of total reflection is found in the mirage. This reflection may take place whenever a ray of light passes from one layer of air to another of different density. The image of an inverted ship is observed commonly enough at sea before the ship itself comes over the horizon. The images of distant shores may be seen in like manner. The rays of light from the ship pass upward and reach some stratum of air which is warmer and consequently rarer than the air above the water immediately surrounding the vessel. From this rarer medium the image is bent down by total reflection and projected to some distant point. In the sandy plains of Egypt and other hot countries a similar phenomenon is due to similar causes. In this case, however, the image formed is reflected from a cooler stratum of air than that immediately above the burning sand of the desert. The inverted picture of trees thus formed in the sky is precisely analogous to the reflection of trees on the shore of a still lake. The reflecting medium in both cases is denser than that surrounding the object.

As the amount of light varies inversely as the square of the distance from the source, so it also varies with the angle at which the light falls. If the rays are projected vertically upon a surface, the amount of light will be greater than that received when they reach the surface at an angle. Hence the amount of light, as well as the amount of heat, which reaches the polar regions is far less than that which falls upon the equator. The same amount of light is spread over a large surface.

Anything like accurate measurement of the amount of light received upon an object must always take into account the light due to reflection—for every visible surface reflects; if it did not it would not be visible. The scattering of the rays which results from a rough surface is utilized in minimizing the glare from a too brilliant source of light, such as the incandescent mantle of the Welsbach gaslight or the dazzling core of the electric arc. Ground glass globes enclose the lights and diffuse the intense brightness by scattering the rays which pass through the roughened surface. The great difficulty from an economic standpoint, with this method of softening the radiated light, is that nearly one-half of the illuminating power is wasted in the resistance offered by the semi-opaque glass globe. Diffuse reflection takes place at all points of the roughened surface.

The famous Mirror Maze, composed of several mirrors at various angles and scores of panes of clear glass, is so confusing that even extreme watchfulness will not prevent the observer from running into a pane of glass, not being able to perceive it. The reflection of any object in a plane mirror is a virtual, not a real image. There is no actual image where the object appears to be, and the virtual image so formed will be exactly as far in the rear of the mirror as the object itself is in front of it. This would follow inevitably from the well-known Law of reflection, which, so far back as the time of Archimedes, was well understood as a fundamental principle of all mirrors of every shape and description.

If two mirrors are placed so as to touch at right angles, a candle placed in the angle will show three images reflected, no matter how the observer stands. By making the angle of the mirrors continually smaller, more and more images will be brought into view. When the angle of the mirrors is 60 degrees (the angle of an equilateral triangle) five images will appear, and seven if the mirrors are inclined at an angle of 45 degrees. When the angle is made small enough so that the mirrors are almost parallel, the number of reflections become practically infinite. An interesting and striking fact with regard to these multiple images is that every image so formed, as well as the luminous object itself, will lie on the circumference of a circle of which the juncture of the mirrors is the exact center. This, again, may readily be shown to be an obvious result of the familiar Law of Reflection.

Sir David Brewster, of the University of Edinboro, invented early in the nineteenth century a reflecting instrument through which he became better known than by any of his more elaborate contributions

REFLECTION AND REFRACTION

to science. The kaleidoscope, a simple little device to be had to-day in almost any toy shop, was constructed by him with three plane mirrors. These were made of equal width and length, and fitted into a tube closed at one end by a disk or plate of ground glass, behind which irregular bits of colored glass or porcelain were allowed to tumble and turn in any direction. The latter were held in place by another disk of clear glass. When viewed from a small aperture in the farther end of the tube these bits of colored glass showed by their multiple reflections in the three mirrors an amazing variety of beautiful symmetrical designs apparently without number or end. So great at one time was the demand for these kaleidoscopes that it was found impossible to supply it. A more complicated series of images of great diversity is made by placing six mirrors together so as to form a regular hexagon, each angle of which is exactly twice the angle of an equilateral triangle, or 120 degrees. This is the form in which mirrors have been combined to produce the remarkable vistas of crystal mazes, of which a noteworthy example has recently been constructed in Paris, wherein the turn of a lever transports the observer from a forest grove to the interior of a Hindu temple or the wonderful Arabian palace of Aladdin.

The image formed by a glass mirror is not reflected by the glass. Back of every such mirror will be found a thin layer of some metallic substance, which forms a much better reflecting surface than the glass. A beam of light falling on the mirror will be partly reflected from the front surface of the glass, but mainly from the metallic hinder surface. Thus it becomes apparent why a mirror, especially a thick one, forms two or more distinct images of an object seen at an angle in the glass. A consideration of the law of Total Reflection will show how many such images may actually be formed, reflected back and forth from the two surfaces of the mirror, and growing rapidly dimmer, so that usually not more than one or two are plainly to be seen.

A certain astronomical observer, not many years ago, betrayed in this connection an unconscious vein of humor. By means of the reflections from a plate of clear glass he announced the discovery of a large satellite circling the planet Venus! On account of these repeated images in glass mirrors, they are usually replaced, in physical observatories, by metallic reflectors.

The great law of Reflection, that the Angle of the Incident Ray equals the Angle of the Reflected Ray, was found to hold true for all angles and all surfaces. The law applies with equal rigor to a plane mirror or to a reflecting surface of any other type, spherical, cylindrical, conical, concave or convex. Nearly a thousand years ago the famous Image Problem of the Arab Al Hazen, to which reference has already been made, was formulated, calling for a proof of the images formed in plane, spherical and conical mirrors. The spreading of the rays of light will obviously change the appearance of the image formed in any convex reflecting surface, while the opposite effect will produce an opposite change in the image formed in a concave reflector.

The image formed by looking in the bowl of an ordinary spoon is seen to be inverted. No matter which way the spoon is held, sidewise or upside down, this will always be found true—unless the spoon is large and brought very close to the face. Looking at the back of the spoon, however, the image is seen to be erect, no matter how near or how far away the spoon is held. The reason is easily seen. Every ray of light from an object must glance off from the polished metallic surface at the same angle as that at which it strikes. In a concave surface, such as the hollow of a spoon, these rays must evidently meet somewhere and then cross. Evidently the image formed after they cross will be upside down and left side right. Such an image is real, for it is actually formed where it appears to be, and in this respect differs from the images formed in plane or convex mirrors, which apparently exist where experience proves they cannot exist, viz., behind the reflector. If the reflection in a concave surface is made by an object held close to the mirror, it will form an enlarged erect virtual image; the rays of light do not pass through the focus, or crossing point of the mirror, hence there is no inversion, and the image, but for the enlargement, is exactly like that formed in a plane mirror. It appears behind the surface.

Parabolic mirrors which have come into such general use for powerful lighting purposes—as, for example, in the headlights of automobiles and locomotives—show but a slight modification of the concave spherical mirror. The change, tho slight, is important, for all the rays of light from the lamp within the reflector now strike the side walls at such an angle that they pass out in parallel lines; therefore, except for the light lost in absorption, at the metallic surface every bit of illumination is centered in the one direction. The illuminating power of these reflectors, when furnished with a brilliant light, is enormous. The parabolic mirror is said to have been known since the time of Archimedes.

The convex surface of the back of an ordinary spoon forms, as has been said, an erect image, which appears reduced and at a distance of several inches behind the spoon. Withdraw the spoon slowly, and the image continues to recede and diminish, until at a certain point the diminution seems to stop and the image remains constant no matter how far away the spoon is moved. Here, as before, a converging point of the rays of light will be found, this time behind the mirror; but there will be no crossing, for the rays will exactly meet and the image be reduced to a point only when the object has been removed to a distance theoretically infinite.

REFLECTION AND REFRACTION

In general, it has been said of all real images that they are those formed by the reflected rays themselves, whereas virtual images are formed by their imaginary prolongations. The real image is always inverted and the virtual image erect. By analogy with the phenomena of images in convex and concave mirrors, the process of image formation through the ordinary convex lens will readily be understood. The process here, as has been shown, is one of refraction, not of reflection of light. But the bending of the rays to a focus on either side of the lens will determine, as before, the form of the image, whether erect or inverted. Images formed by refraction through a convex lens must in all cases when the object is outside the focus be real, since the figure is actually formed and may be shown on a screen exactly where it appears to be.

If the object is placed inside the focus of the lens—*i.e.*, between the focus and the lens itself—an enlarged virtual image will be seen. This is the case in ordinary reading glasses; the light rays from all extremities of the object (letters or what-not) under examination are twice refracted by the double convex surface of the lens, and the eye sees these points of the object along the line last traveled by the light. Hence the object appears greatly magnified—its extremities appearing to be much farther apart than in reality they are. The more convex the lens the greater is its magnifying power, but the greater, at the same time, the difficulty in using it without some correction of the spherical aberration which increases with the curvature of the lens. Double convex lenses, used as magnifying glasses, are frequently called simple microscopes, as distinguished from the powerful compound microscope, which by the aid of brilliant illumination produces an image many thousand times larger than the original. The focus of all convex lenses was seen to be the place where rays of light traveling straight to the lens are bent together by refraction and meet. There will evidently be two such foci formed, one on either side of every double convex lens. These are the so-called conjugate foci of the lens. In concave lenses there is no real focus possible, since all rays will be refracted in a direction away from the perpendicular through the center of the lens. All images through such a lens will therefore be virtual images.

The earliest lenses were made in Europe of rock crystal, altho lenses of glass appear to have been known to the Greeks. The lenses of Hans Lippersley, of Middleburg, the inventor of the binocular telescope, were made of rock crystal. (These small instruments, it is interesting to note, sold at that time (1608) for the large sum of 900 gulden.) Galileo's lenses, one of them concave the other convex, were made of glass. Sparing neither expense nor labor, he succeeded in constructing an instrument which magnified an object nearly a thousand times and brought it more than thirty times nearer. He went to Venice to display his telescope. "Many noblemen and senators," says he, "altho of great age, mounted the steps of the highest church towers at Venice to watch the ships, which were visible through my glass two hours before they were seen entering the harbor."

In the early telescopes lenses were made with very great focal lengths—the beams converging in some cases at a distance of 10, 20, 30, 40 and in one instance of 123 feet from the center of the lens. These lenses were mounted on high poles, and being unprotected by a tube gave very inferior results. The purpose of these great clumsy objectives was the avoidance of the color dispersion which is always observable at the edges of a simple lens of pronounced curvature. Since the prism has shown that the blue rays of light are bent more than red, they must come to a focus behind a lens a little sooner than the red rays. This explanation of the fact that so many common lenses, reading glasses, etc., make it appear that the objects behind them are surrounded with a colored halo. This is more noticeable in lenses of much curvature, for the difference in focus between the red rays and the blue is then emphasized.

Leonhard Euler suggested that lenses made out of two different materials of different refractive powers would probably cure this "chromatic aberration." He tried to produce such a lens, but failed. A London optician, John Dolland, taking up Euler's idea, began a series of tests in making lenses which were achromatic—*i.e.*, showing no color dispersion. Years of repeated failure in this direction were finally crowned with success, and Dolland produced a lens made of crown and flint glass which was perfectly free from color and entirely accurate. His accomplishment created a sensation throughout Europe and greatly facilitated from that time the growth of astronomy. Lenses began to increase in diameter and telescopes in size. Herschel, the discoverer of the two inmost moons of Saturn, added immense concave mirrors to his telescopes whereby the light-gathering power of the instrument was vastly increased. At Parsontown in Ireland was completed a gigantic reflecting telescope with a mirror 6 feet across and a tube 58 feet long and 7 feet in diameter, so that a certain ecclesiastic, Dean Peacock, once walked through it with uplifted umbrella.

The achromatic lenses which made possible these great telescopes were likewise instrumental in the development of microscopes, to which they were early applied. The first microscope was constructed in the beginning of the seventeenth century by Zacharias Johannides, a Dutch optician. The eyepieces of his microscope were made at first concave; subsequent improvements made both lenses convex.

Spectacles also were manufactured with achromatic lenses, greatly increasing their comfort and serviceability. The inventor of spectacles must rest his claim to this honor upon an inscription dated some three hundred years before the invention of achromatic lenses. Upon the tomb of Salvino Armato in Florence is carved below the bust of this nobleman the inscription:

> Here lies
> SALVINO ARMATO D'ARMATI,
> of
> FLORENCE,
> INVENTOR OF SPECTACLES
> May God pardon his sins
> A.D. 1317.

In the tall lighthouses that to-day guard the coast of every civilized country is found the peculiar échelon or annular lens. To avoid the spherical aberration, and the loss of light inevitable in refractors of such magnitude as those of the lighthouse lights, these lenses are made in concentric rings of glass, which focus in one point, the outermost ring being some two feet in diameter. The light placed in this focus is not too widely distributed, and becomes brightly visible over a distance of more than forty miles. Some conception of the power of these lenses may be had from the fact that when inverted and used to condense the solar rays, gold, platinum and quartz are melted in the intense heat, and less refractory substances, as lead, tin and zinc, are almost immediately reduced to a vapor.

Far more perfect than any previously produced were the glass lenses made in Munich by Joseph Frauenhofer. The talented son of a poor glazier, Frauenhofer combined a thoro practical skill with an unusual degree of theoretic insight. "By his invention of new and improved methods, machinery and measuring instruments for grinding and polishing lenses, by his having the superintendence, after 1811, also the work in glass melting, enabling him to produce flint and crown glass in larger pieces, free of veins, but especially by his discovery of a method of computing accurately the forms of lenses, he has led practical optics into entirely new paths, and has raised the achromatic telescope to a perfection hitherto undreamed of." So writes Lommel in his preface to Frauenhofer's "Gesammelte Schriften."

Among the many other applications of the lens which have made a necessary place in present-day life, the camera deserves especial notice. Baptista Porta, a Neapolitan physician and contemporary of the great Gilbert, invented an instrument now familiar enough to every school boy of a practical turn of mind—the camera obscura. A simple box, light proof, and painted black within and without, received through a lens the image of external objects and reflected it from a sloping white paper screen on to a plate of ground glass in the top of the box. To imitate in the form of a fixed photograph the beautiful colored image thus thrown on the plate was achieved in the second decade of the twentieth century by several successful processes, but the commercialization of color photography for the amateur is handicapped by the difficulty of the process.

The camera obscura may hardly be considered the antecedent of the photographic camera of to-day, which resembles the pin-hole camera in structure more nearly. Yet the essential principle of the modern camera was not different from that of the camera obscura. With an adjustable or focusing lens and the substitution of a sensitive film or plate for the former plate of ground glass, the transformation was accomplished. In modern days many people take photographs, and there is more or less familiarity with the nature of the chemical changes that are worked by the exposure to the light of the silver salts upon the "sensitive" plate. If exacting Reason, however, demand in this connection an explanation of why the change takes place, it must be answered in brief that the energy of the light ray probably effects a rapid alteration of the structure of the atoms of the silver salt employed, in much the same way as has been noted before in the different forms of copper and iron. When the velocity of waves of light is remembered, it becomes clear that a 1/10 second exposure means that these atoms have been hammered thousands of times by light waves in that brief period.

The art of photography is of very recent development, depending of necessity upon a certain advance in the science of chemistry. Pictures on metal were produced in 1827 by Joseph Nicephore Niepce, whose assistant and successor in this work, Daguerre, has given his name to the improved metallic photographs which are still called, after him, daguerreotypes. These first efforts at a photograph were clumsy contrivances, requiring from five to seven minutes' exposure, during which the photographee must sit with iron face and rigid figure, immovable. The face of the sitter had also to be dusted with white powder, and the print, when completed, was faint, and in certain lights invisible, on account of the brilliant polish of the metallic surface upon which the print was made. Tinting the picture was commonly resorted to in the endeavor to make the result more life-like. From the slow and troublesome methods of the old daguerreotype to the magnificent black and white instantaneous carbon prints of to-day is a long stride.

It frequently happens in human history that after the invention has been made and perfected, the further progress of knowledge reveals the fact that the wonderful invention already existed in Nature in a state of development far more advanced. The old scoop dredge, tho it still has its special use, has been largely replaced by a huge iron hand like a man's hand; the phonograph is a clumsy imitation of the auricular nerve and tympanum of the human ear; the eye has been described as a camera with a self-adjusting shutter and focusing automatically. Without going too minutely into the physical structure of the eye, its essential parts may briefly be summed up.

Covering all the exposed front of the organ is a tough elastic membrane (cornea), which lets through the light, but protects the delicate mechanism immediately behind. This interior part it is which lends character and color to the eye, the iris or colored ring of various hues—as ranging from a light gray-blue, which is largely destitute of the orange-brown coloring pigment, to a brown so deep as almost to seem black. "Helmholtz," writes Cajori in his history already referred to, "irreverently disclosed the fact that in blue eyes there is no real blue coloring matter whatever; the deepest blue is nothing but a turbid medium. The optic action is the same as in the case of smoke which appears blue on a dark background, tho the particles themselves are not blue; or in case of the sky, which, according to Newton, Stokes and Rayleigh, looks blue through the agency of extremely fine dust suspended in the air. This dust, when illuminated by sunlight, reflects a greater proportion of the shorter waves of bluish light and transmits a greater proportion of longer waves of reddish light."

The "pupil" of the eye is the shutter, which, by the expansion or contraction of the iris, lets in more or less light to the sensitive film or "retina" at the back of the organ. Close behind the pupil and its encircling iris the crystalline lens refracts incident light from objects near or remote, and by the aid of the enveloping "ciliary" muscle may be so far contracted as to focus the vision with equal readiness upon a tiny shell in the hand or a mass of rocks on a far-distant mountain. Through the glassy liquid which fills all the remaining interior of the eye the light is transmitted to the retina, where a chemical change is constantly being effected upon the exposed film of this optical photographic camera, the optic nerves reporting to the brain at every moment the nature of these changes.

With all its beauty and delicate adjustment, however, the human eye has many imperfections. No voice has spoken of the physics of the eye with more authority than has the extraordinarily versatile and learned Helmholtz. To him the eye is indeed a crude instrument. The German physicist indicates its defects with considerable force. "A refracting surface which is imperfectly elliptical," he says, "an ill-centered telescope, does not give a single illuminated point as the image of a star, but according to the surface and arrangement of the refracting media, elliptic, circular, or linear images. Now the images of an illuminated point, as the human eye brings them to focus, are even more inaccurate: they are irregularly radiated. The reason of this lies in the construction of the crystalline lens, the fibers of which are arranged around six diverging axes, so that the rays which we see around stars and other distant lights are images of the radiated structure of our lens; and the universality of this optical defect is proved by any figure with diverging rays, being called 'star-shaped.' It is from the same cause that the moon, while her cresent is still narrow, appears to many persons double or threefold."

"Now, it is not too much to say," he remarks again, "that if an optican wanted to sell me an instrument which had all these defects, I should think myself quite justified in blaming his carelessness in the strongest terms and giving him back his instrument."

The mechanical process of the eye has never, until comparatively recently, been understood. Helmholtz and others, basing their experiments upon the observations of Thomas Young, Louis Joseph Sanson and Max Lagenbeck, have explained the manner in which the eye focuses and the means employed to control the admission of light. The sense of color, however, is still a matter of controversy. The most acceptable theory of color sense is that promulgated by Young and developed by Helmholtz, based on the phenomenon of color blindness to the three shades which occupy respectively the ends and the center of the prismatic ribbon, viz., red, green and violet. Color blindness to red is common and to green not uncommon, while the inability to recognize violet is known. Young showed that the rotation of colored disks of equally combined, red, green and violet produces the impression of gray. Under a certain proportion this gray approaches white. These, therefore, may be taken as the three primary colors, by combination of which all the intermediate colors may be produced.

CHAPTER VIII

THE NATURE OF LIGHT

To THE phenomenon of total reflection was added in the very beginning of the nineteenth century another bit of evidence which the exponents of the corpuscular theory of light found difficult to explain away. This was the phenomenon of interference. Two plates of glass touching at one end and separated at the other by a fine hair will form between them a thin wedge of air. If a bright light is held near the plates they will be seen crossed with dark and bright bands. Thomas Young, a brilliant young English physicist, experimenting with these plates and studying the dark bands, stated in a famous paper on light that they were due to the interference of light waves from the two surfaces of the wedge of air included between the plates of glass. He showed how the waves of light from these two surfaces might be proved to meet at intervals and produce the appearance of darkness, just as two sound waves may be combined to produce silence.

This remarkable paper, by far the most valuable contribution to the study of optics since the time of Newton, attracted no favorable attention and was received with open scorn and contempt by the editor of the Edinboro Review. The young scientist is represented by this illustrous organ as deficient in "the powers of solid thinking" and his theories dismissed as "feeble lucubrations without any traces of learning, acuteness or ingenuity." John Tyndall, that great and fascinating Irish scientist, writes of Young: "For twenty years this man of genius was quenched—hidden from the appreciative genius of his countrymen—deemed, in fact, a dreamer, through the vigorous sarcasm of a writer who had then possession of the public ear. To the celebrated Frenchmen, Fresnel and Arago, he was first indebted for the restitution of his rights." The soundness of Young's reasoning has been abundantly attested to by the verdict of later investigators, and the known fact of the "interference" of light is today held to be one of the compelling arguments in favor of light as a form of vibration.

Difficult of explanation as the fact of interference proved from a corpuscular basis, still more did prismatic dispersion prove itself an occasion of falling. Every one is familiar with the beautiful color effects obtainable with the aid of a triangular prism of glass, and has noted how a beam of "white" light may be spread out into a band of colors as the ray is bent through the prism. In this spreading out it is evident that some of the rays are bent more than others. Unless the corpuscles of light were infinite in variety, this would be simply inexplicable as a corpuscular phenomenon. The prism as an instrument of optical study found its first great master in Isaac Newton. The observation of its effects had been noted by the Roman philosopher Seneca, and in the period of the Renaissance the breaking up of white light into colors was discussed by Grimaldi, Descartes, Hooke and others. But it required the supreme genius of Newton to make clear the true idea of the dispersion of light. With rough appliances fashioned by his own hands he conducted his experiments. In his treatise on "Opticks" he quaintly remarks, "I procured me a triangular glass prisme, to try therewith the celebrated phenomena of colors. And in order thereto having darkened my chamber, and made a small hole in my window-shuts to let in a convenient quantity of the sun's light, I placed my prisme at his entrance, that it might be thereby refracted to the opposite wall."

He goes on to say how surprised he was to find that the ray of light, after passing through the prism, instead of being thrown upon the wall in the form of a round spot, was spread out into a beautiful colored ribbon, or spectrum, red at one end, yellow in the middle, and bluish green at the other end. "Comparing the length of this colored spectrum with its breadth," he continues, "I found it about five times greater—a disproportion so extravagant that it excited me to a more than ordinary curiosity of examining from whence it might proceed.

"Then I began to suspect, whether the rays, after their trajection through the prism, did not move in curve lines, and according to their more or less curvity tend to divers parts of the wall. And it increased my suspicion, when I remembered that I had often seen a tennis ball struck with an oblique racket, describe such a curve line. For, a circular as well as a progressive motion being communicated to it by that stroke, its parts on that side, where the motions conspire, must press and beat the contiguous air more violently than on the other, and there excite a reluctancy and reaction of the air proportionately greater. And for the same reason, if the rays of light should possibly be globular bodies, and by their oblique passage out of the medium into another, acquire a circulating motion, they ought to feel the greater resistance from the ambient æther, on that side, where the motions conspire, and thence be continually bowed to the other. But notwithstanding this plausible ground of suspicion, when I came to examine it, I could observe no such curvity in them. And besides (which was enough for my purpose) I observed that the difference betwixt the length of the image and the diameter of the hole through which the light was transmitted was proportionable to their distance.

THE NATURE OF LIGHT

"The gradual removal of these suspicions at length led me to the experimentum crucis, which was this: I took two boards, and placed one of them close behind the prism at the window, so that the light might pass through a small hole, made in it for the purpose, and fall on the other board, which I placed at about twelve feet distance, having first made a small hole in it also, for some of that incident light to pass through. Then, I placed another prism behind the second board." On turning the first prism about its axis, the image which fell on the second board was made to move up and down upon that board, so that all its parts could successively pass through the hole in that board, and fall upon the prism behind it. The places where the light fell against the wall were noted. It was seen that the blue light, which was most refracted in the first prism, was also most refracted in the second prism, the red being least refracted in both prisms. "And so the true cause of the length of that image was detected to be no other than that light is not similar or homogeneal, but consists of difform rays, some of which are more refrangible than others."

No more complete or illuminating explanation of the nature of light through the agency of the prism has ever been given than this. Newton showed here the real reason of the dispersion, adducing the analogy of the rainbow, altho he clung through it all to the corpuscular theory, postulating the existence not only of the flying particles constituting light, but also of an ether—all the mechanism, in fact, needed for the wave theory, and more.

It was not until the beginning of the present century that this experiment of Newton's (repeated as it had been in the meantime by many philosophers) was found by Dr. Wollaston to possess certain peculiarities which defied all explanation. He found that, by substituting a slit in the shutter of the darkened room for the round hole which Newton had used, the spectrum was intersected by certain dark lines. This announcement, altho at the time it did not excite much attention, led to further experiments by different investigators, who, however, vainly endeavored to solve the meaning of these bands of darkness. It was observed by the great Munich optician that they never varied, but always occupied a certain fixed position in the spectrum; moreover, he succeeded in mapping them to the number of nearly six hundred, for which reason they have been identified with his name, as "Frauenhofer's lines."

It was one of the greatest contributions to science. Accidentally he discovered in the spectrum of a lamp the double line in the orange, now known as the sodium, line. He was endeavoring at the time to determine how the refraction through glass would take place for different colored lights. The observation of the sodium line was a chance incident of his experiments. In oil and tallow light, and in fact in all firelight, he saw this same bright, sharply defined double line "exactly in the same place and consequently very useful." Examining the spectrum of sunlight cast through a small telescope upon a prism, he remarked "an almost countless number of strong and feeble vertical lines which, however, were darker than the other parts of the spectrum, some appearing to be almost perfectly black." He also examined starlight with his primitive spectroscope and found many of the solar lines in the spectrum of the planet Venus. For nearly forty years the scientific world, absorbed in theories concerning the nature of light itself, or the newly announced atomic theory of Dalton and the laws of chemical combination and composition, failed to see the meaning and significance of this discovery of Frauenhofer. The great astronomer J. F. W. Herschel, the eletrician Wheatstone, William Henry Fox Talbot, Sir David Brewster and others remarked on various similar phenomena in spectral experimentation, but none succeeded in finding the clue to the mystery. Many famous men between 1850 and 1860 turned their attention to this riddle.

Herschel pointed out that metals, when rendered incandescent under the flame of the blowpipe, exhibited various tints. He further suggested that as the color thus shown was distinctive for each metal, it might be possible by these means to work out a new system of analysis.

Bunsen and Kirchoff in 1860 discovered that each metal when in an incandescent state exhibited through the prism certain distinctive brilliant lines. They also found that these brilliant lines were identical in position with many of Frauenhofer's dark lines; or to put it more clearly, each bright line given by a burning metal found its exact counterpart in a dark line on the solar spectrum. It thus became evident that there was some subtle connection between these brilliant lines and the dark bands which had puzzled observers for so many years. Having this clue, experiments were pushed on with renewed vigor, until, by happy chance, the vapors of the burning metals were examined through the agency of the electric light. That is to say, the light from the electric lamp was permitted to shine through the vapor of the burning metal under examination, forming, so to speak, a background for the expected lines. It was now seen that what before were bright bands on a dark ground were now dark bands on a bright ground. This discovery of the reversal of the lines peculiar to a burning metal, when such metal was examined in the form of vapor, led to the enunciation of the great principle that "vapors of metals at a lower temperature absorb exactly those rays which they emit at a higher."

To make this important fact more clear, suppose that upon the red-hot cinders in an ordinary fire-grate is thrown a handful of saltpeter, also called nitrate of potash or more commonly niter. On looking through the spectroscope at the dazzling molten mass thus produced (instead of the colored ribbons which the sunlight gives) all is black, with the exception of a brilliant violet line at the one end of the spectrum and an equally brilliant red line at the other end. This is the spectrum peculiar to potassium; so that, if not previously aware of the presence of that metal, and if requested to name the source of the flame produced, the spectroscope would have enabled such answer without difficulty. Now suppose this burning saltpeter to be again examined under altered conditions. Place the red-hot cinders in a shovel and remove them to the open air, throwing upon them a fresh supply of the niter. If the vapor now be examined while the sunlight forms a background to it, it will be seen that the two bright colored lines have given place to dark ones. This experiment will prove the truth of Kirchhoff's law so far as potassium is concerned, for the molten mass first gave the bright lines, and afterward by examining the cooler vapor it was evident that they were transformed to bands of darkness; in other words they were absorbed.

The simple glass prism as used by Newton, altho it is the parent of the modern spectroscope, bears very little resemblance to its gifted successor. The complicated and costly instrument now used consists of a train of several prisms, through which the ray of light under examination can be passed by reflection more than once. By these means greater dispersion is gained; that is to say, the resulting spectrum is longer, and consequently far easier of examination

Since the middle of the nineteenth century the analytical eye of this wonderful instrument has looked into the material universe and aided the chemist to the discovery of elements previosuly unsuspected and unknown. It has shown the composition of sun and stars, by the correspondence of their spectra with those of terrestrial matter, to be in general identical with that of the earth. Nor are its services to be measured merely in qualitative units, for, in examining incandescent bodies, by a careful study of the absorption lines a very exact estimate of the "quantity" present can be arrived at. This method of analysis is so delicate that in experiments carried on at the mint a difference of one ten-thousandth part in an alloy has been recognized. Neither must it be supposed that the services of the spectroscope are confined to metals, for nearly all colored matter can also be subjected to its scrutiny. Even the most minute substances, when examined by the microscope in conjunction with the prism, show a particular spectrum by which they can always be identified.

While the spectroscope succeeded in proving that a certain yellow flame was the flame of sodium and a certain reddish flame was that of calcium, it did not show why the flame of one kind of substance should be brighter than another. The flame of burning wood, for instance, is less bright, generally speaking, than that of a burning kerosene lamp; the flame of phosphorus burning in oxygen is dazzling in its brilliancy; a ribbon of the metal magnesium (commonly used as a powder in flashlight photographs) burns in ordinary air with an intensely brilliant white light. The brightness of these flames cannot be due wholly to temperature, as has often been maintained, for there may be a solid such as iron or carbon burning in oxygen at a high temperature, with brilliant incandescence, or glowing, but without flame, while on the other hand the lambent flame of boric methide or of camphor shows that flame may exist without a high temperature. A piece of burning camphor, in fact, may easily be held in the unprotected palm by changing it from hand to hand—a trick sometimes resorted to by stage jugglers. Again, the ordinary Bunsen burner found in every chemical laboratory will produce, by adjusting the air supply, either a yellow, luminous flame of relatively low temperature, or a much hotter, non-luminous flame, whereas the temperature in the exceedingly brilliant electric arc is extreme, reaching in the electric furnace as high as 3,000 degrees Centigrade.

The real nature of flame was long a matter of conjecture. The "phlogiston" (fire-substance) of the eighteenth century, in fulfilment of the hope expressed by that erratic genius, Count Rumford, is today interred, it is true, in the same tomb with "caloric" (heat-substance). But the death of phlogiston did not bring with it the explanation of the luminosity of flame. Sir Humphrey Davy—inventor of the Davy Safety Lamp—regarded the luminosity as due to the incandescence of solid particles suspended in the flame, and this theory, until about the middle of the nineteenth century, went unchallenged. The presence of solid particles, either in the flame itself or in immediate contact with the burning gas, was held to be essential.

There is no doubt that the introduction of solid particles in a fine state of division into a flame of feeble luminosity will usually impart to it a considerable degree of brilliancy by the incandescence of the solid particles, or perhaps in some cases by reflection of the light from their many surfaces, and it is usual to refer to the black deposit which is formed upon a glass rod or similar body, when held in the flame of a candle or gas, as a proof that such flames contain solid particles.

Nevertheless luminous effects have been produced where the solid particle hypothesis could not account for them, such, for example, as the luminosity of the flame of hydrogen burning in oxygen under pressure; moreover, in many of the brightest flames the temperature is such that fuliginous matter could not exist in them. In many cases it seemed, therefore, to be a more satisfactory explanation, that the luminosity of flames depends on the existence of a comparatively high temperature and on the presence of gases or vapors of considerable density.

The effect of high temperature is seen in the greater brightness of the flames of sulphur, phosphorus, and, indeed, all substances when burnt in pure oxygen, as compared with the result of their combustion in air. Direct evidence of the effect of high temperature is also afforded by the combustion of phosphorus in chlorine, for while at ordinary temperatures only a feeble light is produced by this combustion, strongly heated phosphorus vapor burns in hot chlorine with a dazzling white light.

A comparison of the relative densities of gases and vapors shows that the brightest flames in general are those which contain the densest vapors.

Hydrogen burning in chlorine produces a vapor more than twice as heavy as that resulting from its combustion in oxygen, and the light produced in the former case is stronger than in the latter. Carbon and sulphur burning in oxygen produce vapors of still greater density, and their combustion gives a still brighter light. Phosphorus, also, which has a very dense vapor, and yields, in burning, a product of great vapor density, burns in oxygen with a brilliancy almost blinding.

The luminosity of a flame is increased by compressing around it the surrounding gaseous atmosphere, and it is diminished by rarefying it. Thus, mixtures of hydrogen and carbonic oxide with oxygen emit but little light when they are burnt or exploded in free air, but exhibit intense luminosity when exploded in closed vessels so as to prevent expansion of the gases at the moment of combustion.

The density, then, of the gases formed in combustion, and the temperature at which combustion takes place, were thus held by some physicists, notably E. Frankland, to be the sole determining factors in the brilliancy of a flame. As for the particles of solid matter, it is known that while in some instances they may increase the luminosity, in other cases they produce the opposite effect, rendering the flame less bright. All these known facts were thought during the latter half of the nineteenth century completely to have disposed of the solid particle idea in the brightness of flames. As a matter of fact, it is evident that the "dense vapor" theory advocated by E. Frankland and others, while it adds interesting information to what already is known of the nature of flame, does not in the least disprove the fact that a flame is bright when it contains particles of solid glowing carbon, and it is not luminous when it does not.

Such brilliant and thorough investigators as Heumann, Burch, Smithells, Techla, and especially Vivian B. Lewes, established the fact toward the end of the century that in the burning of ordinary illuminating gas that remarkable illuminant acetylene is first formed and subsequently decomposed. Lewes' careful experimentation showed that in the dark part of the flame there occurs a transformation of gases, and that at the point where luminosity just begins seventy to eighty per cent. of the compounds formed is acetylene, and this in a gas flame in which less than one per cent. of acetylene is originally present. Immediately above this point the increasing heat of the flame breaks up the acetylene gas into its two constituents, carbon and hydrogen. The hydrogen burns in contact with the oxygen of the air. The carbon is heated to incandescence by the combined influence of the burning hydrogen and the so-called "latent heat" of the chemical separation—hence the flame.

The real nature of flame is even to-day very commonly misapprehended. A popular idea exists that wood burns. Wood, strictly speaking, does not any more burn in air than it floats in water. The flames seen burning at the surface of a wood fire are due to the combustion of volatilized solid material, and their luminosity is generally conceded to-day to be due, as above shown, to the presence of finely divided particles of glowing carbon. Dr. Percy has accurately defined flame thus: "Ordinary flame is gas or vapor of which the surface, in contact with atmospheric air, is burning with the emission of light." This definition leaves little to be desired, for it very properly directs attention to the gas or vapor necessary to a flame, as well as to the fact that the flame itself is hollow.

Dr. Robert Montgomery Bird has summed up the essential teachings of modern study of flame briefly as follows:

When the hydrocarbon gas leaves the jet at which it is burned those portions which come in contact with the air are consumed and form a wall of flame, which surrounds the issuing gases. The unburnt gas in its passage through the lower heated area undergoes a number of chemical changes, brought about by the heat radiated from the flame walls; the principal change being the conversion of hydrocarbons into acetylene, hydrogen and methane. The temperature of the flame rapidly increases with the distance from the jet, and reaches a point at which it is high enough to decompose acetylene into carbon and hydrogen with a rapidity almost that of an explosion. The latent heat so suddenly set free is localized by the proximity of carbon particles, which by absorbing it become incandescent and emit the larger part of the light given out by the flame; altho the heat of combustion causes them to glow somewhat until they come into contact with oxygen and are consumed. This external heating gives rise to little of the light.

There have been opponents to this theory of the cause of luminosity —as there are, fortunately, of all theories—but the evidence is so strong and covers so many points, and so many investigators have confirmed one part or another of the work, that it has been generally accepted as a true statement of the facts with which it deals.

Visible light, as Frauenhofer long since pointed out, reaches the eye in vibrations numbering from 4,000 to 7,000 billion per second.

THE NATURE OF LIGHT

No other vibrations are useful to us for seeing purposes, for no others have any effect upon the retina of the eye. The analysis of the apparently white light of the sun and the combining of the spectral colors so formed to reproduce white light dates back to the time of Newton. Frauenhofer, however, devised a means of studying the solar spectrum without a prism. On plates of glass he ruled very fine parallel lines very close together, making the first grating. The beautiful iridescence of such substances as mother-of-pearl has been shown by the simple microscope to be due to a multitude of fine lines in the surface, the refracting edges of which disperse the prismatic colors like any true prism. Such a surface was the grating of Frauenhofer, and the great advantage of this instrument over the prism lay in the fact that the lower part of the spectrum where the red rays occur was very much spread out, whereas the simple prism dispersed the red end of the spectrum so little that examination of its characteristics was rendered difficult. Frauenhofer also experimented successfully with gratings made of very fine wire, .04 to .6 mm. (.002 to .03 inch) in thickness.

By the aid of similar gratings, John William Draper, of New York, not only confirmed the measurements of the light waves which Frauenhofer had made, but determined the temperature (525° C.) at which all solid and liquid substances become incandescent and glow with a red heat. He proved also that below this red heat invisible rays are emitted whose vibration lengths may be measured. Lewis Morris Rutherford, whose magnificent work in radio-activity has rendered him justly famous, produced other and better gratings made of thin sheets of metal, and Henry A. Rowland, of Johns Hopkins University, within very recent years ruled gratings so fine that they contained more than 100,000 lines to the inch—from fifty to a hundred in the width of a fine human hair—gratings which have never been surpassed. With the aid of these wonderfully fine gratings Rowland has prepared large photographic maps of the solar spectrum and prepared a system of standard wave lengths universally adopted. The wave length of every line in the solar spectrum has been measured through this means, and there are few of the common terrestrial elements which have not now been identified in the atmosphere of the sun.

The discovery of the invisible rays below the red of the solar spectrum dates back to Sir William Herschel, who in 1800 determined their existence by means of a thermometer. He noticed that the thermometer rose regularly when it was moved from the violet toward the red end of the spectrum, and it occurred to him to try the region beyond the extremes of the visible colors. To his delight he found a regular series of radiations below the red. "It is sometimes of great use in natural philosophy," the great astronomer observed, "to doubt of things that are commonly taken for granted, especially as the means of resolving any doubt, when once it is entertained, are often within our reach."

"This discovery," says Thomas Young in his "Lectures" of 1807, "must be allowed to be one of the greatest that has been made since the days of Newton." Yet the majority of physicists failed for more than half a century to see the importance of this discovery of Herschel. It was only a few years after the discovery by Herschel of infra-red radiation from the sun that Johann Wilhelm Ritter and Wollaston proved the existence of dark chemical rays in the ultra-violet region of the spectrum. Macedonio Melloni, the inventor with Leopoldi Nobili of the thermopile, was the first to arrive at a thoro realization of the identity of radiant heat and light. "Light," said he, "is merely a series of calorific indications sensible to the organs of sight, or vice versa, the radiations of obscure heat are veritable invisible radiations of light." He argued that where there is light of any sort there must be some heat, and moonlight ought to show some heat effects. He experimented, at first unsuccessfully, in this direction, but finally with a lens more than three feet in diameter succeeded in getting feeble indications of heat from the rays of the moon. The thermopile which he used was a simple instrument based on the well-known principle that a cold wire is, in general, a better conductor of electricity than a warm wire. Hence any simple galvanometer or other current-measuring apparatus showed by a deflection of the needle when any part of the electric conductor was heated.

The measurements of radiant heat made by Melloni in solids and liquids were paralleled by the investigations of Tyndall upon the diathermancy of gases. Tyndall possessed extraordinary powers of popularizing difficult scientific subjects. His first great lecture, delivered in 1853 in England, took his audience by storm. He came to America and delivered in 1872 and 1873 several lectures on light which were enthusiastically received. His famous "Belfast Address" brought upon the brilliant Irishman the charge of "infidelity," for he was as independent in thought as outspoken in expression and held ever to the principle that Truth has nothing to fear from its enemies.

Tyndall pointed out (as had Melloni before him) an error of wide prevalence concerning the influence of color and absorption. Benjamin Franklin records of himself that having placed patches of different-colored cloth of the same weight upon snow and allowed the sun to shine upon them, he found that they absorbed the solar rays to different degrees and sank to different depths in the snow. He concluded from this experiment that dark colors were the best absorbers and light colors the worst. For the visible rays of the sun this conclusion is in general true, but the solar rays consist of radiations running outside the visible spectrum, about seven times the length of the solar spectrum having been detected in the infrared radiations, and perhaps twice as much as is visible in the invisible ultra-violet.

The visible spectrum of "white" light has been shown by recent measurements to be only about one-tenth of the actual measurable solar spectrum. In the invisible region of the spectrum effects are often observed which are the exact opposite of those seen in the prismatic spectrum. Tyndall proved this in a clever manner. He coated the bulb of a delicate mercury thermometer with the white powdered alum and the bulb of a second thermometer with powdered iodine. Exposing both bulbs at the same distance to the radiations from an ordinary gas jet, he found the alum-coated thermometer rose nearly twice as high as the other; alum was a better absorber than iodine. "The radiation," he remarked, "from the clothes which cover the human body is not at all, to the extent sometimes supposed, dependent on their color. The color of animals' fur is equally incompetent to influence radiation."

Some of the first results of the invention of Langley's bolometer were to show that the maximum heat of the solar spectrum is in the orange, not in the infra-red, as Herschel had supposed. It proved, moreover, that the white light from the sun is not the sum total of the solar radiations—that the sun's true color is blue and only the orange veil of the terrestrial atmosphere works through its selective absorption on sunlight letting through the red rays and absorbing the blue, to produce the effect of white. Strictly speaking, we should say with Professor Langley that the atmosphere absorbs all the colors, but selectively taking out more orange than red, more green than orange, more blue than green. "As there are really an infinite number of shades of color in the spectrum," says Langley, ". . . it is merely for brevity that we now unite the more refrangible colors under the general word 'blue,' and the others under the corresponding terms 'orange' or 'red.'"

Newton showed that white light is compounded of blue, red, and other colors; by turning a colored wheel rapidly all blend into a grayish white. Arrange them so that there is too much blue, and the combined result is a very bluish white, that of the original sun ray. Alter the proportion of colors so as to virtually take out the excess of blue, and the result is colorless or white light. White, then, is not necessarily made by combining the "seven colors," or any number of them, unless they are there in just proportion (which is in effect what Newton himself says); and white, then, may be made out of such a bluish light as we have described, not by putting anything to it, but by taking away the excess which is there already.

Langley and T. W. Very showed by studying the radiations of the firefly "that it is possible to produce light without heat, other, than that in the light itself; that this is actually effected now by nature's process; that nature produces this cheapest light at about one four-hundredth part of the cost of the energy which is expended in the candle flame, and at but an insignificant fraction of the cost of the electric light."

Langley showed also that the amount of energy necessary to produce the sense of color varies enormously with the color. The sensation of red, for example, requires that the energy of the waves which enter the eye shall be 100,000 times as great as the energy necessary to produce the impression of green. Far down below the visible red of the solar spectrum the delicate filament of Langley's bolometer groped its way until a point was reached at which the solar radiations seem to be suddenly cut off. From terrestrial sources, however, he obtained still further wave lengths which exceeded in length .03 of a millimeter (or more than .001 of an inch).

Rubens and Nichols, using a modified form of Crookes' radiometer, found still longer wave lengths, equal to about 1/100 the length of the shortest Hertzian waves. Thus radiations of almost every length, from the great electric oscillations of Hertz several miles long down to the ultra-violet rays less than .000009 of an inch, have been definitely measured. Enormous strides have been made in the measurement of all kinds of radiations, thanks to the invention of the Hertz receiver—the "electric eye," as Sir W. Thompson calls it—a simple instrument, "nothing but a bit of wire or a pair of bits of wire adjusted so that when immersed in strong electric radiations they give minute sparks across a microscopic air gap." Thus Sir Oliver Lodge. It was the theory of that great mathematician James Clerk-Maxwell, that light and electricity are fundamentally one, upon which Hertz conducted his studies leading to the production of those wonderful waves which to-day, through the improvements of Marconi, convey messages a thousand miles through empty air. In a lecture delivered a few years before the close of the nineteenth century Lodge said of such oscillations:

"Light is an electro-magnetic disturbance of the ether. Optics is a branch of electricity. Outstanding problems in optics are being rapidly solved now that we have the means of definitely exciting light with a full perception of what we are doing and of the precise mode of its vibration.

"It remains to find out how to shorten down the waves—to hurry up the vibration until the light becomes visible. Nothing is wanted but quicker modes of vibrations. Smaller oscillators must be used —very much smaller—oscillators not much bigger than molecules. In all probability—one may almost say certainly—ordinary light is the result of electric oscillation in the molecules of hot bodies, or sometimes of bodies not hot—as in the phenomenon of phosphorescence.

"Any one looking at a common glowworm must be struck with the fact that not by ordinary combustion, nor yet on the steam engine and dynamo principle is that easy light produced.

"So soon as we clearly recognize," he concludes, "that light is an electric vibration, so soon shall we begin to beat about for some mode of exciting and maintaining an electrical vibration of any required degree of rapidity. When this has been accomplished the problem of lighting will have been solved."

CHAPTER IX

SOUND

THERE is no more general instinct in man than the love of the music of Nature. Often, too, the light accents of almost inaudible sounds are more eloquent and persuasive than the louder vibrations heard in a world where every smallest particle of matter vibrates. The whole physical universe is but a fathomless ocean of vibrations, altho only a few of these appear as audible sound. Yet in human history no physical sense has had such fateful influence as that of hearing. The vocal Memnon of Egypt, the oracles of Greece, the war-trumpets of Rome, the vibrant harp-strings of the Scandinavian skald, the shrill call of the bagpipes, the booming tree-drums of the South American Indians, the violin of Rouget de Lisle, the triumphant crash of the modern regimental band or massed symphony orchestra, finally the human voice in all time—it needs but a glance at a few such examples to prove how surpassing is the influence of the sounds that impinge upon the ear of the mind.

It is said that Apollo was once wandering along the shore of the Mediterranean Sea, and found there the shell of a dead turtle with a few strings of dried flesh stretched across it. He held it up and delighted himself with the musical sound which it made in the wind. He plucked the strings, and found they made a pleasing sound together. Such was the origin of the lyre. Pythagoras constructed on this model an instrument of a single string—the monochord—which was capable of producing notes of various pitch. The string was stretched above a board, and running over a bridge was attached to weights by means of which the tension on the string could be adjusted.

Strange theories the Greeks had as to the nature of sound. Not the least curious of these theories was that enunciated by Alcmaeon of Crotona, who wrote: "We hear with the ear because it contains a vacuum"! Little as they knew of what is called to-day the science of sound, however, the Greeks carried the theory of music to a high degree of development. They were familiar with the diatonic scale of C and wrote massive bass melodies, using the natural notes, these melodies being classified as "modes," according to the note upon which the melody ended. They had six such modes ending on every note of the scale except the seventh. The accompaniment was put in above the melody in a manner exactly the reverse of that now generally in use. The so-called Ioman Mode corresponded to the modern scale of C natural, the Mixolydian to that of G natural, the Æolian to the scale of A minor. These same modes, adopted from the Greek by St. Ambrose and added to by St. Gregory, became the basis of many of the grand melodies still extant in the ritual of the Catholic Church. The Greeks also recognized three genera or varieties of modulation— the Diatonic, the Chromatic and the Enharmonic. The latter contained intervals smaller than a semi-tone—the least difference of pitch to which modern ears are accustomed. The peripatetic school of philosophers held that the higher the pitch of a sound the greater was its velocity; they also believed that the source of a sound determined the speed of its transmission, errors which were not disproved until early in the seventeenth century.

Oracles played an important part in the history of Grecian development, as in fact in that of most ancient nations. The simple device of a speaking tube made it possible to produce those mysterious voices whose supernatural revelations so swayed the imagination of an unsophisticated people. Such were the cryptic and potent utterances of the famous Greek oracle at Delphi. To the modern mind, accustomed to wonder at nothing, to explain everything, the faith of men in the oracular utterances of antiquity seems as barbarous, childish; yet the roar of trains and machinery, the whistles, bells and rattling wheels of commerce cannot drown the quiet voice of the savant, the man who knows. The oracle still speaks, but speaks to-day from the mysterious retirement of the laboratory with an authority as absolute as that which bids the Athenians defend their city with wooden walls.

It is apparent that the multitude of sounds which reach the ear must be conveyed to it by some material medium. In most cases this medium is the air; indeed, the striking fact has long since been pointed out that but for this atmospheric ocean the world would be plunged for us in perpetual silence. The bell-jar experiment of Francis Hauksbee, made in the seventeenth century, proved that no sound is audible in a vacuum. The ringing of a bell became rapidly fainter when the air was exhausted from the bell-jar under which it was placed.

The fact that air is not the only conductor of sound nor the best is well known. Tapping a table, the sound is heard much more distinctly when the ear is placed close to the wood; the Indian places his ear near the ground to note the sound of approaching footsteps; an oncoming train is heard through the rails long before the sound of it reaches through the air; the detonation of a distant explosion comes with a double shock, the sound traveling faster through the earth than through the air. In general, then, the more dense the medium is, the better conductor does it become of sound waves. Liquids transmit the vibrations of sound better than gases. Stones clapped together under water produce a sharp stunning effect upon the ear placed under water to hear them. The bell signals installed on the American coast give practical evidence of the superior transmitting power of water over air.

The velocity of sound in air was investigated in the sixteenth century by Martin Mersenne. Noting the difference in time between the flash and the report of fire-arms at known distances, he got 1,380 feet feet per second as the speed of propagation of sound waves. This result was far from accurate. Pierre Gassendi, making similar experiments, used guns large and small and disproved the Aristotelian theory that the velocity of sound was dependent upon source and pitch. To any one indeed in modern days this idea of the peripatetic school must appear absurd, for the pitch and the source of sounds from a modern orchestra are as various as musical genius can make them, yet when played together the sounds of all reach the ear at the same moment.

That the source of sound does not affect the speed of its transmission is not, however, universally true. Captain Parry, on his Arctic expedition, found that violently loud sounds would travel faster than softer ones. During artillery practice it was shown that by persons at distance from the guns the report of the latter was heard before the command of the officer to fire. In a series of experiments upon the velocity of sound in rocks Mallet showed that with a charge of 2,000 pounds of gunpowder the average velocity of the sound of a blast was 967 feet per second, while a charge of 12,000 pounds produced a speed of transmission of 1,210 per second. Through iron the speed of sound has been shown to be still faster. M. Biot, experimenting with an iron tube 3,120 feet long, found the speed of sound through this tube to be 9 or 10 times as fast as in air. It is now generally conceded that the speed of sound in iron is actually about five times as fast as in air and through water about four times as fast.

The great law of Inverse Squares which has been shown to be so general in physics applies also to Sound. If four bells of the same kind are placed at a distance of 20 yards from the ear and another at a distance of 10 yards the single bell produces a sound as loud as that of the four. How far a sound is audible depends upon its loudness. The report of a volcano at St. Vincent was heard at Demerara, 300 miles away, and the cannons of the siege of Liège in Belgium in 1914 were audible in London.

The study of sound in music, the classification of tones and their combination reached a high point of development long before any complete analysis had been made of the cause of sound and the manner of its transmission. About the end of the seventeenth century Joseph Sauveur, a poor adventurer who found his way on foot to Paris seeking his fortune, became professor of mathematics at the Collège Royal. He published important papers on the discovery of "overtones" in strings, using paper riders to locate the points of greatest and least motion when the strings were set in vibration. He had observed and explained the phenomenon of sympathetic vibration. From the "beats" produced by organ pipes of nearly equal lengths he determined the vibration rates of the notes given forth by each. Two pipes were tuned in the ratio of 24÷25. When air was blown into these four beats per second were observed, from which Sauveur concluded that the higher pitched pipe was producing 100 vibrations per second.

The experiments of William Noble and Thomas Pigott at Oxford had proved that the vibration of a string is greatest at the center and that it may also be made to vibrate in halves, thirds, fourths, fifths, etc. The strings of a harp or piano, for example, vibrate chiefly as a whole—that is, throughout their entire length. The harder the string is plucked or struck, the louder is the sound and the more ample is the motion of the string. Thus amplitude of vibration was seen to be a determining factor in the loudness of a sound.

Not only nearness and amplitude of vibration, but echo as well may increase the intensity of a sound. Speaking tubes, megaphones and such devices depending upon this principle were in use long before the theory of sound was generally understood. The effect here is evidently one of reinforcement by echo, which in smooth tubes is so great that M. Biot observed that a conversation could be carried on in a low tone through a small tube 1,040 yards long. For very long distances, however, it is evident that the speaking tube is not a practicable device, as it would require 8 minutes for the sound to travel from one town to another 100 miles away—less than 1/10 of the distance easily and instantly bridged to-day by the wireless telegraph.

The "father of acoustics" introduced about the end of the eighteenth century a new chapter in the study of sound. Ernst Florens Friedrich Chladni, educated for the law, proved himself a much better scientist than lawyer. He experimented with vibrating plates covered with sand. The collection of the sand at the nodes, or points of least vibration, formed the famous "figures of Chladni." These were exhibited before Napoleon, and the conqueror of Europe presented him with 6,000 francs to enable him to translate into French his Akustik. Chladni invented a torsional pendulum in which the motive force of gravity was replaced by the molecular resistance of a rod to the effect of twisting; he made many calculations of the absolute rate of vibration of sounding bodies and determined the velocity of sound in other gases than air by filling organ pipes with the gas and noting the resulting pitch.

Felix Savart, the greatest master of his time in the theory of sound, invented a simple but effective instrument to show that the vibration rate of a body is the sole factor in the pitch of the note which it produces. A toothed wheel was made to rotate rapidly against the edge of a card. By increasing or decreasing the speed of rotation the pitch of the note produced could be raised or lowered at will. A dial indicated the number of shocks per second made by the teeth of the wheel striking the card.

Caignard Latour invented about the same time an instrument often heard to-day in connection with steam whistles—the siren—so called because it could produce sounds audible in water as well as in air. A current of air blown through holes in a swiftly revolving disk produced notes which could be regulated to give any desired pitch. This apparatus of Latour was used by Savart with certain improvements to determine the limits of audible sounds. He found that he could hear tones of bodies vibrating at the rate of 48,000 per second. The lower limit of audible vibration he placed at 16 or 14 per second. With the same velocity the siren gives the same sound in water as in air and all gases. Thus the number of vibrations per second, irrespective of the material of the vibrating body, was proved to be the sole factor in determining pitch. It is interesting to note that the siren has been applied to find the rapidity of motion in the buzzing wings of insects. The tiny gauze pinions of the gnat have thus been found to vibrate 15,000 times in a second.

About the middle of the last century was invented an instrument so similar to the human ear that it deserves some attention. E. Léon Scott produced an apparatus which he called the Phonautograph, so beautifully constructed as to register not only the vibrations produced by solid bodies, but also those produced by wind-instruments, by the voice in singing, and even such noises as that of thunder or the report of a gun. A small cask of plaster of Paris, perhaps a foot and a half long, was closed at one end but for a small circular space over which was fitted a flexible membrane. Plaster of Paris was selected on account of its absence of elasticity and its very slight susceptibility to vibration. A stylus or blunt needle in contact with the membrane recorded the vibrations of the latter upon a revolving cylinder. A movable piece, called the subdivider, enables the experimenter to adjust at will the arrangement of the lines of greatest and least vibration. Comparing the ellipsoid cask with the auditory canal, the stretched membrane with the tympanum or drum of the ear and the subdivider with the chain of little bones which touch the tympanum, the likeness of this instrument to the organ of hearing becomes singularly apparent.

Before the researches of Savart it was generally assumed that sounds above 18,000 per second and below 32 per second were inaudible to human ears. M. Despretz, investigating the same subject, disputed Savart's results, maintaining that the higher and lower limits of audible sounds were respectively 73,700 vibrations and 32 vibrations per second. It is probable that the ears even of trained experts will vary greatly in their sensibility to sounds of extreme pitch. The intensity of a sound will also evidently make it audible when another less intense sound of the same pitch cannot be heard at all.

The question of the quality of sounds was first clearly explained by the great Helmholtz. His "Lehre von den Tonemfindungen" has gone through many German and English editions. This wonderful investigator, mathematician and physicist showed that musical tones were due to regularity of vibration, discordant tones to irregularity. Musical tones he distinguished by their Intensity, Pitch and Quality. The Quality of a sound he found depended upon the number of "upper partials," or "overtones," present in the vibration of any body. The electrician Georg S. Ohm was the first to point out that there is only one form of vibration which will give rise to no "overtones," but consists only of the fundamental note. This was the vibration peculiar to the pendulum and tuning fork. Helmholtz's experiments showed analytically the composition of vowel qualities, how the infinite subtleties of inflection in the human voice are due not so much to the loudness or softness of the instrument as to the number and position of these upper tones present with and sounding with the fundamental. "If only the unevenly numbered partials," says he, "are present (as in narrow stopped organ pipes, piano strings struck in their middle points, and clarinets), the quality of tone is hollow, and, when a large number of such upper partials are present, nasal. When the prime tone predominates the quality of tone is rich, but when the prime tone is not sufficiently superior in strength to the upper partials the quality of tone is poor." Helmholtz designed a series of glass globes, "resonators," which he had made of such size as to correspond with the vibration numbers of the upper partials of a given fundamental tone. When the fundamental tone was sounded, he held each one of these resonators to his ear, and if that particular overtone were present it would at once be reinforced and exposed by the resonator. Thus he proved beyond question the fact that it is the overtones of any given note which lend to it its peculiar character, tone-color or timbre.

Rudolf König, the eminent instrument maker of Paris, constructed a series of resonators which were an improvement upon the design of Helmholtz. He made his resonators cylindrical in form, having over one end a close-fitting cap, by means of which the cylinder could be drawn out and tuned to a nicety. Then he conceived the brilliant idea of arranging these resonators on a frame connected with a manometric mirror, whereby the presence of each and every overtone could be instantly detected by the dentations of the flame.

But Helmholtz was not content with the analysis of tones according to their quality. He verified his results by the synthesis of the same tones from their constituents. By means of a series of electromagnets he succeeded in making all possible combinations of overtones and producing notes of every quality.

Professor Ganot's Eléments de Physique thus summarizes the facts which the inestimably valuable researches of Helmholtz have contributed to the study of tone-color:

1. Simple tones, as those produced by a tuning-fork with a resonance box, and by wide covered pipes, are soft and agreeable without any roughness, but weak, and in the deeper notes dull.

2. Musical sounds accompanied by a series of harmonies, say up to the sixth, in moderate strength are full and musical. In comparison with simple tones they are grander, richer and more sonorous. Such are the sounds of open organ pipes, of the pianoforte, etc.

3. If only the uneven harmonics are present, as in the case of narrow covered pipes, of pianoforte strings struck in the middle, clarinets, etc., the sound becomes indistinct; and when a greater number of harmonics are audible the sound acquires a nasal character.

4. If the harmonics beyond the sixth and seventh are very distinct the sound becomes sharp and rough. If less strong, the harmonics are not prejudicial to the musical usefulness of the notes. On the contrary, they are useful as imparting character and expression to the music. Of this kind are most stringed instruments and most pipes furnished with tongues, etc. Sounds in which the harmonics are particularly strong acquire thereby a peculiarly penetrating character, such as those yielded by brass instruments.

M. Jul. Ant. Lissajous designed a method of tracing by means of a stylus the vibrations of two tuning forks, known as "Lissajous figures." Nathaniel Bowditch, of Salem, Mass., had also previously to Lissajous' experiments succeeded in producing the same figures.

From the evidence of the researches of Helmholtz it is evident that a pure tone is almost never heard. The notes of a violin, or of a beautiful voice, or of piano sound, it is true, like simple tones. They are not simple—in fact, the most pleasing tones which can be heard are as a rule very complex. A note struck on the piano sounds forth simultaneously a number of other notes. These may not at first appear, but if the note struck is held down for a few minutes even the untrained ear will infallibly distinguish other notes of higher pitch which seem to take shape and stand forth separately from the sounding interior of the instrument. These auxiliary tones are frequently classed under the general head of "harmonics." Helmholtz called them "upper partials." Tyndall gave them the name of "overtones." The strings of a violin or 'cello may likewise be made to produce different notes by setting them into vibration with the bow in the usual way and merely touching the vibrating string at various points. Violin soloists become phenomenally skilled in the use of these harmonics, which can be produced with equal readiness on the stopped or on the open strings. The same effects may be observed in a piano if the string happens to be accessible. From any string under tension harmonic effects may be obtained. Let the A string of a 'cello, for example, be bowed and at the same time lightly touched in the middle by a finger. A note will at once appear which is the octave above the open string, and the string will be seen to be vibrating in two sections in place of one. A paper rider will remain quiet when placed in the middle of the string, but if the latter is made to vibrate throughout its whole length the rider will be violently thrown off. Again, the string may be divided by a touch and made to vibrate in thirds or fourths or fifths. Dividing the string in thirds is clearly equivalent to multiplying its vibration number by 3. Each of these divisions will therefore give out a note whose vibrations are three times as frequent as those of the fundamental; in musical terms this note is said to be an octave and a fifth above the open string. If the vibration number of the A string be taken at 213 vibrations per second, the octave and fifth (E′) will then vibrate three times as frequently, giving 639 vibrations per second. (These figures, while not quite accurate, are close enough to illustrate by a rough computation how the values of harmonics were determined.) Dividing the same string of 213 vibrations per second into four parts, a note is obtained two octaves above the open string (A′), and the vibration number of this note will, in the same manner, be four times that of the fundamental, giving therefore the number 852. The division of the string into fifths produces a note which has five times the vibration frequency of the fundamental. This note will prove to be C″♯—two octaves and a third above the original note. A little careful experimentation will show that several still higher harmonics may readily be produced by this one string. The harmonics produced by sounding a note on the piano and listening for its overtones will usually appear the wrong order, the higher harmonics, on account of their more dissonant relation with the fundamental coming to the fore first.

The natural series of overtones follow in whole tones after the seventh. But none of these are exactly in tune, and after the G″ A″ B″ C‴♯ have been passed a partial tone appears which cannot be located by the notation in common use to-day.

In the pitch generally recognized by physicists C′ has a vibration frequency of 256 per second. "International Standard Pitch," so called, is made slightly higher than this, in the endeavor to lend a more brilliant quality to the instruments. The pitch of a given note, therefore, is not always constant. A brief consideration, however, will show that not only is this the case, but that the tone-relations of a note are not constant, and that the same note in different natural scales must have a different vibration-rate. The fact is that the natural scale in use to-day is not natural, but artificial; the diatonic scale is not diatonic. For purposes of modulation it became necessary to "temper" the natural series of notes which would occur as overtones from a given fundamental. Thus the "perfect fifth" (G) above the note C is actually about 1/50 of a semi-tone flat, and the F next below it is made sharp to a still greater extent, while the other notes of the scale are tempered more than these. A perfectly "tuned" piano has not a single note (excepting the octaves) in tune. The complex nature of the apparently simple major scale may easily be made apparent.

The scale from C to C' has in it eight natural notes (white) and five "accidentals" (black). Excluding the octave, this makes then twelve notes. Theoretically, the major scale was originally derived from the first few overtones of a given fundamental. All the natural notes of the scale, except the seventh, are found in the overtones of the note C. But the interval from the first to the second note of the scale is not the same as the interval from the second to the third. The introduction of minor melodies and a minor scale made the problem still more difficult, for the ratio between E♭ in the "perfect" scale and C is not at all the ratio between D♯ in the "perfect" scale and the same note C. Consequently D♯ and E♭ must both be altered to some intermediate note, since in an instrument (like the piano) of fixed pitch the same key must be struck to represent both these notes. The problem was finally solved by dividing the notes from C to its octave above (C') into twelve equal steps or intervals, and by this means producing a "tempered" scale of which the notes, black or white, could be played in any key. For this instrument so tuned Johann Sebastian

	NATURAL	TEMPERED
c	24	24
c♯ d♭	..	25.43
d	27	26.94
d♯ e♭	..	28.55
e	30	30.25
f	32	32.05
f♯ g♭	..	33.96
g	36	35.98
g♯ a♭	..	38.12
a	40	40.38
a♯ b♭	..	42.80
b	45	45.33
c	48	48

Bach, the greatest of all great composers, wrote his Das Wohltemperirte Klavier, showing that with these fixed and tempered notes music could be played in any key whatsoever. It is related of the great Handel that he could not bear to hear music played in the tempered scale, and had constructed for himself an organ provided with keys to produce every one of the notes theoretically necessary for a perfect scale. This would really require a keyboard containing about twenty notes to the octave, and more than this if such accidentals as double sharps and flats be accurately represented! A glance at the accompanying table will show how each note of the tempered scale compares with its true value in the natural scale.

It is a problem for the "musical" physicist of the future to devise a keyboard adapted to play in perfect tune the perfect scale in every key.

Musical instruments are among the earliest recorded human inventions. In the Hebrew scriptures mention is made of one Jubal, who became "the father of all such as handle the harp and the organ." The Hebrews had many musical instruments—harps, trumpets and flutes of various styles. The Egyptian inscriptions likewise portray types of all these instruments. They developed also an organ, a set of panpipes with bellows. From the Phenicians the Greeks are said to have imitated the cithara, zither or lyre. The Sabeca of the Chaldeans was the precursor of the modern harp, the Psautêrin of the clavichord, from which evolved the modern piano. The bagpipes were known from the very beginning of history in Syria, Phenicia and Egypt. Such early instruments as these were designed rather to accompany singing and religious ritual than for solo performances. The use of instruments unaccompanied by the human voice is an essentially modern idea.

The infinite combinations of tone heard in a modern orchestra are the product of four main classes of instruments:

(1) The Strings.
(2) The Wood Wind Instruments.
(3) The Brass Instruments.
(4) The Percussion Instruments.

More than half of a well-balanced orchestra to-day is made up of stringed instruments—the Violin, Violas, 'Cellos and Bass Viols. As the latter three are identical in general construction with the violin, the difference being mainly one of size, a word concerning the latter will of course apply to all in this group.

The vibration of the strings alone of a violin, made by drawing a bow across them, would have so little resonant value that the sound would be almost inaudible and the instrument about as serviceable in an orchestra as a jew's-harp. The tone must therefore be reinforced, and this is done by the body of the violin, every part of which is forced into vibration when the strings vibrate. A just proportion in the construction of the violin "box" is the secret which the great

VIII

Cremona violin makers—the Guarnerii and Stradivarii—discovered. The wood must not be too thick, for the vibration then will be dull and smothered, nor too thin, for then the tone of the instrument lacks body, richness, mellowness. The material must be perfectly seasoned, so that no subsequent contraction of the fiber may strain and destroy the perfect proportion of the parts of the instrument. The adjustment of the bass-bar beneath the heaviest string and supporting one foot of the bridge; of the sound post which supports the other foot of the bridge; the adjustment, carving out and proportioning of the bridge itself; the length of neck and size of head; the varnish which fills and protects the surface of the wood; the shape of the body; the position, size and shape of the sound-holes—all these and other conditions affect the construction of a perfect instrument. By bowing nearer to or farther from the bridge the tone is made either bright or soft and mellow. If the vibration is excited near the bridge, a large number of the higher overtones are brought out; if farther away, the fundamental and primary overtones assume greater prominence, for the larger the segments in which the principal vibrations occur the less will the tone be affected by the higher partials. If the string is bowed too far from the bridge it loses its sonorous quality, and becomes feeble in tone. The violin string, therefore, is bowed at points which vary from ⅛ to 1/12 of the string-length from the bridge, and the instrument is thus able to produce more varieties of tone-color than are found in any other one instrument.

In the others of this class the quality of tone grows gradually more somber as the instruments increase in size and weight, and the greater size of string necessitates bowing farther from the bridge. Even the bass viol (or violone), however, may be used occasionally as a solo instrument, giving a magnificently rich, ponderous tone.

The production of sound in the brass instruments depends upon the use of overtones. The fundamental ("pedal") notes of these instruments are seldom heard. In the bugle, the simplest of the brasses, the second, third, fourth and fifth overtones are alone used. For example, a C bugle will produce among its natural overtones the notes G, C′, E′, G′, and with these four notes, by aid of a change of rhythm, all the military signals may be produced. A trombone, if in this key, would add to these notes the octave C. Here, however, a new principle is introduced—by means of the slide the length of the trombone tube may be increased. Suppose the slide to be pushed out about an inch and a half, it is clear that the pitch of the whole instrument will be lowered; it will give exactly the same series of overtones, but each will be found about a semi-tone below its original pitch, thus producing the notes F♯, B, D♯, F♯. (It should be noted that a trombone is exactly an octave lower than a bugle, cornet or trumpet in the same key). Pushing the slide out another inch and a half again lengthens the tube and again lowers the instrument a semi-tone, giving the series F, B♭, D, F. This is actually the key in which the orchestral trombone lies with slide closed. By repeating this process of lowering the slide all the semi-tones in the scale may be produced as far as the compass of the instrument extends. The pedal note of the trombone may similarly be lowered by means of the slide.

In all the brass instruments other than the slide trombone the overtones are lowered by means of finger valves which introduce different lengths of pipe into the vibrating tube. The trombone is not infrequently (especially in brass bands) provided with such valves in lieu of the slide, and the physical principal of the instrument then becomes identical with that of the French horn, cornet, trumpet and tuba.

The French horn produces a tone singularly soft among the brasses, sounding often more like some wood wind instrument. The quality of tone of this instrument has been explained on the basis of the conical bore of the tube and the immense bell at the end of it. The sound is softened and mellowed by the oblique reinforcement of echo from the walls of the tube. The trumpet, on the contrary, by far the most brilliant instrument in existence, is said to owe its superiority in this regard to the cylindrical bore and small bell of the tube. The vibrations are not lost as in the spreading walls of the French horn, cornet, etc.

The wood wind instruments are of three types. The flute and piccolo (or octave flute) are made to sound by the breath of the player blown across a hole in the instrument and striking the opposite edge. Different notes are produced by the keys, which open holes in the side of the flute, thus causing the air within to vibrate in various sections at the will of the player.

The oboe, English horn (or tenoroon) and bassoon have two thin reeds in the mouth-piece which set into vibration the column of air within the instrument. The extremely reedy tone of this instrument has caused it to be used a great deal for pastoral effects in what is called "descriptive" music. This penetrating, soft, but reedy quality, when brought down into the bass register as in the bassoon, has an effect sometimes ludicrous, sometimes terrifying, always peculiarly characteristic. The "flutes" of the Egyptians are believed by some authorities to have been in reality of the oboe type. It is probable that they frequently used reeds in the end of the pipes and that the latter would be classed to-day as either oboes or clarinets.

The clarinet principle is not essentially different from that of the oboe, except that it has one reed instead of two. The instrument is made in several pitches. A high clarinet in E♭ is much favored in band music, but appears seldom in orchestra. There are also a bass and an alto clarinet which are recognized by composers, these instruments being identical in principle with the A and B♭ clarinets of an orchestra. The quality of these instruments partakes of both the soft floating notes of the flute and the highly nasal character of the oboe.

Altho there is probably no instrument so primitive as the drum, yet the kettle drums of the modern orchestra are by no means primitive instruments. Their value is chiefly in the tremendous energy which they add to rhythmic effects, but they can also be tuned through a surprisingly wide range of notes, altho of low pitch and dull quality of tone, producing no definite musical tone-color. The copper hemisphere above which the sheepskin head is stretched acts on a perfect resonator, and the tone of the drum, partly on account of this large reflecting surface, has an amazing carrying power.

Of other percussion instruments, such as the cymbals, snare drum, tambourine, xylophone, etc., which have come down with little or no change from the earliest times, only passing mention need be made.

A familiar but very beautiful instrument, different in principle from any of those heretofore mentioned, is the Æolian harp. In this the strings are set in motion by the varying currents of wind upon them. Since no resonator reinforces the tone of the strings, the quality of the sound is exceeidngly soft and ethereal, altho distinct enough in point of pitch.

The mechanical phonograph may be mentioned here, for its exact reproduction of sound is the direct result of modern investigation into the vibrational character of sound-waves.

Sound, therefore, like Light and Heat, may be considered in a double aspect, that of the physicist and that of the artist or musician. The Laws of Physics cannot be considered merely as cold abstractions, for the reason that they are so intimately related to the esthetic interests of life and the advancement of human well-being. The better understanding of the Properties of Matter has led to this era of Mechanical Knowledge; the comprehension of the principles of heat has enabled man to obviate much climatic inclemency; the length of available time for labor and pleasure has been increased by artificial lighting, and speech is dependent upon the hearing of the Sound. And even yet the vast domain of these great subjects is scarcely known, but half explored, and the twentieth century waits to welcome the Newton of the future.

ELECTRICITY

By

Prof. Wm. J. Moore

ELECTRICITY

CHAPTER I

THE NATURE OF ELECTRICITY

So RAPIDLY have the applications of electricity to the wants of industry followed one another during the past thirty years that it may seem as tho the whole science had been practically developed in that time, and yet the real foundation work, which made the almost innumerable electrical contrivances of to-day possible, was mainly laid long before that period. It is Gilbert, Franklin, Volta, Galvani, Davy, Arago, Faraday, Maxwell, and many others, who have enabled the modern experts to put much of the science on a mathematical basis, and who made long strides toward the final goal which is still so far away—the answer to the question, What is Electricity?

Many are the philosophers who are still devoting their lives to it, and occasionally some fact is discovered which disarranges many existing ideas and leads to new and unexplored fields. The new theories which have been advanced, however, have striven rather to elucidate some unexplained points of the old theories than to disprove them.

Thales in 600 B.C., who discovered the attraction of amber for light bodies, said that amber had a soul. Gilbert, in 1600 A.D., is accredited with the following hypothesis: Friction, because it heats a body, causes it to emit rays of a subtle unctuous material, which is cooled again on coming into contact with the air, loses its expansive force, and draws itself together again, bringing back such light bodies as come in the way of the electrified body. According to Hauksbee, the emanations of matter which start from an electrified body spread in the form of rays or physical lines, which possess a kind of continuity in themselves so that those parts of each ray or line which reach out furthest into space receive the impulse from those parts which are nearest to the body.

The eighteenth century brought out two theories which for a time seemed to explain most of the phenomena then observed: one was the two-fluid theory of Symmer and the other the single-fluid theory of Franklin. Both these theories assumed electricity to be a fluid.

Franklin assumes the existence on one electric substance or fluid which attracts the particles of ordinary matter, but repels itself. In the ordinary state, bodies are charged with a normal quantity of this electrical substance. If this charge be either increased or decreased, the body becomes "electrified"; if it be increased, the body is charged with a "plus" or positive charge; if the body has a less quantity of electricity than in its normal state, it is said to be charged with a "minus" or negative charge.

The two-fluid theory thought out by Symmer supposes that instead of there being one fluid there are two fluids having opposite properties to each other. The molecules of either fluid repel one another, but attract those of the opposite kind of fluid. Bodies in their normal condition, or when unelectrified, contain equal quantities of both fluids held together by their mutual attraction, so neutralizing each other. By friction or by induction the two fluids may be separated; the positive fluid passes to one of the bodies and accumulates on its surface, thus leaving an excess of negative electricity on the other. These two theories were convenient to use in explaining the action of frictional and influence machines, the electrophorus, the condenser and many other forms of electrostatic apparatus. Indeed, these theories are still applied to a certain extent as affording a convenient means of expressing these electrostatic actions. They contain a large element of truth, and the later theory of Maxwell and the electron theory are elaborations of them.

Franklin's opinion on the nature of electricity may best be stated in his own words, and the following is an extract from his paper entitled "Opinions and Conjectures concerning the properties and Effects of Electrical Matter arising from Experiments and Observations made at Philadelphia, 1749":

"(1) The electrical matter consists of particles extremely subtile, since it can permeate common matter, even the densest metals, with such ease and freedom as not to receive any perceptible resistance.

"(2) If any one should doubt whether the electrical matter passes through the substance of bodies, or only over and along their surfaces, a shock from an electrified large glass jar, taken through his own body, will probably convince him.

"(3) Electrical matter differs from common matter in this, that the parts of the latter mutually attract, those of the former mutually repel each other. Hence the appearing divergency in a stream of electrified effluvia.

"(4) But tho the particles of electrical matter do repel each other, they are strongly attracted by all other matter.

"(5) From these three things, the extreme subtility of the

electrical matter, the mutual repulsion of its parts, and the strong attraction between them and other matter, arise this effect, that when a quantity of electrical matter is applied to a mass of common matter, of any bigness or length, within our observation (which hath not already got its quantity), it is immediately and equally diffused through the whole.

"(6) The common matter is a kind of sponge to the electrical fluid. And as a sponge would receive no water if the parts of water were not smaller than the pores of the sponge, and even then but slowly, if there were not a mutual attraction between those parts and the parts of the sponge; and would imbibe it still faster if the mutual attraction among the parts of the water did not impede, some force being required to separate them; and fastest, if, instead of attraction, there were a mutual repulsion among those parts which would act in conjunction with the attraction of the sponge—so is the case between electrical and common matter.

"(7) But in the common matter there is (generally as much of the electrical as it will contain within its substance. If more is added, it lies without upon the surface, and forms what we call an electrical atmosphere, and the body is said to be electrified.

"(8) 'Tis supposed that all kinds of common matter do not attract and retain the electrical with equal strength and force, for reasons to be given hereafter. And that those called electrics per se, as glass, etc., attract and retain it strongest and contain the greatest quantity.

"(9) We know that the electrical fluid is in common matter because we can pump it out by the globe or tube. We know that common matter has near as much as it can contain because when we add a little more to any portion of it, the additional quantity does not enter but forms an electrical atmosphere. And we know that common matter has not (generally) more than it can contain, otherwise all loose portions of it would repel each other as they constantly do when they have electric atmospheres. . . .

"(15) The form of the electrical atmosphere is that of the body it surrounds."

Such are the essential parts of Franklin's primitive theory, propounded for the purpose of giving a consistent account of the phenomena of electric attraction and repulsion so far as they were known in this time. It is curious to observe how some of his ideas were quite in keeping with the latest theory—the electron theory—described later.

Various theories were propounded from time to time for a long time after the enunciation of the single and two fluid theories, but none served better as a working basis. In the later part of the nineteenth century, however, a new theory dealing with electricity as obeying the laws of mechanics was formulated by Clerk Maxwell, the great English physicist. Maxwell's ideas were founded on the observations made by Faraday, who discovered that the nature of the insulating material, or dielectric, between the plates of a condenser had a great deal to do with the quantity of electricity which would flow into it under the influence of a given electromotive force. This fact led Maxwell to believe that the dielectric was the real seat of the charge, that the conductor acted merely to distribute the charge over the different portions of the dielectric in contact with it. When a flow of current takes place along a wire it is due to the differences existing in the dielectric about the wire. The following extract from "Maxwell's Theory and Hertzian Oscillations," by H. Poincaré, translated by Frederick K. Vreeland, may serve to give some idea of the action in and about an electric circuit.

"If we undertake to compress a spring," he says, "we encounter an opposing force which increases as the spring yields to the pressure. If, now, we can exert only a limited pressure, a moment will arrive when we can no longer overcome the reacting force; the movement will cease, and equilibrium will be established. Finally, when the pressure is removed, the spring will regain its original form, giving back all the energy that was expended in compressing it.

"Suppose, on the other hand, that we wish to move a body immersed in water. Here again we encounter a reaction, which depends upon the velocity, but which, if the velocity remain constant, does not go on increasing as the body yields to the pressure. The motion will thus continue as long as the motive force acts, and the equilibrium never be established. Finally, when the force is removed, the body does not tend to return to the starting point, and the energy expended in removing it cannot be restored; it has been completely transformed into heat through the viscosity of the water.

"The contrast is manifest, and it is important to distinguish between elastic reaction and viscous reaction. Now, the dielectrics behave toward the motion of electricity as elastic solids do toward the motion of matter, while the conductors behave like viscous liquids. Hence there are two kinds of currents: the displacement currents of Maxwell, which traverse the dielectrics, and the ordinary conduction currents which flow in conductors.

"The former, having to overcome a sort of elastic reaction, must be of short duration, for this reaction increases as long as the current continues to flow and equilibrium must soon be established.

"Conduction currents, on the other hand, must overcome a sort of viscous resistance, and hence may continue as long as the electromotive force which produces them.

THE NATURE OF ELECTRICITY

"To take a hydraulic analogy, suppose that we have a closed vessel containing water under pressure. If we put this vessel in communication with a vertical pipe, the water will rise in it, but the flow will cease when the hydrostatic equilibrium is established. If the pipe be large, there will be no appreciable friction nor loss of head, and the water thus raised may be used to do work. We have here an illustration of displacement currents.

"If, on the other hand, the water be allowed to run out through a horizontal pipe, the flow will continue as long as there is water in the reservoir; but if the pipe be small, there will be a considerable loss of energy, and heat will be produced by the friction. This illustrates the action of conduction currents.

"Altho it is impossible and unnecessary to try to imagine all the details of the mechanism, we may say that all takes place as if the displacement currents had the effect of compressing a multitude of minute springs.

"When the currents cease, electrostatic equilibrium is established; and the tension of the spring depends upon the intensity of the electrostatic field. The energy accumulated in these springs—that is, the electrostatic energy of the field—may be restored whenever they are allowed to unbend; and it is thus that mechanical work is produced when charged conductors are allowed to obey their electrostatic attractions. These attractions are thus due to the pressure exerted on the conductors by the compressed springs. Finally, to pursue the analogy to the end, a disruptive discharge may be attributed to the breaking of some springs which are unable to stand the strain.

"On the other hand, the energy expended in producing conduction currents is lost, and converted into heat, like the work done in overcoming friction or the viscosity of fluids. This is why a conductor is heated by the passage of a current.

"From Maxwell's point of view, none but closed currents exist. To the early electricians this was not the case. They considered as closed the current which circulates in a wire joining the two terminals of a battery. But if, instead of joining these terminals directly, they were connected respectively to the two plates of a condenser, the momentary current which flowed while the condenser was being charged was considered as unclosed. It flowed, they said, from one plate to the other through the wire connected to the battery, and stopped at the surfaces of the plates. Maxwell, on the contrary, considers that the current continues in the form of a displacement current, across the insulating layer which separates the plates, and is thus completely closed. The elastic reaction which the current encounters in traversing the dielectric explains its short duration.

"Currents may manifest themselves in three ways: by their heating effects, by their action on magnets and on other currents, by the induced currents which they generate. We have seen above why conduction currents produce heat and displacement currents do not. Yet, according to Maxwell's hypothesis, the currents which he imagines should, like ordinary currents, produce electromagnetic, electrodynamic, and inductive effects.

"Why could these effects not be observed? Because a displacement current, however feeble, cannot continue long in one direction; for the tension of our hypothetical springs, continually increasing, will soon check it. Thus we cannot have in a dielectric either a continuous current of long duration or a sensible alternating current of long period; but the effects should be observable if the alternations are very rapid.

"And here we have, according to Maxwell, the origin of light: A light wave is a series of alternating currents, flowing in a dielectric, in the air, or in interplanetary space, changing their direction 1,000,000,000,000,000 times in a second. The enormous inductive effect of these rapid alternations produces other currents in the neighboring portions of the dielectric, and thus the light waves are propagated from place to place. The velocity of propagation may be known analytically to be equal to the ratio of the units—that is, to the velocity of light.

"These alternating currents are a kind of electrical vibration; but are they longitudinal, like those of sound, or transverse, like those of Fresnel's ether? In the case of sound, the air undergoes alternate condensations and rarefactions; but the ether of Fresnel acts as if it were composed of incompressible layers, capable only of sliding upon each other. If the currents flowed in unclosed circuits, the electricity would necessarily accumulate at one end or the other of the circuits, and we should have a condition analogous to the condensations and rarefactions of air; the vibrations would be longitudinal. But, as Maxwell admits only closed currents, those accumulations are impossible, and the electricity must behave like the incompressible ether of Fresnel: its vibrations must be transverse.

"Thus we reach all the conclusions of the wave theory of light. This, however, was not enough to enable the physicists, who were attracted rather than convinced, to accept absolutely Maxwell's ideas: all that could be said in their favor was that they did not conflict with any known facts, and that it were indeed a pity if they were not true. The experimental confirmation was lacking, and remained so for twenty-five years.

"It was necessary to find, between the old theory and that of Maxwell, a discrepancy not too minute for our crude methods of observation. There was only one such from which an experimentum crucis could be derived. To do this was the work of Hertz."

Maxwell's electromagnetic theory, which led to the recognition of light as an electrical phenomenon and to many other grand generali-

THE NATURE OF ELECTRICITY

zations, was more a mathematical than a physical theory. What it chiefly accomplished was to express, in mathematical language, the experimental results of Faraday. Maxwell, however, avoided giving any description of the molecular constitution of the media through which electrical energy was transmitted.

Professor Fleming, in his pamphlet on the "Electronic Theory," says:

"It seems tolerably clear from all the facts of electrolysis that electricity can only pass through a conducting liquid or electrolyte by being carried on atoms or groups of atoms which are called ions—*i.e.*, wanderers. The quantity thus carried by a hydrogen atom or other monad element, such as sodium, silver, or potassium, is a definite natural unit of electricity. The quantity carried by any other atom or group of atoms acting as an ion is always an exact integer multiple of this natural unit. This small indivisible quantity of electricity has been called by Dr. Johnstone Stoney an electron or atom of electricity. The artificial or conventional unit of electric quantity in the centimeter-gram-second system, as defined by the British Association Committee on Electrical Units, is as follows:

"'An electrostatic unit of electric quantity is the charge which, when placed upon a very small sphere, repels another similarly charged sphere, the centers being one centimeter apart, with a mechanical force of one dyne. The dyne is a mechanical unit of force, and is that force which, acting for one second on a mass of one gram, gives it a velocity of one centimeter per second. Hence, by the law of inverse squares the force in dynes exerted by two equal charges Q at a distance D is equal to Q^2/D^2. Two other units of electric quantity are in use—the electromagnetic unit, which is thirty thousand million times as great as the electrostatic unit, and the practical unit, called the coulomb or ampere-second, which is three thousand million times the electrostatic unit. We can calculate easily the relation between the electron and the coulomb—that is, between Nature's unit of electricity and the British Association unit—as follows:

"'If we electrolyze any electrolyte, say acidified water, which yields up hydrogen at a negative electrode, we find that to evolve one cubic centimeter of hydrogen at 0° C. and 760 mm., we have to pass through the electrolyte a quantity of electricity equal to 8.62 coulombs. For 96,540 coulombs are required to evolve one gram of hydrogen and 11,200 cubic centimeters at 0° C. and atmospheric pressure weigh one gram. The number 8.62 is the quotient of 96,540 by 11,200.

"'From various sources calculations indicate that the number of molecules of hydrogen in a cubic centimeter is probably best represented by the number twenty million million million $= 2 \times 10^{19}$. Hence it follows, since there are two atoms of hydrogen in a molecule, that in electrostatic units the electric charge on a hydrogen atom or hydrogen ion is

$$\frac{96540 \times 3 \times 10^9}{11200 \times 4 \times 10^{19}} = \frac{65}{10^{11}} \text{ of a C. G. S. electrostatic unit} = \frac{22}{10^{20}} \text{ of a coulomb.}$$

"'Accordingly, if the above atomic charge is called one electron, then the conventional British Association electrostatic unit of electric quantity is equal to 1,540 million electrons, and the quantity called a coulomb is nearly five million million million electrons. The electron or the electric charge by a hydrogen atom or ion is evidently a very important physical constant.'

"It is, in fact, Nature's unit, from which all other physical units may be brought into agreement with natural quantities. And thus we see that electricity is atomic in nature and in structure; that is to say, we can have it only in amounts which are all exact multiples of a certain unit, which unit cannot be subdivided, and 1,540 millions of these units equal one coulomb.

"For long it was held that the atom of matter was the smallest particle in nature and indivisible, but now we must assume that atoms are composed by smaller particles. We are compelled by all the known facts to admit that Professor Crookes was right when he declared the cathode rays to be a stream of matter shot from the cathode. Professor J. J. Thomson, by measuring the deflection of the stream (of "radiant matter," as Crookes called it) in a known magnetic field, shows that, if the radiant matter consists of corpuscles or particles, each carries a charge of one "electron," and has a mass of about 1/1000 of a hydrogen atom, and their velocity is from $\frac{1}{5}$ to $\frac{1}{3}$ the velocity of light.

"So far as the effects in high vacua are concerned, Professor Crookes discovered all we know about cathode rays, but Lenard conceived the idea that these rays could penetrate the walls of the vessel containing the vacuum, and by inserting a window of aluminium in the vessel he found the rays penetrated the aluminium and that they are active outside the vessel as they are inside.

"Electrons are found in the mass of gas through which Röntgen rays have passed. Röntgen discovered that if the rays from the cathode struck a conductor in the vacuum bulb, they penetrated the glass bulb enclosing the vacuum, and that they also penetrate many opaque bodies outside, and produce photographs on active plates.

"The atom, it seems, can be divided into two parts of very unequal size. The small part is negatively electrified, and is always the same, no matter from what chemical atom it comes. The remaining larger part is positively electrified, but is different in nature, depending on the elementary atom broken up. It is not settled whether the particle and its negative charge are separable. It is, however, becoming common to speak of the two together as the 'electron.'

"From this point of view the theory of electricity originates is called the electronic theory. The principal objects of consideration

THE NATURE OF ELECTRICITY

in this theory are these electrons which constitute what we call electricity. An atom of matter in its neutral condition has been assumed to consist of an outer shell or envelope of negative electrons associated with some core or matrix which has an opposite electrical quality, such that if an electron is withdrawn from the atom the latter is left positively electrified.

"A neutral atom minus an electron constitutes the natural unit of positive electricity, and the electron and the neutral atom minus an electron are sometimes called negative and positive ions. Deferring for a moment a further analysis of possible atomic structure, we may say that, with the above hypothesis in hand, we have then to express our statements of electrical facts in terms of the electron as the fundamental idea.

"On this theory the difference between conductors and non-conductors is accounted for by assuming that an electric current is a procession of electrons, so that a conductor is a substance through which electrons can easily move; in non-conductors the electrons may be moved, or vibrated, or displaced to some extent, but spring back again into their former place.

"The electronic or any theory must account for the waves set up in the ether around a variable current. This is explained on the hypothesis that a moving or vibrating electron, while its motion is being accelerated or reduced, radiates ethereal waves, and that a flying column of electrons produces a magnetic field in circles round the moving electrons as a center."

Ordinary gases or mixtures of gases, such as air, contain scarcely any ions. Under the influence of X-rays or other rays of short wavelength, their numbers increase considerably. The positively charged particles attract clusters of neutral molecules and so form positive ions. The electrons which have been set free also attract clusters of neutral molecules, so forming negative ions. They move and by collision these charges neutralizing each other and the clusters resolve into simple gaseous molecules.

CHAPTER II

ELECTROSTATICS—ATMOSPHERIC ELECTRICITY

In the early days of electrical science many of the experiments in electrostatics were developed which still form a considerable part of the course usually taught in present-day schools. The attraction of amber when rubbed for light bodies was known to the ancient Greeks as long ago as 600 B.C. About the year 1600, Gilbert, who had made several discoveries concerning the properties of the magnet, discovered in glass, sulphur, resin and various precious stones the same attractive power known to be possessed by amber. From that time innumerable physicists have extended Gilbert's discoveries and have found a great number of curious phenomena previously entirely unknown, and in this way have contributed to found that branch of physics which, under the name of Electricity, has attained such important dimensions in modern times.

"If he had used a ball of glass or sulphur previously rubbed," suggests Guillemin, "he would have known of the reciprocity of attraction in the same way as he had shown that soft iron attracts a magnet. But Gilbert greatly extended the list of bodies capable, like amber, of being electrified by friction; to those that we have already mentioned he added shellac, rock salt, alum and rock crystal. He also found that electrical attraction took place not only between light bodies, but between certain solid bodies, drops of liquids, gaseous bodies, and dense vapors. Again, he discovered the influence of atmospheric conditions on electric phenomena.

"Boyle discovered the reciprocity of attraction between non-electrified bodies and electrified bodies. A very simple experiment, on the mechanical principle of action and reaction being equal and opposite, led to this discovery. On a pivot was placed a small shellac needle, electrified by being rubbed by catskin. Then, on holding his finger near one end, he found the needle drawn toward his finger. Otto von Guericke, who made the first fractional electrical machine, was the first to observe the phenomena of repulsion, and he also drew from the globe of sulphur of his machine visible sparks, accompanied by a crisp crackling sound, which was, in fact, the noise of the electric discharge. Here we had for the first time in these early experiments the production of sparks similar to those which constitute the electric arc; tho it is a long step from these feeble sparks to the dazzling splendor of the electric light. The experiments of the celebrated burgomaster of Magdeburg date from the middle of the seventeenth century. At the commencement of the eighteenth century, that was to witness such brilliant discoveries in electricity, Dr. Wall succeeded in producing most vivid sparks and far louder crackling; he also had some ideas of the great discovery which made Franklin so celebrated. 'This light and that crackling,' said he, 'are the same thing as thunder and lightning.' The analogy was indeed striking, and it was not long before it was verified and confirmed.

"Numerous observations on the electrical phenomena were due to Hauksbee. Among them are very interesting experiments on the light which is produced in a vacuum or in a rarefied medium when one introduces some bodies into it, and develops on their surface electricity by friction; or when one excites the exterior of a globe of glass, the interior of which is a vacuum.

"He observed in particular the effect of heat on the development of both attractive and repulsive forces. The attractions and repulsions of pieces of tinsel by a tube of glass, rubbed with paper, were found to be more energetic when the glass had been heated by friction. The effects of moisture and warmth that Gilbert had discovered were proved beyond doubt by the experiments of Hauksbee, Dufay and Gray. The following passage occurs in Hauksbee's Physico-Mechanical Experiments: 'When the tube became hottest by the strongest Attrition, the Force of the Effluvia was rendered manifest to another Sense, too, namely, that of feeling. They did not then only produce all the forementioned Effects in a more remarkable manner, but were also plainly to be felt upon the Face, or any other tender part, if the rubbed Tube was held near it. And they seemed to make very nearly such sort of stroaks upon the Skin, as a number of fine limber Hairs pushing against it might be supposed to do.'

"The discovery of electrical conductivity was made in the early part of the eighteenth century by Stephen Gray. While looking for the reason of the difference between the two classes he came upon the general fact that all bodies, without exception, are capable of being electrified, but that the circumstances must be varied to suit the substances.

"Let us rapidly review the points that led Gray to this important discovery. Having electrified a piece of glass tube, the ends of which were stopped with corks, he was surprised to find that the corks, which had not rubbed, picked up light bodies just as the tube itself did, showing that the electricity passed from the glass to the cork. Gray followed up this experiment by lengthening the corks with sticks of ivory, wood or metal, yet he had the same phenomena even with stems which ended in a ball of ivory. Hung from a balcony by a long cord fastened to the tube the ball still was electrified. He then varied his experiment to greater and greater distances, until he found the same effect at the end of a cord 765 feet long. But Gray found that in order to succeed, certain conditions had to be fulfilled; the cord which carried the electricity had to be suspended by silk strings, as he found that he got no electrification at all if he suspended it by means of metal wires.

"One more experiment of Gray's that was soon repeated in all laboratories was to show that the human body conducts electricity. It explains the impossibility that had always been found in trying to electrify such substances as the metals. Having suspended a child by hair cords, and having touched him with his electrified tube, he found that all parts of the child's body had acquired the power of attracting light bodies. The same effect was produced when the child stood on a cake of an "electric" substance, such as resin, as was produced when he was suspended by the hair cords. From these experiments, which were then varied in innumerable ways, two very important conclusions were drawn.

"The first, that electricity obtained by friction could be transmitted to a distance through any substance that could not itself be electrified; the second, a corollary to the first, that this transmission is impossible, or very difficult, if the transmitting body is one of those capable of being electrified by the method described above.

"We quoted above Gray's first experiment, which established the electrical conductivity of the body. It was a French physician, Dufay, a member of the Academy of Sciences, who drew the first spark from the human body. 'Being suspended by silk cords, he found, when electrified, that, if any one brought his knuckle near to him, he felt a stinging sensation like a pin-prick, also that the person's knuckle felt the same sensation. When the experiment was performed in the dark a little spark was observed.'

"Gray took up the experiments of Dufay and in his turn found that he could draw sparks from any insulated body which had been put into contact with rubbed glass; if these bodies terminated in a point a small luminous cone was seen, accompanied by a slight noise. In reference to this Gray repeated Wall's comparison between the spark followed by the crackling sound and the lightning followed by thunder."

"Newton's grand discovery of the law of the universal attraction of matter, when he showed that the force was proportional to the mass and that it varied in the inverse ratio of the square of the distance, incited the physicists of the eighteenth century to discover the law which governed the strength of electrical forces. Dufay, Hauksbee, Muschenbroek, Æpinus, and Cavendish were all more or less instrumental in attaining this end; but we are indebted to Coulomb for

ELECTROSTATICS

an exact experimental demonstration of these laws. Coulomb used for this purpose a similar apparatus to the magnetic balance. It consisted of two spheres so arranged that they could be charged and the force of repulsion between them balanced by the torsion of the suspension.

By means of this instrument Coulomb was able to prove the two laws of electrical attraction:

1. The repulsion between two electrified bodies charged with the same electricity varies inversely as the square of the distance between them.

2. The attractions and repulsions vary in the ratio of the products of the quantities of free electricity—that is to say, of the electric charges of the two bodies.

The action of points on metallic conductors in increasing the density of the charge at the point received the attention of Franklin. The following quotation from his "Experiments and Observations on Electricity, made at Philadelphia, 1774," describes Franklin's own experiments on this subject:

"Place an iron shot of three or four inches diameter on the mouth of a clean, dry glass bottle. By a fine silken thread from the ceiling, right over the mouth of the bottle, suspend a small cork ball, about the bigness of a marble; the thread of such a length as that the cork ball may rest against the side of the shot. Electrify the shot, and the ball will be repelled to the distance of four or five inches, more or less, according to the quantity of electricity. When in this state, if you present to the shot the point of a long, slender, sharp bodkin, at six or eight inches distance, the repellency is instantly destroyed and the cork flies to the shot. A blunt body must be brought within an inch and draw a spark to produce the same effect.

"To prove that the electrical fire is drawn off by the point, if you take the blade of the bodkin out of the wooden handle and fix it in a stick of sealing-wax, and then present it at the distance aforesaid, or if you bring it very near, no such effect follows; but sliding one finger along the wax till you touch the blade, and the ball flies to the shot immediately. If you present the point in the dark you will see, sometimes at a foot distance and more, a light gather upon it, like that of a firefly or glowworm; the less sharp the point the nearer must you bring it to observe the light; and at whatever distance you see the light, you may draw off the electrical fire and destroy the repellency. If a cork ball so suspended be repelled by the tube, and a point be presented quick to it, 'tis surprising to see how suddenly it flies back to the tube. Points of wood will do nearly as well as those of iron, provided the wood is not dry; for perfectly dry wood will no more conduct electricity than sealing-wax.

"It is calculated that the density of electricity at an infinitesimally fine point would be infinitely great, since it is impossible to charge a pointed conductor in the air with electricity; this is proved by experiment. As fast as electrification is produced, it is given off the point into the air and disappears. When we examine the extremity of a point in the dark, there is seen a luminous crest. If, while the point is in communication with the source of electrification, one places one's hand before it, a draft is at once perceptible, arising from the motions of the particles of air. This can be still better shown by holding a candle-flame in front of a long-pointed conductor. The electric wind is sufficient to bend the flame sharply down, or even to put it out.

"This movement of the air at the points on electrified conductors has always been attributed to the accumulation of electricity, which has been compared to a fluid; but the following explanation seems to us preferable, as it involves no hypothesis on the nature of electricity, and, besides, it is found to agree with known phenomena. The molecules of air, in contact with a point electrified to a great electric density, become charged with the same electrification as the conductor itself. Hence the nearest molecules are repelled and others fill their place, which become electrified in their turn, and so on. Hence the current of air, which only lasts as long as the electricity is being supplied. It can be stopped by putting a cap of sealing-wax over the point."

The explanation of the attraction of an electrified body for an unelectrified one was not well understood until the middle of the eighteenth century. John Canton, of Stroud, seems to have been the first to give the true explanation.

It may be well here to point out the difference between a conductor and a dielectric, or non-conductor. A conductor merely connects different parts of the dielectric which surrounds it and with which it is in contact. If, therefore, this dielectric be suddenly charged in one place this charge cannot remain at that place because it is in contact with the conductor, but must flow into the conductor, along it, and then out into the dielectric surrounding it, and takes place at every point of contact between the conductor and the dielectric. The office of the conductor, then, is to distribute the charge to the dielectric. If the conductor be spherical in shape and there is no other charge near by, the dielectric will be charged uniformly all about the sphere. If the conductor tapers to a point, the charge in the dielectric will be most intense about the point. Or if the charge about the sphere is influenced by a neighboring charge, the conducting sphere allows it to move as the charged body may dictate.

This principle of electrical influence was soon made use of in constructing a machine for the production of electric charges and which was the forerunner of the modern electrical influence machine. This was the **electrophorus** of Volta, who gave it the name of "perpetual electrophorus" because it preserves for a long time the charges that it has received.

"It consists of two parts: a cake of insulating material, such as resin, sulphur or india-rubber, cast into a wooden or metal tray, and a metal disk fixed to an insulating handle of glass or to silk cords. Frequently the disk is of smaller diameter than the cake, and sometimes it is made not of metal but of wood, covered on both edge and faces with tinfoil.

"To use the electrophorus, remove the metal disk and rub the insulating cake with flannel, woolen cloth or fur, best of all with a catskin. This produces negative electrification on the resinous cake. This you may prove if you bring your finger near the cake, for you will observe small sparks and crackling sounds. Now take the metal disk by the insulating handle and place it on the rubbed insulating cake.

"Now pause a moment: let us think what has happened in this action. While you were putting down the lid on the cake, even before it touched the cake, it was under influence. The cake is negative, hence as you hold the lid over it there will be a displacement and a rush of electricity in the lid, causing a positive charge to accumulate on the lower side, leaving the upper side negative. This effect will of course increase as the disk is lowered. It will be noticed that the metal dish in which the cake stands is also under influence; but this is of no importance.

"You must now touch with your finger the top of the lid. Your finger will also be under influence during this action, a $+$ charge accumulating on its tip and then discharging itself with a small spark to fill up and neutralize the $-$ charge on the top surface. Now lift up the lid by the handle. You will find that it is positively electrified, and you can carry away the charge and use it to give a big spark to any other conductor. You can then put the lid down again on the cake, touch it, lift it up again and take another spark as often as you please, the cake remaining all the time charged with its original charge. The length of spark is roughly proportional to the size of the electrophorus.

"Mascart in his treatise says that Lichtenberg constructed an electrophorus with a cake six feet across and the disk was five feet across, and the sparks drawn from it fourteen to sixteen inches long. Another very large electrophorus was made by Kleindworth for the University of Göttingen; the cake of resin was 2.25 meters in diameter and the conducting disk 2 meters.

"The cake sometimes preserves its charge for months, if it be kept in a cupboard where the air is perfectly dry. We have said that the insulating cake of the electrophorus is made of resin, sulphur or india-rubber. All good insulators can be used; mixtures of these substances are generally used in order to make the cake less brittle."

A short description of the principal static machines which have been developed is taken from Professor S. P. Thompson's "Elementary Lessons in Electricity and Magnetism."

"For the purpose of procuring larger supplies of electricity than can be obtained by the rubbing of a rod of glass or shellac, electric machines have been devised. All electric machines consist of two parts, one for producing, the other for collecting, the electric charges. Experience has shown that the quantities of $+$ — electrification developed by friction upon the two surfaces rubbed against one another depend on the amount of friction, upon the extent of the surfaces rubbed, and also upon the nature of the substances used.

"The earliest form of electric machine was devised by Otto von Guericke of Magdeburg, and consisted of a globe of sulphur fixed upon a spindle, and pressed with the dry surface of the hands while being made to rotate; with this he discovered the existence of electric sparks and the repulsion of similarly electrified bodies. Sir Isaac Newton replaced Von Guiericke's globe of sulphur by a globe of glass. A little later the form of the machine was improved by various German electricians; Von Bose added a collector or "prime conductor," in the shape of an iron tube, supported by a person standing on cakes of resin to insulate them, or suspended by silken strings; Winckler of Leipzig substituted a leathern cushion for the hand as a rubber; and Gordon of Erfurt rendered the machine more easy of construction by using a glass cylinder instead of a glass globe. The electricity was led from the excited cylinder or globe to the prime conductor by a metallic chain which hung over against the globe. A pointed collector was not employed until after Franklin's famous researches on the action of points. About 1760 De la Fond, Planta, Ramsden and Cuthbertson constructed machines having glass plates instead of cylinders. All frictional machines are, however, now obsolete, having in recent years been quite superseded by the modern influence machines.

"The cylinder electric machine consists of a glass cylinder mounted on a horizontal axis capable of being turned by a handle. Against it is pressed from behind a cushion of leather stuffed with horsehair, the surface of which is covered with a powdered amalgam of zinc or tin. A flap of silk attached to the cushion passes over the cylinder, covering its upper half. In front of the cylinder stands the "prime conductor," which is made of metal, and usually of the form of an elongated cylinder with hemispherical ends, mounted upon a glass stand. At the end of the prime conductor nearest the cylinder is fixed a rod bearing a row of fine metallic spikes, resembling in form a rake; the other end usually carries a rod terminated in a brass ball or knob. When the handle is turned the friction between the glass and the amalgam-coated surface of the rubber produces a copious electric action, electricity appearing as a + charge on the glass, leaving the rubber with a — charge. The prime conductor collects this charge by the following process: The + charge being carried round on the glass acts inductively on the long insulated conductor, repelling a + charge to the far end; leaving the nearer end — ly charged. The effect of the row of points is to emit a — ly electrified wind toward the attracting + charge upon the glass, which is neutralized thereby; the glass thus arriving at the rubber in a neutral condition ready to be again excited. This action of the points is sometimes described, tho less correctly, by saying that the points collect the + charge from the glass. If it is desired to collect also the — charge of the rubber, the cushion must be supported on an insulating stem and provided at the back with a metallic knob. It is, however, more usual to use only the + charge, and to connect the rubber by a chain to "earth," so allowing the — charge to be neutralized.

"The friction of a jet of steam issuing from a boiler, through a wooden nozzle, generates electricity. In reality it is the particles of condensed water in the jet which are directly concerned. Sir W. Armstrong, who investigated this source of electricity, constructed a powerful apparatus, known as the hydro-electrical machine, capable of producing enormous quantities of electricity, and yielding sparks 5 or 6 feet long. The collector consisted of a row of spikes, placed in the path of the steam jets issuing from wooden nozzles, and was supported, together with a brass ball which served as prime conductor, upon a glass pillar."

After the invention of the electrophorus by Volta, the idea naturally suggested itself of performing mechanically the several operations of bringing the plate near the charged bed, of touching its upper side, and of removing it to a large metallic body where the charge could be stored. One of the first of these mechanical arrangements was the revolving doubler of Nicholson, invented in 1788, consisting of a revolving apparatus in which an insulated carrier can be brought into the presence of an electrified body, there touched for an instant while under influence, then carried forward with its acquired charge toward another body, to which it imparts its charge, and which in turn acts inductively on it, giving it an opposite charge, which it can convey to the first body, thus increasing its initial charge at every rotation.

"In the modern influence machines two principles are embodied: (1) The principle of influence, namely, that a conductor touched while under influence acquires a charge of the opposite kind; (2) the principle of reciprocal accumulation. This principle must be carefully noted. Let there be two insulated conductors, A and B, electrified ever so little, one positively, the other negatively. Let a third insulated conductor, C, which will be called a carrier, be arranged to move so that it first approaches A and then B, and so forth. If touched while under the influence of the small positive charge on A it will acquire a small negative charge; suppose that it then moves on and gives this negative charge to B. Then let it be touched while under the influence of B, so acquiring a small positive charge. When it returns toward A let it give up this positive charge to A, thereby increasing its positive charge. Then A will act more powerfully, and on repeating the former operations both B and A will become more highly charged. Each accumulates the charges derived by influence from the other. This is the fundamental action of the machines in question. The modern influence machines date from 1860, when C. F. Varley produced a form with six carriers mounted on a rotating disk of glass. This was followed in 1865 by the machine of Holtz and that of Toepler, and in 1867 by those of Lord Kelvin (the 'replenisher' and the 'mouse-mill'). The latest forms are those of Mr. James Wimshurst."

At the present time these machines are used to a limited extent as a source of high voltage for such work as operating vacuum tubes, X-ray apparatus, and the like; but their uncertainty of action, small power, and the irregularity of their discharge, make the high-tension transformer or Ruhmkorf coil preferable.

Cuneus, a pupil of Muschenbroek, a celebrated physicist of the eighteenth century, was one day trying to electrify some water in a wide-necked bottle. For this purpose he held the bottle in one hand, after having placed in the bottle a metal rod connected to the machine. When he thought the water was sufficiently electrified, he tried to remove the iron rod with one hand without loosing his hold on the bottle with the other hand. He received a shock that surprised him. Muschenbroek repeated Cuneus' experiment, but the shock that he received in his arms, shoulders and chest was so great that he lost consciousness and was so frightened that in writing to Réaumur about this then new discovery, he wrote that for nothing in the world, not even for the crown of France, would he go through it again. But some other physicists were less fearful. Allaman, Lemoinnier, Winckler and the Abbé Nollet variéd the experiment in all sorts of ways, and so a new piece of apparatus was added to electrical science. This apparatus, called the Leyden jar, is named after the place where the experiment was first performed in 1746.

The Leyden jar is only a form of electric condenser, the essential properties of which have already been explained in connection with Maxwell's theory.

It is again to Franklin that science is indebted for an experiment which shows where the charge in such a jar resides. Franklin constructed a Leyden jar having both internal and external metallic coatings removable. Having fitted them to the jar, he connected the inner coating with an electrical machine and the outer coating with the earth and charged the jar in the usual manner. He then separated the metallic coatings and the jar, and examining each one for electrification, he found the metallic coating practically unelectrified, while the glass jar proved to be highly electrified. Upon replacing the coatings in the jar, he was able to obtain a bright spark, just as tho the coatings had not been removed. This experiment clearly proved that the important part of such a Leyden jar or condenser was the glass or dielectric and that the function of the conducting coatings was merely to spread the charge over the glass. Taking such a view, it will be readily seen that the larger the jar, the greater is the quantity of electricity which may be stored therein. Large jars are, however, often inconvenient to handle, so that a "battery" of such jars is used having their inner coatings all connected together to form one large coating, and the outer ones similarly connected.

From time to time it has been attempted to use for the dielectric materials other than glass, and thousands of condensers using paraffined paper are in use on modern telephone and telegraph circuits. Larger condensers are used on power circuits. None of these other materials is, however, as satisfactory as glass, being liable to be disrupted if the pressure of the charge is too great. The opportunities for using condensers to advantage are rapidly increasing at present and considerable energy is being directed toward their development. The desirable qualities of such a condenser are that its dielectric should be capable of containing a very large charge, that it should stand very high electric pressure without disruption, and that its coatings should be in the most intimate contact with the dielectric. In some recent condensers, made in Switzerland, the metal coatings are made by chemically depositing silver upon the inner and outer surfaces of the glass.

The ancients, who knew nothing of electricity, could not conceive of thunder as anything but the result of a purely mechanical shock. Seneca, speaking of the fact that two hands struck together produced a loud noise, concluded from that that the collision of two enormous clouds ought to sound with a very great crash. Again, he compares thunder, "the sound of which is very sharp, even penetrating, to the noise made by the bursting of a bladder on a person's head." Lucretius also explains thunder by the shaking of the clouds or their tearing asunder.

The identity of lightning with electricity was first shown by

Benjamin Franklin in a paper published in 1749, two years before his experiments with the storm clouds. At that epoch he had just recognized the power of points. Two ingenious experiments in which this power was put into play furnished him with a new analogy and suggested to him to verify by the storm clouds the truth of his conjectures. Having suspended by silk threads to the ceiling of his room a tube of gilt paper, 10 feet in length and a foot in diameter, Franklin charged it with electricity. Then, presenting to the tube, at the distance of a foot, the point of a needle, the tube was instantly discharged; if, on the contrary, he presented to it a blunt body, an iron bolt or punch rounded at the end, he found it was necessary to put it within three inches before it could cause the discharge, which then, he said, took place with a sudden crackling. Suspending in the same way some great brass scales, the pans of which were supported by silk cords a foot from the floor, he electrified one of the pans. The twisting of the suspending cord caused the scales to turn; he placed the iron punch underneath, below a point of the circumference described. When the pan which was electrified passed over it, it lowered itself, came in contact with it and thus discharged itself. But if the end of the punch was furnished with a needle, the point uppermost, the pan passed above it without approaching, and the discharge took place silently, or if in its course the pan had come near enough for a spark to strike, it could not, because it would have been discharged beforehand.

"Now," says Franklin, "if the fire of electricity and that of lightning be the same, as I have endeavored to show at large in a former paper, this pasteboard tube and these scales may represent electrified clouds. If a tube only 10 feet long will strike and discharge its fire on the punch at two or three inches distance, an electrified cloud of perhaps 10,000 acres may strike and discharge on the earth at a proportionately greater distance. The horizontal motion of the scales over the floor may represent the motion of the clouds over the earth and the erect iron punch a hill or high building, and then we see how electrified clouds passing over hills or high buildings at too great a height to strike may be attracted lower till within their striking distance. And lastly, if a needle fixed on the punch with its point upright, or even on the floor below the punch, will draw the fire from the scale silently at a much greater than the striking distance, and so prevent its descending toward the punch; or if in its course it would have come nigh enough to strike, yet being deprived of its fire it cannot, and the punch is thereby secured from the stroke.

"I say, if these things are so, may not the knowledge of this power of points be of use to mankind in preserving houses, churches, ships, etc., from the stroke of lightning by directing us to fix on the highest parts of those edifices upright rods of iron made sharp as a needle, and gilt to prevent rusting, and from the foot of those rods a wire down the outside of the building into the ground, or down round one of the shrouds of the ship, and down her side till it reaches the water? Would not these pointed rods probably draw the electrical fire silently out of a cloud before it came nigh enough to strike, and thereby secure us from that sudden and most terrible mischief?"

And thus it is that this discovery of Franklin's has been the means of saving much property from destruction. It is only of recent years that much has been added to the knowledge of the action of lightning rods and of their proper design and application. Hertz's experiments in electrical oscillations and the proof that lightning discharges were also oscillatory in their character, enabled us to gain a better understanding of how to handle these tremendous discharges. It is now known that lightning discharges have a frequency of oscillation of about 500,000 periods per second.

A recent and most beautiful application of condensers to the conduction of these lightning discharges to earth may not be out of place here. If a lightning discharge strikes an electric line in its course to earth it may find it easier to pass back to the generator at the power station, jump through the insulation to the frame and then to the earth, than to leap over the insulators and down the pole to the earth; the result being to destroy the generator. If, however, condensers are connected at various points along the line, it may be well to see what should happen.

Every time that a condenser is charged and discharged a current flows through the wire leading to it, one way on charging, the other on discharging. If this succession of charges and discharges takes place slowly, only a small amount will flow into and out of the condenser, but if it takes place rapidly the current is proportionately increased without the pressure being any higher. Suppose such condensers to be connected on a line in which the current has a frequency of 60 oscillations or cycles per second: a small current will then flow continually. This current is of such a character that it does not mean a waste of power—but this is too advanced to be here explained. If, however, a lightning discharge having a frequency of 500,000 per second strikes the line, it will pass readily to earth through the condensers instead of disrupting the insulation of the generators, the condensers being able to pass 500,000/60 as much current as would be passed from the line. There is still much to be learned of electrical disturbances in the atmosphere and little is yet known of the causes producing them. It is a field of vast possibilities and one whose study may result in giving Man a partial control over atmospheric conditions.

CHAPTER III

FUNDAMENTAL DISCOVERIES

There are in all sciences some discoveries which seem to open vast fields for exploration, and which appear suddenly to increase the power of mankind. In electrical science the benefits conferred by the discoveries of Volta and Galvani, Davy, Arago, Ampere, Faraday, Seebeck, Maxwell and Hertz are only just beginning to be realized Volta and Galvani started the investigation of electric currents, and to-day the earth is full of applications of them, each one the servant of a human brain. Each day sees a new device based upon them, and each application presents them in a new light, which again leads to another useful appliance of the principles involved.

One hundred years ago men were not so well organized for scientific research as they are at present, and it may seem strange that such a simple discovery as electromagnetic induction should have taken so long to develop after the production of electric currents. It must be remembered, however, that organization was loose, not bound tightly together as it is now, when mankind is, as it were, united into one large concentrated brain. If a discovery is made at the present time the world knows of it in a few days, and thousands of men stand ready to apply it to all kinds of industries; and many men can bring their vast experience to the immediate aid of the discoverer, so that the discovery is quickly perfected. All this power of self-improvement is owed, however, to those whose works have united men so closely. Scientific research has developed into a business. Large companies have gathered together the best brains of the world, money and conveniences are placed at their disposal, the needs of industry are presented to them and are quickly filled. The scientific brain is kept in constant touch with the wants of life, and there is at last accomplished that union of the scientist and the man of the world—the one with needs, the other with the means of fulfilling them—that was lacking in the earlier days.

There are, in general, two classes of scientists. One is possessed of a mathematical mind, delighting in the abstract solution of a problem, and caring not whether the result turns out one way or another. He is concerned rather with the proof of the similarity of processes than with any difference of detail. To the man with the mechanical

FUNDAMENTAL DISCOVERIES

mind, however, the detection of differences is all-important. He finds his pleasure in observing differences in phenomena by the process of experiment, and his whole idea is to obtain a definite and useful result. Both classes of men are necessary. Maxwell developed a beautiful mathematical theory of great comprehensiveness, but the proofs waited for the experimental demonstrations of Hertz. The groundwork of the science is, however, usually developed through that property of so few minds—the power of observation.

The discovery of the electric current was an event. Galvani, an eminent doctor and professor of anatomy at the University of Bologna, was, one evening in the year 1780, busy in his laboratory, with some friends, making experiments relating to a nervous fluid in animals. On a table, where there was an electric machine used for the experiments, there had been placed by chance some recently skinned frogs, intended to make broth of. "One of Galvani's assistants," says P. Sue, in his "Histoire du Galvanisme," "casually put the point of his instrument near the internal crural nerves of one of the animals; immediately all the muscles of the limbs seemed to be agitated with strong convulsions. Galvani's wife was present; she was struck with the novelty of the phenomenon; she thought she saw that it occurred just at the moment when a spark was taken from the electric machine. She warned her husband, who hastened to verify this curious fact, and he recognized that the muscular contractions of the frog took place, in fact, every time that a spark appeared, but ceased while the machine was at rest."

This observation was the beginning of many experiments with the doctor by which he tried to prove the identity of the nervous fluid of animals with the supposed electric fluid. In 1786 he again continued researches of this kind. "Being anxious one day," says A. Guillemin in his "Electricity and Magnetism," "to see whether the influence of atmospheric electricity on the muscles of frogs would be the same as that produced in machines, he had for that purpose hung up a number of skinned frogs' legs on the balcony of a terrace of his house. He hooked the hind legs to the iron of the balcony by a copper wire which passed under the lumbar nerves. Galvani remarked with surprise that every time that the feet touched the balcony the frogs' limbs were contracted with quick convulsions, tho at that moment there were no signs of a stormy cloud, and, therefore, no particular electric influence of the atmosphere."

These facts suggested to Galvani the idea that there existed an electricity belonging to animals, inherent in their organization; that this electricity, secreted by the brain, resides specially in the nerves, by which it is communicated to the entire body; "that the principal reservoirs of this electricity are the muscles, each fiber of which may be considered as having two surfaces, and possessing by that means the two electricities, positive and negative, each of them representing besides, so to speak, a small Leyden jar, of which the nerves are the conductors." Hence the comparisons he makes between the muscular contractions in frogs and other animals and the commotions produced by the discharge of a Leyden jar.

Alexander Volta, then Professor of Natural Philosophy at Pavia, repeated Galvani's experiments, but he very soon modified his explanations. According to Volta, the electricity developed was of the same nature as that which an electric apparatus produces. It is the contact between dissimilar metals which gives place to the production of electricity, one of the metals being charged with a positive, the other with a negative electrification; these charges combine in traversing the middle conductor of muscles and nerves. Then arose between the two celebrated philosophers a discussion, a struggle, honorable to both, and, above all, profitable to science, which thereby became enriched by a multiude of new facts. The invention of the marvelous apparatus which received the name of Voltaic pile at last caused the theory of the professor of Pavia to prevail, tho Galvani's hypothesis on the existence of a sort of animal electricity is now recognized as partly true. On the other hand, Volta's ideas have been somewhat modified.

The outcome of these contentions was the invention of Volta's pile, first made in 1800. Here, for the first time, was produced a means of generating a steady and continuous flow of electric current. Volta's construction was as follows: Disks of copper, zinc and flannel were cut out and arranged in a pile in the order, copper, flannel, zinc, and this order was successively repeated, the flannel being first dipped in sulphuric acid so that its function was merely to connect the copper and zinc by the acid. This arrangement gave a feeble electromotive force between the elements of each set, which increased when one connection was made at the lower end of the pile and the other was moved toward the top. Volta's idea of the action of the pile was, however, not as it is known to-day. He believed that the source of the electromotive force was at the contact of the copper and the zinc disks, and that the moistened cloth served merely as a means of connecting them, whereas the real seat of this force is at the contact of the acid with the zinc.

This discovery of Volta's was the starting point of many investigations, in which the metals and the liquids were tried in all sorts of combinations, many of which were quite successful, and soon batteries were developed which were capable of furnishing quite powerful currents. For sixty years these batteries were the only source of current available for conducting the brilliant experiments of that period.

As soon as a source of current was obtainable it was natural to ascertain the effects of this current on various bodies. One of the first of these was that of Carlisle and Nicholson, in 1800, on the decom-

FUNDAMENTAL DISCOVERIES

position of water. Having passed the current of a volatile pile, formed of disks of silver and zinc, through water, they noticed that at the end of the copper wire which came from the negative pole of the pile some gaseous bubbles were given off, which they ascertained to be hydrogen; the other wire became rapidly oxidized. On substituting for copper, platinum, which is not attacked by oxygen, bubbles of this latter gas were given off in the same way from the positive wire. That is to say, when two platinum wires were used, oxygen gas was given off in bubbles from the surface of the wire by which the current entered the water, and hydrogen gas was at the same time given off in bubbles from the surface of the wire by which the current left the water.

The next fact of great importance was brought to light twenty years after the discovery of Volta's pile by Oersted, professor in the University of Copenhagen. This accomplished savant found that the electric current acted on the magnetic needle. "For a long time," says Guillemin, "there had been a suspicion of the existence of a relation between magnetic phenomena and electricity; people had remarked the occurrence of perturbations by the mariner's compass on ships struck by lightning, or when their masts presented the phenomenon known by the name of St. Elmo's fire. It was known that discharges of batteries of Leyden jars affected magnetic needles placed near the apparatus." But these facts only gave vague ideas of the relation mentioned above.

In 1820, the year after that in which Oersted made his discovery, Ampere studied and described the laws of this action, and showed besides that the currents themselves acted on currents, and later Arago, Dacy and Sturgeon discovered the magnetizing of steel and soft iron under the influence of the current from a battery. The experiments of these men were so many points of departure for a multitude of new experiments which in a short time completely changed the aspect of this part of the science by showing that magnetism and electricity are different manifestations of the same cause.

Oersted expressed his discovery by saying that a current acts "in a revolving manner" on a magnetic needle. He does not, however, seem to have understood that the electric current carried about in a magnetic field, and that it was the mutual action of this field and of the magnetism in the needle that produced the deflection. Oersted expressed the law of the deflection as follows: When an electric current acts on the magnetic needle, the north pole of the needle is urged toward the left of the current.

Ampere was the first to use Oersted's discovery to measure the intensity of currents; but to Schweigger and to Poggendorf, working independently, is due to happy thought of multiplying the action of electricity on the magnetizing needle so as to detect the existence of the feeblest current. This instrument, then termed the multiplier, is now called the galvanometer, and its importance as a factor in the further development of the science is seldom appreciated. From this developed the Thomson galvanometer, in which the needles were made extremely small and light and having a mirror attached, upon which a beam of light was thrown, and the reflected beam was made to pass over a scale. The galvanometer was thereby furnished with a long weightless pointer, whereby the smallest motion of the needle was multiplied many times, and extremely small currents could be detected.

In September, 1820, a little while after the discoveries of Oersted and Ampere, Arago made the following experiment: He plunged into a mass of iron filings a copper wire which was connected to the two poles of a battery; on drawing out the wire, without interrupting the current, he found it to be covered over its whole surface with particles of filings arranged transversely. As soon as the current was broken the iron particles became detached from the copper and fell down. To assure himself that this was really temporary magnetism, and not the attraction of an electrified body for light bodies, he substituted for the iron filings a non-magnetic substance, such as copper dust or powdered glass, and found that the phenomenon did not take place. On placing needles of soft iron, and then of tempered steel, very near the copper wire and across it, he saw that the action of the current transformed them into magnetic needles, having their south poles always to the left of the current, a result in conformity with the earliest experiments of Oersted. Shortly afterward Arago and Ampere noticed that magnetism of iron or steel is developed much more energetically by placing the needle inside a spiral coil of wire through which the current flows. This was the origin of the electro-magnet which was later developed by Sturgeon and Henry.

The discovery of the greatest value to electrical science was that made by Faraday in 1831. He reasoned that if magnetism could be produced by the action of the electric current, the converse should also be true, and after some experimenting he was successful in demonstrating it. An interesting account of his experiments is given below, being an extract from Professor Tyndall's "Faraday as a Discoverer":

"In 1831 we have Faraday at the climax of his intellectual strength, forty years of age, stored with knowledge and full of original power. Through reading, lecturing and experimenting, he had become thoroly familiar with electrical science; he saw where light was needed and expansion possible. The phenomena of ordinary electric induction belonged, as it were, to the alphabet of his knowledge: he knew that under ordinary circumstances the presence of an electrified body was sufficient to excite, by induction, an unelectrified body. He knew that the wire which carried an electric current was an electrified body, and still that all attempts had failed to make it excite in other wires a state similar to its own. What was the reason of this failure?

"Faraday never could work from the experiments of others, however clearly described. He knew well that from every experiment issues a kind of radiation, luminous in different degrees to different minds, and he hardly trusted himself to reason upon an experiment that he had not seen. In the autumn of 1831 he began to repeat the experiments with electric currents which, up to that time, had produced no positive result. And here, for the sake of younger inquirers, if not for the sake of us all, it is worth while to dwell for a moment on a power which Faraday possessed in an extraordinary degree. He united vast strength with perfect flexibility. His momentum was that of a river, which combines weight and directness with the ability to yield to the flexures of its bed. The intentness of his vision in any direction did not apparently diminish his power of perception in other directions; and when he attacked a subject, expecting results, he had the faculty of keeping his mind alert, so that results different from those which he expected should not escape him through preoccupation.

"He began his experiments 'on the induction of electric currents' by composing a helix of two insulated wires, which were wound side by side round the same wooden cylinder. One of these wires he connected with a voltaic battery of ten cells, and the other with a sensitive galvanometer. When connection with the battery was made, and while the current flowed, no effect whatever was observed at the galvanometer. But he never accepted an experimental result until he had applied to it the utmost power at his command. He raised his battery from ten cells to one hundred and twenty cells, but without avail. The current flowed calmly through the battery wire without producing, during its flow, any sensible result upon the galvanometer. During its flow—and this was the time when an effect was expected; but here Faraday's power of lateral vision, separating, as it were, from the line of expectation, came into play—he noticed that a feeble movement occurred when he made contact with the battery; that the needle would afterward return to its former position and remain quietly there unaffected by the flowing current. At the moment, however, when the circuit was interrupted the needle again moved, and in a direction opposed to that observed on the completion of the circuit."

This result and others of a similar kind led him to the conclusion, in his own words, "that the battery current through the one wire did in reality induce a similar current through the other; but that it continued for an instant only, and partook more of the nature of the electric wave from a common Leyden jar than of the current from a voltaic battery." The momentary currents thus generated were called

VIII

induced currents, while the current which generated them was called the inducing current. It was immediately proved that the current generated at making the circuit was always opposed in direction to its generator, while that developed on the rupture of the circuit coincided in direction with the inducing current.

"It appeared," says Tyndall, "as if the current on its first rush through the primary wire sought a purchase in the secondary one, and by a kind of kick impelled backward through the latter an electric wave, which subsided as soon as the primary current was fully established. Faraday, for a time, believed that the secondary wire, tho quiescent when the primary current had been once established, was not in its natural condition, its return to that condition being declared by the current observed at breaking the circuit. He called this hypothetical state of the wire the electrotonic state; he afterward abandoned this hypothesis, but seemed to return to it in after-life. The term electrotonic is also preserved by Professor DuBois Reymond to express a certain electric condition of the nerves, and Professor Clerk Maxwell has ably defined and illustrated the hypothesis in the tenth volume of the 'Transactions of the Cambridge Philosophical Society.'"

The mere approach of a wire forming a closed curve to a second wire through which a voltaic current flowed was then shown by Faraday to be sufficient to arouse in the neutral wire an induced current; the withdrawal of the wire also generated a current having the same direction as the inducing current; those currents existed only during the time of approach or withdrawal, and when neither the primary nor the secondary wire was in motion, no matter how close their proximity might be, no induced current was generated.

"Faraday," remarks Tyndall, "has been called a purely inductive philosopher. A great deal of nonsense is, I fear, uttered in this land of England about induction and deduction. Some profess to befriend the one, some the other, while the real vocation of an investigator, like Faraday, consists in the incessant marriage of both. He was at this time full of the theory of Ampere, and it cannot be doubted that numbers of his experiments were executed merely to test his deductions from that theory."

Starting from the discovery of Oersted, the celebrated French philosopher had shown that all the phenomena of magnetism then known might be reduced to the mutual attractions and repulsions of electric currents. Magnetism had been produced from electricity, and Faraday, who all his life long entertained a strong belief in such reciprocal actions, now attempted to effect the evolution of electricity from magnetism. Round a welded iron ring he placed two distinct coils of covered wire, causing the coils to occupy opposite halves of the ring. Connecting the ends of one of the coils with a galvanometer, he found that the moment the ring was magnetized, by sending a current

FUNDAMENTAL DISCOVERIES

through the other coil, the galvanometer needle whirled round four or five times in succession. The action, as before, was that of a pulse, which vanished immediately. On interrupting the current, a whirl of the needle in the opposite direction occurred. It was only during the time of magnetization or demagnetization that these effects were produced. The induced currents declared a change of condition only, and they vanished the moment the act of magnetization or demagnetization was complete.

The effects obtained with the welded ring were also obtained with straight bars of iron. Whether the bars were magnetized by the electric current, or were excited by the contact of permanent steel magnets, induced currents were always generated during the rise and during the subsidence of the magnetism. The use of iron was then abandoned, and the same effects were obtained by merely thrusting a permanent steel magnet into a coil of wire. A rush of electricity through the coil accompanied the insertion of the magnet; an equal rush in the opposite direction accompanied its withdrawal.

The precision with which Faraday describes these results and the completeness with which he defined the boundaries of his facts are wonderful. The magnet, for example, must not be passed quite through the coil, but only half through, for if passed wholly through the needle it is stopped as by a blow, and then he shows how this blow results from a reversal of the electric wave in the helix. He next operated with the powerful permanent magnet of the Royal Society, and obtained with it, in an exalted degree, all the foregoing phenomena, and now he turned the light of these discoveries upon the darkest physical phenomenon of that day.

Arago had discovered, in 1824, that a disk of non-magnetic metal had the power of bringing a vibrating magnetic needle suspended over it rapidly to rest, and that on causing the disk to rotate, the magnetic needle rotated along with it. When both were quiescent, there was not the slightest measurable attraction or repulsion exerted between the needle and the disk; still, when in motion the disk was competent to drag after it not only a slight needle, but a heavy magnet. The question had been probed and investigated with admirable skill by both Arago and Ampere, and Poisson had published a theoretic memoir on the subject; but no cause could be assigned for so extraordinary an action. It had also been examined in this country by two celebrated men, Mr. Babbage and Sir John Herschel; but it still remained a mystery. Faraday always recommended the suspension of judgment in cases of doubt.

"I have always admired," he says, "the prudence and philosophical reserve shown by M. Arago in resisting the temptations to give a theory of the effect he had discovered, so long as he could not devise one which was perfect in its application, and in refusing to assent to the imperfect theories of others." Now, however, the time for theory had come. Faraday saw mentally the rotating disk, under the operation of the magnet, flooded with his induced currents, and from the known laws of interaction between currents and magnets he hoped to deduce the motions observed by Arago. That hope he realized, showing by actual experiment that, when his disk rotated, currents passed through it, their position and direction being such as must, in accordance with the established laws of electromagnetic action, produce the observed rotation.

Introducing the edge of his disk between the poles of the large horseshoe magnet of the Royal Society, and connecting the axis and the edge of the disk each by a wire with a galvanometer, he obtained, when the disk was turned round, a constant flow of electricity. The direction of the current was determined by the direction of the motion, the current being reversed when the rotation was reversed. He now states the law which rules the production of currents in both disks and wires, and in so doing uses for the first time a phrase which has since become famous. When iron filings are scattered over a magnet, the particles of iron arrange themselves in certain determined lines called magnetic curves.

In 1831 Faraday for the first time called these curves "lines of magnetic force," and he showed that to produce induced currents neither approach to nor withdrawal from a magnetic source, or center, or pole was essential, but that it was only necessary to cut appropriately the lines of magnetic force. Faraday's first paper on Magneto-electric Induction, which is here briefly condensed, was read before the Royal Society on the 24th of November, 1831.

Faraday delighted in investigation for the sake of the processes themselves. He had no inclination to follow up his discoveries with their practical application. The attitude of his mind is best described in his own words. "I have rather," he writes in 1831, "been desirous of discovering new facts and new relations dependent on magneto-electric induction than of exalting the force of those already obtained, being assured that the latter would find their full development hereafter."

CHAPTER IV

ELECTRO-MAGNETO MACHINERY

As previously related, the relations of electricity and magnetism were established by the investigations of Oersted, Ampere, Arago, Faraday, and others; but the one to whom the most credit is due is Faraday. He not only made discoveries of the greatest importance, but he followed up these discoveries with such true explanations of their principles that these explanations have become the basic laws of electro-magnetic induction. Faraday, however, did not care to make practical use of his discoveries, being sure that others would do so. What were some of these discoveries which have been of such great value to succeeding generations? One of them was a modification of Arago's experiment in which Faraday rotated a metallic disk between the poles of a magnet, and, by connecting one wire to the shaft of the disk and another in rubbing contact with its rim, produced a steady deflection on the galvanometer. This was really the first electro-magnetic generator. Here Faraday produced a continuous current without that drawback to direct current machines of the present day— the commutator.

It has from time to time been attempted to build machines based on Faraday's experiment, but the voltage generated was not sufficient for practical purposes. Recently, however, owing to the introduction of the steam turbine with its high speed, generators have been built of large powers and voltages of 600 or more which are based on this principle. In this experiment of Faraday's, then, was the beginning of the modern electric generator with its almost unlimited power of changing mechanical into electrical energy or vice versa. Faraday did not at first use an electro-magnet, but in his first public demonstrations used a very powerful permanent magnet. Faraday made many other experiments in the induction of currents, culminating in the production of an apparatus known as Faraday's ring, the ancestor of the modern alternating current transformer.

"The first development of Faraday's discovery," says Henry Morton in his "Electric Lighting," "was made by Pixii, of Paris, who in 1832 constructed an apparatus in which a large steel magnet was rotated so that its poles continuously and successively swept past those of an electro-magnet, or U-shaped bar of soft iron whose ends were surrounded with coils of copper wire. This motion generated in the copper wire rapidly alternating electric currents, which were 'commuted' or made to pass out of the machine in a constant direction by a simple 'commutator' on the axis of the revolving magnet, which shifted the connections each time the direction of the current was changed.

"In the machine of Pixii, near the top, are seen the copper-wire coils wound on cores of soft iron, like thread on a spool. Immediately below these is the permanent magnet, of a U shape and so supported that it can be rapidly rotated about a vertical axis midway between its poles, so that each pole is caused to approach, pass and recede from in succession each of the iron cores of the coils. Immediately below the bend of the U-magnet are the commutator segments, pressed upon by the contact brushes, and below these again is the gearing by which the magnet is made to rotate. Machines operating on the same principle, but varying in construction (as, for example, by rotating the electro-magnet or coils of copper wire while the steel permanent magnet remained stationary), were brought out by Saxton, of Philadelphia, in 1833; by Clark of London, in 1834; and by Page, of Washington, in 1835. None of these machines, however, was of sufficient size to be available for the production of a practical electric light, altho they all exhibited a capacity for this effect on a minute scale.

"The first magneto-electric machine of a magnitude sufficient to operate a practical electric lamp was that produced by the united labors of M. Nollet, Professor of Physics at the Military School of Brussels, and his assistant constructor, Joseph van Malderen, under the auspices of a corporation composed of French and English capitalists and known as the 'Alliance Company.' Strange to say, this machine was built with the absurd object of using it to decompose water and employ the resulting gases in the production of light."

This machine, with some modifications by Mr. Holmes, of England, was, under the superintendence of Faraday himself, introduced into two of the English lighthouses, at South Foreland and at Dungeness. Its preliminary trial was made in 1857. The electric light was first thrown over the sea from the South Foreland on the evening of December 8, 1858, and from Dungeness on the 6th of June, 1862.

The electric light was not introduced into the French lighthouses until December 26, 1863, when it was installed at La Heve, near Havre. It was also used for lighting works of construction, such as the Cherbourg Docks, and on some vessels, for example, on the Lafayette and the Jerome Napoleon. Altho Faraday lived to see the little spark which he had developed from a magnet and coil of wire in his laboratory grow into these magnificent illuminators of sea and land, it was not until after many years and numerous new developments that the electric light approached the commercial utility which it today possesses. These Alliance machines, on account of their great size and multitude of parts, were very expensive. Thus the two machines placed in the Dungeness lighthouse, with their engines, appliances, and lamps or "regulators," cost £4,760, or nearly $24,000. The two located at Souter Point in like manner cost £7,000, or about $35,000, and the machines and accessories for the two lights at South Foreland cost £8,500, or about $42,500. The same characteristics caused them to be liable to accident and injury and costly in repairs. The world therefore waited for some further development before it could enjoy generally the advantages of electricity as a means of illumination.

The first of these came when Dr. Werner Siemens, of Berlin, constructed a machine in which the revolving coil or armature was made of the form shown in Fig. 13, and was entirely enclosed between the ends of the permanent magnets. To construct this armature a long, solid cylinder of soft iron is taken, and two deep grooves are cut on opposite sides through its entire length, so that its cross-section is such as appears at F in the accompanying figure. Insulated copper wire is then wound lengthwise in these grooves, its ends being united to the section x, y of the commutator. Journals on which this armature rotates are provided at either end, and at one end also a pulley by which it may be driven by a belt.

This armature secured a great concentration of action by bringing the revolving armature into a highly concentrated field of magnetic force and allowing it to have a very rapid angular velocity of rotation. But the chief value of this improvement consisted in its serving as a step toward another, which was most remarkable in its results and excited the liveliest interest all over the world when it was announced.

This next step was taken by Wilde, of Manchester. He took a small magneto-electric machine, such as had been constructed by Siemens, and carried the current from its commutator to the coils of very large electro-magnets, which constituted the field magnets of a similar machine, which, however, differed from the other, or Siemens machine, both in size and in having its field constructed of electro-magnets in place of permanent magnets. The first or small magneto-electric machine was mounted on the top of the other, and sent the current from its commutator through the coils of the electro-magnet below, between whose expanded poles another Siemens armature was made to revolve. Under these circumstances the current developed in the armature of the upper machine by its permanent steel magnets will develop a more than tenfold greater magnetic force in the poles of the electro-magnet of the lower machine; and the second armature, rotating in this powerful magnetic field between the poles of this large electro-magnet, will develop a more than tenfold greater current than that of the smaller machine. This method of multiplying or creating magnetic force was a wonderful discovery, and, combined with the use of electro-magnets in place of permanent magnets for the production of magnetic field, gave an important increase in power and efficiency to the machine; for as compared with permanent magnets the power of electro-magnets is vastly greater.

This advance, made by Wilde on April 13, 1866, was quickly followed by another, made almost simultaneously in Europe by Varley, Siemens, and Wheatstone, and nearly a year earlier in this country by Mr. M. G. Farmer, whose work in another department of electric lighting is to be treated in more detail farther on. This development may be indicated by the term "self-exciting," and consisted in the discovery that if the commutator is so connected with the coils constituting the field magnets that all or a part of the current developed in the armature will flow through their coils, then all permanent magnets may be dispensed with, and the machine will excite itself or charge its own field magnets without the aid of any charging or feeding machine.

There is in all iron, unless special means have been taken to remove it, a little magnetic force. This small magnetic force, called "residual magnetism," in the iron cores of the field magnets will produce a little current in the armature when it is revolved. This current flowing through the coils of the field magnets will increase their magnetic force, and thus cause them to develop more current in the armature, which in turn, flowing through the coils of the field magnets, will further increase their magnetic force, and so on until maximum, determined by the structural conditions of the machine and the amount of driving force applied to the pulley of the armature, is reached. In practice such machines are each complete within themselves. When started they develop for a few moments only very feeble currents; but within a few seconds they "wake up" by degrees, and reach their maximum in less time than it takes to read this paragraph.

One other radical improvement in dynamo-electric machines remains to be recorded, namely, that due to the French inventor Gramme. The essence of this lay in the structure of the armature. While previous to Gramme all armatures had been constructed either like spools of cotton or like balls of yarn wound on blocks, he made his armature by starting with an iron ring (itself consisting of a coil of soft iron wire), and winding the copper wire on this by passing the end of the wire again and again through the ring. The copper wire is continuous throughout as regards its electric connection, but at frequent intervals a loop of this wire is carried out and attached to a segment of the commutator.

This armature being rotated in a magnetic field—*i.e.*, between the poles of powerful field magnets—tends to deliver a substantially continuous current to "brushes" touching the commutator segments at points midway between the poles of the field magnets. It will be remembered that the iron ring constituting the core of the Gramme armature was made of iron wires, and not of a solid piece or ring of iron. The object of this was to prevent the formation of electric currents in this ring-core itself, commonly called Foucault currents, which would be a cause of inconvenience by heating the armature and of loss by wasting energy in the useless production of this heat. The Siemens armature had so such provision, and accordingly very serious difficulties were experienced in the running of machines using such armatures by reason of the intense heat there produced. Arrangements were in fact made in many machines to relieve this symptom by running cold water through the armature, made hollow for that end; but this did not cure the disease or prevent the loss of efficiency caused by the conversion of the driving energy into useless heat in place of useful current. The desirable end was, however, soon secured by "laminating the armature core"—that is, making it up out of a great number of thin sheets of iron insulated from each other and held together by one or more bolts. The merit of this invention appears to have been assigned by the United States Patent Office to Edward Weston, September 22, 1882.

In comparing a Weston generator of about 1890 with a modern machine, the most marked feature is the large and heavy field magnet. Edison's first generators, of which some are still in operation, also contain these tremendous field magnets. These large field magnets were made necessary because the idea of embedding the wires in the armature in shots had not yet been originated. The fields were therefore made powerful in order to force the requisite magnetic flux across the large air gap into the armature.

By the later improvement of embedding the wires in slots in the armature, the air gap was much reduced and the fields made proportionately higher. This decreased very considerably both the weight and the cost of the machine.

A change in the design of direct current generators of considerable importance was occasioned by the desirability of connecting them to slow-speed engines of the Corliss type—engines of low steam consumption. To accomplish this many poles were arranged in a circular yoke, and these were called "multipolar" generators. Upon the introduction of the high-speed steam turbines, however, the number of poles was again decreased to two, four, or six, and the weight of a machine of given power was greatly reduced. Herein lies one of the advantages of the steam turbine for driving generators.

The dynamo is first of all a generator of alternating currents, and the commutator was added for the purpose of rectifying them. This commutator was always a source of trouble, mainly on account of sparking and the wearing away of the brushes and commutator surface. On the other hand, continuous currents are, in many cases, much easier to handle than alternating ones, and it was this fact which caused so much effort to be spent on the development of direct current apparatus. Direct currents could be transmitted with less loss of voltage in the line and direct current motors were quite well developed before 1890. These two very important facts caused the direct current to reign supreme. In the latter part of the 80's, however, its overthrow began, and ever since it has gradually been declining before the advance of its more flexible rival—the alternating current. At that time Nikola Tesla took out patents covering the principles of the induction motor—a motor which, on account of its mechanical simplicity, rapidly found favor, altho inferior to the direct current motor in many respects. The fundamental principle of these motors lies in the production of a rotating magnetic field, which field drags along with it, at a somewhat slower speed, a cylindrical armature called the rotor.

An idea of how a rotating field is produced by the action of polyphase currents is given in Professor S. P. Thompson's "Elementary Lessons in Electricity and Magnetism." "It is obviously possible," he says, "by placing on the armature of an alternator two separate sets of coils, one a little ahead of the other, to obtain two alternate currents of equal frequency and strength, but differing in phase by any desired degree. Gramme, indeed, constructed alternators with two and with three separate circuits in 1878. If two equal alternate currents, differing in phase by one-quarter of a period, are properly combined, they can be made to produce a rotary magnetic field. And in such a rotatory field conductors can be set rotating, as was first suggested by Baily in 1879.

"Consider an ordinary Gramme ring (Fig. 17) wound with a continuous winding. If a single alternating current were introduced at the points A A' it would set up an oscillatory magnetic field, a N pole growing at A, and a S pole at A', then dying away and reversing in direction. Similarly, if another alternate current were introduced at B B' it would produce another oscillatory magnetic field in the B B' diameter. If both these currents are set to work but timed so that the B B' current is ¼ period behind the A A' current, they will then combine to produce a rotatory magnetic field, tho the coil itself stands still. This is quite analogous to the well-known way in which a rotatory motion, without any dead points, can be produced from two oscillatory motions by using two cranks at right angles to one another, the impulses being given ¼ period one after the other. The above combination is called a diphase system of currents. If the B B' current is ¼ period later than the A A' current the rotation will be right-handed.

"Another way of generating a rotatory field is by a triphase system (or so-called 'dreh-strom') of currents. Let 3 alternate currents, differing from one another by ⅓ period (or 120°), be led into the ring at the points A B C. The current flows in first at A (and out by B and C), then at B (flowing out by C and A), then at C (out by A and B), again producing a revolving magnetic field. This is analogous to a 3-crank engine, with the cranks set at 120° apart."

One of the important features of these motors is their successful operation at high voltage—11,000 or more. Another feature is their mechanical simplicity, there being no commutator, rings, brushes or other parts to collect dirt and thus interfere with the operation of the machine. As previously stated, alternators are usually wound to generate two or three phase currents, altho they may be built for other

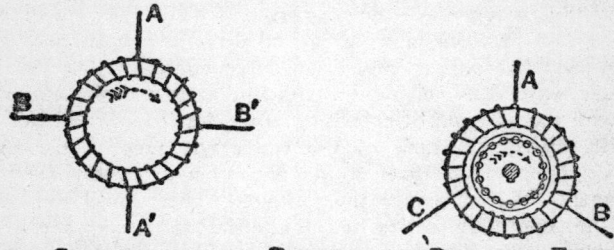

Fig. 17 —Connections for Producing a Rotating Field From Two-phase Currents.

Fig. 18 —Connections for Producing a Rotating Field From Three-phase Currents.

phases. In the last few years, however, the three-phase generator has practically controlled the field on account of the wide use of three-phase currents. Historically the generators have developed in the order of single, two, and three phase.

The first generators to come into commercial use were single-phase —i.e., had a single winding in the armature. A notable instance of the use of these generators was the first plant of the Telluride Power Company in Colorado, where a single-phase generator was connected to a water wheel and the electrical energy developed again converted into mechanical energy by an exactly similar machine used as a motor. When an alternating current generator is used as a motor it is called a synchronous motor, for the reason that its speed must be absolutely synchronous with that of the generator. Alternating current generators are thus reversible in their action, just as are direct current generators. They are not, however, usually self-starting, but require auxiliary motors to bring them up to speed.

After the development of the induction motor—it being necessary to have polyphase currents for the production of the rotating magnetic field—two-phase generators came into use. Probably the largest of these are located in the first and second Niagara Falls power houses, where there are twenty-one, each one being of 3,750 kilowatts or 5,000 horse-power capacity. In transmitting this power to Buffalo, it is first changed to three-phase by a simple connection of transformers—known as Scott's connection—because 25 per cent. of copper is saved thereby. In the more recently constructed generators three-phase windings are almost exclusively used, principally because of the advantage of three-phase transmission. It is a notable fact, however, that these generators were used in the Frankfort-Lauffen transmission of 1891 in Germany, transmission being effected, then as now, by three wires. These alternators are now built in sizes as large as 7,500 and 10,000 kilowatts, or 10,000 and 13,300 horse-power.

In 1893 the rotary converter was brought out. This machine is the connecting link between alternating and direct currents, usually serving to convert alternating into direct current, altho it may be used in the reverse way. In construction it is similar to a direct current generator, with the addition of collecting rings for the introduction of the alternating current. Many of the converters now in use are six-phase, the change from three to six phase being accomplished by the transformers used to reduce the voltage. These machines serve to connect the superior qualities of the alternating current for transmission purposes with the more perfect ones of the direct current motor for traction purposes. On account of the degree of perfection which has been attained recently with the alternating current motor, it would seem that the days of the rotary converters are numbered.

The induction coil and the alternating current transformer are found on the same principles, but differ somewhat in the purposes to which they are applied. Each depends upon the fact that if the magnetic flux passing through a coil is changed in value, an electromotive force will be set up in the coil which will be proportional to the rapidity of that change. There are several ways of producing the flux through the coil. One is by the introduction of a magnet into the coil, in which case the magnetic flux may be caused to change by moving the magnet in and out of the coil, there being established an electro-motive force in one direction upon its introduction, and in the reverse direction upon its withdrawal. Another method is to cause the flux created by another coil to pass through the first one and to vary this flux by changing the current in the second coil. The coil causing the flux is called the primary, and that in which the electro-motive forces are set up, the secondary coil.

The best way of making the flux set up by the primary coil pass through the secondary coil is to wind the two coils on the same core It will here be evident that an electro-motive force will be induced, not only in the secondary coil, but in the primary as well, since each turn of wire surrounding the changing magnetic flux is equally affected. This electro-motive force is called the electro-motive force of self-induction, and acts in such a way as to retard the establishment of a current in a coil, and to maintain it when it is attempted to stop it. In other words, it causes the circuit to act as tho it possessed inertia. From these statements it would appear, then, the more rapidly the electro-motive force which it is desired to set up, the more rapidly must the magnetic flux be changed and the greater must be its value. A flux withdrawn from a coil infinitely fast would produce an infinitely high electro-motive force, but this is no more possible than it is to stop a heavy fly-wheel instantly. Having now in mind what is desired in an induction coil, let us see how the various methods for producing these results gradually developed.

The credit for all discoveries in electromagnetic induction is usually given to Faraday. One should not, however, in this connection, forget Professor Henry, whose discoveries were made without a knowledge of Faraday's works, and but a few months after them. Faraday discovered the effect of one coil upon another, but Henry was the first to discover the electromotive-force of self-induction, and published his discovery in 1832. In his first experiments Henry used copper tape or ribbon, wound in the form of a spiral, and, upon passing a current through this spiral, and suddenly interrupting it, he obtained a bright spark, and if the two ends of the coil were touched by the hands at the instant of break, a shock was felt. When the current was alternately made and interrupted by rubbing one of the wires over a rough metal plate, vivid sparks were obtained. In 1836 the Rev. N. J. Callan, of Maynooth College, constructed an electromagnet with two separate insulated wires, one thick and the other thin, wound on the iron core together. The thick wire was copper, and through this the current was passed. The thin wire was iron, having one end attached to the thick winding. Upon making and breaking the current, he obtained severe shocks from the iron wire circuit. Later he extended his experiments by constructing a larger apparatus of sufficient power to kill small animals.

In 1837, Sturgeon, the inventor of the electromagnet, constructed a coil on Callan's plan, but of a shape resembling the wooden coil. He applied to his coils a make-and-break arrangement, consisting of a wire dipping in a mercury cup in one case and of a notched zinc disk in the other. He made experiments with solid iron cores, and noticed that when the interruptions of the current became too rapid, the effect was much diminished. He draws attention to the fact that G. H. Bachhoffner had tried a divided iron core and had observed that a bundle of fine iron wires used as a core gave far better shocks than when a solid iron bar was employed. Sturgeon therefore made use of the iron wire core in constructing his coils, one of which was exhibited to the London Electrical Society in August, 1837.

The next advance was made by Callan in September, 1837, when he constructed two coils, each with its primary and secondary windings separate. These coils he connected together with their primaries in parallel and their secondaries in series, so that the secondary electromotive forces added together. He surmises that if a hundred such induction coils could be arranged with their secondaries in series and their primaries in parallel, it would be possible to have a shock equal to 100,000 or 200,000 single cells.

In 1838, Professor Page, of Washington, constructed a coil closely resembling modern coils. The two windings were entirely separate and he used the iron wire core. In addition he made a very important improvement. It has been seen that the value of the electro-motive force depends upon the suddenness of the collapse of the magnetic flux. Page noticed that the spark produced in his mercury contact breaker was quite prolonged, so that the current producing the flux in the core was not stopped as suddenly as it should be, and he conceived the idea of covering the mercury with oil or alcohol in order to suppress the spark, and this proved a valuable addition. This device was revived many years after by other inventors, particularly by Foucault. Page was the first to notice that when a metallic sheath or tube is interposed between the primary and secondary circuits, it more or less annuls the action. Between 1838 and 1850 Page made many induction coils. With one of his coils he found he could obtain sparks ½ inch long in air. He also noticed the effect of rarefying the air upon the length of the discharge. With a coil giving only 1/16-inch sparks in air, he obtained a discharge of about 4½ inches in rarefied air. In 1850 he constructed a very large coil, from which he obtained sparks 8 inches long with a battery of 100 Grove cells.

It is to Ruhmkorff, a skillful mechanician of Paris, that modern electricians are indebted for many of the mechanical improvements in coil construction, and for the addition of the condenser which is used to suppress the spark at the break of the primary circuit, thus performing the same function as the coil on the mercury in Page's interrupter. So many of these coils were constructed by Ruhmkorff that this type of coil is commonly called by his name. One of the largest of these coils was made by him in 1867, the secondary containing 62 miles of wire. This coil could give sparks 16 inches in length. In its construction Ruhmkorff employed a method of winding the secondary so that no two neighboring parts should be at a very different potential. He had before been troubled with internal sparking of the secondary. Instead of winding the wire in layers, he wound it in small flat sections which were placed side by side on the core and connected in series. This method of winding was also employed by

E. I. Ritchie, of Boston, who constructed a large coil in 1860 capable of producing sparks of 21 inches with only three bichromate cells. One of the largest of this type of coil ever built was constructed by A. Apps in 1876, and is known as the Spottiswoode coil. The secondary of this coil contained no less than 280 miles of wire in 341,850 turns, and produced sparks 42 inches in length.

The evolution of the alternating current transformer from the induction coil was but a short step. The first intimation of it came in 1856, when C. F. Varley, of London, took out patents on an induction coil in which the iron wire core was extended and folded back on itself outside the coil, so that the ends overlapped and completed the magnetic circuit. J. B. Fuller, of New York, seems, however, to have been the first to recognize the value of the transformer as early as 1879, but his death caused the failure of his plans. A number of other inventors attempted to adapt the induction coil to the operation of lights, but they all worked with the idea of connecting the primaries in series, but the loading of each secondary was found to affect all the others, and the plan was not successful. The last experiment with this series arrangement of primaries was made in 1883 on the Metropolitan Railway in England. A Siemens alternator was put down at the Edgeware Road Station, and a high-pressure alternating current was led through the primary circuits of a series of secondary generators which reduced the pressure. The high-pressure current was transmitted through the primary coils of secondary generators. The length of the primary circuit was 16 miles and the primary coils of the secondary generators were placed in series upon it. Incandescent and arc lamps were worked at these various stations. The impossibility of independent regulation prevented the system from being a success.

The advantages of operating the transformer primaries in parallel from the same mains were first pointed out by Rankin Kennedy in 1883, but were not appreciated and acted upon until they were again brought forward in 1885 by Messrs. Ziperowsky, Deri and Blathy, of Budapest.

In August, 1885, the investigations of these gentlemen were made known in a series of technical papers, and in which the reasons for adopting the parallel mode of arranging induction coils were given fully, as well as descriptions of transformers suitable for this method of working. In the summer of 1885 the Inventions Exhibition was held at South Kensington, and part of the exhibit of the Edison and Swan United Electric Company consisted of a pair of 10 hp. Ziperowsky-Deri transformers working in parallel between a pair of high-pressure leads, and reducing the pressure from 1,000 to 100 volts. The currents for these transformers was supplied by a self-exciting alternator, and the primary current was conveyed by a pair of No. 10 B. W. G. insulated copper wires a distance of 800 yards to the place where the transformers were placed. The system was set in operation in London in July, 1885. The transformers were closed magnetic circuit transformers and the lamps were arranged on the secondary circuit in parallel.

"This was the first occasion," says J. A. Fleming in his "Alternate Current Transformer," "on which transformers with their primary circuits arranged in mains were exhibited operating incandescent lamps arranged in parallel on their secondary circuits. This small installation was worked throughout the summer and autumn of 1885 with perfect success. From and after this date the system of parallel working was universally adopted."

Transformers may be divided into four classes, depending on the disposition of the iron core. These are:

(1) Transformers with open or incomplete iron magnetic circuits.
(2) Transformers with closed or complete iron magnetic circuits.
(3) Transformers with an iron core.
(4) Transformers surrounded by an iron shell.

The first type was soon found to produce poor results, altho good for the induction coil, and closed magnetic circuits were used.

There are two common types of transformers, viz., constant potential and constant current. The first are used in such work as incandescent lighting, operating motors, etc., in which the voltage must be held constant. The second are employed to supply arc lamp circuits in which it is necessary to keep the current constant but vary the voltage to suit the number of lamps. Both transformers may operate from the same constant potential mains. In the constant potential transformer both primary and secondary windings remain fixed and the windings are interlaced as much as possible, so that all the magnetic flux created by the primary winding must also pass through the secondary winding. In the constant current transformer, however, this magnetic leakage is utilized to prevent the increase of the secondary current. The fact that the secondary and primary currents in a transformer are opposite in direction and cause a repulsion between the two coils is here utilized to bring about this result. The secondary coil is movable and its weight is nearly balanced. Any attempt of the current to increase creates a greater repulsive force between the windings, and the secondary moves away from the primary so that less flux from the primary passes through the secondary and the voltage of the latter is reduced. Such transformers are now made which produce an almost constant current in arc lighting circuits. Since 1885 transformers have gradually developed in size, efficiency, regulation of voltage, and ability to withstand high voltage. Transformers of 3,000 kilowatts capacity are now quite common. The voltage regulation is almost one per cent.—*i.e.*, the fall in voltage from no load to full load is only one per cent. Operation is successfully carried on at 110,000 volts.

What were some of the details which had to be developed to produce these large transformers? One of the first things done was to immerse them in oil. The first transformers were exposed to the air, from which the coils absorbed moisture, thus causing them to break down easily. The oil prevented this absorption, and also acted to insulate the windings, as it is very much harder for a spark to pass through oil than through air. In the very high voltage transformers the oil is exposed to a vacuum, and the last trace of moisture in it is extracted.

As the size of the transformer increased, greater difficulty was found in keeping it cool, for altho a large transformer is more efficient than a small one, yet the actual loss increases with the size, but without a corresponding change in bulk. For example, take the case of a 3,000-kilowatt transformer. Altho the loss is only about two per cent., this means an actual loss of 60 kilowatts, or as much heat as would be developed by 1,000 incandescent lamps of 16 candle power. To get rid of this heat, cold water is circulated in pipes through the oil or air is forced over the transformer.

CHAPTER V

THE DEVELOPMENT OF POWER TRANSMISSION

THE location of a convenient spot for the economical generation of electric power usually does not coincide with the center of its consumption, so that the connection of the two points presents a problem which has consumed the energies of many engineers. Among the natural available sources of energy to-day which are most prominent are coal and liquid fuels and the fall of water. Coal and the liquid fuels, can without much expense, be brought to many industrial centers, and the power plant is then erected at these points. In many cases, however, as in the western part of this country, the cost of cartage is prohibitive. On the other hand, water powers are abundant, but are not usually found at points where manufacturing may with profit be carried on.

The power available in such waterfalls, and which has been wasted for centuries, is at last being utilized through the medium of electrical transmission and has become an immense addition to the sources of energy. With the enormous amounts of power now required, the natural resources of fuel are fast becoming exhausted, and America would soon be left without the means of carrying on civilization had not methods of distributing the inexhaustible supply of energy in waterfalls been developed. The importance of the work which has been done and is still being done by those engaged in the design of these power lines is appreciated by few.

Some of the essential parts of such a system of power distribution need consideration. The power-house must be located on a stream which has at all times a sufficient flow to operate the generators at their full capacity. Failing in this, an artificial lake or storage reservoir may be constructed. In order that the power may be economically transmitted, the voltage of the line must be high, and the higher the better. The loss in the line varies as the square of the voltage, so that with the same line loss the power may be transmitted four times as far by doubling the voltage. The practical limit of generator voltage is about 13,000 volts. This is due to the difficulty met in insulating against higher voltages in the limited space available in the generator. The present tendency, where generators are turbine driven, as is the usual case, is to reduce the generated voltage. The high speeds incident to turbine operation make it cheaper to generate at a lower voltage and step up the current through a transformer on the outside.

The next important factor is the transformer, and in the perfecting of this piece of apparatus a great deal of attention has been centered. By its means, the voltage may be raised to almost any degree with a very slight loss of power, the limit being the ability of its insulating materials to resist breakdown. The advance in the art of constructing transformers has been such that they may now be built with the same assurance for 100,000 volts as formerly of 3,000 volts. There is, however, prospect of their successful operation at 500,000 volts.

Why, then, are lines not yet operating at 500,000 volts? Now comes the weakest part of the system, viz., the insulation of the line. The development of insulating materials has not been able to keep pace with that of the means for producing high voltages, altho it has been rapid. Insulators for carrying the lines have increased in size and cost until they have assumed great importance. Wooden poles have been replaced by steel towers, and rights of way have been granted through which the lines may pass. They are regularly patrolled by men whose business it is to report immediately to the power station any defects observed.

Operation of these lines in actual practice has not been as difficult as laboratory experiments tended to prove. There has been less leakage from the line than was expected and also fewer breakdowns. One of the main difficulties in the operation of these long lines has been due to lightning discharges, but even these are fast being eliminated. New lines are usually troubled with malicious persons who delight in shooting off the insulators, but these have been cured by the severe punishment inflicted. Large birds have sometimes caused arcs to start between the line wires by approaching too close.

Each year sees the limit of successful operating voltage raised. What would have been considered impossible a few years ago is now an accomplished fact. The highest practical operating voltage is 110,000, though successful experiments were made with 200,000 volts in Switzerland. For testing purposes, as high as 500,000 volts has been used. There is no standard voltage, lines being operated at 15,000, 60,000 or 100,000 voltage.

In reviewing the development of power transmission, an idea of its rapidity may be gained by observing the work of the pioneer plants. Altho much of the work was done in Europe, America has accomplished her share and has developed the alternating current system of power distribution to the point where it has finally triumphed over the European direct current system.

During the years from 1880 to 1890, power transmission was effected almost entirely by direct current. Electricity for power and lighting was sent out over the same lines, and the power load usually consisted of a number of small motors. The generators were wound for low voltage so that the lamps could be operated directly from them. Power stations were erected at the centers of distribution. As the load increased the size of the conductors necessary to give any kind of regulation became very large and the cost of the copper was enormous.

Edison was the first to devise a means of effecting an economy in the weight of copper necessary to transmit a given amount of power, and brought out the Edison 3-wire system, by which it was only necessary to use about three-eighths of the copper employed with the old 2-wire system. This system is still used in both direct and alternating current distributions for lighting. Edison made use of the fact that by doubling the voltage only one-fourth the weight of copper would be necessary, but he added a middle or neutral wire, whose voltage was half-way between the outside wires, so that the voltage between the outside wires was 240, and between either outside and the neutral was 120. The lamps were connected between either outside wire and the neutral, the neutral serving merely to carry the difference in the currents. If, therefore, the number of lamps on each side was the same, the neutral carried no current. If the lamps were properly distributed, it was possible to make the unbalancing current small, so that the neutral wire could be made smaller than the two outside wires. At the power station the 120-volt machines were connected in series and the neutral wire ran from the middle connection.

This was, of course, a great step ahead, as it permitted the transmission of power to greater distances, but the main advantage was the improved regulation—*i.e.*, the increased steadiness of the lights. Even this system, however, was only good for several miles, and therefore did not enable the power station to be removed to a location where fuel and water could be more economically obtained. The system is, however, good for congested districts where the lines are short.

Upon the introduction of the electric railway, the necessity for high voltage was forcibly impressed, and 500-600 volts soon became standard and has remained so until the present time. With this increased voltage it became possible to remove the power station to a point of convenient water and fuel supply.

For several years previous to 1890, Nikola Tesla had experimented with alternating currents with a view to the production of an alternating current motor, and was at last successful. About the same time transformers for raising and lowering the voltage were brought out, and the rotary converter for changing alternating into direct current was exhibited in 1893. This completed the steps in the development of the present alternating current system. The high voltage alternating current generator in the railway power-house gradually displaced the direct-current, and the power became concentrated in one large station, resulting in a more economical production of power. During this evolution the railway lines remained in operation on direct current at 600 volts. It is now standard. Interurban and long distance railways operate on 11,000 volts single phase alternating current. Recently direct current voltages of 1,200 and 2,400 volts have been adopted for long distance railway work.

The railroads radically increased the radius of transmission. Sub-stations were erected, and in these were installed the rotary converters. The power from the central station was all sent out at high voltage as alternating current to transformers, from the low voltage sides of which it entered the rotary converter, which changed it into 600-volt direct current. Each sub-station therefore acted as a supply station, but without the large cost of a generating station. The lines supplied by each sub-station were comparatively short and the voltage of the circuit remained much more nearly constant than before. A large and modern example is that of the Interboro Rapid Transit Co. of New York City.

Each of the generating units consists of a compound engine and a generator of 3,750 kw. capacity, delivering 25 cycle alternating current at 11,000 volts. The power is sent out at this voltage directly without the use of raising transformers and delivered to sub-stations along the subway lines. At these stations it is then reduced by means of lowering transformers to such a voltage that when applied to the rotary converter direct current will be delivered at 600 volts, which current operates the railway motors.

This system may be said to have become standard for large cities. Cables for underground use can now be made which are entirely reliable and satisfactory on 11,000 volts. This voltage is, however, as high as engineers will willingly guarantee and dispenses with the use of the large raising transformers necessary with lower voltage generators.

The first transmission of power to a distance in the United States was made in the year 1890, one year before the Frankfort-Lauffen experiment. This station is at the falls of the Willamette River in Oregon, thirteen miles from Portland, where water-power estimated at 225,000 horse-power is obtainable.

In 1893 it had been in successful operation for three years with satisfactory results, both as to the working of the apparatus and the cost of maintenance, the operation of the dynamos being described as admirable and the transformers not having cost a cent for repairs.

The plant, however, to which much of the present knowledge of conditions affecting high-voltage operation is due is that of the Telluride Power Co. in Colorado. This plant operates under particularly severe conditions, and in the overcoming of the obstacles encountered much valuable information was gathered. Here, for the first time, men were systematically trained for operating the plant, each man receiving a general education in all the branches of engineering connected with it. Much of its success was, therefore, due to the knowledge and skill of its operating force. Here that natural enemy of long-distance transmission—lightning—was met and conquered.

"Near Telluride, Colorado," says Atkinson, "is a waterpower station from which power is electrically transmitted to the Gold King mill, nearly three miles distant, where it is employed for operating crushers and stamps. It was equipped, when first constructed, with a Westinghouse alternating-current dynamo of 100 hp., operated by a Pelton turbine wheel driven by water received through a steel pipe 2 feet in diameter, under a head of 320 feet. The general construction of this dynamo is the same as that of the dynamos employed at the Willamette Falls station, but its field winding is composite, part of the magnets being excited by the armature current of a separate direct-current machine and the others by a current from its own armature, which is made by an apparatus equivalent to a two-segment commutator, the adjustment being such that the e.m.f. of the current delivered through the mains rises as the current strength increases, compensating for the fall of potential in the line and keeping the e.m.f. at the motor constant at 3,000 volts. The speed is 83 revolutions per minute, producing 10,000 alternations of current.

"The main current flows directly to the motor at the mill without transformation, the only transformers employed being the small ones connected with the indicators on the shunt circuits. The motor is the same in size, horse-power and general construction as the dynamo, and runs in synchronism with it, but is excited by a current from its own armature, obtained from a special winding parallel with the main armature coils, and connected with the field coils by a circuit in which the current is made direct by a commutator. A small Tesla motor of special construction is employed as a starter for the large motor, and is connected with the mains by a parallel circuit, as shown. The armatures of both motors are belted to a countershaft on which the ratio of size between the pulleys is such as to give the armature of the large motor a little higher speed than that of the small one.

"When the circuit of the small motor is closed its armature quickly attains its normal speed, putting the armature of the large one in rotation, at a speed somewhat higher than that of the dynamo, and causing it to generate a self-exciting current at the normal e.m.f. of the circuit. The small motor is then switched off and the speed of the large one gradually decreases till it is approximately equal to that of the dynamo, the relative speed of each machine being indicated by the degree of illumination in incandescent lamps connected in series with the secondary coils of two transformers whose primary coils are connected respectively, with the circuit of each machine, as shown; the illumination decreasing, from decrease of current, as the speeds of the two machines approach equality. When the proper relative speed, as thus indicated, is attained, the main circuit of the large motor is closed by its switch and it is connected with the mill machinery by its fricton clutch, the small motor having been disconnected by its clutch and brought to rest. The whole operation of starting is accomplished in about two minutes by one man.

"If the speed of the motor, on starting, should happen to be a little lower than that of the dynamo it may rise to the proper speed; but if much lower, it will continue to decrease, in which case the switch of the large motor is opened and that of the small one closed, and the speed thus restored. The field current of the motor, as indicated by the ammeter, is regulated, on starting, by a rheostat, and requires no further adjustment for the varying loads. The line runs across a rough country, ascending a mountain at the power station to a height of 2,500 feet, at an angle, in some places, of 45 degrees, and parts of it are practically inaccessible in winter, the snow being sometimes on a level with the tops of the poles. Special protection is required against lightning, to which this region is peculiarly liable, 40 discharges through the lightning arresters having, on one occasion, occurred in 40 minutes. The successful operation of the plant under these unfavorable line conditions, and with a comparatively new type of electric apparatus, since its completion in June, 1891, has inspired such confidence that extensive additions have been made both for power and lighting, which indicates that for the former purpose as well as the latter the employment of the alternating current with long-distance transmission has passed from the experimental to the practical stage." Since the above writing many trials of high voltage have been made at this plant, until it is now operating at 40,000 volts.

The Niagara Falls Power Transmission was one of the earliest, and is still the largest. The first station was built on the American side, and contains ten 5,000-hp., two-phase, 25-cycle, 2,200-volt alternating-current generators. Each of these generators is mounted at the top of a long, vertical shaft, at the lower end of which is the turbine. Since the weight of the generator and turbine is very great, too great to be supported by a bearing, the turbine is so constructed that the action of the water tends to balance this weight. The armatures of the generators are stationary and the field magnets revolve outside the armature, being shaped like an umbrella. The best engineering skill in the world was employed in designing the plant, and its success is largely due to that fact. Turbine wheels and generators of that size were practically unknown, and the starting of the plant marked the beginning of a new era in the development of large water-powers. Since the construction of the first plant another similar one has been built containing eleven units of the same capacity, making the total output of the two plants 105,000 hp. Two other plants also have been constructed on the Canadian side of the river, which deliver part of their power to towns in the United States.

Most of the power from the two American plants is consumed by local manufactories which have sprung up there; 30,000 hp. is sent to the city of Buffalo, about 25 miles away. Since power can be transmitted with 25 per cent. less copper with three-phase than with two-phase current, the two-phase current, generated at 2,200 volts, is changed by transformers to three-phase and the voltage at the same time is raised to 22,000. The distance to which Niagara Falls is transmitting its power is increasing daily, the greatest distance being to Syracuse, 160 miles away, where the power in 1916 was delivered at 60,000 volts.

A typical water-power station, with a transmission line surpassed in length by few is that of the Bay Counties Power Co. of California. It was the first of the big long-distance lines, and was put in operation on April 27, 1901. The company supplies power from three plants operated in parallel. Power is transmitted at 40,000 volts to Oakland, a distance of 142 miles from the main generating station, and power is supplied to the Standard Electric Company for transmission to various points along San Francisco Bay, the farthest of which is Stockton, 218 miles distant from the main power plant." It was ten years before this was outdistanced by the Southern Power Co., at Charlotte, N. C., at 100,000 volts, the line transmitting 240 miles.

Altho long-distance power transmission by continuous currents is practically unknown in this country, there are many examples of this type in Europe which have operated in competition with alternating current. Most of these plants are located in Switzerland and France, and are in satisfactory operation. Much of the development in continuous current working has been due to M. Thury, a French engineer, and the originator of the system. In this system a number of series-wound generators are connected in series, so that their voltage add together. It is evident, therefore, that any voltage may be generated by connecting together a sufficient number of such machines, and 60,000 volts have in this manner been obtained. Direct-current generators of this type can be built which will operate satisfactorily as high as 4,000 volts. In obtaining the 60,000 volts above mentioned sixteen of these generators are connected in series. Each machine is substantially insulated, both from the floor and from its driving turbine. The Thury system is known as a "constant-current" system, because the current is held constant no matter what the load may be; but the voltage is varied, so that at light loads the voltage is low, and reaches its maximum only at times of full load. The advantages of this are obvious.

The line is very simply constructed, consisting of two wires, and in case of accident to one wire the earth may be used as a return. The line, therefore, presents a much simpler construction than that for an alternating-current system requiring three wires. At the receiving end the electrical power is converted into mechanical power through a number of series motors connected in series across the line. A centrifugal governor attached to each motor holds its speed constant by varying its field strength. For this purpose a portion of the current (which is always the same) is shunted from the field through a resistance.

What are the advantages and disadvantages of this system? The chief advantage claimed for it by its advocates is the simplicity of its line construction. With direct current the insulation of the line is only subjected to the effective voltage of the line, while in an alternating-current transmission the voltage which the insulators must stand is at least 1.4 times the effective line voltage; and, in addition, surges of waves of voltage are liable to occur which may double this value. It will therefore be apparent that the direct-current line has a decided advantage. Another advantage claimed for it is its ability to operate during lightning discharges, since more effective arrangements may be made to prevent the lightning from entering the stations.

Coming to the stations, however, the direct-current system has serious drawbacks. It has not been found practicable as yet to build the generators larger than 400 kw. output. To equal one of the Niagara Falls power stations in output would, therefore, take 125 such generators. Advocates of the alternating-current system have always considered these stations too complicated for satisfactory operation. It must be admitted, however, that M. Thury, through persistent work, has simplified the station to such an extent as fully to meet this objection.

On the whole, alternating-current transmissions seem to be more satisfactory than the direct current, and this advantage will increase as alternating-current motors reach the perfection attained by direct-current machines and line insulation becomes so perfected as easily to withstand the voltages imposed upon it.

Regarding recent developments in high-voltage transmission and its future limits, the "Engineering Record" may be quoted. It said:

"At last the next great step has been taken, thanks to the enterprise of the insulator maker, and especially to the construction of the suspension type of insulator, which makes relatively easy pressures before difficult. The pin insulator, when constructed of dimensions adequate for very high voltage, became unwieldy and mechanically troublesome; not so the suspension insulator, which actually leads to improvements in line construction. It will probably be found, too, as is often the case, that the precautions now considered necessary in going to very high voltages will prove to be more than adequate in the light of practical experience. It is a fact that in Continental practice surprisingly small and simple insulators have been found entirely successful for pressures considerably higher than would be attempted with the same material here. American engineers attach great importance to preserving a high line insulation, as they should, but they went through a period in which the size of insulator was all out of proportion to their quality and design. Now, practice is settling into sounder lines and will go on to better and better results. The fact is that at every stage of progress toward high voltage advance has proved to be easier than seemed at first possible. Difficulties that seemed insuperable have been, time and again, overcome with comparative ease, so that now one is not beside the mark in counting upon a very general advance in the near future. Of course, the plants in which 100,000 volts or more is a figure commercially necessary are relatively few. As time goes on, however, and the more remote powers are utilized, high voltage will become more and more necessary, and will be more generally employed.

"As to the limits which may be reached one would be unwise to prophesy. At 100,000, or about there, a condition is reached where, save for large powers and long wires, further increase would lead to wires too small to be desirable mechanically. In addition, it is undesirable, for electrical reasons, to use anything much below a quarter inch in diameter at very high pressure, so that there is a natural limitation to the number of very high voltage plants. Yet, for the really big work of the future, success depends on just such bold achievements as the one here considered. The next step will probably be in the direction of a very long line at extreme voltage. Here, again, is a debatable ground, owing to line difficulties. No one has yet operated a line of such wave length as to be a material fraction of the natural wave-length corresponding to the frequency. There is a possibility of a new class of troubles arising under such circumstances, and new devices may be required to meet it. It is on such very long lines that the use of high-tension continuous current has found some advocates. Severe requirements as to the use of cables is a possible source of future trouble, but here also the manufacturer may be counted on to push ahead; 20,000-volt cable is in use in England to the extent of several hundred miles, and 40,000-volt cable has been successfully worked, so that if the time should demand underground lines at 100,000 volts or more, it is safe to say that they would be forthcoming."

CHAPTER VI

THE HISTORY OF ELECTRIC LIGHTING

The history of electric lighting begins soon after the discovery of electric currents. In 1800 Sir Humphrey Davy, while experimenting with the effects of currents, obtained bright sparks between two charcoal points upon breaking the contact between them. The number of cells with which he worked was, however, insufficient to produce a continuous light. After a few years he increased the number of cells in his battery until it was composed of 2,000 elements. With this powerful source of current he was able to obtain a continuous discharge between carbon points which sustained itself across a gap of 7 inches and emitted a dazzling light. This light was exhibited in 1813 at the Royal Institution. Davy found that the conducting power of the charcoal points was improved by extinguishing the charcoal under mercury. The consumption of these points was very rapid. The name "voltaic arc" came from this experiment of Davy's, from the fact that the stream of vapor formed itself into a bow, the charcoal points being horizontal.

Owing to the high cost of producing the electrical current no one seems to have cared either to develop a lamp or to ascertain the properties of the arc itself until 1844, when Foucault constructed a lamp using carbons from the retorts of gas works, which were much harder and more compact than Davy's charcoal points and less easily consumed.

Thomas Wright, of London, devised the first apparatus (1845) in which the adjustment of the carbons is brought about automatically. W. C. Staite used the electric current for the regulation of the carbons in 1848. In 1858 Faucault devised a lamp in which the carbons were made to approach automatically by means of a clockwork feed, the clockwork being controlled by an electromagnet. As the current diminished in strength, due to the increase in the length of the arc as the carbons burned away, a magnet in series with the arc weakened and released the escapement of the clockwork, thus moving the carbons together. In this lamp both carbons moved, and were so regulated in their motions as to maintain the arc in a fixed position. In later lamps, used for general illumination, this was not considered necessary, and the regulating mechanism was considerably simplified.

The lamps were known as "focussing" or "self-centering" lamps, and are still necessary in some cases, such as stereopticon work.

Before proceeding with the history some of the properties of the arc may be examined. If it is attempted to produce an arc by means of a battery of few cells, the attempt will be unsuccessful. It is necessary that a difference of potential of about 40 volts should exist between the carbons before any stream of vapor will be formed. The longer the arc produced the higher is the voltage necessary to maintain it. In the ordinary carbon lamp practically no light comes from the arc itself; it is all emitted from the white-hot carbon points. If the source of current is direct or continuous, most of the light is radiated from the positive carbon, or that by which the current enters, and this carbon is consumed about twice as rapidly as the other. From the fact it will be seen that in such lamps as Foucault's it was necessary to arrange the mechanism so that the positive carbon should move at about twice the rate of the negative. Another peculiarity is the manner in which the carbon points burn away. When the combustion takes place in the air the positive carbon has a depression or "crater" formed in it, and upon the negative is produced a nib. This seems to be due entirely to the fact that combustion takes place in air, as the phenomenon disappears when the arc is enclosed, and both carbons become blunt. This seemingly slight difference was, however, a factor of considerable consequence, as the greater part of the light is emitted from the intensely hot crater of the positive carbon, so that in the open arc much of the light is cut off from the horizontal direction by the rim of the crater, which is removed by enclosing the arc. The temperature of the arc is the greatest of all earthly temperatures, about 7,000° F. Nearly all substances volatilize instantly at it.

Arc-lamp development was stimulated by the construction of the magneto-electric machine, which greatly decreased the cost of power. The introduction of the dynamo, however, completely solved the problem of power, and the field was immediately opened for the electric light.

One of the first successful lights was the electric candle of Paul Jablochkoff, invented in 1876. This is probably the simplest of all electric lamps. It consisted of two carbon rods placed parallel, and separated from each other by plaster of paris, the rods having brass tubes at their lower ends which make contact with springs set in the holding device. To start the candle a thin plate of graphite was laid across the tip, this being heated by the passage of the current sufficiently to start the arc. Difficulty was, of course, encountered in operating these lamps on direct current on account of the unequal rates of burning of the positive and negative carbons. It was attempted to overcome this by making the positive twice as thick as the negative carbon, but the ratio not being exact, and liable to variation, caused the failure of this method. They were therefore operated on alternating current, and over 4,000 were in use in Paris alone. The lamps, however, were not satisfactory, and inventors gradually reverted to the lamp with the adjusting mechanism.

As soon as arc lamps had to be operated over a considerable territory it was seen that the mode of connection, known as "series," wherein a single wire is used to connect the lamps together, was preferable to the "parallel" system, which required two wires, both in economy of wire and in saving of power. This required a special arrangement of the lamp mechanism. On the series system the same current passes through each lamp, and since it requires about 50 volts to operate a lamp the generator must develop as many times 50 volts as there are lamps. This necessitated the construction of a generator which should develop a high voltage, as there were often as many as 125 lamps on one line, requiring 125×50, or 6,250 volts. Such a suitable generator was devised by Mr. Charles Brush, and is known as the Brush arc-lighting dynamo.

Returning to the mechanism of the lamps suitable for such a circuit, one of the first of these was constructed by Hefner Alterneck, and is known as the Siemens differential lamp. This type of regulator is still in use, altho, of course, modified and improved. The lower solenoid is known as the "series" coil, and carries the same current that passes through the arc. The upper solenoid has many turns of fine wire and is connected across the arc. The two coils act upon the same core in opposite directions, hence the name "differential." If the carbons approach too closely the current in the series coil increases and pulls them apart, but as the length of the arc is increased thereby the voltage across it grows greater and the upper solenoid receives more current. This prevents the series coil from producing too great a motion, and the carbons are held by the balancing action of the two coils. The upper carbon alone is fed down by the action of gravity, the lower carbon being fixed. This style of lamp was also developed by Brush in America, and many thousands have been used. The combination of the Brush high-voltage generator and the differential-series lamp was quite satisfactory as a means of lighting, and many of these arrangements are in use at the present time, altho they are fast being replaced by more modern systems.

With the open arc lamp of the Brush type the replacement of the carbons was required daily, and became quite an item in the total expense of operation. About 15 years ago arcs enclosed by a thin glass were introduced which required trimming only once in ten or fifteen days. At first it was thought that the enclosing glass would cut off so much of the light as to seriously impair the efficiency of the lamp. The fact previously mentioned concerning the flattening of the carbon tips and a consequent better distribution of the light here came to the aid of the enclosed lamp, so that altho there was some loss of light due to the glass, the improved distribution overbalanced that effect. A grave fault, however, was the deposition of the silicious impurities of the carbons on the enclosing glass, with a consequent diminution in the light. Efforts were accordingly directed toward the improvement of the carbons, and altho it has not been found possible to produce carbons free from such materials, that fault is not at the present time serious.

Altho the series system of operation is the only practicable one over long distances, it is often required to operate arc and incandescent lamps on the same circuit, as in buildings, etc. For such work the differential mechanisms of the series system is not suitable. In that system the lamps act to steady one another, for with so many in circuit the fluctuations of one lamp do not appreciably affect the current in the circuit. The operation of a simple lamp requires, therefore, something to replace the steadying action of the other arcs, and this is accomplished by means of a dead resistance. Some energy is, of course, wasted in this resistance (about 25 per cent.), but the operation is very satisfactory.

The ordinary carbon arc lamp, altho one of our most efficient sources of light, is still far from the ideal. Of the total energy radiated from it only about 10 per cent. has the proper frequency of vibration to affect the eye as light. The ideal light would emit rays all of which would affect the eye. One means of effecting this increase is to raise the temperature of the heated body; another, to employ a different material, since all materials do not emit equal light at the same temperature. Attempts to utilize the latter principles resulted in the production of "luminous" and "flaming" arcs. Some of the most prominent workers on this subject are Bremen, Auer, Nernst, Blondel, Whitney and Steinmetz.

The luminous arc is composed of two electrodes which supply a stream of light-giving vapor. One of the most prominent examples of this type is that developed by Mr. Steinmetz, and known as the magnetic arc. The positive electrode is a rod of copper, the negative a rod of magnetite, or iron ore. The light given off is an intense greenish white, the efficiency being several times that of the ordinary arc. They have recently been established on a commercially operative basis, altho still unsatisfactory in some respects. They can operate only on direct current, which usually involves the rectification of the alternating current, now almost universally generated.

The flaming arc is almost invariably produced by utilizing the intense heat of the carbon arc to render incandescent various refractory materials. For this purpose either one or both of the carbons are impregnated with metallic salts having great light-giving power, as calcium, titanium, strontium, etc. The most efficient of these are the salts

HISTORY OF ELECTRIC LIGHTING

of calcium, which emits dazzling yellow rays. For some purposes—as interior lighting—these rays are objectionable on account of the distortion of color which they produce, and the salts of titanium are preferred, as they emit a beautiful white light, altho of less intensity. The lamps may be operated on either direct or alternating current. The objectionable features of these lamps are the increased cost of the carbons and their short life. For that reason they have not yet come into general use for street lighting. In respect of life the magnetic arc has the advantage, its life being about the same as the enclosed carbon arc—150 hours.

Developments in arc lighting have followed one another with such rapidity during the last seven or eight years, and are still progressing so swiftly, that one hardly knows where they will stop. The fine organizations of engineering and scientific skill under the control of large electrical enterprises have made possible these rapid developments of the last few years.

"Admirable as is the system of electric-arc lighting for use in streets and open spaces, and in workshops or large halls," says Henry Morton in his "Electricity in Lighting," "it is entirely unfit to take the place of the numerous lights of moderate intensity employed for general domestic illumination. For this purpose it was at a very early period perceived that the incandescence, or heating to luminosity, of a continuous conductor by an electric current was the most promising method. It was also at a very early period perceived that the conductor to be used for this purpose must be one which would admit of being raised to a very high temperature without being melted or otherwise destroyed. The first material which was thought of in this connection was platinum, or one of its allied metals, such as iridium, which have the highest melting points among such bodies, and are, besides, entirely unacted upon by the air at all temperatures.

"In 1848 W. E. Staite took out a patent for making electric lamps of iridium, or iridium alloys, shaped into an arch or horseshoe form. One of the most serious difficulties, however, even with these materials, was that to secure from them an efficient light it was necessary to bring them so near to their fusing points that a very minute increase in the current would carry the temperature beyond this and destroy the lamp by fusing the conductor.

"An escape from the difficulty was offered by the use of hard carbon, such as that employed for the electrodes of arc lamps; but here the compensating drawback was encountered that this substance, when highly heated, was attacked by the oxygen of the air, or, in other words, burned. To meet this plans were devised for the replacement of the consumed carbon in a non-active gas or in a vacuum. Thus, in 1845, a patent was taken out in England by Augustus King, acting as agent for an American inventor named J. W. Starr, for an incandescent lamp, the important parts of which are represetned in Fig. 23. Here a platinum wire is sealed through the top of a small glass chamber constituting the upper end of a barometer tube. This platinum wire carries at its power end a clamp, which grasps a thin plate or rod of carbon, and also a non-conducting vertical rod or support, which helps to sustain another clamp, which grasps the lower end of the carbon strip and connects it by a wire with the mercury in the barometer tube below. By passing a current through the platinum wire, and thence through the upper clamp, carbon strip, lower clamp, wire and mercury, the carbon strip could be made incandescent, and was to a certain extent protected by the surrounding vacuum. Tho this lamp produced a brilliant light, it proved in various respects unsatisfactory, and was abandoned after numerous trials. Other inventors, as, for example, Konn, of St. Petersburg, continued to work with rods or pencils of hard carbon and achieved a limited success, but the irregularity and brittleness of the material seem to have been an insuperable objection and drawback, and the problem of commercial electric lighting by incandescent conductors yet remained without a solution.

"This was the state of affairs even up to the fall of 1878, when, as is claimed, William E. Sawyer, in combination with Albon Man, after many preliminary experiments, produced their first successful incandescent lamp with an arch-shaped conductor made of carbonized paper. In their application for a patent, filed January 8, 1889, these inventors use the following remarkable language in their fourth claim: 'An incandescing arc of carbonized fibrous of textile material.' This indicates that they realized the importance of what seem to be the common features of the present electric incandescent lamps, namely, the arc or arch or bow or loop form, and the carbonized fibrous or textile material. They also specially refer to carbon incandescent conductors made from paper.

"After a long and hotly contested interference, the United States Patent Office has granted them a patent in which these points are broadly stated. The lamp brought out by Messrs. Sawyer and Man, soon after their application for a patent, and described and shown in that application, was a rather large and complicated structure, and had no improvement and simplification of this structure been made the present immense development in electric lighting would no doubt have been unattainable. It is to T. A. Edison, without doubt, that we owe many of the simplifications and modifications which, by cheapening the lamp and diminishing its weight, have extended its range of use and its usefulness to a remarkable degree. On his return in the fall of 1878 from the far West, where he had gone in company with Dr. and Mrs. Henry Draper, Dr. George P. Barker and the present writer, to observe the total solar eclipse of that year, Mr. Edison visited the shops and laboratory of William Wallace, at Ansonia, Conn., where many experiments with electric-arc lights and dynamo-machines were in progress, and while studying these was impressed with the desirability of producing an incandescent electric lamp. Like so many before him, he first turned to platinum and platinum alloys, and devised a form of lamp admirable for its simplicity, but, unfortunately, open to a fatal objection.

"The announcement of a new system of electric lighting, made by Mr. Edison and his friends on the foundation of this device, attracted universal attention, and even caused a serious fall in the value of 'gas stocks' in this country and abroad. It is, indeed, amusing now to look back upon the extravagant assertions and predictions made at that time and widely circulated when we realize how more than frail was their foundation. In fact, Mr. Edison very soon found out that this simple device was entirely insufficient for the purpose proposed, because the heated platinum wire gradually stretched by its own weight, and thus was constantly getting out of adjustment, and finally would become attenuated and break.

"It also happened that, though the secret of this great invention was carefully guarded, some inkling of it escaped, and this enabled those who were familiar with such subjects to perceive the close similarity between this Edison lamp and a similar device constructed and used by Dr. J. W. Draper prior to 1847, and described and figured in articles published by him during that year in the American Journal of Science and Arts, The London, Edinboro and Dublin Philosophical Magazine, and Harper's New Monthly Magazine. This apparatus was used by Dr. Draper as a source of light or lamp with which he determined the relations between temperature and luminosity. At the conclusion of his article Dr. Draper says: 'An ingenious artist would have very little difficulty, by taking advantage of the movements of the lever, in making a self-acting apparatus in which the platinum should be maintained at a uniform temperature notwithstanding any change taking place in the voltaic current.'

'It also appeared that precisely the same idea had occurred to another inventor, Hiram S. Maxim, who has developed such a marvelous improvement in magazine or repeating guns, and who, on December 22, 1879, filed an application for a patent which, after an interference litigation with Edison, was finally issued to Maxim on September 20, 1881. It has also been shown that in 1858 M. G. Farmer, one of the veteran electricians of America, to whose work in connection with the dynamo-electric machine allusion has been made before, lighted a room in his house at Salem, Mass., for several months with platinum lamps of similar structure controlled by automatic regulators. During 1878 and 1879, however, Mr. Edison was most diligently at work, and perceiving the imperfections of his first ideas, sought in every way to overcome them. It thus came to pass that by December 21, 1879, at which date he made his first revelation to the public, in the pages of the New York Herald, he had perfected a platinum lamp, as well as some other forms substantially like it.

"But these platinum conductor lamps were not the only outcome of Mr. Edison's work between the fall of 1878 and December, 1879. As this Herald article also related, Mr. Edison, like many before him, having experienced the insuperable difficulties present in metallic conductors, has turned his attention to carbon in various forms; and, like Sawyer and Man, had found fibrous textile materials, when carbonized, to be most convenient, and paper especially to be, in the first instance, the most available substance. Like Sawyer and Man, he had also found the arch, or horseshoe form, to be the most desirable. Tho working with the same materials and form, Edison produced a structure very different in appearance from that of Sawyer and Man, which was the first one whose electric properties were accurately measured, these measurements having been made at the Stevens Institute of Technology, early in 1880, by the present writer, acting in his capacity as Chairman of the Committee on Scientific Tests of the United States Lighthouse Board, that body desiring information as to this new light, and deputing the work of investigation to this committee.

"In this lamp the carbon conductor is supported on platinum wires and held in minute platinum clamps at the ends of these wires, which are sealed through the walls of the pear-shaped enclosing tube in the manner which has been familiar for twenty years in the construction of the beautiful toys known as 'Geissler tubes.' The interior of this glass vessel had likewise been exhausted and hermetically sealed, in the manner usual with many Geissler tubes and with the radiometers of Dr. William Crookes."

From the date of its invention until about 1908, the Edison carbon-filament incandescent lamp held a practical monopoly. About this time, other lamps, using metallic filaments and giving greater efficiencies, were put on the market, and the years from 1908 to 1912 saw intense competition for supremacy between the various lamps. With 1914 began a new period.

Edison's first filaments were made of carbonized thread or paper. It is obvious that such filaments could not be made with any great uniformity. A great many experiments were made and are still being made to determine the best method of making them. They are all, however, made by what is called the "squirting" process, of which an outline follows.

Pure cellulose, as cotton-wool or blotting paper, is dissolved in a concentrated solution of zinc chloride until a jelly-like mass is obtained. Great care is required to obtain pure materials, and the various processes must be closely watched. This mass is filtered by forcing it through a suitable filter such as glass-wool, fine wire-gauze, or flannel. It is then heated under a vacuum to free the viscous material from air carried into it by the cotton-wool or cellulose. It is then squirted, under fairly high pressure, through a fine orifice, which just dips below the surface of acidified alcohol contained in a tall glass jar. The alcohol hardens the cellulose, which forms a fine thread of a diameter depending on the size of the orifice. By revolving the jar, the thread is coiled in it. When hard, it is removed and washed, and wound on drums to dry. When dry, it has the appearance of catgut. It is then given the desired shape by being wound on molds and baked. Bundles of filaments are then packed in carbon powder in plumbago crucibles which are raised to as high a temperature as possible.

The carbonized filaments are gauged for diameter and the legs cut to the required length, after which they are ready for mounting on to the leading-in wires. There are two methods for doing this. In one, the ends are laid against the leading-in wires and a drop of paste composed of graphite mixed with a binding material is applied, the paste being afterward dried in an oven; in the other, by heating the joint red-hot in an atmosphere of benzene, the benzene having decomposed and carbon deposited.

The filament is then "flashed" in order to make it more uniform and increase its life. Flashing is accomplished by placing the filament under a bell-jar filled with hydrocarbon vapor, and raising it to incandescence by the passage of a current, whereupon the vapor is decomposed and a firm compact coating of carbon is deposited upon it. The greatest deposit takes place where the filament is thinnest, as the current causes it to heat most in that part. Flashing, therefore, smooths out the irregularities of the filament.

The filaments are next sealed into bulbs and the bulb exhausted. In the early days, Sprengel mercury pumps were used, but these were very slow, altho very perfect. Nowadays, a little phosphorus dissolved in alcohol is introduced into the stem, which is then connected to a mechanical air-pump having oil-sealed valves and exhausted as far as possible. The stem is then sealed a short distance below the bulb and the phosphorus vaporized by a little heat into the bulb, where it combines with the remaining oxygen and completes the exhaustion. The lamp is then properly sealed off.

The first patents covering the principle of the Nernst lamp were taken out by Professor W. Nernst in 1897 and 1898. In its first form it was very crude, serving mainly to show the fact that the filaments could be produced and that their efficiency was about twice that of the ordinary carbon filaments. This was the first incandescent lamp to threaten the life of the Edison carbon filament lamp. Much was promised for it at first, and its development was vigorously taken up in this country, England and Germany. Altho the lamps are still manufactured, very few are in use, and it is probable that the manufacture of them will soon cease entirely. The recent introduction of the tungsten lamp has made its existence unnecessary, as it is surpassed by the tungsten lamp in efficiency, life and first cost. It contains, however, a very interesting principle, viz., the employment of an electrolytic conductor as the incandescent body. This conductor or glower, as it is called, is practically non-conducting at ordinary temperatures and requires to be heated before it will allow the passage of current through it. This fact is probably the principal cause of its failure commercially, as the heating apparatus is quite complicated, of uncertain life, and the time consumed in lighting (sometimes half a minute) is in many cases objectionable. This is the only electric lamp that can be started with a match and blown out.

The glower of the American form of Nernst lamp is said to consist of the oxides of several rare metals, such as yttrium, ytterbium, thorium, etc., altho the true composition is known only to a few. The glowers are in the form of a short, thick filament, cemented to flexible platinum terminals by which it is suspended below and close to heating coils, consisting of porcelain tubes in which are imbedded resistance wires. These resistance coils are, of course, necessary to bring the glower up to the temperature at which it begins to conduct. The heating resistance is connected in shunt with the glower, which has in its immediate circuit an electro-magnetic switch for opening the heater circuit. When the glower becomes sufficiently heated to conduct, the current in this portion of the circuit operates the electro-magnetic switch and automatically cuts out the heating coils.

As the glower conducts electrolytically rather than as a solid, up to the present it has given a much shorter life when used on direct or low frequency alternating current circuits than with higher frequencies. Altho up to the present time these lamps cannot be called a commercial success, recent developments and improvements in constructional details have made the efficiency of the lamp equal to that of the tungsten. If a method of producing a lamp free from the complicated starting apparatus which now prevails is discovered, these lamps may be heard from again.

These lamps have followed one another in such rapid succession that some of them, altho full of promise, have never been long in the commercial field, having been succeeded by others still better. Incandescent electric lamps with metallic filaments are older than carbon-filament lamps. As long ago as 1840 lamps were constructed with filaments of platinum, and for thirty years after that date various attempts were made to construct a practical lamp, using either platinum or iridium wires for the filaments, the only two metals at all suitable which were obtainable at the time. None of these attempts met with any commercial success, and the use of metals was finally abandoned in favor of carbon by the experimenters who developed the carbon-filament lamp in 1879-1880.

The success attained with carbon caused all consideration of metallic filaments to be put on one side for nearly twenty years. The introduction of the Nernst lamp appears to have then stimulated research afresh, and many inventors turned their attention to the metals, to find the field greatly widened by the chemical progress which had been made in the meantime. Instead of only two possible metals to work with, there were now numbers known with sufficiently high melting points to suggest great possibilities. After much painstaking effort and laborious work, carried out by inventors who deserve the highest possible praise for both their ingenuity and their perseverance, three commercial metallic-filament lamps have been evolved which have given a new set of possibilities to the electric lighting industry.

While the metallic filament lamp was still in the laboratory stage, a form of carbon lamp known as the metallized-carbon-filament lamp was introduced. This lamp at first threatened to take the place of all other filament lamps. It was sold under the trade name of the Gem lamp and developed efficiencies far above those of the pure carbon lamp. The metallized filament was baked a second time, after flashing in a carbon dust packed crucible at a temperature of 5,400° F. These filaments took on an elastic coat over the outer surface which exhibited some of the properties of graphite and some peculiar to itself. The osmium lamp is the invention of Dr. Auer von Welsbach, and the earliest patents relating to it were taken out in 1898. The earlier reports in reference to the osmium lamps appeared in the technical press in 1901, but the lamp did not appear to have been manufactured commercially until 1903, and it was not until 1905 that it was introduced here by the General Electric Company.

"The method of manufacture may be gleaned from the patents and from a paper read by Dr. Fritz Blau before the Elektrotechnischer Verein in 1905. The method finally adopted was that of pressing finely-divided osmium, mixed with an organic binding agent, through small diamond or sapphire dies. The thread thus formed is carbonized, and the carbon is then driven off by incasing the filament in an atmosphere of steam and hydrogen.

"The filaments have to be raised to a very high temperature in order to 'sinter' together the osmium particles into a practically homogeneous filament. Sintering may be described as a sort of modified welding process; the metal does not fuse, but the particles raised almost to their melting point bake together and bind very firmly; as a matter of fact exactly the same phenomenon occurs with carbon filaments, which after the first stages of baking are highly porous, but become dense and homogeneous on further raising their temperature. The osmium filaments are mounted in bulbs in the same way as carbon filaments, the mount being made by fixing together by means of an arc the end of the osmium filament and the leading-in wire. The osmium lamp has been described on account of its interesting position as the first of the new metallic filament lamps. The lamp is already obsolete.

"The earliest patents in relation to the tantalum lamp were taken out by Messrs. Siemens and Halske in 1901 and 1902, but the lamp was not introduced commercially until 1905. The tantalum lamp can certainly claim to be the first metallic filament lamp which proved to the full its suitability by the development of the tungsten lamp, and it will continue to be remembered as the first lamp to afford solid ground for the hope of a marked advance in electric incandescent lighting. The filament of the tantalum lamp is made from pure drawn tantalum wire, and one of the difficulties in its manufacture is the preparation of the pure tantalum in a form suitable for drawing.

"Tantalum metal is obtained in a powdery form by reducing potassium-tantalo-fluoride; the power is then fused electrically in vacuo, the process serving not only to produce the metal in a coherent form but also to drive off the occluded gases. The fused ingot is drawn into wire. The metal oxidizes readily, and when heated burns completely to oxide; the filament must therefore be mounted in an exhausted tube, and the difficulty of disposing of the necessary length in the bulb has been overcome in an ingenious manner (rendered possible by the flexibility of the wire) by winding it on a frame.

"The earliest patents relating to the production of filaments of tungsten appeared in 1904. The most important are those taken out by Just and Hanaman, Kuzel, and Welsbach. The credit for the development of a commercial lamp rests with the inventors already named, and lamps are now manufactured by all three of the processes which they devised."

Tantalum and tungsten lamps were both extensively manufactured for about three years. During this period the carbon lamp was still in use and the metallized filament continued to grow in favor. The carbon lamp held its position because of its cheapness and rugged construction.

The tantalum lamp had the marked advantage over both types of carbon filament because it was longer lived and gave an efficiency somewhat better than the metallized. Its principal disadvantage was its high first cost. When used in an alternating current it showed a tendency to deteriorate and thus shorten its life.

During this experimental period, the tungsten lamp had the double disadvantage of being high in first cost and fragile. The latter fact forbade its use in any place where the lamp was liable to vibration of

HISTORY OF ELECTRIC LIGHTING

any marked extent. These disadvantages were offset by its high efficiency.

Tungsten is exceedingly hard and is worked with difficulty. Early filaments were made by sintering finely divided tungsten reduced from tungsten oxide. This process produced the fragile filament mentioned. During 1910, methods of drawing tungsten filaments were devised which have overcome the principal disadvantages and have allowed tungsten lamps to be used in practically all places to which carbon lamps were adapted. In 1912, tungsten lamps were used successfully in the New York subway and elevated trains. The life of these filaments is very long, averaging about 1,000 hours of continuous burning. This type of lamp is now sold under the trade name of "Mazda." Tungsten lamps are now manufactured in sizes from 100 watts to 2,000 watts; the lamp efficiencies vary from 0.65 watt per candle in the smaller to 0.50 watt per candle in the larger.

The idea of producing light from incandescent vapors has always been an attractive one. Theoretically it is possible to obtain a far more efficient light from these vapors than from incandescent solids, because the emanations are more nearly of the same frequency than those from solids. Discharges in vacuum tubes have been tried for many years and there was developed a form of tubes, known as Geissler tubes, in which the most beautiful effects were produced by discharges through rarefied gases, but their brightness was never sufficient for practical lighting.

About twenty years ago, Peter Cooper Hewitt, making use of the fact that a column of mercury vapor is a good conductor, succeeded in constructing a mercury vapor lamp of great power and efficiency. This lamp consists of a long glass tube, having two electrodes, the negative of which is mercury. The arc is formed between these electrodes and completely fills the tube. This is, therefore, a true arc lamp. The lamp must be burned in an inclined position, the mercury being in constant circulation. It is vaporized at the lower end, condensed at the upper, and runs back to the lower again. One feature, which for general lighting is objectionable, is the color distortion produced by this light. Since there are no red rays in it, red bodies appear black, and all objects have a greenish-blue appearance. For purposes of photography, for drafting-rooms, etc., it is, however, admirable, being rich in the upper rays of the spectrum. The past few years have seen such rapid development in filament lamps that the mercury arc is seldom installed in places where the cheapest efficient illumination is the prime consideration.

Following out the idea of producing light from discharges in a vacuum, MacFarlane Moore has succeeded in producing a lamp which is extremely ingenious. The chief advantage claimed is the improved distribution of the light, the light being nowhere intense. The tubes may be made a hundred or two feet long and may be fitted to suit the shape of the room. The discharge is effected by means of a high-pressure voltage. The tubes give off a pleasing light of a pink color. It is necessarily installed in large sizes, breaks easily, and is short lived.

The nitrogen lamp is the most recently developed filament lamp. Three structural differences mark it from the ordinary tungsten lamp. The bulb is filled with nitrogen gas instead of evacuated; the bulb is provided with a long cylindrical neck and the filament is made of a helical winding of extremely fine tungsten wire, instead of straight wire of a larger diameter. The presence of the nitrogen gas around the filament allows of operation at a higher temperature, because this gas is absolutely inert and displaces all the oxygen, which could never be done by evacuating. The gas also establishes connection currents which flow upward into the cylindrical neck. These currents carry with them the particles of disintegrated filament and deposit them in the neck, where they are out of the line of effective light rays. The helical filament adds strength and gives a large area of radiating surface, thus reducing the intrinsic brilliancy of the light.

CHAPTER VII

THE DEVELOPMENT OF ELECTRO-CHEMISTRY

THE striking effects brought about by electricity formed the subject of much study about the middle of the eighteenth century. At that time friction electrical machines were in use, and in order to intensify the effects produced, very large machines were constructed. The most famous of these is still to be seen in the Teyler Museum in Haarlem. Pater Beccaria, some one hundred and thirty years ago, by using such machines, found that metals could be revivified (*i.e.*, reduced) from their calces (oxides) when the electric spark was passed between two pieces. In this way he obtained zinc and mercury. Some time later, Priestley investigated the action of the electric spark on air, and observed that an acid was produced; he mistook this for carbonic acid, until Cavendish recognized it as nitric acid. Van Marum studied the behavior of several other gases in this path of the electric spark (which led him to notice the formation of ozone), and made experiments also by passing the spark through liquids. Before him, Priestley had discovered that in oil and ether the electric spark produces gas, and proved that this gas contained hydrogen.

The first actual electrolysis was made by Deimann and Paets van Troostwyk in Haarlem in 1789, in which they successfully decomposed water into hydrogen and oxygen. In their experiments, the water was contained in a cylindrical tube closed at the top, and having a metal wire sealed into its upper end. Another metal wire was introduced into the lower end of the tube, which dipped into a basin of water. When the sparks struck through the water, bubbles of gas were disengaged from the metal wires, and, rising in the tube, gradually displaced the water. As soon as the column of water sank below the upper electrode the gas, which was a mixture of hydrogen and oxygen, exploded. This experiment was later repeated by Ritter, using silver wires and a solution of a silver salt, and he observed that the negative pole became coated with precipitated silver. On changing the poles, silver was dissolved from one and deposited on the other (now the negative pole). In Deimann's experiment, oxygen and hydrogen were simultaneously formed both at the positive and at the negative poles, so that the process was not a true electrolytic one like that of Ritter's.

The whole state of the science was changed in a great degree by the discoveries of Galvani, and particularly by those of Volta. In 1795, Volta arranged the metals in a series according to their behavior in galvanic experiments, and in 1798 Ritter showed that the same series is obtained when the properties of the metals to separate other metals from their salt solutions are compared.

"After the introduction of Volta's pile (in 1800) the physiological and optical phenomena were less studied," remarks Sven Arrhenius in his "Text Book of Electric Chemistry," "and more attention was paid to the chemical actions. As opposed to the electrical machines, these piles gave large quantities of electricity at a comparatively low potential. Nicholson and Carlisle, in 1800, studied the evolution of oxygen and hydrogen in salt solutions at immersed gold electrodes which were connected with the poles of a voltaic pile, and observed that litmus in the neighborhood of the positive pole was turned red by the acid produced there.

"Some years later Davy made his brilliant electro-chemical discoveries. He succeeded in decomposing the oxides of the alkali and alkaline earth metals, which had previously been regarded as elementary substances, and in preparing the pure metals. Further progress in obtaining the more difficultly reducible metals in this way was later made by Bunsen and his pupils."

At the time of Davy's discovery of the alkali metals Berzelius was just beginning his scientific investigations. In one of the first of these, carried out jointly with Hisinger, he studied the action of the electric current upon solutions of various inorganic substances, resulting chiefly in the establishment of the first electrochemical theory. This theory dominated the science of chemistry for many decades. According to it, every chemical atom, when in contact with another, possesses, like a magnet, an electropositive and an electronegative pole. Moreover, one of these poles is usually much stronger than the other. Consequently, an atom behaves as if it possessed but one pole, either electropositive or electronegative, according as the positive or negative pole, respectively, predominates in strength. The magnitude and sign of this resultant polarity upon the atoms of a given element determines its chemical behavior. If, for instance, the atoms of an element are electropositive, it will react with elements whose atoms are electronegative, and conversely. During this reaction the two kinds of electricity neutralize each other, more or less completely according to the degree of inequality existing between the positive and negative charges upon the reacting atoms. If complete neutralization does not take place, the resulting compound itself is electropositive or electronegative according as the electropositive are greater or less than the electronegative charges upon the component atoms. Compounds which thus possess a resultant polarity may then enter into further combinations with each other, in such a way as to form a complex compound which is more nearly or quite neutral. Thus the theory explains not only the formation of simple compounds from their elements, but also the formation of complex compounds, such as double salts, from their component simple compounds. According to this theory, chemical and electrical processes are closely related, and all compounds have a dualistic nature, being formed of an electropositive and an electronegative components. This theory is, therefore, known as the electro-chemical, or dualistic theory. It was applied throughout the domain of inorganic chemistry, which at that time was practically the entire science of chemistry, and altho it contained many arbitrary assumptions, it performed a great service to science because of its systematizing influence.

For several decades after the establishment of the dualistic theory no considerable advance was made in electro-chemistry. This lack of progress was soon counter-balanced by the important discoveries which were made by Faraday about the year 1835. He was the first to show that whether electricity is produced by friction or by means of a voltaic pile, it is capable of producing the same effects. This fact convinced him that there exists but one kind of positive and one of negative electricity. He next attempted to discover a relation between the quantity of electricity flowing through a circuit and the magnitude of the chemical and magnetic effects which it could produce. His results may be expressed as follows:

The magnitude of the chemical and magnetic effects produced in a circuit by an electric current is proportional to the quantity of electricity which passes through the circuit.

A further discovery was made by Faraday by comparing the quantities of different substances in solution which are decomposed by the same quantity of electricity. This comparison may be made in a very simple manner, by connecting into one circuit a series of solutions of different substances so that the same quantity of electricity passes through each solution. The chemical decomposition produced by the electric current in each solution may then be determined by analysis. The results obtained may be summarized as follows:

The quantities of the different substances which separate at the electrodes throughout the circuit are directly proportional to their equivalent weights, and are independent of the cencentration and the temperature of the solution, the size of the electrodes, and all other circumstances.

Those who first recognized the decomposition of water by the electric current sought an explanation for the simultaneous appearance of hydrogen at one electrode and of oxygen at the other. It was not until 1805, however, that a comprehensive theory for this phenomenon was put forward. During that year such a theory was published by Grotthus. According to this theory the electric current charges one electrode positively and the other negatively, and these charged electrodes then exert an electrical influence upon the water molecules. Under this influence the water molecules acquire a polarity, the hydrogen atom becoming charged with positive and the oxygen atom with negative electricity. The positive electrode then attracts the negatively charged oxygen atom, and the negative electrode the positively charged hydrogen atom, causing the water molecules to arrange themselves in a row or chain.

As science gradually developed, the imperfections of the theory advanced by Grotthus became more and more apparent. According to this theory the splitting of the molecule, which is necessary for the condition of electricity, cannot take place until the electro-motive force is sufficiently great to overcome the affinity or cohesion between the two components of a given compound. As a matter of fact, however, it was found that, under suitable conditions of experiment, it is possible to cause an electric current to pass through a solution even when the electro-motive force of the current is extremely small.

Clausius was the first to direct attention to the disagreement of the Grotthus theory or conception of electrolysis with facts. Basing his conclusions upon the experimental results already obtained, he declared "every assumption to be inadmissible which requires the natural condition of a solution of an electrolyte to be one of equilibrium, in which every positive ion is firmly combined with its negative ion, and which at the same time requires the action of a definite force in order to change this condition of equilibrium into another differing from it only in that some of the positive ions have combined with other negative ions than those with which they were formerly combined. Every such assumption is in contradiction to Ohm's law."

At about the same time that Clausius advanced this theory Hittorf began work upon the migration of the ions, and a little later Kohlrausch commenced experiments upon the electrical conductance of solution. The work of these investigators greatly increased the knowledge of the process of electrolysis. Making use of their work, Arrhenius, in 1887, replaced the theory of vibrating ions of Clausius by the theory of free ions.

According to the material conception of electricity, an ion may be considered to be a compound of positive or negative electrons with the element in question. The formation of an ion is, then, entirely analogous to the formation of a compound from two ordinary elements. For instance, in the formation of ions from sodium iodine the sodium atoms combine with positive and the iodine atoms with negative electrons. This conception is very comprehensive, for according to it the law of electro-chemical change (Faraday's law) appears as a consequence of the laws of definite and multiple proportion. Altho the theory of electrolytic dissociation was not spared great opposition in its early years, it has successfully advanced until at the present time by far the greater number of investigators accept it and recognize its value.

"It would be impossible to give in a few words a clear conception of all the reasons which led Arrhenius to adopt his now almost universally accepted views," says Langbein in his "Electro-Deposition of Metals," "and a short statement of these views must, therefore, suffice. He discovered that according to the degree of dilution and the nature of their combination, salts in aqueous solutions are to a more or less far-reaching extent decomposed into independent portions, *i.e.*, the ions, and the term electrolytic dissociation is applied to this phenomenon.

"Only combinations which dissociate—are decomposed and thus form ions—can be conductors of the current, the progressive motion of the latter being solely taken care of and effected by the ions. The ions are supposed to be charged with a certain quantity of electricity —the kathions with positive, the anions with negative, electricity—and so long as current passes through to the electrolyte, they move free in the latter. However, when a current is conducted through the electrolyte, the ions are attracted by the electrodes, the positively-charged kathions by the negatively-charged cathode, and the negatively-charged anions by the positively-charged anode. By reason of these movements of the ions to the electrodes this phenomenon is called migration of the ions.

"The ions, on reaching the electrodes, are freed of their charge, *i.e.*, they yield their electricity to the electrodes. They lose thereby their ion nature, being transformed by their separation on the electrodes into the allotropic or isomeric form of the element or combination."

After the true action of Volta's pile had been discovered, the first modification was to immerse the plates of copper and zinc in the liquid. This arrangement gave a more powerful and lasting effect than the original pile. Volta arranged the cells in a circle and called such a battery a "crown of cups." In 1806, the Royal Institution of London became possessed of a battery of 2,000 elements on the trough system. It was with this apparatus that Davy succeeded in decomposing potash and soda. This simple type of cell would, however, only work for a short time on account of the collection of bubbles of gas on the plates; *i.e.*, the cells became "polarized." Becquerel studied this effect and succeeded in overcoming it to a great extent in 1829, by employing two different liquids separated by a porous partition, each of which enclosed one of the electrodes. In 1863, Professor Daniell invented the cell known by his name and which is one of the most constant current cells ever made, altho not so powerful as some. The zinc and copper electrodes are here separated by a jar of porous earthenware, the zinc being surrounded by dilute sulphuric acid and the copper by a saturated solution of sulphate of copper. This latter solution is the "depolarizer," acting to prevent the bubbles of hydrogen from collecting on the copper plate, as would be the case in the simple cell. Instead of hydrogen being thrown out at the copper pole, copper is deposited from the sulphate of copper depolarizer so that this solution becomes constantly weaker and the copper heavier. To prevent the weakening of the sulphate, crystals are added occasionally. This battery has been much employed in telegraphic work. A form of this cell, known as the "gravity" cell, has been much used for this purpose, the porous partition having here been done away with, and the separation of the liquids effected by the difference in their densities.

In 1839, Grove introduced a cell in which the depolarizer was strong nitric acid, which surrounded a platinum plate. This is a much more powerful depolarizer than sulphate of copper, and the cell was very energetic. It had, however, the disadvantage of high cost, and gave off disagreeable fumes. The first drawback was overcome by Professor Bunsen, in 1843, who substituted for the platinum plate one of gas-retort carbon. The fumes, however, still remained. This battery was useful to the early experimenters, as it furnished a strong and constant current.

Another good depolarizer is chromic acid. This is used in the same manner as nitric acid in the carbon-zinc cell of Bunsen. It does not, however, give off fumes and yet is almost as powerful as the Bunsen cell. Various forms of this cell have been made and they have been extensively used, especially for telephone work. They deteriorate only slightly on standing.

Perhaps the most extensively used primary cell is the LeClanche. This is also a zinc-carbon cell, but sal-ammoniac is used to replace the sulphuric acid of the preceding cells and the depolarizer is the black oxide of manganese. This depolarizer is slow in its action and the cell is, therefore, not good for constant current work, but it has a very slow rate of deterioration. This cell is very extensively manufactured in the "dry" form in which the exciting fluid is held as a moist paste. The cell is not entirely dry, however, as is sometimes supposed, for if it dries out it ceases to work.

One of the most recent primary cells as well as the best is the zinc-copper-oxide cell of Lalande. In the Edison form of this cell, the copper oxide is pressed into plates and mounted in the cell between two zinc plates. The exciting fluid is caustic potash. The copper oxide acts as the depolarizer and is reduced to metallic copper. The cell is very efficient, has a long life, and does not deteriorate on standing. Thousands are now in use for such work as operating railway signals, sparking gas engines, etc.

The existence of secondary currents was discovered by Ritter in 1803. Having substituted to the actions of a Volta's pile another pile formed only of disks of copper, separated by moist cloth, he remarked that this second pile, though inactive by itself, gave in its turn an electric current, in the opposite direction to the current of the first pile.

This current was of but short duration, and the electro-motive force was lower than that of the pile used in charging it. In 1826, De la Rive also found that a secondary or inverse current could be obtained from plates of platinum upon which oxygen and hydrogen had been disengaged in the experiment of the decomposition of water by a battery. This phenomenon took the name of "polarization of the electrodes" and the current itself that of the "current of polarization."

After that, secondary currents were the object of many researches made by physicists, among whom may be mentioned Faraday, Grove, Wheatstone, Poggendorff, E. Becquerel and Gaugian.

He experimented on voltameters with wires of copper, silver, tin, aluminum, iron, zinc, gold and platinum, and for each of them varied the nature of the liquid into which the electrodes were placed. He found that "all the metals oxidizing at the positive pole of the cell, the secondary current, obtained after the interruption of the primary current, was as much more intense as the oxidation was more complete, if the oxide formed remained adherent and insoluble in the acidulated liquid of the voltameter." Even gold and silver did not resist the action of the oxygen of the pile; they were covered with dark deposits of oxide, and furnished an energetic secondary current. Platinum did not oxidize, it is true, in a visible manner, but the secondary inverse current was of shorter duration than that of the metals which were covered with a layer of adherent oxide; an effect which was explained by the rapid decomposition of the oxygenated water produced around the positive electrode of the voltameter. The action of the hydrogen was, on the other hand, stronger with platinum than with all the other metals, for the electrode around which this gas was disengaged furnished, with another neutral electrode, a more intense secondary current than when any other metal was employed.

The most important result of these interesting researches is that which assigns the greatest intensity to the secondary current produced by a voltameter with electrodes of lead, and dilute sulphuric acid as the liquid. Measuring the electro-motive force developed in such a voltameter, after the rupture of the primary current, Plante found that it was equal to about one and a half times (more exactly, 1.48-1.49) that of the most energetic voltaic element, such as a Grove or Bunsen. This suggested the idea of constructing secondary cells, and uniting them in a battery, so as to store up or accumulate the work of the voltaic pile, in the same way that static electricity is condensed by the aid of conductors of great surface separated by an insulating material.

The action in a storage cell is as follows: When the battery is charged, the positive plate consists of lead peroxide and the negative of pure lead in a spongy condition. When the cell discharges, both plates become a form of lead sulphate. Upon being charged by having reverse current sent through them, they are reformed into lead peroxide and sponge lead. If the plates were platinum, oxygen would be given off where the current enters, and hydrogen where it leaves, but with the lead sulphate plates the oxygen and hydrogen combine, thus oxidizing one and reducing the other.

Storage cells have many uses. They are employed in large sizes in central power stations to equalize the load on the machinery, serving to help the engines carry the maximum loads so that they are not strained. Electric automobiles are largely used, and the new Edison storage battery has solved the problem of the weight of the battery. This cell is made up of a positive plate having as an active agent a high nickel oxide, a negative plate having as the active material powdered iron and an electrolyte consisting of dilute potassium hydrate solution. These batteries are made in sizes from 40 ampere-hours to 450 ampere-hours. The energy delivered per pound of battery varies from 10.4 watt-hours in the 40-ampere battery to 13.2 watt-hours in the 450-ampere. Storage batteries are used in lighting trains, operating locomotives, supplying telephone lines and igniting gas engines.

CHAPTER VIII

THE TELEPHONE

In 1854 a Frenchman, Charles Bourseul, predicted the transmission of speech, and outlined a method correct save in one particular, but for which error one following his directions could have produced a speaking telephone. His words at this date seem almost prophetic:

"I have asked myself, for example, if the spoken word itself could not be transmitted by electricity; in a word, if what was spoken in Vienna may not be heard in Paris. The thing is practicable in this way:

"Suppose that a man speaks near a movable disk, sufficiently flexible to lose none of the vibrations of the voice; that this disk alternately *makes and breaks* the connection from a battery: you may have at a distance another disk which will simultaneously execute the same vibrations."

The words "makes and breaks" in Bourseul's quotation have been italicized by the present writer. They form the keynote of the failures of those who subsequently followed Bourseul's directions literally.

Philip Reis, a German inventor, constructed what he called a telephone in 1861, following implicitly the path outlined by Bourseul. He mounted a flexible diaphragm over an opening in a wooden box, and on the center of the diaphragm fastened a small piece of platinum. Near this he mounted a heavy brass spring, with which the platinum alternately made and broke contact when the diaphragm was caused to vibrate. These contact points formed the terminals of a circuit containing a battery and the receiving instrument. His receiver assumed various forms, prominent among which was a knitting needle wrapped with silk-insulated copper wire and mounted on a cigar box for a sounding board. Its operation was as follows:

The sound waves set up in the air struck against the diaphragm of the transmitter, causing it to vibrate in unison with them. This caused the alternate making and breaking of the circuit at the point of contact between the platinum and the spring, and allowed intermittent currents to flow through the receiver. These caused a series of sounds in the knitting needle by virtue of "Page effect." The sounding board vibrated in unison with the molecular vibrations of the needle, and the sound was thus greatly amplified.

Reis' telephone could be depended upon to transmit only musical sounds. The question as to whether it actually did transmit speech has been the subject of much discussion, but if it did this at all it was very imperfectly. "The cause of its faliure," says K. B. Miller in his "American Telephone Practice," "to successfully transmit speech will be understood from the following facts: A simple musical tone is caused by vibrations of very simple forms, while sound waves produced by the voice in speaking are very complex in their nature. Sound possesses three qualities: pitch, depending entirely on the frequency of the vibrations; loudness, depending on the amplitude of the vibrations; and timbre, or quality, depending on the form of the vibration. The tones of a flute and a violin may be the same as to pitch and loudness and yet be radically different. This difference is in timbre, or quality."

Reis' transmitter, as he adjusted it, was able only to make and break the circuit, and a movement of the diaphragm barely sufficient to break the circuit produced the same effect as a much greater movement. The current therefore flowed with full strength until the circuit was broken, when it stopped entirely. The intermediate strengths needed for reproducing the delicate modulations of the voice were entirely lacking. This apparatus could therefore exactly reproduce the pitch of a sound, but not its timbre and relative loudness. For the next fifteen years no apparent advance was made in the art of telephony, altho several inventors gave it their attention.

In 1876 Professor Alexander Graham Bell and Professor Elisha Gray almost simultaneously invented successful speaking telephones. Gray has been one of the principal claimants for the honor of being the first inventor of the telephone, but Bell has apparently established his right to it, and has also reaped the profit, for, after long litigation, the United States Patent Office and the courts have awarded the priority to him as against Gray and many others.

Bell possessed a greater knowledge of acoustics than of electrical science, and it was probably this that led him to appreciate wherein others had failed. His instrument consisted of a permanent bar magnet having on one end a coil of fine wire. In front of the pole carrying the coil a thin diaphragm of soft iron was so mounted as to allow its free vibration close to the pole.

"Two points will be noticed," says Miller in the work before cited, "which have heretofore been absent; that no battery is used in the circuit and that the transmitting and receiving instruments are exactly alike. When the soft-iron diaphragm of the transmitting instrument is spoken to, it vibrates in exact accordance with the sound waves striking against it. The movement of the diaphragm causes changes in the magnetic field in which lies the coil, which changes, as already pointed out, cause currents to flow in the circuit. These currents flow first in one direction and then in the other, varying in unison with the movements of the diaphragm, the waves being very complex as represented graphically. Passing along the line wire, these electrical impulses, so feeble that only the most delicate instruments can detect them, alternately increase and decrease the strength of the permanent magnet of the receiving instrument, and thereby cause it to exert a varying pull on its soft-iron diaphragm, which, as a result, takes up the vibrations and reproduces the sound faithfully."

Bell's earlier instruments were exhibited in 1876 at the Centennial in Philadelphia. The receiver consisted of a tubular magnet, composed of a coil of wire, surrounding a core, and inclosed in an iron tube, which was about 1¾ inches in diameter and 3 inches long. This tube was closed by a thin iron armature, or diaphragm, which rested loosely on the upper face of the iron tube, the length of the core being such as not quite to touch the diaphragm when in this position. The whole was mounted on a base, arrangements being made to adjust the air gap between the pole of the core and the diaphragm by means of a thumbscrew.

The transmitter consisted of an electromagnet in front of the core, on which was adjustably mounted a diaphragm of goldbeater's skin carrying a small iron armature at its center. A long mouthpiece, into which the sounds to be transmitted were spoken, served to convey the sound waves more directly to the diaphragm.

"Nearly all books and articles on telephones," says Miller, "that treat of Bell's early receiver at all, show and describe it as having the diaphragm fastened at one edge by a single small screw to the upper face of the iron tube, and sprung away from the tube at its opposite side. This mistake occurred in the first two editions of this work, and would have been in this one but for Thomas D. Lockwood, who was kind enough to call attention to it. The origin of the error is explained in the following interesting extract from a letter written by Mr. Lockwood to the writer of this book:

"'This mistake first appeared in the account given by Engineering of Sir William Thomson's address to the British Association in September, 1876, and has been universally copied. The origin of the mistake is very odd. The screw of the instrument given to Sir William Thomson, and which he exhibited in England on his return, was put through a hole in the edge of the diaphragm and engaged with a threaded hole of the tube, for the purpose of attaching the diaphragm while in transit, to prevent it from getting lost. No one, however, notified Sir William of this, it probably having been forgotten; and Sir William seems to have forgotten what the instrument, as he saw it in Philadelphia, looked like. Finally, in knocking about among Sir William's luggage, the free end of the diaphragm was apparently, and without doubt unintentionally, bent upward, as the picture shows. But when so bent, being at the same time rigidly fastened at the opposite edge, it would not and could not work; and when Sir William showed it in England he couldn't make it work.'"

Bell's instrument in a modified form is the standard of to-day. It is now used as a receiver only, a more efficient transmitter, depending upon entirely different principles, having been invented. In speaking of Bell's invention, Sir William Thomson, Lord Kelvin, said: "Who can but admire the hardihood of invention which devised such very slight means to realize the mathematical conception that if electricity is to convey all the delicacies of quality which distinguish articulate speech, the strength of its current must vary continuously as nearly as may be in simple proportion to the velocity of a particle of air engaged in constituting the sound?"

Much has been said and books have been written on the rights of Reis as the inventor of the speaking telephone. The validity of Bell's controlling patent was the subject of many attacks, the litigation finally reaching the Supreme Court of the United States. In the opinion of this court (October term, 1887) the following brief but comprehensive statement is found:

"We have not had our attention called to a single item of evidence which tends in any way to show that Reis or any one who wrote about him had it in his mind that anything else than the intermittent current caused by the opening and closing of the circuit could be used to do what was wanted. No one seems to have thought that there could be another way. All recognized the fact that the minor differences in the original vibrations had not been satisfactorily reproduced, but they attributed it to the imperfect mechanism of the apparatus used, rather than to any fault in the principle on which the operation was to depend.

"It was left for Bell to discover that the failure was due not to workmanship, but to the principle which was adopted as the basis of what had to be done. He found that what he called the intermittent current—one caused by alternately opening and closing the circuit—could not be made under any circumstances to reproduce the delicate forms of the air vibrations caused by the human voice in articulate speech, but that the true way was to operate on an unbroken current by increasing and diminishing its intensity. . . . Such was his discovery, and it was new. Reis never thought of it, and he failed to transmit speech telegraphically. Bell did and he succeeded. Under such circumstances it is impossible to hold that what Reis did was an anticipation of the discovery of Bell. To follow Reis is to fail, but to follow Bell is to succeed. The difference between the two is just the difference between failure and success."

A very interesting fact, and one which might have changed the entire commerical status of the telephone industry, is that in 1868 Royal E. House, of Binghamton, N. Y., invented and patented an "electro-phonetic telegraph," which was capable of operating as a magneto-telephone, in the same manner as the instruments subsequently devised by Bell. House knew nothing of its capabilities, however, unfortunately for him. The instrument is provided with a sounding diaphragm of pine wood stiffened with varnish, mounted in one end of a large sound-amplifying chamber, so formed as to focus the sound waves at a point near its mouth, where the ear was to be placed to receive them. The electro-magnet adapted to be connected in the line circuit had its armature connected by a rod with the center of the wooden diaphragm. By this means any movements imparted to the armature by fluctuating currents in the line were transmitted to the diaphragm, causing it to give out corresponding sounds; and any movements imparted to the diaphragm by sound waves were transmitted to the armature, causing its movements to induce corresponding currents in the line. Two of these instruments connected in a circuit would act alternately as transmitters and receivers in the same manner as Bell's instruments.

It has been shown that in order to transmit speech by electricity it is necessary to cause an undulatory or alternating current to flow in the circuit over which the transmission is to be effected, and that the strength of this current at all times be in exact accordance with the vibratory movements of the body producing the sound.

Bell's magnetic transmitter was used as the generator of this current, as a dynamo, in fact, the energy for driving which was derived from the sound waves set up by the voice. The amount of energy so derived was, however, necessarily very small and the current correspondingly weak, and for this reason this was not a practical form of transmitter, except for comparatively short lines.

Elisha Gray devised a transmitter which, instead of generating the undulatory current itself, depended for its action on causing variation in the strength of a current generated by some separate source; this variation in current strength always being in accordance with the movements of the diaphragm.

He mounted on his horizontal vibrating diaphragm a metal needle, extending into a fluid of low conductivity, such as water. The needle formed one terminal of the circuit, the other terminal being a metal pin extending up through the bottom of the containing vessel. The vibration of the diaphragm was supposed to cause changes in the resistance of the path through the fluid on account of the varying distance between the points of the electrodes and therefore corresponding changes in the strength of the current.

Bell also used a liquid transmitter in which a conducting liquid was held in a conducting vessel, forming one terminal of the circuit. The other terminal was a short metallic needle, carried on the diaphragm, and projecting slightly into the liquid, so that the area of contact between the liquid and the needle would be varied to better advantage by the vibration of the diaphragm than if the needle were immersed a greater distance into the fluid.

Bell's liquid transmitter depended on variation in the extent of immersion of the electrode, while Gray's instrument, owing to the great extent to which the pin was immersed, depended rather on the variation in the length of the conducting path through the liquid itself, a faulty principle for this purpose.

Bell's liquid transmitter was also exhibited at the Philadelphia Centennial in 1876, and, unlike that of Reis, simply caused variations in the resistance of the circuit, and thereby allowed a continuous but undulatory current to pass over the line, the variations in which were able to reproduce all the delicate shades of timbre, loudness and pitch necessary in articulate speech.

Gray and Bell embodied, or attempted to embody, in these instruments the main principle upon which all successful battery transmitters are based. A battery furnished the current, and the transmitter, actuated by the voice, served to modulate it. It was not long, however, before a much better means was devised for putting this principle into practice.

In 1877 Emile Berliner, of Washington, D. C., filed a caveat, and later in the same year applied for a patent on a transmitter depending upon a principle pointed out in articles published in 1856, 1864 and 1874 by the French scientist Du Moncel, that if the pressure between two conducting bodies forming part of an electric circuit be increased, the resistance of the path between them will be diminished, and conversely, if the pressure between them be decreased, a corresponding increase of resistance will result.

Soon after this Edison devised an instrument using carbon as the medium for varying the resistance of the circuit with changes of pressure. Edison's first type of carbon transmitter consisted simply of a button of compressed plumbago bearing against a small platinum disk secured to the diaphragm. The plumbago button was held against the diaphragm by a spring, the tension of which could be adjusted by a thumbscrew.

A form of Edison's transmitter, devised by George M. Phelps in 1878, is shown in Fig. 38. The transmitting device proper is shown in the small cut at the right of this figure, and is enclosed in a cup-shaped case formed of the two pieces, A and B, as shown. Secured to the front of the enlarged head, e, of the adjustment screw, E is a thin platinum disk, F, against which rests a cylindrical button, G, of compressed lampblack. A plate of glass, I, carrying a hemispherical button, K, has attached to its rear face another platinum disk, H. This second platinum disk rests against the front face of the lampblack disk, G, and the button, K, presses firmly against the center of the diaphragm, D. The plates, F and H, form the terminals of the transmitter, and as the diaphragm, D, vibrates, it causes variations in the pressure and corresponding changes in the resistance of the circuit, thus producing the desired undulations of current.

Professor David B. Hughes made a most valuable contribution tending toward the perfection of the battery transmitter. By a series of interesting experiments he demonstrated conclusively that a loose contact between the electrodes, no matter of what substance they are composed, is far preferable to a firm, strong current. The apparatus used in one of his earlier experiments, made in 1878, is shown in Fig. 39, and consists simply of three wire nails, of which A and B form the terminals of the circuit containing a battery and a receiving

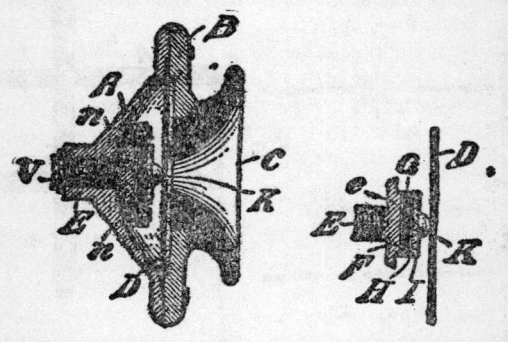

Fig. 38 —Phelps-Edison Transmitter. (From Miller's American Telephone Practice.)

instrument. The circuit was completed by a third nail, C, which was laid loosely across the other two. Any vibrations in the air in the vicinity caused variations in the intimacy of contact between the nails, and corresponding variations in the resistance of the circuit. This was a very inefficient form of transmitter, but it demonstrated the principle of loose contact very cleverly.

It was found that carbon was, for various reasons, by far the most desirable substance for electrodes in the loose-contact transmitter, and nothing has ever been found to approach it in efficiency and desirability.

Another form of transmitter devised by Hughes, and called by him the microphone, is shown in Fig. 39. This consists of a small pencil of gas carbon, A, pointed at each end, and two blocks, B, B, of carbon fastened to a diaphragm or sounding board, C. These blocks are hollowed out in such a manner as to loosely hold between them the pencil, A. The blocks, B, B, form the terminals of the circuit. This instrument, tho crude in form, is of marvelous delicacy and is well termed microphone. The slightest noises in its vinicity, and even those incapable of being heard by the ear alone, produce surprising effects in the receiving instrument. This particular form of instrument is, in fact, too delicate for ordinary use, as any jar or loud noise will cause the electrodes to break contact and produce deafening noises in the receiver. Nearly all carbon transmitters of to-day are of the loose-contact type, this having entirely superseded the first form devised by Edison, which was then supposed to depend on the actual resistance of a carbon block being changed under varying pressure.

In speaking of Professor Hughes' work on loose contacts and the

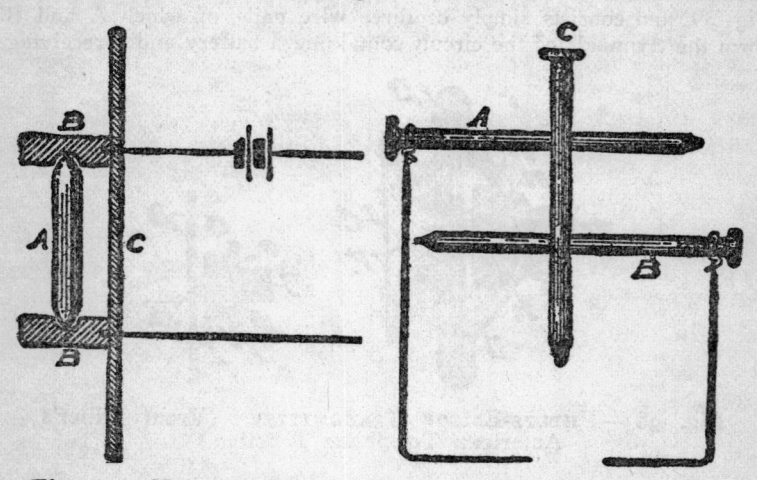

Fig. 39 —HUGHES' CARBON AND NAIL MICROPHONES. (From Miller's American Telephone Practice.)

microphone, the Telegraph Journal and Electrical Review, an English electrical paper, says in its issue of July 1, 1878: "The microphone is a striking illustration of the truth that in science any phenomenon whatever may be turned to account. The trouble of one generation of scientists may be turned to the honor and service of the next. Electricians have long had sore reasons for regarding a 'bad contact' as an unmitigated nuisance, the instrument of the evil one, with no conceivable good in it, and no conceivable purpose except to annoy and tempt them into wickedness and an expression of hearty but ignominious emotion. Professor Hughes, however, has, with a wizard's power, transformed this electrician's bane into a professional glory and a public boon. Verily, there is a soul of virtue in things evil."

Professor Hughes, in an article in Nature, June 27, 1878, thus

THE TELEPHONE 273

describes the conditions necessary for microphonic action: "If the pressure on the materials is not sufficient, we shall have a constant succession of interruptions of contact, and the galvanometer needle will indicate the fact. If the pressure on the materials is gradually increased the tones will be loud but wanting in distinctness, the galvanometer indicating interruptions; as the pressure is still increased, the tone becomes clearer, and the galvanometer will be stationary when a maximum of loudness and clearness is attained. If the pres-

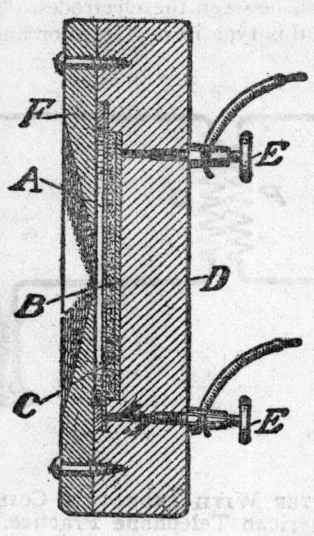

Fig. 40—HUNNING'S GRANULAR CARBON TRANSMITTER. (From Miller's American Telephone Practice.)

sure be further increased, the sounds become weaker, tho very clear, and, as the pressure is still further augmented, the sounds die out (as if the speaker was talking and walking away at the same time) until a point is arrived at where there is complete silence."

Only one radical improvement now remains to be recorded. In 1881 Henry Hunnings devised a transmitter wherein the variable resistance medium consisted of a mass of finely divided carbon granules held between two conducting plates. His transmitter is shown in Fig. 40. Between the metal diaphragm, A, and a parallel conducting plate, B, both of which are securely mounted in a case formed by the block, D, and a mouthpiece, F, is a chamber filled with fine granules of carbon, C. The diaphragm, A, and the plate, B, form the terminals of the transmitter, and the current from the battery must therefore flow through the mass of granular carbon, C. When the diaphragm is caused to vibrate by sound waves, it is brought into more or less intimate contact with the carbon granules and causes a varying pressure between them. The resistance offered by them to the current is thus varied, and the desired undulations in the current produced. This transmitter, instead of having one or a few points of variable contact, is seen to have a multitude of them. It can carry a larger current without heating, and at the same time produce greater changes in its resistance, than the forms previously devised, and no ordinary sound can cause a total break between the electrodes. These and other advantages have caused this type in one form or another to largely displace all others.

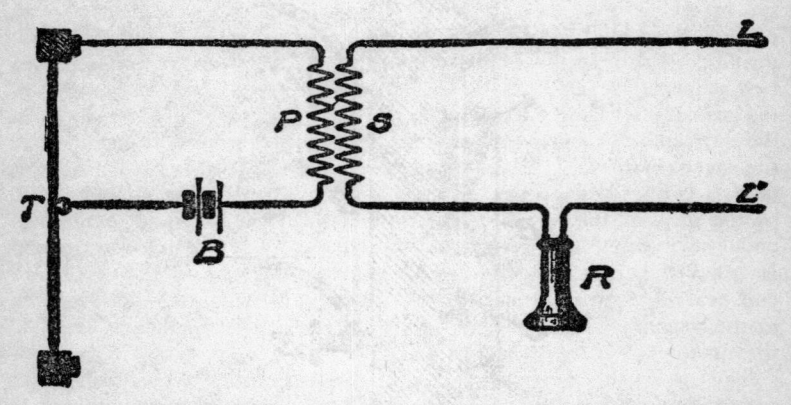

Fig. 41 —TRANSMITTER WITH INDUCTION COIL. (From Miller's American Telephone Practice.)

At first the practice was to put the transmitter, together with the receiver and battery, directly in circuit with the line wire. With this arrangement the changes produced in the resistance by the transmitter were small in comparison with the total resistance of the circuit, especially in the case of a long line, and the changes in current were therefore small. Edison remedied this difficulty by using an induction coil in connection with the transmitter.

The induction coil used then and now is made as follows: Around a core formed of a bundle of soft-iron wires is wound a few turns of comparatively heavy insulated copper wire. Outside of this, and entirely separate from it, is wound another coil consisting of a great number of turns of fine wire, also of copper, and insulated. The transmitter, together with the battery, is placed in a closed circuit with the coarse winding of a few turns, while the fine winding of many turns is included directly in circuit with the line wire and the receiving instrument. The coarse winding is usually termed the primary winding, because it is associated with the primary source of current, the battery; while the fine winding is usually termed the secondary winding, because the currents flowing in it at the transmitting station are secondary, or induced currents. In coils of this kind the coarse winding is almost invariably termed the primary for the above reason, altho many conditions exist in electrical work and in telephone work where the high-resistance winding is in reality the primary coil.

The circuit arrangement spoken of is shown in Fig. 41, in which T is a transmitter, B a battery, P and S primary and secondary windings, respectively, of an induction coil, L', L' the line wires, and R the receiving instrument. It is well to state here that the usual way of indicating the primary and secondary of an induction coil in diagraphic representation of electrical circuits is by an arrangement of two adjacent zigzag lines, as shown in Fig. 41. A current flowing in the primary winding of the induction coil produces a field of force in the surrounding space, and any changes caused by the transmitter in the strength of the current produce changes in the intensity of this field. As the secondary winding lies in this field, these changes will, by the laws of Faraday and Henry, cause currents to flow in the secondary winding and through the line wire to the receiving instrument. In good induction coils the electro-motive forces up in the secondary coil bear nearly the same ratio to the changes in electro-motive force in the primary coil as the number of turns in the secondary bears to the number of turns in the primary.

The use of the induction coil with the transmitter accomplishes two very important results: First, it enables the transmitter to operate in a circuit of very low resistance, so that the changes in the resistance produced by the transmitter bear a very large ratio to the total resistance of the circuit. This advantage is well illustrated by contrasting the two following cases:

Suppose a transmitter capable of producing a change of resistance of one ohm be placed directly in a line circuit whose total resistance is 1,000 ohms; a change in the resistance of the transmitter of one ohm will then change the total resistance of the circuit one one-thousandth of its value, and the resulting change in the current flowing will be but one one-thousandth of its value. On the other hand, suppose the same transmitter to be placed in a local circuit, as above described, the total resistance of which circuit is five ohms; the change of one ohm in the transmitter will now produce a change of resistance of one-fifth of the total resistance of the circuit, and cause a change of one-fifth of the total current flowing. It is thus seen that fluctuations in the current can be produced by a transmitter with the aid of an induction coil which are many times greater than those produced by the same transmitter without the coil.

The second advantage is that by virtue of the small number of turns in the primary winding and the large number in the secondary winding of the induction coil, the currents generated in the secondary are of a very high voltage as compared with those in the primary, thus enabling transmission to be effected over much greater length of line, and over vastly higher resistances than would be possible if the transmitter were forced to vary the current flowing through the entire length of the line.

Neither the telephone receiver nor the transmitter have undergone any radical changes since their early days. Various minor details have received the attention of engineers and inventors, but the magneto-telephone is still the receiver and the variable resistances of the carbon contacts the means of transmission.

The principal developments have been in the means of intercommunication. The growth of the telephone industry has been very rapid, and from being a luxury the telephone has become a business necessity. The tendency has been toward the simplification of the subscriber's station and the improvement of the central office. The "telescribe" and "transophone" are inventions of 1914, the first writing a telephone message and the second recording it automatically on a phonograph. Both of these are Edison patents.

The telegraphone or telephonograph is an instrument which records magnetically sounds produced at a distance. It was originated by Mr. Poulson, a Danish inventor. Either a steel band is used or a long steel wire rolled from one drum to the other under the recording magnet, which receives the talking currents and engraves them magnetically upon the steel wire. To reproduce the message it is only necessary to pass the steel wire under the producing magnet connected to a telephone receiver, the reproduction being very perfect. The message may be erased from the wire by means of the obliterating magnet supplied with an alternating current.

CHAPTER IX

ELECTRIC RAILWAYS

ALTHO the earliest recorded experiments date back three-quarters of a century, the electric railway is essentially a modern development, for it achieved a recognized position less than twenty years ago, long after the telephone, the arc and incandescent lamp, and the stationary electric motor had been thoroly established. This is but natural, for it is the logical outcome of the establishment of certain cardinal principles and practices in the kindred arts.

The first roads to carry passengers commercially were built in Europe, but the first railway experiments and the modern commercial impetus, as well as most of the essential and distinctive features of the art as it stands to-day, an example of almost unprecedented industrial development, are distinctively American, as Frank J. Sprague pointed out in his paper before the Electrical Congress of 1904, from which much of the following matter is taken.

Brandon, Vt., birthplace, and Thomas Davenport, blacksmith, father, are the names first on the genealogical tree of the electric railway, in the year 1834. A toy motor, mounted on wheels, propelled on a few feet of circular railway by a primary battery, exhibited a year later at Springfield, and again at Boston, is the infant's photograph. This was only three years after Henry's invention of the motor, following Faraday's discovery, ten years earlier, that electricity could be used to produce continuous motion.

The records of Davenport's career, unearthed by the late Franklin Leonard Pope, show this early inventor a man of genius, deserving a high place in the niche of fame, for in a period of six years he built more than a hundred operative electric motors of various designs, many of which were put into actual service, an achievement, taking into account the times, well nigh incredible.

For nearly two score years various inventors, handicapped with the limitations of the primary battery, and in utter ignorance of the principles of modern dynamo and motor construction, labored with small result. The invention by Pacinotti, in 1861, of the continuous-current dynamo may properly be said to date all modern electric machines. These were developed in their earliest forms by Gramme and Siemens, Wheatstone and Varley, Farmer and Rowland, Hefner-Alteneck and others, and brought into existence the elements essential to any possible commercial success. Yet notwithstanding that the principle of the reversibility of the dynamo-electric machine and the transmission of energy to a distance by the use of two similar machines, said to have been discovered and described by Pacinotti in 1867—the same year in which Prof. Farmer described the principle of the modern dynamo in a letter to Henry Wilde—and demonstrated independently at the Vienna Exposition by Fontaine and Gramme in 1873, many years more passed before the importance and availability of this principle were generally recognized.

From 1850 to 1875 is a long period, relatively, and yet there seemed to have been practically an entire cessation of experimental electric railway work until, in the latter year, George F. Greene, a poor mechanic of Kalamazoo, Mich., built a small model motor, which was supplied from a battery through an overhead line, with track return, and three years later he constructed another model on a larger scale. Greene seemed to have realized that a dynamo was essential to success, but he did not know how to make one and did not have the means to buy it.

Shortly afterward, in 1879, at the Berlin Exposition, Messrs. Siemens and Halske constructed a short line about a third of a mile in length, which was the beginning of much active work by this firm. The dynamo and motor were of the now well-known Siemens type, and the current was supplied through a central rail, with the running rails as a return, to a small locomotive on which the motor was carried longitudinally, motion being transmitted through spur and beveled gears to a central shaft from which connection was made to the wheels. The locomotive drew three small cars having a capacity of 20 people and attained the speed of about eight miles an hour.

Perhaps more than to any other the credit for the first serious proposal in the United States should be awarded to Field. Curiously enough, patent papers were filed by Field, Siemens and Edison, all within three months of each other, in the spring and summer of 1880. Priority of invention was finally awarded to Field, he having filed a caveat a year before. He had been actively interested in electric telegraphs, and in an account of his work published some 20 years ago, it is stated that he early constructed two electric motors and had in mind the operation of street cars in San Francisco, but had not been able to do anything in the matter because of a realization that a dynamo must be used instead of a battery. In 1877 while in Europe he saw some Gramme machines, and on his return two of them were ordered but not delivered. Later a dynamo was ordered from Siemens Brothers in London which was lost, and this was replaced by another which arrived in the fall of 1878. Meanwhile two Gramme machines were placed at his disposal, and shortly afterward an electric elevator was operated. In February, 1879, he made plans for an electric railway, the current to be delivered from a stationary source of power through a wire enclosed in a conduit, with rail return, and in 1880-81 he constructed and put in operation an experimental electric locomotive in Stockbridge, Mass.

Pending the settlement of patent interferences between Edison and Field (the Siemens application being late was rejected), the two interests were combined in a corporation known as "The Electric Railway Company of the United States," and the first work of the company was the operation of an electric locomotive at the Chicago Railway Exposition in 1883. This locomotive, called the "Judge," after the late Chief Justice Field, ran around the gallery of the main exposition building on a track of about one-third of a mile in length.

The motor used was a Weston dynamo mounted on the car and connected by beveled gear to a shaft from which power was transmitted by belts to one of the wheels. The current was taken from a center rail, with track return. A lever operated clutches on the driving shaft, and the speed was varied by resistance. The reversing mechanism consisted of two movable brushholders geared to a disk operated by a lever, each arm carrying a pair of brushes, one of which only could be thrown into circuit at a time, to give the proper direction of movement.

Meanwhile several other inventors were getting actively into the field of transmission of power and electric railways. In the summer of 1882 Dr. Joseph R. Finney operated in Allegheny, Pa., a car for which current was supplied through an overhead wire on which traveled a small trolley connected to the car with a flexible cable, and about the same time in England Dr. Fleming Jenkin, following a paper by Messrs. Ayrton and Perry before the Royal Institution on an automatic railway, proposed a scheme of telpherage which was developed by those gentlemen.

In the early part of the same year the writer, Mr. Sprague, then a midshipman in the United States Navy, who had in 1879 and 1880 begun the designing of motors, was ordered on duty at the Crystal Palace Electrical Exhibition then being held at Sydenham, England. While in London he became impressed with a belief in the possibility of operating the underground railway electrically. He first considered the use of main and working conductors, the latter being carried between the tracks, with rail return, but noting the complication of switches on certain sections of the road, conceived the idea of a car moving between two planes, traveling on one and making upper pressure contact with the other, those planes being the terminals of a constant potential system. For practical application the lower of the two planes was to be replaced by the running track and all switches and sidings, and the upper plane by rigid conductors supported by the roof of the tunnel, and following the center lines of all tracks and switches, contact to be made therewith by a self-adjusting device carried on the car roof over the center of the truck and pressed upward by springs.

In 1882 he applied for a patent on the first idea, which was but a variation from that shown in other patents, but the second laid dormant for nearly three years because of central station work and the development of the application of stationary motors.

Meanwhile in the United States Charles J. van Depoele, a Belgian by birth and a sculptor by original trade and an indefatigable worker, had become interested in electric manufacture and soon energetically attacked the railway problem. His first railway was a small experimental line constructed in Chicago in the winter of 1882-83, the current supplied from an overhead wire. In the fall of 1883 a car was also run at the Industrial Exposition at Chicago.

A year later a train pulled by a locomotive and taking current from an underground conduit was successfully operated at the Toronto Exhibition to carry passengers from the street car system, and again in the year following Van Depoele operated another train at the same place, using on this occasion an overhead wire and a weighted arm pressing a contact up against it.

Experiments were also carried on by him on the South Bend Railway in the fall of 1885, where several cars were equipped with small motors, and also in Minneapolis, where an electric car took the place of a steam locomotive. Other equipments were operated at the New Orleans Exhibition and at Montgomery, Ala., where the current was at first taken from a single overhead wire which carried a traveling trolley connected to the car by a flexible conductor.

Other equipments were put in operation at Windsor, Ont.; Detroit, Mich.; Appleton, Wis., and Scranton, Pa.

In these several equipments the motors were placed on the front platforms of the cars and connected to the wheels by belts or chains. The cars were headed in one direction and operated from one end only.

In 1888 the Van Depoele Company was absorbed by the Thomson-Houston, which had recently entered the railway field, and Van Depoele continued in its active development until his death in 1892.

Among the early American workers of this period none was for a time more prominent than Leo Daft, who after considerable development in motors for stationary work took up their application to electric railways, making the first experiments toward the close of 1883 at his company's works at Greenville, N. J., these being sufficiently successful to be repeated in November of that year on the Saratoga and Mt. McGregor road. The locomotive used there was called "The Ampere," and pulled a full-sized car. The motor was mounted on a platform and connected by belts to an intermediate shaft carried between the wheels, from which another set of belts led to pulleys on the driving axles. A center rail and the running rails formed the working conductors. Variation of speed was accomplished by variation of field resistance, this being accentuated by the use of iron instead of copper in some of the coils.

In the following year Daft equipped a small car on one of the piers at a New York seaside resort, and a little later another one at the Mechanics' Fair in Boston, the motor for this last being subsequently put on duty at the New Orleans Exposition. In 1885 work was begun by the Daft Company on the Hampton branch of the Baltimore Union Passenger Railway Company, where in August of that year operations were begun, at first with two and a year later with two more small electric locomotives which did not carry passengers themselves, but pulled regular street cars. A center and a running rail were used for the normal distribution, but at crossings an overhead conductor was installed and connection made to it by an arm carried on the car and pressed against it. The driving was by a pinion operating on an internal gear on one of the axles.

Daft's most ambitious work followed when a section of the Ninth Avenue Elevated Road was equipped for a distance of two miles, on which a series of experiments were carried on during the latter part of 1885, with a locomotive called "The Benjamin Franklin." The motor was mounted on a platform pivoted at one end, and motion was communicated from the armature to the driving wheel through grooved gears held in close contact partly by the weight of the machine and partly by an adjustable screw device. This locomotive, pulling a train of cars, made several trips, but the experiments were soon suspended. This work was followed by street railway equipments at Los Angeles and elsewhere, using double overhead wires carrying a trolley carriage.

Meanwhile Bentley and Knight, after some experiments in the yards of the Brush Electric Company at Cleveland in the fall of 1883, installed a conduit system in August, 1884, on the tracks of the East Cleveland Horse Railway Company. The equipped section of the road was 2 miles long, the conduits were of wood laid between the tracks, and two cars were employed which were each equipped with a motor carried under the car body and transmitting power to the axle by wire cables.

These equipments were operated with varying degrees of success during the winter of 1884-85, but were abandoned later. The work was followed by a double overhead trolley road at Woonsocket, the motors being supplied by the Thomson-Houston Company, and later by a combined double trolley and conduit road at Allegheny, Pa.

In 1884-85 J. C. Henry installed and operated in Kansas City a railway supplied by two overhead conductors, on each of which traveled a small trolley connected to the car by a flexible cable. The motor was mounted on a frame supported on the car axle, and the power was transmitted through a clutch and a nest of gears giving five speeds. In the following year a portion of another road was equipped. A number of experiments seem to have been conducted there and on some the rails were used as a return. The collectors were of different types, and it is said that among others there was one carried on the car. The final selection was a trolley having four wheels disposed in pairs in a horizontal plane, carried by and gripping the sides of the wires; this feature, but using one wire and rail return, characterized a road installed by Henry in San Diego, Cal., opened in November, 1887.

Meanwhile work had begun in Great Britain, where the first regular road to be put in operation was that known as the Portrush Electric Railway, in Ireland, installed in 1883 by Siemens Brothers, of London. Power was generated by turbines, and the current was transmitted by a third rail supported on wooden posts alongside of the track, the running rails constituting the return. The pressure used was about 250 volts.

This was followed in the same year by a successful short road at Brighton, installed by Magnus Volk, the current being transmitted through the running rails. Then came the railway installed at Bessbrook, Newry, in 1885, under the direction of the Messrs. Hopkinson, and at Ryde in 1886, in which latter year was also installed the Blackpool road by Holyroyd Smith. In this latter case the conduit system was used with complete metallic circuit. The motor was carried underneath the car between the axles and connected by chain gearing. Fixed brushes with end contact were used for both directions of running.

Reverting to work in the United States, Sprague again took up the electric railway problem, and in 1885, before the Society of Arts, Boston, advocated the equipment of the New York Elevated Railway with motors carried on the trucks of the regular cars, and work was actually begun on the construction of experimental motors. Shortly afterward a regular truck was equipped and a long series of tests made on a private track in New York City. In May, 1886, an elevated car was equipped with these motors and a series of tests begun on the Thirty-fourth Street branch of the road.

These motors may be considered the parent models of the modern railway motor. They were centered through the brackets on the driving axles, connected to them by single reduction gears, and the free end of the motor was carried by springs from the transom, the truck elliptics being interposed between this support and the car body. The truck had two motors; they were run open; had one set of brushes and were used not only for propelling the car but for braking it. The motors were at first shunt wound, but later had a correcting coil in series with the armature at right angles to the normal field to prevent shifting of the neutral point. The car was operated from each end by similar switches, current at 600 volts was used, and increase of speed was effected by cutting out resistance in the armature circuit and then by reducing the field strength. This enabled energy to be returned to the line when decreasing from high speed. It being impossible to interest the railway management, the experiments were finally suspended. Soon afterward a locomotive designed by Field had a short trial on the same section of the elevated.

Sprague then turned his attention to building a locomotive car of 300 hp. capacity, each truck to be equipped with two motors, each having a pair of armatures geared to the axle, but this evidently being ahead of the times, and the possibilities of street tramway traction becoming evident, these equipments were abandoned, and he began the development of the type of motor finally used in Richmond, one crude form of which was first used in storage battery experiments in Philadelphia and others in New York and Boston in 1886.

Reviewing the conditions at the beginning of 1887, statistics compiled by T. Commerford Martin show that, including every kind of equipment, even those of a fraction of a mile long and operated in mines, there were but nine installations in Europe, aggregating about 20 miles of track, with a total equipment of 52 motors and motor cars, none operated with the present overhead line or conduit, and seven cars operated by storage batteries, while in the United States there were only ten installations, with an aggregate of less than 40 miles of tracks and 50 motors and motor cars, operated mostly from overhead lines with traveling trolleys flexibly connected to the cars. These were partly Daft, but principally Van Depoele roads. Almost every inventor who had taken part in active work was still alive. The roads, however, were limited in character, varied in equipment and presented nothing sufficient to overcome the prejudices of those interested in transportation and command the confidence of capital.

As a result of all these experiments the series wound motor soon became universal because of its ability to start a car with the least expenditure of energy, and has held its place to the present time with minor improvements in its structure and method of gearing; 550-600 volts has become standard for the operation of the motors, this value having been found the most satisfactory. Altho higher voltages are desirable for economy of transmission, the difficulties encountered in the construction of the motors offset any advantage gained thereby.

As previously explained, the higher the voltage used, the further may the power be economically distributed. In the direct current system the voltage is limited to about 600. With this comparatively low voltage, cars could be economically operated only within a few miles of the generating station. The development of the alternating current transformer, by means of which the voltage could be raised or lowered without mechanism, showed the way to new developments. The direct current generators in the power stations were gradually removed and alternators substituted. Power could be generated at either low or high voltages, stepped up by means of transformers sent over the line at a high voltage to a sub-station, dropped to a lower voltage again by the transformers, and changed to direct current by means of rotary converters, from which the car lines were fed. This is the system at present in use in all the large cities. The most unsatisfactory part of this system is the sub-station with its rotary converter, which increases the cost.

Beginning with 1903, the application of alternating current motors to railway work was begun. The motors used in this service are of three general types: (1) the single phase series motor; (2) the single phase repulsion motor; (3) the three-phase induction motor. American practice seems to favor the first two of these types of motors, though engineering opinion differs as to their relative merits. Either of these types of motor is adapted to economical high tension power transmission, and the outlook for equipping long railways now employing steam locomotives is good. Several roads have electrified divisions of their lines and are operating them successfully.

In May, 1905, the Westinghouse Company completed the first heavy locomotive to be operated by single-phase alternating current. This locomotive complete weighs 136 tons. It was built in two halves, each having three axles, each axle driven by a 225-hp. single-phase series motor having single reduction gears with a ratio of 18 : 95. The current required to operate this locomotive (6,600 volts, 25 cycles) is collected from the trolley wire by means of a pneumatically operated pantagraph trolley, with sliding contact, and carried through an oil switch and circuit breaker to an auto-transformer. In this transformer it is reduced to 325 volts, at which pressure it is used in the motors. This locomotive, being designed for heavy freight service, develops a draw-bar pull of 50,000 pounds at a speed of from 10 to 12 miles per hour.

Following several other successful applications of these motors, the New York, New Haven & Hartford Railroad decided to equip its road as far as Stamford, Conn., a distance of 22 miles, with the Westinghouse system. The locomotives used weigh 70 tons and are each equipped with four gearless motors of 250 hp. each. These locomotives operate over 12 miles of track in the city of New York by means of 600-volt direct current and over 22 miles of track supplied with alternating current at 11,000 volts, 25 cycles. Each locomotive is capable of hauling a 200-ton passenger train in accommodation service, requiring one stop every two miles, at a schedule speed of 26 miles per hour and a maximum speed of 45 miles per hour. In express service a maximum speed of 60 to 75 miles per hour can be attained.

The most notable example of repulsion motor equipment is that of the New York, Westchester & Boston Railway. That company has 63 miles of track, four locomotives and several motor cars, all of which take 11,000-volt, single-phase A.C. current directly from the trolley. This equipment is used for local passenger and freight service.

During 1907, the first high voltage D.C. railway equipment was tried out. Now there are a large number of roads operating on 1,200-volt D.C. current, with a mileage (on January 1, 1916) of 800 miles. This mileage is distributed among 14 lines. Recently the Chicago Great Northern Railway adopted 2,400-volt D.C. current for hauling heavy traffic over a division with steep grades.

CHAPTER X

THE ELECTRO-MAGNETIC TELEGRAPH

As early as 1774, Lesage constructed an electric telegraph consisting of twenty-four wires, at the end of each of which was a pith-ball electroscope; and in 1816 Ronalds constructed a line of one wire, using pith-balls and two synchronous wheels. He endeavored to bring the matter to the attention of the British government, and received the really exquisite reply that "telegraphs of any kind are now wholly unnecessary, and no other than the one now in use will be adopted." A very important step was taken in 1828 by Harrison Gray Dyar, of New York, who invented a method of recording in which a discharge was made to pass through a sheet of moistened litmus paper moving at a uniform rate. A line was actually set up and experimented upon in the same year. In all of these systems it was proposed to use frictional electricity; but, even with the present vastly increased power of production and control of this species of electricity, a successfully operating telegraph would hardly be possible.

The real electric telegraph began with Galvani and Volta, and, as already intimated, more than one system has been fairly successful, the fundamental principles of which were understood before the close of the first decade of the present century. The complete solution of the problem, however, would unquestionably have been postponed for many years but for the discovery of Oersted in 1820. Immediately on its announcement, the telegraph became the dream of many men in many countries. "Concerning its origin and growth," says T. C. Mendenhall in his "Century of Electricity," "the great majority of Americans have been singularly mistaken. The popular impression seems to be that it is exclusively an American invention, and that in America it was almost exclusively the product of the genius of one man. It hardly need be said that these impressions are extremely erroneous.

"Ampère, whose genius had accomplished so much in the early development of the theory of electro-magnetism, was probably the first to suggest its use in telegraphy. His method was founded on Oersted's experiment. If a needle could be deflected by an electric current, if this could be accomplished by a wire or wires of great length, and if these movements of the needle could be converted into a code by means of which letters or words could be expressed, then the electro-magnetic telegraph was possible. Ampère's suggestion was to employ a number of wires and to deflect a number of needles. Considerable attention was given to the development of this idea for a number of years following the discovery of its fundamental principle. The progress of the invention was seriously retarded by the publication of an investigation by Barlow, of the Woolwich Military Academy, in 1825, in the course of which he discovered that there was an enormous diminution in the power of a current to produce effects with an increase of distance, and which led him to declare that the project of an electro-magnetic telegraph could not possibly be successful."

The invention of the electro-magnet by Sturgeon apparently offered a new solution of the problem; but, owing to the imperfect construction of his magnets, the difficulty of overcoming distance was not diminished. This obstacle, which seemed for a time to be insurmountable, was conquered by Joseph Henry in the manner already described. Out of Oersted's experiment grew the needle-telegraph—a form which prevailed for several years in Europe, until it gave way before the evident superiority of that founded on the electro-magnet, which grew out of the researches of Henry, and which is generally known as the Morse or American system.

The needle-telegraph was first in the field, and its working will first be considered. Many of its earlier forms appear as suggestions only, no attempt having been made to put them in practical operation. In 1832, however, Baron Schilling, a Russian counselor of state, had a working system in which thirty-six needles were used, and which included an ingenious alarm for calling the attention of the receiving operator. It consisted of a device by means of which the movement of one of the needles released a small ball of lead, which, by dropping upon the mechanism of the alarm, set it in operation. A model of this system was exhibited before the emperors Alexander and Nicholas.

A little later the two illustrious German philosophers, Gauss and Weber, established a successfully operating line at Göttingen. It was two or three miles long, and a double wire was used. Magnetic needles or bars, freely suspended, were used as receiving instruments, and the arrangement included a device for setting off an alarm-clock. The current from a battery was first used, but afterward the secondary or induced current was substituted. This line was in working order in 1833, and was established mainly for experimental purposes. The practical development of the scheme was given over to Steinheil, in whose hands it grew with rapidity. In 1837 he had constructed several miles of telegraph, extending from Munich to various points in the vicinity. His work appears to have been officially sanctioned by the government, and his wires doubtless constituted the first electric telegraph ever erected for commercial purposes. The system included a method of recording the message as received, which might also be read by sound, the signals being distinguished from each other by the use of bells differing in pitch.

"But altogether the most valuable contribution made by Steinheil," says Mendenhall, "was the discovery that the use of a double wire was unnecessary, it being possible to establish electric communication between two points by the use of one wire, whose terminals were joined to the earth through plates of metal, or other conductors exposing considerable surface. As it largely reduced the cost of construction, this discovery was of prime importance. It was really a repetition of what Franklin had long before accomplished when he stretched his wire across the Schuylkill River, but the relation between the two experiments was not at the time appreciated or fully understood."

Both the science of electricity and the art of telegraphy owe much to the genius of Sir Charles Wheatstone, whose interest in and connection with telegraph enterprises began in 1835, in which year he exhibited one of Schilling's telegraphs in his lectures, and in the year 1837, when he formed a copartnership with W. F. Cooke, for the purpose of introducing the electric telegraph into England. Their first patent was taken out in 1837; and the system required five needles, with as many wires for their manipulation, and a sixth wire for the "return current." Wheatstone developed numerous improvements during the next few years, and as early as 1840 a dial instrument showing the letters of the alphabet was patented. Numerous difficulties were encountered and overcome, and by 1844 the enterprise was on a sound financial basis.

The operation of working a telegraph was at first naturally regarded by most people as a mystery and by many as a fraud. When communication was established between Paddington and Slough, a distance of about twenty miles, the wires were insulated partly by silk and were suspended through goose-quills attached to posts along the Great Western Railway. The telegraph company not only invited the patronage of the public in a legitimate business way, but it also exhibited its apparatus as a novelty. This short line speedily established itself in the good graces of the people through its instrumentality in securing the arrest of a criminal.

The construction expenses incident to the use of a large number of wires, to say nothing of other difficulties, led to the reduction of the number of needles employed to two, and one in which a single wire was sufficient. A single needle is now almost universally employed wherever the needle system has survived competition with other forms. The movements of the needle are readily applied to signaling the alphabet by combinations of swings to the right and to the left. It will be remembered that in Oersted's experiment a reversal of the current through the wire reversed the direction of the deflection of the needle. The operating key is so arranged that when its handle is turned to the right a current is sent through the line which deflects the needle in the same direction; and when the opposite movement is made the current is reversed, and the needle swings to the left. The alphabet may, and generally does, correspond with what is known as the "Morse Code." A swing to the right is interpreted as a long signal or dash, and one to the left as the short or "dot" signal of the Morse system.

For many years the needle system of telegraph was used almost exclusively in Great Britain, altho it never succeeded in gaining a foothold on the continent of Europe or in any other part of the world. Its principal advantage is the comparatively feeble current required to work it; but it is slower than the Morse system, and does not lend itself to sound-reading, or to methods of securing written records of the messages which it transmits. It has, therefore, almost entirely given way to other systems, even in Great Britain, altho, as will be seen, it is retained in connection with long ocean cables, and within a few years a self-recording device has been successfully applied to it.

The system of telegraphy now almost universally in use is one which originated in America, and whose development was nearly contemporaneous with that of the needle system. In England the fundamental experiment about which the telegraph grew was that of Oersted; while in America the electro-magnet, as constructed by Sturgeon and improved by Henry, was made the basis of the invention. As there has been much misunderstanding concerning the distribution of credit for the evolution of this system of telegraphy, it may not be out of the way to consider at some length its more important phases.

Much credit must always be accorded Professor S. F. B. Morse, through whose indefatigable labors and persistent faith the commercial value of the enterprise was first established. Born in the last century, he reached the age of forty years before having apparently given a single thought to what was to be the great work of his life. His early training was that of an artist, although he was always fond of scientific pursuits. He studied in London under the best masters, and was highly successful in his chosen profession, some of his works bringing him great renown. His first conception of an electro-magnetic telegraph seems to have arisen out of a conversation with a friend on board the packet ship Sully, on a voyage from Havre to New York in 1832. In this conversation some experiments of the French were described, in which electricity had been transmitted through long distances. Some one remarked, "It would be well if we could send news in this rapid manner"; to which Morse at once replied, "Why can't we?" And from that moment he devoted his energies to accomplishing the desired end.

During the remainder of the voyage he made drawings of forms of apparatus and considered the transmission of signals into an alphabet. He does not appear to have been familiar with the principles of electro-magnetism at that time, and it is affirmed that the use of an electro-magnet was suggested to him by the gentleman with whom this first discussion was held. On reaching New York, he began experimenting upon the subject, and in 1835 he had completed a working model of his recording instrument. It was not until 1837, however, that he was able to put two of them in operation at the extremities of a short line, so as to be able to both receive and send signals. In that year his apparatus was exhibited to many people in the University of New York. In the following year he made an unsuccessful effort to secure aid from Congress to establish an experimental line between Washington and Baltimore. He then visited Europe, but failed to secure patents for his inventions. During the session of Congress of 1842-43 he again struggled to secure recognition and an appropriation to enable him to build his experimental line. The scheme was considered quixotic by many members of Congress, and at the last moment he despaired of success; but during the midnight hour of the last night of that session, March 3, 1843, a bill was passed appropriating thirty thousand dollars for the line from Washington to Baltimore.

In the meantime many apparently insuperable obstacles had been encountered in the attempt to secure the successful working of the apparatus. In the beginning, Morse used a magnet with a few turns of wire, as Sturgeon had done, and a single cell of battery. With this his instrument failed to work through more than a few feet of wire. This difficulty was surmounted by taking advantage of the researches of Henry, using what he called an "intensity" magnet and many cells of battery instead of one. Altho by this method signals could be transmitted through a comparatively long distance, they were still too feeble to print themselves upon the moving strip of paper. To overcome this difficulty it was only necessary to introduce the device known as the "relay," by means of which the work on the main circuit was reduced to making and breaking the current of a local battery, on the circuit of which was the recording machine. In this short circuit the current was easily made strong enough to operate the registering instrument. This method of working had been devised nearly ten years before by Henry, and it had also been used by Wheatstone in his needle system.

In Morse's first attempt to build his experimental line from Washington to Baltimore in 1844, the wires were placed underground instead of upon poles; but the former method was soon abandoned for the latter, which had already been in use for several years in Europe and elsewhere. In Morse's first instrument the "transmitter" was mechanical; that is to say, the message to be sent was first "set up" in "dots and dashes" by arranging long and short type in proper order in a line, and by the regular movement of this line of type the circuit was closed for periods of time necessary to the reproduction of the dots and dashes at the other end. Morse did not imagine that signals could be made by the hand with sufficient regularity to produce legible records. This was soon discovered to be possible, however, and for the clumsy mechanical transmitter the simple key of to-day was substituted, by the skillful manipulation of which the operator produces dots and dashes with such regularity and rapidity as to leave nothing to be desired.

The statements made above, derived from papers of an official character, may be summarized as follows: In the Morse telegraph are found the battery, for which credit must be given primarily to Volta, and then to Daniell, who in 1836 devised a battery nearly constant in its strength—an essential requisite to its application to the telegraph; the key, or transmitter, which, except in details of construction, is practically that in use since experiments on electricity were begun; the receiving instrument, of which the essential feature is the electromagnet, due primarily to Sturgeon, but modified and improved so as to be available for this work by Henry; the relay, by means of which the local current is put in operation, which was used by Henry and also by Wheatstone; the line wire suspended on poles—a method first practically used by Dr. W. O'Shaughnessy at Calcutta in 1839.

While it appears, therefore, that Morse cannot justly claim priority in the discovery of a single scientific principle involved in the telegraph, it must be admitted on all hands that he played a most important part in its development. In Europe all effort had been in the direction of the use of the needle system. Morse was quick to see the advantages of the electro-magnet, and especially the ease with which it could be made to leave a permanent record of the message. His use of a simple armature with to-and-fro motion, armed with a style, or pencil, which marked long or short lines upon a moving slip of paper, and his alphabet made up of these dots and dashes, show great ingenuity and mechanical judgment. As a measure of the value of his system, compared with the English, it is sufficient to repeat that to-day it has driven nearly every other from the field.

As the popularity of the telegraph increased and the number of line wires grew large, attempts were made to make one line wire transmit more than one message at the same time. Various schemes have been tried, most of which have failed by reason of the complications of the apparatus and the consequent troubles attending them.

The step in the direction of utilizing the line wire more fully was the invention of the duplex system by Dr. Wilhelm Gintl in 1853. This system was improved by Carl Frischen, of Hanover, until it lacked only one essential element—means to overcome the condenser-like action of the long line wire. It was not until 1872 that this was supplied by Joseph B. Stearns, of Boston, who introduced a condenser into the artificial line of the duplex system and, by adjusting it, made the artificial line behave like the line wire itself. This important addition made the system entirely successful, so that it became possible to transmit two messages in opposite directions at the same time.

Following the success of the duplex system, there was developed a method by which two messages could be sent simultaneously in the same direction, and it was but a step to combine these two systems so that two messages could be sent each way simultaneously. This last is known as the quadruplex system, and was immediately successful because there were no delicate adjustments to be made and no rotating parts as in some of the synchronous telegraphs which have been tried from time to time.

As early as 1852 Moses G. Farmer, of Salem, Mass., devised a synchronous-multiple telegraph in which he proposed to employ two rotating switches, one at each end of the line, to successively and simultaneously join the several operators at one station with those of another. The idea was to connect two operators for an instant, pass on to the next two, and so on, returning to the first two operators so quickly that the relay of the receiving operator would not have had time to change nor the key of the sender to make a dot. The impulses of the current had therefore to be made with great frequency, and the control of this impulsive current was the principal cause of failure. Another difficulty was the maintenance of the rotating switches in synchronism.

The public is occasionally startled with an announcement that some one has invented a telegraph by which a wire may be utilized for twenty or perhaps forty transmissions, but usually it is the old wanderer in a new garb. Speed by this method, however, is limited far within the bounds of these statements. It might seem that it would only be necessary to multiply the number of contacts and to increase the velocity of the rotating arms; but the limit in this direction is soon reached, for only a certain number of impulses can be transmitted over a line within a certain period with force sufficient to produce signals. Many valuable improvements have been made in recent years in this class of telegraphy, but large as the art has grown, the great object of all has been to obtain more perfect synchronism—that is to say, to cause two mechanically independent arms to rotate at the same speed.

One of the most recent of these synchronous telegraphs and which is now being exploited is that invented by Mr. Delaney. The principle is that of Farmer, but the method used to hold the rotating switches in synchronism is extremely ingenious. It is stated that 1,000 words per minute may be transmitted over a single wire. The messages are prepared on a tape by a punching machine and received on a chemically prepared strip of paper.

The idea of printing the despatch is not new. In the early days of the electric telegraph (1841) Wheatstone took out a patent for printing the message in ordinary letters upon a strip of paper. Since then many inventors have followed out the same idea, with more or less success. The most perfect of all these systems, however, is that invented by Professor David E. Hughes, which, in a modified form, is

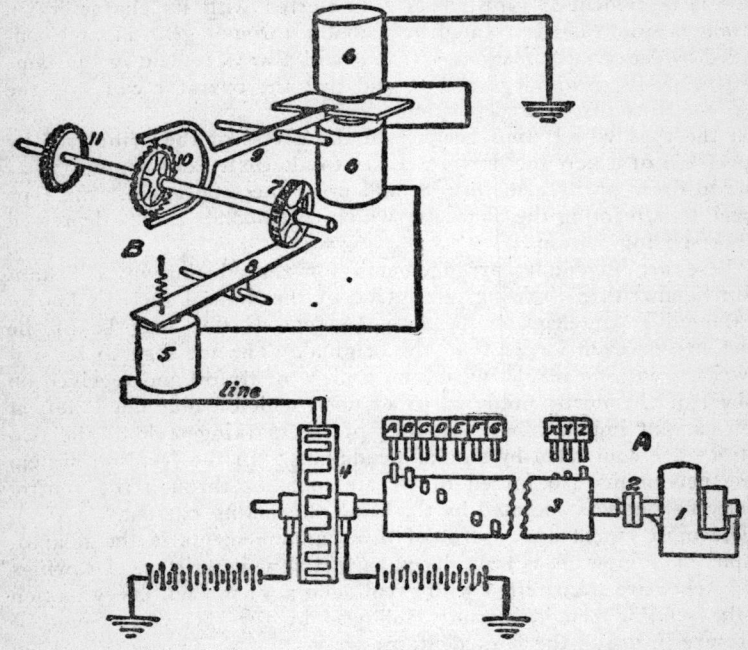

Fig. 45 —Arrangement of a Printing Telegraph or "News Ticker." (From Standard Handbook for Electrical Engineers.)

now very generally used as a news or stock ticker. Fig. 45 shows the connections for such a telegraph.

The sending station is at A and one of the receiving stations at B. The line is fed with an alternating current produced by reversing commutator, 4. This alternating current does not affect printing relay 5, but does operate polar relay 6, which in turn operates the escapement. Reverser 4 is driven by constant-speed motor 1 and has as many segments as there are characters on the type wheel. The escape wheel 10 is provided with an equal number of teeth, so that each revolution of reverser 4 will produce one revolution of type wheel 7. On the shaft with the reverser is rigidly mounted a cylinder provided with a number of pins arranged spirally as shown; each pin is in line with a segment of the reverser and also in line with a pin fastened to the keyboard.

Depressing a given key will always stop the cylinder and therefore type wheel 7 in the same place. The connection to the motor 1 is made with friction clutch 2, which slips when cylinder 3 is stopped. Now it is evident if type wheel 7 is started with its characters in certain position and is rotated by a motor through gear 11 and controlled by escapement magnet 6, that it will always remain in the same relative position with cylinder 3, and that the operator can stop the type wheel in any desired position.

If the type wheel stops because of the arrest of the cylinder 3 by depression of a key, the current ceases to alternate, and magnet 5 has time to draw up its armature, 8, and press the tape against the type wheel, thus printing the character which corresponds to key depressed at the sending station.

These are ingenious arrangements for reproducing at a distant point handwriting, drawing, etc. One of the first of these is known as Casselli's pantelegraph, because the reproduction may be of the same size or even larger than the original. The message to be sent is written with an insulating ink on a piece of tinfoil and received on a sheet of chemically prepared paper upon which a blue dot is left at each current impulse. The motions of the marking style at the two stations are controlled by similar pendulums. In the Denison system these pendulums are forced to vibrate together through the control of electro-magnets operated by the same alternating current.

The most recent and useful of these arrangements is the telautograph. The message is reproduced as fast as it is written. Drawings or sketches are transmitted with great accuracy; in fact, every motion of the sending pen is instantly followed by the receiver. Some of these are in use in the United States army.

The insulation of conductors for use under water was made possible by the discovery of gutta-percha by an English surgeon in India in 1842. It is extremely probable that the widespread use of submarine cables would have been postponed many years had this substance remained unknown. One of the first cables insulated by this material, and possibly the very first, was laid in 1848 across the Hudson River, from Jersey City to New York. In 1850 a cable was laid across the channel, from Dover to Calais, but it was unprotected by any sheathing or armor, and it lasted but a single day.

In the following year the experiment was repeated, this time with a cable protected by a number of heavy iron wires. The operation was successful, and permanent telegraph communication was established. During the next few years the number of submarine cables increased rapidly, as did also their length, altho, on account of ignorance in regard to many conditions necessary to insure the best success, failures were numerous. Many people began to consider the feasibility of a line connecting the continents across the Atlantic Ocean. A few sanguine capitalists combined to further the enterprise, and through the undaunted courage and faith of an American, Mr. Cyrus W. Field, the purely financial obstacles were surmounted. Unfortunately, the electrical and engineering problems to be met with were not understood; and the first cable of 1858, after gasping for breath for a few short weeks, lay dumb forever at the bottom of the sea.

Something of the character of this cable may be learned from the following brief description by Sir William Thomson, to whom, more than to any other one man, the world is indebted for the success of submarine telegraphy: "In the year 1857 as much iron as would make a cube twenty feet wide was drawn into wire long enough to extend from the earth to the moon, and bind several times around each globe. This wire was made into 126 lengths of 2,500 miles, and spun into 18 strands of 7 wires each. A single strand of 7 copper wires of the same length, weighing in all 110 grains per foot, was three times coated with gutta-percha, to an entire outer thickness of .4 of an inch; and this was "served" outside with 240 tons of tarred yarn, and then laid over with the 18 strands of iron wire in long, contiguous spirals and passed through a bath of melted pitch."

An attempt to lay this cable in 1857 resulted in the loss of 400 or 500 miles by breaking from the stern of the ship from which it was run. After some further experimentation, it was determined to employ two ships to lay it in the following year; and accordingly, on the 29th of July, 1858, the Niagara and the Agamemnon, each loaded with half the cable, met in mid ocean, joined the ends, and started, the Niagara for the west and the Agamemnon for the east. On the 5th of August the ends were successfully landed on the opposite shores of the Atlantic.

The cable was known to be in bad condition before the laying was completed, and the earnest but ill-advised efforts which were made to force it to work during its brief period of activity only tended to shorten its life. Communication of a very irregular and unsatisfactory character was maintained for several weeks. The admirable mirror galvanometer, which had just been devised by Sir William Thomson, was for the first time in use at the Valentia end, while for a time the attempt was made to use the ordinary receiving apparatus which had been provided by the company at Newfoundland. Later the galvanometer was put in use on this side, but not before very powerful currents had been used on the cable. In fact, Sir William

Thomson had declared his belief that, if proper methods of handling the cable electrically had been in use from the beginning, its performance would have been lasting and in the main satisfactory.

Owing to the fragmentary character of many of the messages transmitted, a single sentence from that of the Queen to the President having been received on August 16, and the remainder twenty-four hours, later, many persons in both Europe and America became skeptical as to the transmission of signals, and not a few even doubted that the cable had been laid. As a matter of fact, four hundred messages, containing over four thousand words, were sent. On September 1, interchange of messages ceased; but on October 20 the cable spoke its last words— "two hundred and forty"—which were read at Valentia, being part of a message giving the number of battery-cells then on the line. From that date the "splendid combination of matter lay at the bottom of the sea, forever useless." But it had not lived in vain; the possibility of the thing was demonstrated, and it only remained to surmount the obstacles which this trial had shown.

During a few years succeeding this first attempt, the problem was studied in the light of the experience which it had afforded. Another trial was made in 1865, this time by the Great Eastern, a vessel which offered many advantages for cable-laying. After about two-thirds of the distance was run the cable broke and further operations were postponed until the following year, when a complete cable was successfully laid, and that of 1865 picked up, spliced and finished. Since then many other lines have been placed across the seven seas.

One of the difficulties encountered in attempting to send messages through such a long cable was that due to the electrostatic capacity of the cable. The cable acts like a very large condenser, so that when the voltage is applied at one end the current does not instantly rise to its steady value, but takes several seconds, and when the supply of voltage is disconnected the current continues to flow. In order to signal rapidly, therefore, it was necessary to overcome this action and to use very delicate receiving instruments. For this purpose, Sir William Thomson, Lord Kelvin, devised the well-known siphon recorder, which is really a sensitive galvanometer whose moving coil carries a siphon tube filled with ink, the ink being ejected from it in fine drops on a strip of paper. To produce these fine drops the siphon tube is connected to a small electrostatic machine, so that the tube is electrified.

Altho the telephone has made such rapid advances as a means of communication, the telegraph still holds its own field. The greater simplicity of the latter, the less expensive lines, the greater distances to which messages can be transmitted, all combine for its preservation. The tendency of waves to flatten in telephonic communication has been largely overcome by balancing induction coils attached at intervals along the line. This method is due to the work of Dr. Pupin of Columbia University. The value of the induction in each coil is calculated from the characteristics of the line. These coils make possible the transmission of a voice for several hundred miles. In the transcontinental line, at the time of its inauguration, the distance from New York to San Francisco was divided into five sections. At each junction point a repeating apparatus was installed. These repeaters have made voice transmission possible over a distance of nearly 4,000 miles.

CHAPTER XI

WIRELESS TELEGRAPHY AND TELEPHONY

Professor Henry, of Princeton University, was the first to show the oscillatory character of the discharge of a Leyden jar. This single loud spark, which to the eye seems to pass in one direction across the gap, is really a quick succession of current surges, first one way and then the other, and has its mechanical analogy in the pendulum.

At the outset it may be well to analyze this spark discharge, as it is still the most prominent means of radiating the electric waves used to transmit signals. Suppose this pendulum analogy of the spark discharge between two spheres to be taken and the similarity of the two actions noted. If a heavy pendulum be drawn back by means of a light fiber, it will finally strain the fiber to such an extent as to cause it to break. The pendulum being suddenly released gradually acquires motion, which is accelerated until its lowest position is reached, after which it is retarded just as it was accelerated and stops at about the same height at which it started. The process is then repeated, but in the opposite direction. Now compare the action on the two charged spheres. The pressure in the dielectric surrounding the spheres is gradually raised until it suddenly gives way, there being a flow of current from the positive to the negative sphere, which current gradually increases and is greatest at the instant when both dielectrics are at the same potential, just as the motion of the pendulum was greatest at its lowest position. The current then begins to decrease and finally stops when the dielectric is again strained to about the same potential it had at first but reversed in direction. The current then starts back again just as the pendulum again acquired motion.

Now let it be considered what goes on in the space surrounding this action. A current is always surrounded by a field of magnetic force, which field is proportional to the strength of the current. As this current between the two spheres increases there is, therefore, sent out an increasing magnetic field which is radiated into space, reaching a maximum and again decreasing the current. But while the current increases the electrostatic strain about the sphere decreases, thus sending out an electrostatic wave which again increases as the current decreases. It will thus be seen that as these surges take place alternate electromagnetic and electrostatic waves are radiated into space.

Why do not these surges keep on forever? Mainly because the current in its flow across the gap encounters a resistance, and instead of converting all its energy into magnetic waves loses a portion as heat at each surge. This corresponds to oscillating the pendulum in a liquid or viscous material, the energy of its motion soon being converted into heat.

So much for the creation of these waves. But how may their passage through space be detected? One way, is by catching them on a wire. What is the manner of the catching? If a wire be placed so that it cuts the wave transversely to its line of motion, it is clear that the moving magnetic wave will induce in it an electro-motive force. As these waves follow in rapid succession, a series of alternating electro-motive forces is set up in the wire. These oscillatory currents are sometimes called "jigs." How these jig currents make their presence known varies with the style of wave detector used.

Before entering upon the history of this "spark telegraphy," as the Germans called it, it may be well to review some of the experiments which preceded this system. In 1838 Professor Joseph Henry, of Princeton, making with an electrical machine and Leyden jar a one-inch spark in the top room of his residence, set up induced currents in the cellar of the same building. Professor Morse, however, was probably the first to successfully transmit signals without wire. On December 16, 1842, he sent a wireless telegram across a canal eighty feet wide; and in November, 1844, L. D. Gale, acting under instructions from Professor Morse, made wireless signals across the Susquehanna River at Havre de Grâce, a distance of nearly one mile. In the latter experiment Mr. Gale used as a source of energy six pairs of plates in the form of a galvanic battery. He found that the best results were obtained when on each side of the river two plates were immersed near its bank and were connected by an insulated wire stretched along each shore for a distance three times as great as that which measured either path of the crossing signals. A few years later James Lindsay, a Scotchman, repeated Morse's experiments, but without knowing of them. In 1859 he read a paper before the British Association on the subject of "Telegraphing without Wires," and among his hearers were Faraday and Lord Kelvin.

A method of signaling without wires by means of the inductive effect of two parallel circuits was successfully used by Sir William Preece in 1882. The principle of this method is as follows: If two loops of wire are placed parallel to each other and an intermittent current is passed through one of them, waves of magnetic flux are sent out, portions of which thread the second loop and by their fluctuations produce currents in it which may be detected by a telephone or other device. The strength of such signals falls off very rapidly from the source, and such a system can only be made to operate over short distances.

Preece constructed two parallel lines, one on the English coast and one on the Isle of Wight.

The crowning achievement, however, was the work of Hertz, whose early death deprived the world of the aid of a most powerful brain. In 1886 Hertz discovered that if a loop of wire having a small air-gap left in it were placed at a distance from a spark discharge of a Leyden jar, minute sparks would pass across the air-gap of the loop, thus indicating the presence of electric waves. He subsequently made a very complete study of the behavior of these waves and thus gave a tremendous impetus to the development of wireless telegraphy.

Second to the work of Hertz is that of Sir Oliver Lodge, who in 1889 discovered the effect of electric waves on the breaking down of the electrical resistance of two knobs barely in contact, which discovery resulted in the first means used to detect the presence of electrical waves, viz., the coherer.

The development of wave detectors is an important chapter. For these instruments Professor Fleming has suggested the use of the word cymoscope as a general term including all classes of wave detectors. A great number of these have been invented, but they may all be included under the following classes: 1, spark cymoscopes; 2, contact cymoscopes; 3, thermal cymoscopes; 4, magnetic cymoscopes; 5, electrolytic cymoscopes; 6, electrodynamic cymoscopes; 7, vacuum tube cymoscopes.

The first cymoscope invented was that used by Hertz in his investigation of electric waves, and belongs to the first class. It consisted merely of a ring broken at one point and arranged so that the gap might be adjusted by means of a micrometer screw. Tiny sparks across this gap indicated the presence of waves. Since the electromotive force required to produce a spark across even a small gap is very considerable, it will be obvious that such a detector could only operate at a short distance, and would therefore be useless for the purpose of signaling.

The next invention, made in 1890, was the Bramly coherer, which consisted of a small glass tube containing two metallic plugs and separated by a gap partially filled with metallic filings. This is an example of the second class. The metallic filings, when loosely packed, offer a very high resistance to the passage of current through them, but the presence of waves breaks down their contact resistance, which continues after the waves have ceased. In order to again restore their resistance they must be tapped or shaken, an operation known as decoherence. It is obvious that such an apparatus may be used like a key in a telegraphic circuit—a key operated by electric

WIRELESS TELEGRAPHY

waves—and may therefore be used to operate a telegraphic instrument. Such was the first device used. It was defective, however, in that it was necessary to tap it after each signal, decoherence was not certain, it required frequent adjustment, and the result was often a confused lot of signals.

Many arrangements of loose contacts were tried, and the coherer was improved by Marconi, Lodge, Braum, and others. One of the principal troubles being the operation of decoherence, most of the inventors sought to develop a coherer which should be self-restoring, and a number of successful types were invented. One of these was the Hughes coherer, employing carbon granules placed between iron plugs. The most perfect and successful of all these is, however, that devised by Sir Oliver Lodge and Dr. Muirhead, and used in the Lodge-Muirhead system. It consisted of a steel disk, slightly separated from a globule of mercury by a film of oil, the disk being arranged to rotate slowly. The presence of waves breaks down the oil film and establishes contact with the mercury, which contact immediately breaks upon the cessation of the waves. A siphon recorder, placed in series with the cymoscope, is used to record the message.

Altho a number of forms of the magnetic style of detector were devised, it was not until 1902 that a successful working apparatus was produced. For some time before that it was known that the oscillating currents received would annul wholly or in part the magnetic hysteresis of iron when passed through a coil surrounding the iron. Hysteresis acts like molecular friction, so that when a magnetizing current is passed through a coil surrounding an iron core, the magnetization does not increase and decrease with the current in the coil, but lags behind it. If another coil be placed around this same core and the oscillating currents passed through it, this hysteresis will be suddenly removed and the magnetism in the core will suddenly change in value. This sudden change could be detected by a third coil surrounding the core and connected to a telephone receiver, resulting in a sudden click. This was the principle of which Marconi made use in his magnetic detector, and which he has used in his long-distance experiments. The arrangement is shown in Fig. 18. It consists of a band of iron wires passing through two coils, one carrying the jig currents and one connected to the telephone. The wires are magnetized by two permanent magnets, and as they move under that portion where the two poles meet, the magnetic flux in them undergoes a reversal, which reversal, however, always takes place at the same point until the jig currents pass, when the flux is suddenly shifted backward, causing a sound in the telephone.

These detectors have come into very general use on account of their convenience, sensitiveness, and adaptation to rapid signaling. In 1901, Dr. Lee de Forest patented a detector which depends for its operation on the disruption of the minute metallic bridges or "trees" which form, under suitable conditions, between the electrodes of an electrolytic cell. The apparatus, called a "responder," consists in a glass tube similar to that of a coherer, in which are fitted two electrodes, preferably of tin. The space between the electrodes—about 1/64 inch—is filled with a viscous, semiconducting liquid, such as glycerin with a small admixture of water, together with some peroxide of lead as a depolarizer, to prevent the excessive evolution of gas. When a cell of suitable voltage is connected across this "responder," metallic "trees" or bridges are formed, which make a path of low resistance; but upon the passage of the jig currents these "trees" are broken down and the circuit broken, producing a sound in a telephone receiver. Immediately upon the cessation of the jig currents, however, these "trees" again establish themselves.

Another very successful and extremely sensitive detector was invented by Fessenden and Vreeland, and consists of a small platinum cathode containing nitric acid, with a minute anode of platinum wire 1/10,000 inch in diameter. This little electrolytic cell, when polarized to the critical point by being connected to a battery, is remarkably sensitive to jig currents. It has been employed by Fessenden in his transatlantic experiments.

Many other detectors have been developed which have operated successfully, but those described are used most generally.

It would not be possible in a few words to give a comprehensive idea of the various systems in use, as many important improvements which have been made in the last ten years. Those systems which have attained commercial importance are the Marconi, the Fessenden, the De Forest, the Slaby-Arco and the Lodge-Muirhead. The greatest differences are usually found in the receiving apparatus.

The first system used by Marconi employed the coherer as a wave detector and the Ruhmhorff coil to produce the sparks from which the waves were radiated. Experiments with this form of apparatus were first made in 1896 in England, where Marconi went to obtain the assistance of Sir William Preece. These experiments were so successful that trials were made during the next year, at each of which something new was learned whereby the distance of transmission was increased. From some of these experiments Marconi worked out the effect of the height of the antenna, or aerial wire, on the distance of transmission.

In August, 1897, Marconi organized a company known as the Wireless Telegraph and Signal Co., with a capital of $5,000,000. In June, 1897, Marconi went to Rome, and after having undertaken in this city, at the instigation of the Minister of Marine, several experiments from one floor to another with a conductor three yards in height, was invited by the Hon. Brin, Minister of Marine, to undertake, in the presence of a select commission composed of officers who were specialists belonging to the royal marines, some fresh experiments. The place chosen was the Gulf of Spezzia. The experiments took place between the 11th and the 18th of July, 1897. The apparatus made use of for transmitting and receiving was similar to those employed on the Bristol Channel; that is to say, aerial wires ending above in metallic sheets. The coil was less powerful than that used in the former case, giving sparks 10 inches in length only.

The apparatus was located, during the entire series of experiments, in the electrical laboratory of St. Bartholomew, and bore an aerial line about 75 feet in height, which was afterward prolonged to 90, terminating in a square metal sheet of about 8 feet in the side.

On the first three days, viz., 11th, 12th and 13th of July, the experiments were executed on land, which gave very good results up to a distance of 3½ kilometers, or say 2 miles; on the 14th of July the receiver was set up on board a tug, having a mast about 50 feet in height, which bore an aerial wire of equal length ending in a sheet about 8 feet in the side.

The transmitting station was bound to carry out the following instructions: Ten minutes after the start of the tug it was to send for 15 minutes dots and dashes at intervals of 10 seconds; then transmit a phrase, maintaining between each signal an interval of 10 seconds; then to suspend transmission for an interval of 5 minutes, after which it should go through the same round, but with intervals of 5 seconds instead of 10 between each signal.

The tug having started from the little port of St. Bartholomew, the receiver registered some signs even before transmission had begun on land, a fact due doubtless to extraneous causes. She directed her course toward the western mouth of the mole, and continued to receive signals, not however, in order and in the intervals that had been prearranged, but much more frequently. The sky was covered with stormy clouds and in the distance lightning was frequent, hence it was surmised that besides the signals that were really transmitted, others, due to atmospheric influence, were impressing themselves, which rendered the strip of paper on which they were registered illegible.

On again repeating these experiments after the storm clouds had disappeared, correspondence came out very clearly up to a distance of 5,500 meters (nearly 3 miles), with the tug stationary. The tug was again put in motion, so as to interpose between itself and the station at St. Bartholomew the point called Le Castagne, in order to ascertain what effect such a screen would have on signaling.

The signals ceased as soon as the obstacle intervened, to recommence on the tug being moved from its influence. On the return journey the messages continued to come out clear and exact.

On the 17th of July trials were made from the same stations of St.

Bartholomew to the armored ship San Martino, anchored at a distance of about 1¾ miles from the transmitting station, the aerial conductor of which had been carried to a height of about 40 yards, while the ship bore at the receiver an aerial line, first of 20, and then of 30 yards in height.

Transmission succeeded perfectly, independent of the position of the coherer and the receiver; that is to say, even if they were screened at the sending station and surrounded by metallic masses under cover or placed below the water-line in the ship.

It was at once foreseen by many experimenters, among them Sir Oliver Lodge, that with the old forms of apparatus there would be interference between wireless stations, as the receivers would respond to all wave lengths. To understand how it is possible to make a sending or a receiving circuit which will send out or respond to only one kind of electric wave, let the pendulum analogy again be used. In order to set a pendulum in motion it is necessary that the impulsive force should be imparted to it the same number of times per second in which the pendulum naturally oscillates. Even if stray forces are applied, but are not properly timed, the effect on the pendulum will be small, whereas a very minute but properly timed force, acting for some time, will produce considerable motion in a large pendulum. All these characteristics of the pendulum may be applied to the electric circuit—the natural period of vibration, the small effect of a lot of waves differing in length, and the large effect of a succession of feeble but similar waves.

Sir Oliver Lodge, in 1897, took out a patent for a "syntonic system of wireless telegraphy, based directly on his own work on the discharge of Leyden jars and on Hertz's experimental results. The transmitter consisted of two large cones of sheet metal placed with their axes in a vertical line, and having a spark-gap between their apices. In another form of transmitter a single metal sphere, separated by small spark-gaps from the terminals of an induction coil, was used as a radiator. Both types produced direct Hertzian radiation, the latter giving waves of very high frequency. The spherical oscillator was partially enclosed in a copper cylinder, open at one end in order that the rays might be condensed in one direction. The receiver, for use in connection with the large cones, consisted of two similar cones connected through the primary of a small transformer, the secondary of which was connected to the coherer circuit. The dimensions of the transmitter and receiver were adjusted to give equifrequent natural vibrations and therefore resonance. No earth connection was made, as it was desired that the transmission should be purely by means of free radiations. The early conical form of radiator has now given place to the horizontal conductors. Stations in which this latter arrangement has been adopted are now working in various parts of the world.

As soon as Marconi had modified his system of telegraphy he applied it immediately to the conquest of record distances in radio-telegraphic transmission. To this end he set up a station at the Lizard (Cornwall), which was immediately put into communication with Marconi's experimental station at St. Katherine's, Isle of Wight, at a distance of 300 kilometers (about 200 miles), in which he used an aerial conductor consisting of four vertical wires standing about 5 feet from one another, about 144 feet in height, along with a strip of wire netting of the same length.

Under the new system the energy required to telegraph to a given distance was very much diminished, so that 150 watts sufficed to communicate to the 300-kilometer distance.

Encouraged by the results of the experiments in communication between St. Katherine's and the Lizard, Marconi put his whole heart into the attempt to resolve the arduous problem of establishing transatlantic radiotelegraphic communication. Repeated experiments had shown that long waves, either by successive reflection or diffraction, could turn round the surface of the earth, so that their transmission to very great distances resolved itself only into a question of sufficient power in the transmitting apparatus and sufficient sensibility in the receiving; but these necessitated large financial means, which would, however, not be wanting in a man whose business acumen was not less surprising than his experimental ability.

Being largely subsidized by the Marconi Wireless Telegraph Company, Marconi began, early in 1901, unknown to every one, his trials, by establishing two specially powerful stations at Poldhu, near Cape Lizard, in Cornwall, on one side of the ocean, and at Cape Cod, in Massachusetts, on the other side. The results of these first trials are not known, and judging by the silence maintained in this regard they were probably negative. The two stations, that had cost the sum of more than £15,000, were destroyed by storms in September of the same year.

Marconi caused the station at Poldhu to be rebuilt, furnishing it with powerful machines and radiators, and decided to attempt communication with St. Johns, Newfoundland; that is to say, to a lesser distance than that previously chosen, viz., of about 1,500 miles. At St. Johns, Newfoundland, where Marconi had obtained from the Government every facility for making the trials, the installation was of the simplest character, consisting of a receiving station only. The aerial line was maintained at a height of about 400 feet by means of a kite.

Marconi had already agreed with the station at Poldhu that every day, at six o'clock in the evening, a long series of letter S should be sent. This letter, in the Morse alphabet, consists of three dots.

The message was received telephonically. On the 12th of December, 1901, Marconi announced that he had received the different S's at equal and determinate intervals, and he proclaimed that it was practically, physically and mathematically impossible that the signals could have come from any other place but Cape Lizard.

In the summer of 1902 Mr. Marconi made an interesting comparative test of his first (coherer) system and his second (magnetic detector) system. The ship "Carlo Alberto" was fitted out with both sets of receiving apparatus. By previous arrangements a set of signals from the Poldhu station was to be sent out at certain hours of the day. As the voyage toward Kronstadt proceeded the signals diminished in strength, and at a distance of 900 kilometers were not perceptible during the day. At night, however, they continued to be received by both systems until the port of Kronstadt, was reached, when only the magnetic detector responded, and that only feebly. The disturbing action of daylight was very marked in these tests.

Having received an invitation from the Canadian Government to continue his experiments in Canada, Marconi erected a large station at Table Head, on the island of Cape Breton, at the mouth of Glace Bay, and 3,800 kilometers from Poldhu. On Dec. 20, 1902, Mr. Marconi sent the first radiograms across the Atlantic to the Kings of England and Italy. Shortly afterward another station was erected at Cape Cod, in Massachusetts, the distance to the Poldhu station being 3,200 miles, or 660 miles further than the Glace Bay station. On Jan. 16, 1903, a complete radiogram was sent by President Roosevelt to the King of England.

Professor Fessenden commenced in 1897 the development of the system which is now the property of the National Electric Signaling Company. For two years he was engaged by the United States Government for special research in the subject, and had the advantages of all the resources of a government department at his command. His inventions are very numerous, and in many respects original, and his results show a precision and practicality not attained by many other experimenters in the same field.

Magnetic, thermal and electrolytic detectors, methods of exact tuning, and even wireless telephony, are covered by Fessenden's patents. Among these, perhaps that which has contributed most to the success of the system is the barretter. In its original form this was a thermal receiver, depending for its action on the change of resistance in a very fine platinum wire when carrying the jig current. Latterly the continuous wire has been discarded in favor of an electrolytic coil, one electrode of which is an extremely fine point. The apparatus has been described more fully under wave detectors. An important feature of this system, which greatly aids secrecy of trans-

WIRELESS TELEGRAPHY

mission, is the arrangement of the sending key, which does not break the circuit, but merely alters the wave length of the waves given out, by cutting out some inductance. Thus, unless a receiving station is tuned with extreme accuracy to the transmitter, it will receive, instead of signals, only a long, continuous dash; hence only a very sharply tuned receiver will receive a message at all. In the latest forms of apparatus the difference in frequency between the waves sent out during spaces and those sent as signals is only ¼ per cent.; interception by rivals is, therefore, almost impossible. Fessenden is apparently the first to use an aerial consisting of a steel tube standing on an insulating foundation, and held in position by insulated stays.

A report giving a description of the Fessenden system, as applied to transatlantic signaling between Massachusetts and Scotland, may be of interest here:

"The power is developed by a boiler-engine-alternator equipment having a maximum capacity of 25 kw., 60 cycles current. A transformer steps up the voltage to about 25,000, thus charging the condensers, which are discharged by means of a gap adjustable so as to effect the discharge at any desired point of the cycle.

"The receiver used is the liquid barretter in its latest form. The aerial is formed by a tower extending to a height of 415 feet above the ground-level, and supporting a sort of umbrella formed of wires at its top. The tower is essentially a steel tube 3 feet in diameter, supported every 100 feet of its height by a set of four steel guys, there being thus sixteen guys in all. The tower is pivoted at its base on a ball-and-socket joint, and is insulated from the ground for a voltage of 150,000. The guys are insulated from the tower into 50-foot sections by means of strain insulators. One of the most serious problems to be solved was the construction of these strain insulators, which, while capable of safely transmitting the maximum stress of about 20,000 pounds, also resist an electrical tension of 15,000 volts each. The maximum deflection of the top of the tower in a 90-mile hurricane is computed to be 15½ inches. A wave chute containing over 100 miles of wire, and extending over six acres, is a very essential feature of the installation.

"On January 3, 1906, the first signals were received from the American side, and shortly afterward communication was established, so that messages were freely exchanged at night. The intensity of the signals received by telephone was at times so great that the messages could easily be read with the diaphragm three inches from the ears of the operator. A station twenty miles distant from Brant Rock, using about 30 kw., and sending on a wave length differing not much more than 3 per cent, from that of the Scottish station, was cut out while messages were received from Machrihanish."

A system differing in many respects from the other systems has been devised by Sir Oliver Lodge and Dr. Muirhead. The rotating steel disk coherer described under wave detectors is used by them. Another feature is the use of two capacity areas at both sending and receiving stations by the adjustment of which they may be brought into tune.

This system has been installed in many places with great success, and altho it has not yet operated over such distances as the Marconi and Fessenden systems, it compares favorably with them in syntonizing power, and has the advantage of using the siphon recorder.

The Telefunken System is based on the patents of Professors Slaby and Braun and of Count von Arco. It may be considered as striking a mean between the earlier systems of Marconi and Lodge and Muirhead, tho of course with many variations and elaborations in detail. A system of wires, similar to those used by Marconi, forms the aerial, and the earth connection is given by a large capacity, as in the Lodge-Muirhead apparatus. A coherer and receiving circuit in many respects similar to the Marconi arrangements is employed.

The de Forest system has had quite an extended commercial application, especially in the United States. It has the advantage of very rapid signaling, 25 to 30 words per minute having been reached. As early as 1908, communication by this system was established between Manhattan Beach, New York, and Colon, Panama, a distance of 2,170 miles.

The period from 1908 to 1915 has witnessed many improvements in wireless telegraph systems. Most of the improvements have been of a mechanical nature. Practically no changes have been made in the operating principles. Wireless telegraphy is now in common service, both as a safety device and as a commercial organ. Wireless sets have been designed for aerial craft and the results obtained in the European war have demonstrated its reliability under the most severe tests. The Canadian government has established a complete chain of stations from coast to coast. The U. S. government has established wireless communication with all the territorial possessions. Experiments are now being carried on attempting the operation of navigation signals, such as fog horns, by means of wireless.

Wireless systems are now operating successfully over long distances at a rate of 100 words per minute. In 1914 the application of wireless to the operation of fast train traffic was made by the D. L. and W. R. R. It now has trains equipped with aërials and complete sending and receiving apparatus. Train dispatching is carried on from two stations, one at Hoboken, N. J., and the other at Buffalo, N. Y. Attention in wireless circles was centered in 1915 on the development of wireless telephony. Towards the close of that year wireless telephone messages were transmitted a distance of 4,600 miles, thus signally recording the achievement of success in this extremely difficult field, a success that no one had expected would be secured for at least a score of years later.

The extension of wireless telegraphy and wireless telephony and the study of the relations of electrical discharges in radio-active bodies bid fair to the most fruitful of the fields of the immediate future. The Age has been well called the Age of Electricity, and amazement is constantly expressed that Man should so well utilize a force concerning which he knows so little. The complete understanding of the phenomena of atomic force and of radio-activity may go far to unlock many of the closed doors of Nature, and the electrical scientist of to-day is steadily approaching that understanding.

MEDICINE

MEDICINE

CHAPTER I

THE ANCIENTS

The development of anatomy and physiology, since the earliest days of mankind, is so closely interwoven with the history of medicine and philosophy that no consideration of the medical arts is possible without some realization of the strange complications of thought at that early time. It is Science now, but it was Mystery then. Mystery overhung the thinkers of antiquity, and nowhere did this element of magic and of wonder have a stronger hold than in the strange humors of disease, for which they could find none other explanation than that they were punishments inflicted by gods or demons.

With this well-nigh universal conception of the causes of disease, it follows naturally that healing could only attend the propitiation of the gods by suitable sacrifices, prayers and penances, and the offices of priest and physician were unified. But instead of this aggrandizing the doctor's importance, public opinion veered. Inasmuch as so great stress was laid upon the gods to maim or to heal, so much the less power had the physician-priest, for was he not a mere tool of the gods? It was not he that healed. Even to within a century or two ago a "barber-surgeon," as he was called, was held in the greatest contempt, and the development which has led to the medical profession holding a place of eminence in the minds of men is one of the most startling evolutions of modern times.

This sudden elevation reveals a public consciousness of the worth of true knowledge. Whereas the physician of the ancients was also priest, philosopher and scribe, and could not specialize or attain distinctive knowledge in any one branch of the healing art, for the reason that those branches were incompletely developed and not much was known of them, now the physician is acutely trained to a definite portion of his profession and speaks thereon with authority. Moreover, he must not only know his subject and know it well, but he must be a man of culture, of wide general knowledge and keen understanding of the men and times in which he lives, and he must also be a chemist, a biologist and a physicist, indeed there is not a branch of science which he does not subordinate to his effort to alleviate pain and raise the life-standard of the human race.

The peerless knowledge of the ancients in the Mathematical Sciences and in the Fine Arts naturally raises the question why anatomy, physiology and organic chemistry were not independently studied or worked out with any analytical skill. The structure and functions of the human body were little known and less understood. That the confusion of mind incident upon the commixture of the Art of Medicine with Philosophy and Religion went far to cause this neglect is true, but it seems that an even greater barrier lay in the absence of freedom of study and of expression.

All the religions of the past taught that to lay critical hands upon a body was wrong and even impious, and this idea was so firmly rooted that for centuries such a prohibition is found in civil law. In many cases the dead body was held as more sacred than the living, esteemed peculiarly of reverence and even worship, and even yet the old idea has not entirely died out which considered anatomical research and dissection to be a sacrilege. Knowledge was perilously gained, and with the study of anatomy and physiology thus under ban it is small wonder that the physicians were able to do little to stay the scourges of the appalling epidemics which literally mowed down hundreds of thousands in the Middle Ages. Few developments of human thought show a truer following of a high ideal than the advance made through centuries of toil to stay the pain and alleviate the distress which accrue from "the ills that flesh is heir to."

In proportion to the progress of civilization and refinement, more definite and well-reasoned attempts have been made to remove or alleviate disease and to repair any of the gross injuries to which the human body is constantly exposed. Subject as it is to the influence of various noxious agents and to a consequent derangement of its functions, to many painful affections and to the loss of its powers and actions, men have always been anxious to remove or relieve these conditions. Thus, in the earliest periods of society, mankind must have been aware of the relief which was given in the derangements of alimentation by evacuation and would probably have discovered, incidentally perhaps, that certain vegetable agents promoted this operation. In external injuries they would find that rest, pressure, heat or cold gave relief, as, for example, when pressure stopped an excessive flow of blood. This rude species of medical and surgical practice has been found to exist in newly discovered countries, even when in the most barbarous state, while it has been observed that the improvement in the healing art has been nearly proportionate to the advancement of the other sciences of life and to the gradual progress of knowledge on all subjects connected therewith.

The Egyptians had several divinities who presided over the cure of disease. The principal of these deities, Isis, was at once the sister and the wife of Osiris. She had demonstrated her eminent medical skill by recalling to life her son Horus. Imhotep, the Egyptian Æsculapius, who was one of the Memphis gods, and Chunsu, the counsellor of the sick, were of lower rank. The cat-headed Pacht (Bubastis) and Apis were worshipped as the deities of parturient women or of child-blessedness, for children among the Egyptians were esteemed a great blessing.

The medical knowledge of the ancient Egyptians was tolerably extensive, and, gauged by the measure of those early ages, by no means unimportant. It was at all events quite characteristic. Medicine was divided into the science of higher degree (conjurations, dissolving the charms of the gods by prayer, interpretations of the revelations received by the sick during incubation in the temples) and ordinary medical practice. The former was pursued only by priests, who aimed to get further control over their people by pretending to have command of Nature.

The pathological knowledge of the ancient Egyptians comprised a knowledge of fever and of diseases of the eyes, in the treatment of which their physicians enjoyed special reputation throughout all antiquity. They must therefore be regarded as the earliest oculists. They were even summoned to foreign courts and furnish the earliest examples of practitioners who traveled among foreign people.

In physiology they held that until the age of fifty years the heart gains annually about two drachms in weight, but that afterward it loses about the same amount each year, so that finally, in old people, death is occasioned by this continual loss. Also they assumed that four demons ruled over the body. As Buchta points out, hunger and thirst were not regarded as bodily wants, but as quasi-poisonous substances which forced themselves into the body and required to be neutralized by eating and drinking, in order that they might not destroy it. A similar superstition also prevailed regarding the dead, and thus these too required food.

The Egyptians, who did not shrink from human dissection as much as the Greeks, were indeed acquainted with anatomy, but not to the degree which might be expected from their other medical skill. Yet Athotis, the son of King Menes, who is himself said to have been a physician, had written on anatomy. Both of these were kings and thus furnished evidence of the high estimation of medicine and of physicians in Egypt. The Egyptians assumed theoretically the existence of two kinds of vessels and nerves or tendons, of which there were in the body from twenty-four to thirty-two. Such a nerve extends from the little finger to the heart; hence the custom of dipping this finger in their libations. They were acquainted with the heart, the lymphatic glands and the crystalline lens of the eye.

When the method of embalming is considered, it is manifest that the custom could result in no anatomical knowledge, even if the persons who made embalming their business had been of a different class from that to which, as a matter of fact, they really belonged. The mode of procedure in embalming is clearly known. In the first place it was determined by the friends of the deceased in which of the three prevalent styles the operation should be performed. In the more expensive styles patterns were exhibited for their selection. If the most costly form was selected, one of the sacred scribes marked eight lines, one upon the left side. Following the direction and length of these, an associate from the disreputable and most deeply despised caste of the Egyptians, the "paraschites," with a sharp stone—an evidence of the high antiquity of the custom—made an incision into the cavity of the abdomen. He then ran away, so as not to be stoned for his offence against the dead.

Now began the work of the embalmers, who existed as a guild even to the time of the Roman Empire. The viscera were removed and preserved in canope, *i.e.*, vases of clay, limestone or alabaster, the lids of which were decorated with representations of one of the four genii of the dead—Amset, Hapi, Tuamutef and Khebsennuf—to whom the canope in question was dedicated. After the cranial cavity was cleared of the brain by means of hooks inserted through the nose, the cavities of both the cranium and abdomen were filled with spices, myrrh and cassia. The salters then laid the corpse in a solution of carbonate of soda, where it was left usually for seventy days. At the expiration of this period it was again washed in caustic soda, then coated over with gum and finally wrapped in a cloth of fine linen. In good mummies the hair and nails are preserved, but the eyeballs have obsidian eyes inserted in them.

The corpse, thus prepared, was placed by the friends in a bivalvular wooden coffin, hollowed out to suit the size and form of the body and often adorned with beautiful hieroglyphics. The mummy, thus completed, was then placed in the catacombs, where, as is well known, they have been found in a good state of preservation after thousands of years.

In embalming "'of the second class" method, cedar resin was injected into the unemptied cavities of the body, which was then salted down for seventy days, after which the viscera and resin were removed together. "Embalming of the third class" consisted in simply salting the body after it had been washed. Besides these methods, the Egyptians also often buried their dead in the ordinary way. In fact, the poor were even buried in the sand without any shroud and those possessed of a little means in arched vaults built of brick.

The Egyptians were acquainted with a considerable number of

drugs and had numerous formulæ for their preparation. Prominent remedies were opium, strychnus, squill and vegetable remedies in general, though medicines of animal origin and of a kind disgusting to modern ideas also were employed. The Egyptians made use of metallic preparations such as antimony (a paint for the eyes), verdigris and white-lead. Ointments, oils (which, in consequence of their excellence, were imported from Egypt by even the Greeks in Hippocrates' time), plasters, pills (mixed with honey and afterward rolled into form) steam for inhalations, poultices, enemata, decoctions and such like were recognized preparations.

Mental diseases were blamed upon the demons, and amulets were in common use, especially in the treatment of diseases of the nervous system. Astrology was called into counsel in the treatment of disease, and by reason of the theurgic character of ancient Egyptian character it was susceptible of change with every variation of worship. In the Middle Ages, it is remembered, Egyptian wisdom was regarded as identical with sorcery, the search for the philosopher's stone, alchemy and astrology; while even to-day the gipsy is not a little feared by the ignorant classes.

The astrology of the Egyptian was not comparable with that which developed in the valley of the Euphrates. In the gray dawn of antiquity there immigrated into Babylonia from the north a Turanian people, the Chaldees, whose dominant element consisted of the servants of the deity. The latter thus rose to be an influential priesthood, and accordingly the name Chaldee—the Magi of the Bible—was employed to designate both these immigrants and their priests. The Chaldees enjoyed great esteem as mathematicians, astronomers, astrologers, interpreters of dreams and (theurgic) physicians. Aside from the Chaldean Magi, however, Herodotus avers that the Babylonians had no regular physicians who visited the sick, but the latter were exposed upon the streets and interrogated by those who passed. If any of these visitors had recovered from a similar disease he was expected to counsel the invalid as to the means by which he had been cured.

The Old-Persian medicine too, so far as can be judged from the exceedingly scanty information now possessed, was theurgic in its character. Leprosy was ascribed to offences against the sun, and the sufferer was compelled to live apart from the healthy. Amulets played an important role, for each city and every province had its genius. Sparkling stones were worn for love of the genii, and in this way originated the reliance upon and belief in the virtues of stones. They served to avert evil and were especially useful against the venom of serpents and scorpions; they mitigated the pains of disease and of wounds, since it was believed that fire and water, the male and female Genius of Nature, were active in them. Hence the doctrine of the Magi as to their composition, hence the prescriptions as to their use. The Persians possessed an extensive knowledge of poisons. The Houma-drink—a drink prepared from the plant Houma and which possessed almost divine powers—was prescribed by the physicians for pains in the limbs, catarrhal obstructions and urinary diseases.

In reviewing the medical culture of the Pheoenicians it is importnat to remember that in the papyrus Ebers it is stated that one of its books is the work of a physician of Byblos. What is known of this book permits the conjecture that much more important medical knowledge than has been heretofore suspected was possessed by this Semitic race. Not only was it distinguished for its technical, nautical and meteorological knowledge, as well as for its activity in colonization, its comerce and its luxury, but it also exercised an important influence upon the Greeks, which appears in Greek medicine. That the Phoenicians indulged in an extremely sensual religious worship is known. It is also known that their supreme deity, Baal-Zebub (the god of flies), the Beelzebub of the Bible, was a god of medicine and was interrogated as an oracle of health and disease. His priests were clad in red clothing, possibly the earliest example of the red garments of the physician. The Carthaginians, as Phoenician colonists, differed but slightly in their medical customs from that of the parent stock.

Early Jewish medicine is especially conspicuous for its absence. In consequence of the stern prohibition against contact with the dead, true anatomy was not thought of, the bones and vessels being only very vaguely mentioned, while nothing is known of any Jewish physiology. The almost complete absence of a pharmacology among the Jews is remarkable, for they were acquainted with a great number of plants, and the Egyptians, among whom they had lived, had a large number of remedies which they might have appropriated. Figs, and the heart, liver and gall of fishes are mentioned as medicines, and bathing in the Jordan is deemed a remedy for leprosy. This lack of remedies is doubtless to be explained by the purely theurgic character of Hebrew medicine. Yet the mortality of the Jews was not, for this reason, any greater than that of other people who employed "remedies" in abundance.

The Hebrews, like all other peoples, regarded the prevalence of diseases, and especially of important epidemics, as punishment inflicted by a deity on account of their sins. For relief, therefore, they resorted to repentant prayers and the meditations of their priests. They did not see any need for physicians. But the great lawyer, Moses, while he omitted any surgical or medical practice, gave his people the first elementary code of public hygiene. It contained the specific directions in regard to the kind and preparation of food; the slaughtering of animals; the burial of the dead; the regulation of marriage and sexual relations; the diagnosis and isolation of cases of leprosy and some other contagious diseases. The only surgical procedure given was that of circumcision, which was performed by the priests.

The later knowledge of the Jews is found in the Talmud, the medical contents of which are fairly complete for that period. Its Surgery embraces a knowledge of dislocations of the femur, contusions of the skull, perforation of the lungs, œsophagus, stomach, small intestine and gall-bladder, of wounds of the spinal cord, trachea, pia mater, of fractures of the ribs (all of which were considered very dangerous unless immediate medical aid could be obtained), of oral and nasal polypi, the latter of which were considered a punishment for past sins. In sciatica a curious direction is given to rub the hip sixty times with meat broth. Besides the ordinary operations, *e.g.* venesection, which was performed by mechanics or barbers, mention is made of circumcision and of the operation for imperforate anus. The execution of the latter operation is described very minutely.

The Talmudic pathology ascribes diseases to a constitutional vice, to evil influences affecting the body from without or to the effect of magic. It recognizes, among other things, the origin of jaundice from retention of bile and of dropsy from suppression of urine. The latter in general was divided into anasarca, ascites and tympanites. Prognostically it is declared that hydrocephalus internus, or water on the brain, is always fatal, while hydrocephalus externus is not necessarily so; that rupture and atrophy of the kidneys are followed by death; that hydatids, or cysts of the liver, on the contrary, are not fatal; that suppuration of the spinal cord, induration of the lungs, etc., are incurable—views which may have been based upon the dissection of animals and may be considered germs of pathological anatomy. Sweating, sneezing and dreams promising a favorable termination of existing disease pass from critical symptoms.

In therapeutics natural remedies, both external and internal, were employed, as well as the arts of magic. The rabbis, at other times so strict, allow to the sick even prohibited articles of diet if they have a desire for them. Among their special prescriptions may be noticed onions for worms; wine and pepper in disorders of the stomach; goat's milk in dyspnoea (labored breathing); emetics in nausea; a dog's liver for the bite of a mad dog; injections of oil of turpentine in cases of stone in the bladder; a drop of cold water in the eye in the morning, with warm foot and hand baths in the evening, for sore eyes; bleeding and the warm baths of Tiberias. Asafetida and many other drugs are certainly derived from Grecian medicine, the laying on of hands, prayer and conjurations with less certainty to the same source. In Dietetics it was recommended before the age of forty to take more food than drink, after that age to reverse the habit; after meals to eat salt and then to drink water freely, but not to work too much nor to walk, sleep nor indulge in wine. On the other hand, it is advised to form regular habits, to bathe, anoint and wash frequently.

The Anatomy of the Talmudists is based chiefly upon the dissection of animals, through Rabbi Ishmael, at the close of the first century, dissected, or rather "skeletonized," by boiling the body (dissection in the interests of science was permitted by the Talmud), on which occasion he found 252 (instead of 232) bones. They recogized the origin of the spinal cord at the foramen magnum and its termination in the caura equina; allowed two coats to the œsophagus; included the lungs in two coverings and gave a special coat to the fat about the kidneys.

In Physiology they assume cold, heat, dryness and moisture as component forces. In experimental physiology they point out that removal of the spleen is not fatal, and distinguished between salt solution and albumen by the fact that the former, under the influence of heat, deliquesces, while the latter coagulates.

Hindu medicine is one of the oldest in the world. Like the foregoing, it is also priestly medicine. In its whole extent it grew up upon Indian soil, although at a late period foreign views, especially those of the Greeks, probably were interwoven. The study and practice of the Indian physicians, however, are controlled by regulations, which give evidence of a very earnest and worthy conception of the medical profession and embody truths acknowledged even today.

Certain external requirements were imposed upon the physician, the estimation of which is characteristic of the childlike mind of the people, though the adoption of some of them would seem, if not necessary, at least useful for us of the present day. There were demanded of the physician a fine person, absence of passion, decorum, chastity, temperance, amiability, veracity, consideration for the sick, generosity, diligence, earnestness, freedom from boasting, secrecy, a desire for knowledge which scorns not even the lessons of an enemy, and, above all, reflection and independence of thought.

Moreover, it is said:

"A physician who desires success in his practice, his own profit, a good name and finally a place in Heaven must pray daily for the welfare of all living creatures, first of the Brahmans and of the sacred cow. . . . The physician should wear his hair short, keep his nails clean and cut close and wear a sweet-smelling dress. Let his speech be soft, clear, pleasant. Transactions in the house should not be bruited abroad."

The last advice is found also in the Hippocratic oath.

Medical instruction, which comprises the learning by heart of the medical doctrines taught orally, is imparted by the Brahmans and begins in early youth, a regulation which is found also among the Greeks. The pupil must first select a good text-book and then a good teacher. Instruction embraces the theory of medicine and a practical course at the bedside, with the performance of some operations. The pupil must begin to study early in the morning (after having rinsed his mouth and prayed to the cow and the gods) and cease late in the evening. Conference with fellow students is enumerated among the means adapted to give the student a better insight into his studies.

The general Pathology of the Hindus, says J. H. Baas in his excellent "History of Medicine," points out as the characteristics of health a serene spirit, clear sense and perfect understanding, uniform warmth from a uniform mixture of the fluids and elements and undisturbed regularity of the secretions and functions of the body. Diseases are divided into natural and supernatural (the work of demons), with subordinate classes, as accidental, corporeal, mental, original and complicating, secondary, internal and external. Pain is considered a symptom of all diseases and fever a symptom of all severe affections. Etiologically diseases are ascribed to an unequal or perverted action of the five common elements—ether, air, fire, water and earth. These however, in the first place, through the influence of food, season, conditions of the atmosphere and the climate, form proximate causes of disease, while corruption of the three "elementary fluids," bile, mucus, and air, is looked upon as the remote cause.

Other evils arise from draughts of air, water, the passions, bad habits of life, insufficient clothing and unclean dwellings. Worms also play an important part in the etiology of diseased conditions of the body or its parts and the existing superstition to this effect probably had its origin in this Indian idea.

Operative surgery attained such a position among the Hindus that they did not shrink from the greatest and most difficult operations. First may be noticed the dressing of wounds, concerning which the Ramayana says:

"The wounded in battle should be quickly picked up, carried into a tent, the bleeding stayed and upon the wounds should be dropped an anodyne oil with the juice of healing herbs."

Next may be quoted the apothegm:

"The fire cures diseases which cannot be cured by physic, the knife and drugs."

Their special pathology includes many internal diseases, rheumatism, gout, hæmorrhoids, inflammations, fever, catarrh, diabetes mellitus (first mentioned among the Greeks by Demetrius of Apamea), diarrhœa, jaundice, cough, verminous diseases, epilepsy, mania a potu, the exanthemata, dysentery and phthisis.

Diagnosis was effected by the aid of the senses and by examination of the sick, and the physician was expected to pay special attention to the pulse, the bodily temperature, the color of the skin, the urine and feces, the eyes, the strength of the voice and the noise of the respiration.

Therapeutics were guided by the curability or incurability of the disease. If the disease belonged to the incurable class the physicians did not take the patient under treatment at all, but advised him plainly, honestly and unselfishly. It is said:

"To go forth upon a narrow footpath to the invincible northeastern tongue of land, to live on water and air until this earthly tabernacle sinks down and his soul is united with God."

Herodotus similarly relates:

"Whosoever among the Indians becomes sick goes out into a desert and lays himself down there. No one troubles himself about him, whether he be sick or dead."

If, however, the disease is curable attention must be paid in the cure to the disease itself, the season, the organic fire, the age, bodily habit, the strength, the intelligence (according to the Indian ideas the stupid are cured more quickly than the intelligent, because, thinks the open-hearted Susruta, they are more obedient), nature, idiosyncrasies, remedies and the regions of the earth.

The Materia Medica of the Hindus is most copious, in fact almost as rich as that of to-day. It embraces remedies from the animal, vegetable and mineral kingdoms, together with the arts of magic. Remedies are used both externally and internally; they are divided into pharmaco-dynamic classes and are either simple or (as is more frequently the case) exceedingly complex in their nature. Venesection and cupping, especially the former, play an important part. Even inhalations into the mouth and nose by the aid of tubes are known.

In India the ancients had hospitals. Inoculation of the natural and artificial virus of small-pox was practised with a prophylactic view. The Brahmans always performed this operation in the beginning of the warm season. The skin was rubbed, a few incisions made and virus of the preceding year, with which pledgets of cloth had been saturated, was bound upon the abraded surface. The persons thus inoculated were compelled to remain in the open air (Indian method of inoculation). Boys were inoculated upon the outside of the forearm, girls upon the upper arm. Vaccination is now obligatory in the larger cities, but elsewhere the old plan is generally carried out.

Dietetics are carried to the extreme and carefully regulated. The Hindus are forbidden to eat meat.

Their knowledge of Toxicology is considerable. Such an acquaintance with natural history as is necessary to a knowledge of remedial agents is possessed in a remarkable degree. On the other hand, Anatomy forms the weakest side of Indian medicine. This, however, ought not to occasion much surprise when the prohibition of contact with the dead is considered an offense always to be expiated, though only lightly. The method of preparing bodies and the sole instruments employed in this process are very original, but certainly not adapted to afford a good insight into the structure of the human body.

"Let the physician leave a corpse fastened," it is ordered, "together with its receptacle, in a brook, to macerate in a clear place —a corpse which has a body uninjured, uncorrupted by poison, unshaken by chronic disease, unhandled a hundred times, unclothed—and draw it out when maceration is complete. The corpse at the expiration of seven days should then be rubbed with pieces of bark; he can then with his eyes see the skin and all the external and internal parts."

Hindu medicine must be assigned, at all events, a superiority over the Egyptian and the Talmudic; indeed, it may claim even the very first rank among those examples of medical culture which have not experienced a continuous development. That it was not far behind Greek medicine, both in the extent of its doctrines and in its internal elaboration, furnishes only a very superficial comparison. It cannot fail to command admiration when the very early period in which it developed and attained so high a grade is considered.

The Chinese are little further advanced now than they were ages ago, except in the large cities, where foreign influences cannot help but be felt. The ancient and unlimited liberty of choosing one's occupation in China has resulted in making the medical profession enormous in point of numbers. From the earliest times, therefore, there have been found several physicians in every village. In China any person may be a physician to the poor without having given any previous evidence of his professional competency. Any one, moreover, may assume the title of physician. The court physicians only, as a matter of precaution, are compelled to pass an examination before a college at Pekin.

Chinese apothecaries, before they can carry on their business, must have passed an examination and must exhibit a diploma from the examining board. Powerful remedies, like opium, arsenic, etc., are forbidden to be dispensed by them without the prescription of a physician. The pharmacies are fully supplied with the necessary drugs (a Chinese pharmacopœia contains 650 different kinds of leaves) and they are kept in a very orderly condition. Besides pills as large as musket-balls, their proprietors also prepare love potions. The prescriptions of physicians are prepared by the apothecary, but the latter combines also with his business the occupation of fortune-telling.

Chinese surgery embraces the practice of acupuncture, which is regarded as a universal remedy and has for its object the quickening of the "vital spirits." It is practiced by twisting or driving in a needle inserted into the body. By this operation a free passage is supposed to be made for the "winds." Besides this, Chinese surgery includes the application of moxas, cupping, inoculation (which the physician Go-mei-schan is said to have invented about A. D. 1000) and paracentesis of the eye and bleeding. The latter operation is, however, practiced rarely and is performed with a small lancet, after which tallow and oil are applied to the wound without any bandage. Enemata are not employed, since they are offensive to the modesty of the dignified Chinese. Under ordinary circumstances they make shift with poultices. In this line cats' liver and fowls' entrails are specially popular, while fractures are treated by extension.

Kneading of the muscles (massage) which is also said to have been in use 2,000 years before the present era (though, according to Wernich, of Japanese origin), is likewise practised. The Chinese also claim to have been able for thousands of years to produce anæsthesia by means of the preparation Mago. Inoculation of modified smallpox, too, has been practised by them. Their surgeons are extremely ignorant, are assigned to inferior service and receive little pay.

The pathology of the Chinese is very incomplete. All diseases, especially epidemic diseases, are ascribed to spirits and winds, cold and warm humors, etc., and are assigned, in accordance with their benign or malign character, to Yo (the good principle) or Yn (the evil principle). To Yo belongs acute inflammatory fever, to Yn hectic fever, etc. There are, according to Chinese pathology, 10,000 varieties of fevers. Among their diagnostic procedures are examination of the tongue and the eyes and feeling of the pulse. The pulse flows from the "spirits" of a certain part of the body, which manifest their presence in a given place. By means of it both the cause and the seat of disease are to be found.

The art of feeling the pulse is very old and extremely elaborate. It is performed elegantly by placing several fingers upon a certain point and then raising or depressing each in turn, as is done in playing the piano—the Chinese "play upon" the pulse instead of feeling it. In this practice the changes of the moon and the seasons of the year are considered, according to certain rules. The performance often lasts several hours. In diseases of the heart the left pulse is investigated, in those of the liver the right, etc. Each speck upon the tongue and upon discoloration of this organ points to special diseases and viscera.

Chinese pharmacology contains remedies from the vegetable and animal kingdom almost exclusively and is very copious. It includes elephant's bile, dried spiders, bugs, toads, lizards, snakes, claws, ears, tongues, hearts and livers of numerous animals, excrements, dragonbone, cotton, ivory, musk, rhubarb, gentian, camphor, Chinese seeds, leaves in large doses and innumerable other things. The genuine ginseng-root (worth about $25 an ounce) and the edible nests of the swallow are considered veritable panaceas and are specially prized by the Chinese.

In therapeutics great importance is laid upon strict diet, frequent baths, etc. The chief task of the physician, after making his diagnosis, is to remove the materia morbi, which has entered by way of digestion, the nerves or the circulation. In general the maxim "contraria contrariis" is followed, hence in debility, *e.g.*, the extract of tiger's blood is prescribed. Almost every animal supplies a distinct specific, particularly its blood and its liver. Often too, especially among the wealthy, the whole store of Chinese remedies must be exhibited until the proper specific is found. If the patient dies, according to the Chinese idea, he is indeed cured by the suitable remedy, but the physician has not had the time to rid him of his poisonous drug, and, as the result of this unfortunate want of time, the patient is doomed.

Anatomy and physiology occupy the lowest grade in Chinese medical science, though a few very old and imperfect plates are in existence. In their veneration of the dead, dissection of the human body is of course excluded. The Chinese assume six chief organs in which the "moisture" is located, viz., the heart, liver, two kidneys, spleen and lungs; six others in which is the seat of "warmth," viz., the small and large intestine, the gall-bladder, the stomach and the urinary apparatus. They enumerate three hundred and sixty-five bones. The Chinese, in place of the fire and earth of the Greeks, class wood and metal as elements and heat and moisture (whose union produces life, their separation death) are regarded as fundamental qualities. The circulation flows outward from the lungs five times in twenty-four hours and terminates in the liver. The bile, as it is one of the most powerful remedies so also is it the special seat of courage; the lungs give origin to the voice; the spleen is the seat of reason and, with the heart, furnishes ideas; the liver is the granary of the soul, while the stomach is the resting-place of the mind.

In the pathology of the ancient Japanese medicine external and internal diseases are said to be distinguished. A disease peculiar to the Japanese pathology is the lesion of the spine, called Kakkeh. The most wonderful things are regarded as therapeutic measures—*e.g.*, in small-pox the decoration of the sick-room with red hangings. On the whole, the medicine of the Japanese bore almost as strong a theurgic character as that of the Chinese, from whom, as has already been seen, it was adopted. Both too, may be considered philosophical sciences, inasmuch as neither was ever a sacerdotal medicine proper.

Equally ancient, the Celts and the Teutons possessed a medical mythology displayed among the demi-gods. Thus there is a female Æsculapius, Eira; another goddess, Fricco, invoked for fruitfulness in wedlock, and Holla, the aider of women in labor. On the other hand, Hela, a ghastly form, received all those who died of disease into her residence, Niflheim, which contained the hall, Elidnir (pain); her bed, Koer (disease), and the table, Hungur. Some fragments of genuine medical practice and information of a later period have been preserved. Thus the Scandinavian physicians in cases of dropsy are said to have had recourse to the actual cautery and in asthma to have resorted to venesection, while for bearing the wounded those warriors were selected who possessed soft hands. Their anatomy mentions two hundred and fourteen bones, three hundred and fifteen vessels and only thirty teeth. Their physiology locates love in the liver, passion in the bile, memory in the brain—data which remind of Indian ideas.

CHAPTER II

THE GREEKS

The earliest traces of European medical history are to be found in the Homeric writings, which, although they are Ionic in origin, at the time when they first clearly appear had become indigenous to the soil of Greece. Prominent in the Hellenic pantheon was Æsculapius, one of the sons of Apollo, who was reputed to have the power of restoring the dead to life, but who had been slain by Jupiter at the request of Pluto because he had restored to life an enemy of the god of the underworld. He was the pupil of old Chiron, the centaur, possessed of marvellous powers of healing and of song, and is usually represented seated holding a bundle of medicinal herbs.

He was deified in the Greek life, but only in the anthropomorphic sense of the lesser gods, and while temples were erected in his honor, they were merely nuclei around which were gathered places for the housing and treatment of the disabled and diseased. Those who cared for the sick in these places were called Æsclepiadæ, being both priest and physician. Their duties were mainly the treatment of surgical cases, except that diatetics and climatic therapeutics were well understood. These temples were generally located in healthy situations, the patients enjoyed rest and leisure and diversions were plentiful for the mind. In fact, they were not unlike the modern Spa and health resort.

There seems to have been no writing or recording for future reference. The first physician known to put his thoughts and observations down on paper was Hippocrates. So that it may safely be asserted that the culmination of Grecian mythological medicine is in the great genius of Hippocrates, who really elevated medicine to its proper rank of a science. It is generally admitted that although Greece cultivated the arts and sciences with so much success, yet, in the first place, she borrowed them from the neighboring nations, principally from Egypt and Phœnicia. For a long time those in Greece who wished to acquire a larger share of knowledge, either theoretical or practical, than was possessed by their own countrymen, visited Egypt as the great storehouse of science and learning.

The practice of medicine remained for a considerable time hereditary in the family of Æsculapius and in a great measure confined to it. As the field of healers increased, practitioners were all classed under the general name of Æsclepiadæ, although this may have been narrowed to those who were both priest and physician. The process of treatment was mainly magic and incantations and not based on an exact knowledge of human anatomy or its functions.

In those days of almost constant warfare there must have been wounds of all varieties. Most men were hurt or disabled temporarily than killed outright, so that practical surgery was further developed than any other phase of the medical art, and the treatment of wounds achieved wonderful results. It was efficacious in its simplicity; foreign bodies were removed, the wounded parts were placed in as normal a position as possible and certain healing vegetables, either balsamic or stypic, applied. Wine and other stimulants were used to support the patient in his shock and bandages and splints were applied even as they are nowadays.

Over a long period of several centuries, of which there is scant record and only a hint now and then, there was very little advance in the progress of medicine. The Æsclepiadæ were the sole practitioners—the guardians or superintendents of the many temples devoted to Æsculapius. Of these there were several which became quite famous as schools—those of Cos, Cnidos and Rhodes. The priests connected with these institutions became divided, thus early laying the foundation for the two great sects of Dogmatists and Empirics, which long divided the medical school. The school of Cos assumed more of a philosophical cast, attempting to unite reason with experience, while the school of Cnidos sought mainly to observe and collect mere matters of fact.

The school of Cnidos is said to have laid especial weight upon the subjective statements of the sick, the relation of the symptoms to individual parts of the body and the use of active remedies, especially drastics. Less attention was devoted to diet. It cultivated the science of diagnostics and recognized some auscultatory signs—*e.g.*, the pleuritic friction sound, and it satisfactorily distinguished many diseases, such as phthisis, typhus, diseases of the urinary bladder, the kidneys, the bile, etc. The Cnidians also performed even major operations, like trepanning the ribs and excision of the kidneys, and, though always empirics, they were bold operators. In opposition to the physicians of Cos, however, they discarded venesection.

The school of Cos (which was flourishing as early as 600 B.C.), in contrast to that of Cnidos, cultivated especially objective investigations, symptomatology, prognosis, the relation of the symptoms to the entire body, etiology and expectant and mild therapeutics, though it recommended venesection; in short, it practised all that is worthy of praise in the medicine of Hippocrates and the Hippocratists. These two schools are the first examples of those two opposing tendencies which have characterized medicine down to the present day.

THE GREEKS

The name of Pythagoras, who founded the so-called Italian school, stands preëminent, but even his history is enveloped in much obscurity. He devoted most of his life to the study of natural knowledge and advanced the various departments of science, especially in the knowledge of the structure and actions of the human frame. He is said to have dissected the bodies of animals and to have known something of anatomy. He taught large bodies of students at Crotona and was a man with a mind far above his time. He traveled extensively throughout Egypt, where he learned mathematics and other branches of Egyptian knowledge. He believed that the soul of man emanated from a God and was immortal, that the basis of life was heat.

But while Pythagoras applied salves and poultices to wounds, he did not approve of or practice surgery. Diet and gymnastics, he declared, must maintain health. Disease was due to the demons, hence prayers, offerings and music were used to restore harmony. His followers believed that magic resided in certain plants, especially the cabbage, which was a special food of the sect.

Gymnastic medicine was a phase in the science on which the Greeks laid special stress. There were schools founded for the practice of gymnastic exercises under charge of trainers who supervised the health of their pupils, treated injuries and also internal diseases. They were often capable physicians, but had no standing as such.

Among the pupils of Pythagoras, Alcmaeon of Crotona was the most famous in medicine. He was manifestly the first (animal) anatomist and is said to have discovered the optic nerves and the Eustachian tubes. Health, he affirmed, depends upon the harmony, disease upon the discord of the component parts of the body; of heat and cold, dryness and moisture, bitterness and sweetness, a similar antithesis, a doctrine amplified in later systems of medicine. His theory of hearing is well worth notice:

"We hear with the ear because it contains a vacuum and this occasions the sound. In the cavity, however, the sound is generated, the air resounding against it."

The atomic school presented a widely different purview. This school sought in matter the foundation of the world and of thought; indeed it professed to find the principle of all things in the infinitely minute identical, altho these atoms were not eternal nor illimitably divisible. Within these were believed to reside order, position, form and motion. They differ in size, and to this difference their weight corresponds. The differences of the elements, fire, water, air and earth, depend upon differences in the form and size of the atoms.

The soul, it was said, consists of round and smooth atoms, and its expressions, like life in general, are a result of the motion of the atoms. These smooth and round atoms exist in the whole body. In special parts they are particularly active—*e.g.*, so that the heart occasions wrath, the liver desire, the brain thought. The perceptions of the senses originate in the motion of the atoms of external objects (whose image they are) toward the organs of sense and produce in these organs a palpable impression, the perception. Spirit and body are identical; a healthy condition of the brain implies mental health and disease of the same organ implies mental disease.

To a great extent the way seems to have been prepared for the coming of a leader in science. The power and civilization of Greece had reached its zenith; great military expeditions against Persia had been successful. No other nation had approached her in any field of learning—history, art, philosophy—and she had the world's greatest statesmen. The art of writing had come over from the Phœnicians, so that the records of all sorts were kept. Hippocrates, called the Great (460 B.C.), came from a family of physicians and received a thorough education both at home and abroad. He recognized the great fundamental truth—that the basis of all knowledge is the accurate observation of actual phenomena and that the correct generalization of these phenomena should be the sole foundation of human reasoning. He was thus a mixture of the two great schools which were formed after his death and which divided the medical profession for many years into dogmatists and empirics.

Hippocrates was a patient and very accurate observer and an industrious writer, being the first to keep full records of all his studies and observations. He is justly called the "Father of Medicine." Especially was he the creator of profane, as distinguished from sacerdotal medicine which had prevailed until his day; of public, in place of the preceding secret medicine. In a word, he was the great founder of scientific medicine and of artistic practice.

The general pathological views of the Hippocratists are based upon the assumption of the four elements, water, fire, air and earth, whose mixture and cardinal properties—dryness, warmth, coldness and moisture—form the body and its constituents. To these correspond the cardinal fluids, yellow bile, blood, mucus and black bile, in the order mentioned. (Herein lies the first theory of humoral pathology.) Health consists in a uniform action and reaction, disease in an irregular action and reaction of all these upon and between each other.

Diseases are cured by restoration of the disturbed harmony in being and the action of the elements, elementary qualities, cardinal fluids and cardinal forces. Nature, or the vital force inherent in the body, accomplishes the cure, however, in the best way. If Nature works undisturbed, the disease runs a regular course through the three stages of crudity, coction and crisis. In the first of these a degeneration of the fluids predominates; in the second they are prepared for evacuation; in the third they are removed. If this course fails, and especially if the "crisis" is wanting, there result secondary diseases or incurable conditions. The crises occur particularly upon the odd, so-called critical, days.

Hence the interference of the physician (and in this his art consists) is directed always to choosing the right instant for lending aid. This is especially the case in fevers, which are caused by heating or excess of mucus due to a check of the secretions. Besides the proximate causes of disease mentioned here and above, Hippocrates constructed especially the important doctrine of remote causes. Such are offenses against a judicious mode of life, climatic and meteorological influences the peculiarities of the season, endemic and epidemic constitution, place of residence and similar predisposing causes.

To this was joined dietetics, a science also founded by Hippocrates. This science regarded the age—"old persons use less nutriment than the young"; the season—"in winter abundant nourishment is wholesome, in summer a more frugal diet"; the bodily condition—"lean persons should take little food, but this little should be fat; fat persons, on the other hand, should take much food, but it should be lean," and similar rules. In addition, respect was also paid to the easy digestibility of food—white meat is more easily digested than dark—and to its preparation. Water, barley-water and wine were recommended as drinks. Baths, anointing, gymnastic exercises and the frequent use of emetics were also commended as dietetic measures, and the dietetic principles of Hippocrates in febrile diseases are substantially observed at the present day. By means of such precepts Hippocrates extended the doctrine of indications, which constitutes one of his greatest services to medicine.

The diagnostics of Hippocrates (though he does not recognize any such special branch) was founded especially upon objective investigation by means of the senses and made use of every aid. The ear applied to the chest of a patient suffering with pneumonia supplied a knowledge of the mucous rale ("like the bubbling of boiling vinegar"); the sight furnished a survey of secretion and excretion, the bodily frame, the attitude of the body and its members, the gait, etc.; feeling (the hand upon the chest or abdomen) supplied an idea of the bodily temperature and perhaps likewise of the pulse (though he certainly knew nothing of counting the latter), and the taste and sense of smell equally were put to service.

One of the chief services of Hippocrates to medicine was the foundation of the science of prognosis. This was based upon the excellent maxim:

"In order to be able to prognosticate correctly who will recover and who will die, in whom the disease will be long, in whom short, one must know all the symptoms and must weigh their relative values."

It considered the perspiration, the sleep, mucous rales in the throat, the visage (facies Hippocratica) and the appearance or absence of the "crises" on the appointed days.

In Etiology he paid particular attention to age, constitution, meteorogical influences, etc., as is seen in the following passage:

> "Catarrhs are dangerous in old people when a dry spring follows a winter with south winds and rains. If, however, the summer is dry and north winds prevail, with south winds in a rainy autumn, coughs, hoarseness and catarrhs arise."

The surgical knowledge of Hippocrates was considerable, both as regards the number of diseases recognized by him and their treatment with or without operation. Fractures are handled particularly well as regards the method of reduction and dressing, the mode of repair and the duration of this process. If a fracture is healed with considerable shortening, he is of the opinion that it is better to break the corresponding sound bone, so as to equalize the shortening. The same may be said of dislocations. Hippocrates recognizes dislocations of the humerus inward, downward and outward:

> "The head of the humerus is often luxated (dislocated), but not upward, in consequence of the acromion; nor backward, by reason of the scapula; nor forward, in consequence of the biceps muscle; but rarely inward or outward, yet frequently and chiefly downward."

He employs also a great number of methods of reduction. Diseases of the joints (and their treatment by massage) and wounds, especially of the skull, are well managed. The latter, in consequence of the fact that, until the time of the discovery of explosive weapons, arms designed to strike or cut were used, formed the favorite field of surgical labor. Hippocrates also recognized the fact that wounds of one of the cerebral hemispheres produce paralysis or spasms of the opposite side. The treatment and healing of wounds by first and second intention, fistulæ, ulcers and tumors were also judiciously discussed. Hernia was less fully treated. The hot iron was employed frequently, a practice to which reference is made especially in the famous aphorism:

> "What drugs fail to cure, that the iron (or knife) cures; what iron cures not, that the fire cures; but what the fire fails to cure, this must be called incurable."

His surgical therapeutics recognizes a very judicious plan for reposition of the gut in prolapsus ani. Other surgical remedies were bandages, poultices, plasters, ointments, styptics, caustics, cold and compression, suppositories, pessaries, enemata, cupping, etc. The rudiments of orthopædic surgery are also to be found in Hippocrates, who, as Kroner points out, treats club-foot with suitable manipulations, bandages and proper shoes.

The most brilliant and eternal contributions of Hippocrates to medicine are his therapeutic maxims:

"Follow Nature."

"The physician is a servant, not a teacher of Nature."

"The physician should benefit or at least not injure."

He was not prejudiced nor devoted to a stereotyped system:

"We should examine also the strength of the sick, to see whether they may be in condition to maintain a spare diet to the crisis of the disease."

"Complete abstinence often acts very well, if the strength of the patient can in any way maintain it."

"In the application of these rules we must be always mindful of the strength of the patient and of the course of each particular disease, as well as of the constitution and ordinary mode of life with respect to both food and drink."

In hygienic matters Hippocrates advises one to observe what he tolerates well and what badly, and to manage accordingly; to labor, rest, sleep all in their due season; not to eat too little nor with too absolute regularity, that deviation from the rule may not produce harm; to drink pure spring-water, as well as wine mixed with water more or less, according to the season; occasionally to get a little tipsy, so that accidental excesses may not occasion harm.

Among his numerous remedies (265 have been enumerated, in spite of his constantly emphasizing the assistance of Nature) Hippocrates employed chiefly vegetable substances, though drugs derived from the animal kingdom also were not discarded. Some of these remedies were also articles of food—*e.g.*, the flesh of the horse, ass, fox and dog, cabbage-juice, seven pints of ass' milk as a mild purgative. Metallic remedies were also recognized, such as copper, alum and lead.

The anatomical knowledge of Hippocrates was very imperfect, as must naturally have been the case, inasmuch as it was based upon the dissection of animals only. The different parts were not kept distinct enough from each other, but were often interchanged, intermingled and artificially constructed. In detail the bones were best known, while misty views alone prevailed with reference to the muscles. The intestines were fairly well distinguished. Nerves, sinews and ligaments were confounded together, while as regards the vessels (which contained partly blood and partly pneuma), and especially as to their course, his views were most singularly artificial. He was acquainted with the pericardium, the two ventricles, the thickness of the walls, the muscular nature and internal appearance of the heart; he knew that the left ventricle is empty after death, and he was acquainted with the valves of the great vessels of the heart. He also knew that the auricles do not contract exactly contemporaneously with the ventricles. Four pairs of vessels were assumed, one originating behind from the nape, a second out of the head behind the ears, the third from the temples, the fourth from the brow.

The brain he regarded as a gland which condenses into mucus the ascending vapors, which then flow down through the nose. The kidneys are also glands, connected with the bladder by "veins." The liver is an organ for the preparation of blood and bile, has five lobes and is more vascular than all other parts. The vena cava with several bronchia pass from it to the heart and one vein goes from it to the spleen. Hippocrates was acquainted with the duodenum, the colon, the mesentery, the seminal vesicles and the rectum, but no clear description of them is given anywhere. The nerves are hollow and convey the "spiritus animalis" throughout the body, an idea which occasioned lively discussion as late as the seventeenth century.

Of physiology in the works of Hippocrates it is not easy to speak with propriety. Still the facts may be adduced that it was assumed the food was cooked in the stomach, which possessed a peculiar warmth, increased by the liver; that the blood is "warm" in the left heart, while in the right it is still "cold"; that the cause of its warmth is the pneuma, received from the air by means of the "cold" lungs. Hippocrates' profound comprehension and appreciation of the history of medicine is expressed in the following maxim:

"The physician must know what his predecessors have known,
if he does not wish to deceive both himself and others."

The undying importance of Hippocrates in medicine rests, first of all, not so much upon his enrichment of science with new material (though this honor too is his unquestioned due) as upon the creation of a scientific medicine and art; upon the method and really great principles which he introduced for all time into science and especially into practice. His investigation and determinaton of the phenomena of disease and of the science of etiology, and still more his improvement of professional treatment, have also won for him immortal reputation.

Hippocrates was above all else a practitioner who desired chiefly not to impose upon his fellow-men with showy discoveries and theories, but to assist them to the utmost of his power. And this he did. Hence his words of immemorial value:

"Where is love for art, there is also love toward man."

The maxim alone would raise him to that genuine humanity often ascribed to Christianity alone.

The great philosopher Plato (429 B.C.), perhaps one of the loftiest intellects the world has ever seen, and who illumined with his clear-sighted logic every subject he touched, treated in his philosophy certain points which had a distinct influence on medical thought for centuries to come. He taught that the heart is the origin of the blood vessels, and, as the seat of the mind, receives through them the commands of the superior soul. The lungs, which receive through the trachea a portion of the drink in addition to the air, serve to cool off the heart. The liver serves to lower desires and is for the purpose of divination. The spleen furnishes an abode for the impurities of the blood. The intestine is long and tortuous, in order that the food may remain the longer therein, so that the mind may not be disturbed too often in its contemplation by the renewal of nutriment necessitated frequently by greater shortness of the gut.

Breathing, he declared, takes place by inward pressure of the air, for no vacant space can exist in the body. The muscles, with the bones, serve as a protection to the marrow against the heat and cold. The marrow itself consists of triangles, and its most perfect portion is the brain. Death is occasioned by a separation of the soul from the marrow. Sight originates in a union of the light flowing out of and into the eyes; hearing is a shock of the air (correct even now), which is communicated to the brain and the blood and even to the soul. Taste is due to a solution of rapid atoms by means of small vessels, which latter conduct these from the tongue to the heart and soul; smell, however, possesses no image as its foundation and is therefore very transitory.

Disease, he thought, originated in a disturbance of both the quantity and quality of the fluids. The most frequent cause of disease is the downflow of mucus and acridity; the most dangerous is corruption of the marrow. Another cause is the yellow and black bile, through whose aberrations inflammations arise. Continued fever is occasioned by fire, quotidian fever by air, tertian fever by water, quartan fever by earth. Mental diseases are the result of corporeal evils or of bad education. Besides bodily exercise and diet, remedies are formed from drugs, which constitute an opposing treatment for diseases, before which they flee away. Of physicians he says that they must be rulers of the sick, in order to cure them, but they must not be money-makers.

Praxagoras has acquired immortal fame by his discovery of the distinction between arteries and veins, of which the former were the active agents in the formation of the pulse. He thought, under ordinary circumstances, they contain air only, but in the case of wounds blood is also found in them, having been drawn in from all the surrounding parts. He considered respiration an action designed to strengthen the heart by forcing air into that organ; the brain was a mere dependence of the spinal cord, but the heart was the origin of the nerves. Praxagoras was a "humorist" of the purest water, and as such assumed no less than eleven humors: the sweet, acid, salt, bitter and pungent among them. He sought the source of fever in the great vena cava, and called attention to the differences of the pulse in conditions of health and disease. He practised taxis in every possible way in cases of strangulated hernia and even performed the operations of herniotomy and amputation of the soft palate when diseased. In therapeutics he favored bleeding, though only before the fifth day in inflammation, employed vegetable remedies almost exclusively and laid great weight on the diet.

Plato's greatest disciple was Aristotle (384 B.C.), who was—and indeed still is—an oracle in philosophy and in certain earlier elements of natural science. Having been given eight hundred talents (an enormous sum) for the collection of materials for a "history of animals," he expended it so wisely that he gathered into his own hands almost every item of information possessed by the ancient world. In advancing the knowledge of Nature and insisting on the exactitude of observations, he did more for medicine than even his master Plato. He assumed five elements as the component parts of the body and assigned to them three cardinal qualities: form, substance and motion or rest. Experience, he taught, was the basis of all science; the body is the instrument of the soul, and both body and soul are in essence one and the same. Life is movement; the heart, however, is the seat of warmth, the source of motion, sensibility and desire. It is the "Acropolis of the body."

The investigation of Aristotle in natural science extended especially over the animal kingdom. He was a famous zoologist and the founder of Comparative Anatomy. It is only through Physiology that he comes into contact with medicine, since pathology, particularly that of man, is only slightly and incidentally considered. He refers diseases to the blood and the humors, through the abundance or lack of which, as the case may be, their difference arise. He made observations on the influence of the weather, the season, the food, drugs, etc.

On the other hand, his labors in Anatomy, which he studied in animals, are of great importance. He distinguished the nerves as such, but called them canals of the brain, which latter organ he described as bloodless and of the largest size in man. Yet by the term "neura" he understands tendons and ligaments, which he thinks originate from the heart. He recognized the optic nerve, but explained the auditory nerve as a "vessel."

The common origin of the vessels from the heart is also one of his theses, and he discovered independently the difference between arteries and veins. He gave its name to the aorta and speaks of the great vena cava. Yet he had totally incorrect views concerning the course of the vessels. Thus one ran from the liver to the right arm, another from the spleen to the left arm; hence venesection upon the side of the organ affected by disease was especially efficacious. He described the ureter correctly and the organs of sensations inexactly.

In his Physiology he assumes that vessels and tendons preside over sensations. Chyle originates in the process of coction in the stomach and is thence carried into the heart. In his view the blood is the nutritive material designed for the formation, growth and warming of the body and for the supply of its waste. It is brought to the tissues by the vessels and in its normal condition is an indifferent fluid which contains neither mucus, bile nor water. But in conditions of disease the blood becomes mixed with these extraneous fluids. Sleep is a restrained energy of sensation, with unrestrained capacity therefor. In respiration the pneuma, which serves for the purpose of cooling, passes through the trachea into the heart.

Aristotle emphasizes the necessity and advantage to the physician of a knowledge of the natural sciences. He says:

"It is the business of the naturalist to know also the causes of health and disease. Hence most naturalists see in medicine the conclusion of their studies, and of physicians, those at least who display some scientific knowledge in the practice of their art, begin the study of medicine with the natural sciences."

He also emphasizes the fact that the better class of physicians lay great weight upon anatomy. Yet in spite of his nice knowledge of Nature, Aristotle was not free from the superstition of his age and was a believer in dreams, the happy significance of a sneeze, chiromancy and similar matters which are now set aside.

The school of Alexandria (300 B.C.) presented an entirely new aspect to the ancient world. The science of medicine was cultivated in this school with great zeal, and some improvements are due to its professors. Among the most famous of these are Erisistratus and Herophilus. Little detail is handed down about them, but they are particularly mentioned as being the first who dissected the human body, for which purpose the bodies of criminals were alloted to them by the government. They pointed out the difference between the structure of the human body and that of animals which most resembled it. They ascertained more correctly the structure of the heart and great vessels and of the brain and nerves.

Soon after the establishment of the Alexandrian school the medical profession became divided on the method of treatment and study of disease—the Dogmatists and later the Empirics. The Dogmatic school professed to set out with theoretical principles which were derived from the generalization of facts and observations and to make these principles the basis of practice. Although this is now considered the correct method to pursue the study and practice of medicine, it is a method which if not carefully watched is exposed to the greatest danger of being corrupted by ignorance and presumption. This occasioned the slow formation of the opposing sect—the Empirics—who defended the principle of "experience" as being of chief importance in the development of the methods of medical investigation and treatment. The Empirics rejected as useless all search after the theoretical causes of disease and all knowledge of anatomy—certainly a grave mistake—but, on the other hand, in their emphasis of experience caused the formation of the conception of the physician, not only as a scholar and a student, but also as a man of ripe judgment and understanding.

CHAPTER III

THE ROMANS

For some centuries the Alexandrian school first contributed to the advance of all sciences and then prevented a too early decay of them. The Grecian civilization had begun to decline, and it was during this time that the Roman Empire laid the foundation for its future grandeur. The martial character of Roman life drew the attention away from medicine. "The Roman people," says Baas, "for more than six hundred years were not, indeed, without medical art, but they were without physicians."

This art consisted merely in prayers, dietetic measures, prescriptions from the Sibylline books, charms, etc. That the Romans cherished much grosser superstitions than the Greeks is well known. With rude simplicity they elevated into divinities those evils which especially harassed them and then in the early centuries of Rome worshiped these deities with fervor. Later Romans became dissatisfied with their own gods and worshiped also Phrygian, Egyptian and Grecian medical gods and built for them temples at Rome and in other places.

A Roman of natural talents, educated at Alexandria, acquainted with human nature and possessed of considerable shrewdness and address was Asclepiades (100 B.C.), but he possessed little science or professional skill. He began by villifying the principles and practices of his predecessors, especially Hippocrates, and asserted that he had discovered the most perfect and efficient form of treating diseases. He conceived matter to consist of extremely small atoms, cognizable indeed by the understanding but not by the senses.

Between the particles of the atom he suggested little empty tubes, the "poroi," in which move a multitude of the finest particles which occasion sensation and correspond to the pneuma of others, here considered only atomically. If the motion of these particles is quiet and regular, it is called health, but if it is irregular, feeble or boisterous, sickness arises. Sickness also originates in the air received in respiration and in the food and enters the body in respiration and digestion, by both of which it passes through the "poroi" into the heart and the blood and through this finally into the whole body which it nourishes. The pulse originates in an influx of the particles into the vessels; animal heat, sensation, secretion in a similar way; hunger and thirst, however, originate in emptiness of the pores of the stomach, which, in accordance with varying conditions, may be either empty, full or contracted. According to him, the proximate cause of disease is stagnation of the atoms; on the other hand, he finds in the humors only a secondary cause.

In surgery Asclepiades has won great reputation by his practice of tracheotomy in angina. He also recommended scarification of the ankles in dropsy, as well as paracentesis with the smallest possible wound. He observed, too, spontaneous dislocation of the hip-joint.

In pathology he was the first to distinguish definitely acute and chronic diseases (for example dropsy). The special forms of diseases are based upon the greater or less disproportion of the atoms to the "poroi" and the grade of stagnation thus occasioned. Thus, he said, quotidian fever originates through the largest atoms, tertian through the medium-sized, quartan through the finest.

Upon the size of these atoms depends also the grade of the fever; larger atoms occasion severe, smaller less dangerous fever. Fever heat originates in active movements of the atoms; the chilliness is due to their quiescence. Hemorrhage is a result of putridity or of laceration. Crises, in opposition to Hippocrates, Asclepiades totally denied, a denial which excited the special wrath of Galen. What is said in therapeutics of the activity of nature is, according to Asclepiades, pure sophistry. The physician alone cures and nature simply supplies opportunities.

Those who followed Asclepiades formed a new school, called Methodism, which stood for a course midway between Dogmatism and Empiricism. The theory was that the solids are the seat and cause of disease, in this respect directly opposite to that of Hippocrates, who traced cause of disease to a disturbance of the fluids, the so-called humoral pathology.

The most important Roman author on medical subjects and a compiler of a very high order in his eight books, "De Medicina," was Aulus Cornelius Celsus (between 25-30 B.C. and 45-50 A.D.). He had also written on philosophy, oratory, jurisprudence and history and was in fact an encyclopedist. Tho not a physician by profession, he thought and wrote on medicine as tho he were a practitioner, so that his work may claim the value of an original treatise on medicine.

His descriptive and operative surgery (including also operative dentistry) is considered his best contribution to medical art. It must still be regarded as a "masculine" branch in comparison with the salve-surgery which came into vogue at a later period. It gives also the best idea of the eminent services of the Alexandrians, who furnished the substance of surgical art.

He was the first writer who professedly treats of surgery and its operations, and he shows that the art had attained an astonishing degree of perfection. The state of surgery in his time must have been much further advanced than medicine.

He describes, on the one hand, a large number of surgical ailments, such as diseases of the joints and the bones, wounds, tumors, burns, fistula, abscess, sprains and luxations, for which he recommends reduction before the development of inflammation; fractures, in which, when they fail to unite, he recommends extension and rubbing together the ends of the bone and even cutting down upon the bone so that it heals as an open wound; hernia, which he thinks originates in laceration of the peritoneum; strangulated hernia, where he cautions against cathartics; the radical operation for reducible hernia; foreign bodies in the ears, etc. On the other hand, he notices many operations of the ancients, some of them handed down by him alone, among others, bleeding, double ligation of bleeding vessels and division of the vessels between the ligatures.

In this work of Celsus much of the substance of the lost writings of ancient physicians, and especially those of the Alexandrian age, is preserved. He has manifestly selected from these with ripe judgment only what is reasonable, useful and valuable, and accordingly has paid comparatively little attention to opinions and theories, a point in which he contrasts strongly with Galen, and which impresses upon his work the stamp of practicality and usefulness.

Celsus is the first native Roman physician whose name has been transmitted. Before his time all those who arrived at any degree of eminence were either Greeks or Asiatics, thus suggesting the idea that most native practitioners were of humble rank. This may be attributed to the low state of science in Rome, altho literature had advanced to a high state. All trades and manufactures of Rome were carried on by slaves, and medicine seems to have been placed in the same class.

In opposition to the humoral theory of the "Dogmatists" and the solidism of the "Methodists," the Pneumatic school introduced the aeriform, spiritual principle of the "pneuma" (the world-soul of the Stoics), into their general pathology. Yet they also left the elementary qualities (warmth, coldness, moisture and dryness, which according to their doctrine may be seen and felt and not recognized simply by their effects) a place in their "system." The pneuma comes by way of the respiration as a part of the creative "world-soul" into the heart and is driven thence into the vessels and the whole body, in which it effects in a passive way the diastole of the pulse, while the contraction of the arteries is an active process. When it works regularly and is united with warmth and moisture it occasions health; under contrary circumstances, and mixed with warmth and dryness, it occasions the acute diseases, while mixed with cold and dryness melancholy. This latter condition in its acme introduces death, a state in which everything becomes dry and cold.

Areteus of Cappadocia (about 30-90 A.D.) shows himself a great physician by his conception, even thus early, of the duties of his profession. He was one of the Pneumatic school and an eminent medical writer.

In anatomy he does not differ greatly from the views of his time. Still in his work are found intimations of the tubes of Bellini, while he may have had a correct idea of the decussation of the nerves in the medulla. He knew that the tongue was composed of muscles. In physiology he, with Aristotle, regarded respiration as the process by which the pneuma reached the lungs and thence the heart, the seat of life. The blood was prepared in the liver, the bile in the gall-bladder; in the large intestine a secondary digestion takes place; in the spleen is to be found thick, coagulated blood; the seat of the soul is in the heart. He knew that the contents of the arteries was light-colored, that of the veins dark.

Rufus of Ephesus (about 50 A.D.), who lived shortly after Celsus, practised dissection on apes and other of the lower animals. He discovered the decussation of the optic nerves and the capsule of the crystalline lens and gave, for the time, a very clear description of the membranes and parts of the eye. He taught that the nerves originated from the brain. Physiologically he divided them into nerves of motion and nerves of sensation and ascribed to them all the functions of the body, since he did not distinguish them accurately from muscles and tendons. The heart, whose left cavity he declares to be thinner and smaller than the right, he considers the organ which gives origin to the pulse, and he associates the latter also with the pneuma. He describes the pulse carefully in its varieties as dicrotic, suppressed, innumerable and intermittent. The heart is, in his view, the seat of life and of animal heat, while the spleen is a useless organ. He was also an alienist and wrote on the subject of melancholia. A sick man who believed that he had no head was convinced of its existence by a leaden hat. Moreover, he studies diseases of the urinary bladder and kidneys and medicines—the latter of which he discussed in verse.

The Eclectic school was founded 90 A.D., the main principles being to avoid theories and metaphysical speculations and to select from all preceding schools that which was most reasonable and practically beneficial. The most famous man of this sect was Claudius Galen (131-204 A.D.), one of the most remarkable men in the whole history of Medicine. He made his influence felt both in his time and for centuries to come. He enjoyed a most thoro education at home and abroad; he studied at Alexandria and traveled extensively; he knew all the teachings of his predecessors and he wrote an immense number of medical treatises. At once he attained first rank in medicine, and this rank has been compared not unaptly to that which Aristotle possessed in the world of general science. For centuries after his death his doctrines and tenets were regarded almost in the light of oracles which very few had the audacity and courage to oppose. And it may be stated without exaggeration that the authority of Galen alone was estimated at a much higher rate than that of all other medical writers combined, extending over a period of twelve hundred years.

That he was a man of wonderful intellect and great talents no one can deny. He had studied philosophy very thoroly, and as was the tendency in those days, this was intimately interwoven with his medical beliefs. He was an admirer of Hippocrates and always speaks of him with great respect, professing to act on his principles. Yet, as a matter of fact, the two men could not be more different, the simplicity of the ancient Greek being strongly contrasted with the abstruseness and refinement of Galen.

The general pathological views of Galen are founded upon the four elements to which are attached the primary qualities: To air coldness, to fire warmth, to water moisture, to earth dryness. To these correspond four cardinal humors, among which latter the element water predominates in the mucus, which is secreted by the brain; fire in the yellow bile, which has its origin in the liver; earth in the black bile formed by the spleen, while in the blood, which is prepared in the liver (an important error not discarded until the seventeenth century), the elements are uniformly mixed. Mucus is cold and moist, yellow bile warm and dry, black bile cold and dry, the blood warm and moist.

The life-giving principle is the soul, which as "spiritus," or "pneuma," is taken from and constantly renewed by the general world-soul in the respiration. Arrived in the body, the pneuma becomes in the brain (to which it penetrates through the nose) and in the nerves the "animal spirits"; in the arteries and the heart (to which it comes by way of the lungs) the "vital spirits," and in the liver and the renal veins the "natural spirits." The three fundamental faculties, the "animal," "vital" and "natural," which bring into action and keep in operation the corresponding functions, originate as an expression of the primal force "soul" (pneuma), existing in these three faculties within the body. Besides these, there are for special functions of the body other faculties, subordinate to these three and acting occasionally as the "attractive," the "propulsive," the "retentive" and the "secreting."

Upon these depend nutrition, assimilation, secretion, muscular contraction, in general all the ordinary functions of the body, in which each organ has the property of appropriating to itself, by means of these faculties, that which is necessary for its own existence. There are, besides these, "special forces," which are not derived from the three already named, and which are therefore supernatural. Everything, however, which exists and displays activity in the human body originates in and is formed upon an intelligent plan, so that the organ in structure and function is the result of that plan. Thus the human frame is adapted to the solution of a teleological problem. Indeed, Galen is the father of teleology in medicine.

Galen is of peculiar importance in special pathology from the fact that he first designedly employed experiment for its basis. He was the first physiologist (if we except the accounts of the Hippocratists in embryology) to experiment and vivisect upon scientific principles and founded the physiology of the nervous system. Nerves of motion, which as such are "hard," are represented by the sixty spinal nerves; those of sensation ("soft") by the nerves of the brain. Of the latter he recognized seven. Galen was acquainted with the movement of the brain and assumed that by it the impurities of the "animal spirits," brought to the brain by the carotids, were then expelled, while its more refined portions, the nervous spirits, were prepared in the plexus of the ventricles and thence borne by the nerves thruout the body. The great sensibility of the intestines depends upon the sympathetic nerve. The perception of light he locates in the retina.

Respiration and the pulse serve one purpose—the reception of air. The latter in inspiration comes first into the lungs and thence into the left heart and arteries. On the other hand, during the diastole, or rest of the arteries, air is sucked into them through the pores of the skin. During the systole, or contraction of the lungs and arteries, the "soot" escapes. The air or pneuma received by the lungs is not sufficient by itself to cool the heart, hence air is also received through the skin. The diastole of the heart and arteries and inspiration also conduct pneuma to the blood, while the systole and expiration discharges the "soot" from the blood. Respiration has its origin in the vital, the pulse in the animal sphere. Respiration is effected by means of the diaphragm and the intercostal muscles.

The physiological route of the pneuma (the respiratory process he deemed one of combustion) is developed within the body or the vessels as the circulation, which takes place as follows: From the stomach the food, which has undergone "coction," proceeds to the liver, where it is converted into blood. This blood is now carried to the heart, and the latter organ (whose various parts all contract simultaneously) drives into the lungs, through the pulmonary artery, so much of this blood as may be required for their nutrition. At the same time the remainder of the blood is driven through the veins into the body and a minute portion passes through the pores of the septum into the left ventricle, where it is mixed with the pneuma drawn into the heart through the pulmonary veins in diastole. No blood returns from the lungs to the heart, for all of it is consumed in the nutrition of those organs. From the left heart the blood (mixed with the pneuma) proceeds through the aorta, to be communicated to the veins finally by means of the pore-like anastomoses at the terminations of this vessel. To the veins all the nutrition of the body is due.

The blood conveyed to the body by the veins is principally used up in nutrition, but what little remains, together with the new blood formed in the liver, returns to the right heart by a sort of ebb-tide in the venous circulation. Dilatation and diastole of the heart, as well as of the arteries, are the active factors in the motion of these parts, while systole is the passive element. (Systole is really the active heart-muscle.) Singularly enough, however, no physician, down to the time of Harvey, formed a similar opinion of the theory of circulation of the ancients. The blood is perfected in the heart and supplied with the "calidum innatum" (innate heat) and then passes on into the body. The pulse arises from an active dilating force, pulse-force, communicated to the arteries from the heart.

The heart has no nerves, but is the seat of passion and courage. The brain is the seat of the rational soul and an organ for the secretion of mucus and for cooling the heart. The lungs also serve to cool off the heart. The liver is the place for the preparation of the blood and the seat of love. The "animal spirits" are the cause of the soul's activity. They originate from the blood, but in the brain become the "animal spirits." From the origin of the "animal spirits" the dependence of mental expressions and disturbances upon the bodily condition is also explained. Galen divided these mental disturbances into mania, melancholia, imbecility and dementia.

In direct opposition to what has been said concerning mental activity and its cause and seat, he explains the temperaments by the mixture of the elements, and therefore divides them into (1) the dry and warm (choleric); (2) dry and cold (melancholic); (3) moist and warm (sanguine); (4) moist and cold (phlegmatic). The sensations again are dependent upon the animal spirits. The sight is effected through that portion of these spirits which is found between the lens and the choroid and which intercepts the rays of light in order to conduct them to the optic nerve. The pneuma likewise occasions the smell by forcing its way into the anterior ventricles of the brain, which are the seat of this sense. The hearing originates in the penetration of the pneuma, in the form of waves, into the course of the nerve of hearing.

Much more original is the knowledge of Galen in anatomy, which from his youth up he studied with enduring fondness. His observations were confined entirely to the lower animals, except in regard to the bones, which he had been able to study upon two human skeletons at Alexandria. One of these skeletons had been cleaned by birds, the other by the Nile, and Galen considered it a piece of special good fortune that he had been able to study their structure. His anatomical works—the best among the ancients—continued text-books down into the sixteenth century. He is in many points the first discoverer and always a very careful describer, the latter especially in regard to osteology, the central and peripheral nervous system, the larynx, the intestines and the genital organs, tho he, too, is not free from the confusion and errors of the ancients and readily falls into teleological speculations. He handled the subject of bandaging in detail and introduced the methods known even to-day.

Galen did not greatly advance semeiology, with the exception of the doctrine of the pulse, which he elaborated so extensively that he wrote many treatises on this subject alone. He advanced diagnoses chiefly by his sharper systematic definition of the phenomena of disease, while, so far as the means of investigation are concerned, he did not go beyond the Hippocratists and earlier physicians.

In special pathology Galen added little of importance to the material already existing, tho he constructed his pictures of disease more perfectly through a better analysis of single symptoms, as in phthisis (its different forms and infections (?) character), pneumonia and pleuritis, gout, rheumatism, intermittent fever, varieties of spasm, etc. Cancer he regards as a parasitic being, which occasions both local and general disturbances. Rightly, however, he laid great weight on socalled climatic cures, of which he seems to have been the founder. But even in the treatment of disease he was less a practitioner than a skillful theorist.

One of the most distinguished surgeons of antiquity was Antyllus, the first who, in addition to depression, described the extraction of small cataracts. He also described the so-called Antyllic method of operation on aneurism, as well as the method of practising venesection, cupping, scarification, arteriotomy, subcutaneous section of the ligaments in stiff joints and of the ligaments of the tongue in stammering.

The change which came over the world of thought with the transference of the capital from Rome to Constantinople was not without its effect on medicine, and from the time of Antyllus a new type of medical art is made evident. Naturally the Roman period followed the Greek in its much philosophizing, but there was an earnest desire to learn and what was known was practised simply and without the desire to impress the beholders. The periods to come reveal a vast change in the attitude of the medical profession to the world, the classic medical philosopher disappearing with the fall of Rome.

CHAPTER IV

BYZANTINE AND ARABIAN SCHOOLS

WITH the removal of the "Capital of the World" from Rome to Constantinople (Byzantium) a new epoch was opened upon the world, in which Medicine shared. Constantine I. (312-337), the first Christian emperor, seemed to feel that by investigating theological claims he had secured exemption from scientific interest, and the healing art found little imperial patronage. Indeed, the time generally seemed to be satisfied with the progress that had been made in science, and after the death of Galen, for many years there are no illustrious names, and no discoveries worth the mentioning. Literature had declined rapidly, and the last vestige of Roman patriotism passed away when the empire was divided into an East and a West. Even in the time of Galen, the Roman Empire had begun to decline, and altho it produced a very few scientists, most of the illustrious physicians and surgeons were foreigners—either Greeks or Asiatics. But during the third and fourth centuries of the Christian era, no names are heard, nothing is written—there being merely a few compilations of Galen and the early Greek mediciners. One of these compilers, perhaps the best, was Oribasius, who at the request of the Emperor Julian, made a compilation of all medical works from the time of Hippocrates to Galen.

The city of Alexandria still retained its reputation as the great school of medicine, depending, of course, on its extensive medical library. But this was destroyed by the conquest of the Arabians in the seventh century. The Saracens, in a spirit of blind bigotry, appeared to be actuated by the barbarous desire to eradicate science from the face of the earth. However, in spite of the Saracens, some of the books escaped the fire, and these were carefully hidden by those who appreciated their value. Among these relics were the writings of Galen, and in an early period of the Saracenic Empire, they began to be held in high esteem. This period extended only to the eighth century and was merely a continuation of Galen's wonderful influence. The physicians did not advocate science, merely professing to comment on and copy from the works of their great master.

Aetius (circa 510 A.D.) occupied in Byzantium almost the same position as Oribasius in Rome. He embraced the doctrines of the Christian religion, and these played some part in his treatment of diseases. In surgical therapeutics, Aetius recommended a great number of salves and plasters. The preparation of salves must, however, take place with certain ceremonies. Thus, one should continually repeat, in a loud but solemn tone, the charm "The God of Abraham, the God of Isaac, the God of Jacob, give virtue to this medicament," until the required consistency of the plaster in making is obtained. If a bone is stuck in the throat, the patient should swallow, and then draw out again, a piece of raw meat, to which a pack-thread has been fastened; or the physician should grasp him by the throat (unfortunately the results of this treatment are not given!) and cry in a loud voice, "As Lazarus was drawn from the grave and Jonah out of the whale, thus Blasius, the martyr, commands, 'Bone, come up or go down!'" He practised venesection on both the diseased and the sound side, and in cerebral congestion advises also a stick to draw into the nose of the patient, that the double hemorrhage may render the cure more certain. He further commends the pimpernel in hydrophobia, and pomegranate bark for worms. To detect poison in a wound he makes use of a poultice of walnuts laid upon it and afterward thrown to a fowl; if the fowl eats the poultice, the wound is free from poison; if not, it is not.

Aetius defended the Hippocratic maxim that Nature should be permitted to have her own way, a precept to which very different explanations have been given from Hippocrates' time down to the present day, since it is usually "the masters' own nature" which they ask others to follow. In hectic fevers he advises nutritious food; in febrile diseases generally, coolness of the apartment. Typhoid fever manifests as its chief symptoms stupor and delirium, febris algida, however, an icy coldness.

His doctrine of fever, according to which the seat of fever is in the heart, is most complete. Fever results chiefly from diseases of the stomach and intestinal canal. The general vitality suffers in diseases of special organs only so far as it functionates through these organs. On mania and disease of the mind in general he makes some admirable observations. His methods of diagnosis are comparatively perfect. Thus he employs the pressure of the fingers for the detection of anasarca (the frequent inflammatory nature of which, indeed, he first recognized); palpitation in enlargements of the spleen; inspection in the investigation of urinary sediments, which he discusses fully; percussion in tympanites and succussion in ascites.

The disease occasioned by worms he describes very well, and he also recognizes lung-stones, so that he had evidently made dissections. His views on the place where venesection should be practised give evidence of a freedom from prejudice far in advance of his time. He bled from all parts of the body, and held the opinion that it was perfectly immaterial whether the operation was performed in the vicinity of the diseased parts (as Hippocrates preferred), or (as the Methodists directed) on the opposite side, since all the veins in the body communicate. He admonishes his colleagues not to be dazzled by the glare of "The Authorities."

In striking contrast with these and similar sound principles, however, are his peculiarities and his superstition, in which qualities he was a true son of his time. Thus in gout he recommends a very complicated antidote, the use of which is to be begun in January, and continued for a year and a day. It is to be taken 100 days, then suspended for 30 days, then resumed for 100 days, then suspended 15 days, then it is prescribed again every second day for 260 days, after which 80 similar doses follow. He cures the pains of colic by a stone, upon which is engraved the figure of Hercules strangling the serpent, or by an iron ring, upon one side of which is exhibited an incantation, on the other, the diagram of the Gnostics.

Theophilus (circa 540 A.D.) was one of the most popular physicians and medical authors during the Middle Ages, and his work, "On the Structure of the Body," was often made the basis of instruction in the universities. In it, among other things, the olfactory nerves are first mentioned as a special pair of cerebral nerves; attention is directed to the dependence of the development of the skull and vertebral column upon that of the brain and spinal cord, and reference is made to how the wisdom and goodness of the Divine Being have ordained everything so infinitely perfect as to give to the hand precisely five fingers, and to the skull a spherical form. In general he follows Galen.

Paul of Aegina (circa 560 A.D.) was the last of the Greek physicians who were of any rank in medicine. The military surgery of Paul is very complete, clear, and suited to the weapons of the period. It is evidently based upon a rich experience, for he had seen even the worst injuries do well, and in operations he desires, above all, that the wounded part should occupy the same position which it had occupied at the moment of injury. In order to remove sling-stones, darts, arrow-heads, etc., he cuts or draws them out or pushes them through, and he gives judicious precautions to avoid the injury of any important parts.

Pathology he treats from head to foot, after the method customary in his day. He also describes specially diseases of the skin and heart (without, however, differentiating the individual diseases), epidemic colic, and ascribes gout, very properly, to an inactive life, with too rich food.

From the foregoing it may be inferred that Paul must have been one of the most capable, if not the most daring operator of his age. His experience in this department of the healing art, and particularly at this time, seems the more surprising, since for centuries before him, surgeons had made shift with an apparently inoffensive surgery of plasters and salves, rather than resort to operative measures.

After the destruction of the Alexandrian library and its medical contents, the Arabians turned to Grecian science for instruction in the medical arts. They followed Hippocrates and Galen, translating them both into Arabic. The works of Hippocrates did not obtain much hold, however, on account of the simplicity of this author, whereas the metaphysical refinements and elaborate arrangements of Galen pleased the Arabic taste. After the conquests, the successors of Mahomet rested, and seemed disposed to add to their grand empire by the cultivation of the arts of peace. They even translated the Greek philosophers and studied them. But in spite of all this, they were not open to this form of intellectual advancement, and no additions were made to general science, other than the invention of chemistry or alchemy. They even introduced it into medicine.

Among the special medical branches, practical anatomy was utterly excluded by religious belief, and midwifery and gynecology were then (as almost in the East to-day) forbidden to men. The practice of operative surgery, too, was considered unworthy of a man of honor, and was permitted only to the despised lithotomists and similar persons of the lower class, who in consequence of the fatalism of the Arabians (in spite of the remarkable tolerance of the Orientals, even to-day, for painful operations), were very rarely allowed to have recourse to the knife.

"Operations performed by the hand, such as venesection, cauterization, and incision of arteries," says a writer of this period, "are not becoming a physician of respectability and consideration. They are suitable for the physician's assistants only. These servants of the physician should also do other operations, such as incision of the eyelids, removing the veins in the white of the eye and the removal of cataract. For an honorable physician nothing further is becoming than to impart to the patient advice with reference to food and medicine. Far be it from him to practice any operation with the hands." Even the extraction of teeth was avoided, and, although dentistry was cultivated, as among the ancients, it was practised only by the lower class of physicians, the assistants.

Medicine proper was chiefly taught. Chemistry, pharmacy and materia medica, and indeed, the history of medicine were also well cultivated. They were the first to describe smallpox. They greatly improved drugs, due mainly to their researches in chemistry.

Rhazes (932-1010 [?]) was a prolific writer, but blindly followed Galen. His most important additions to knowledge were in surgery and in pharmacy. His semeiology and prognostics, with the exception of the indications to be derived from the urine and the planets, are famous; yet his anatomical and physiological knowledge never exceeds that of Galen.

BYZANTINE AND ARABIAN SCHOOLS

Avicenna in the tenth century wrote a work which contains substantially the conclusions of the Greeks, and was the text-book and law of the healing, until modern times. It includes anatomy, physiology and materia medica. In it are mentioned camphor, iron in various forms, amber, aloes, manna and many other drugs. He considers gold and silver as "blood-purifiers"; hence gilded and silvered pills are, in his view, specially efficacious.

His pathology makes prominent mention of mental diseases, and notices tic douloureux (described also by other Arabians), tetanus, three forms of inflammation of the chest—pleuritis, muscular rheumatism and mediastinitis—measles and the purples. He is also said (according to Leichtenstern) to have been the first physician to teach the contagiousness of phthisis. In his general pathology and therapeutics he distinguishes, among other matters, fifteen kinds of pain, and preserves the Galenic humoral pathology. In great coldness and in great heat he gives no medicines, and considers the same remedy good in one locality, which would be injurious if employed in another.

In surgery he calls the extraction of a cataract a dangerous operation, but speaks in favor of depression; declines to operate on strangulated hernia; describes puncture of the bladder; the method by which leeches and other foreign bodies when swallowed may be removed from the œsophagus, hardened wax removed from the meatus, etc., while he prefers to loosen the teeth by means of the fats of treetoads, rather than to pull them out. In obstetrics he follows the views of the earlier writers. In military surgery (according to Fröhlich) he taught only very little, and this he borrowed from the Greeks, without giving his own experience.

Albucasis, later in the same century, is the last of the Arabian physicians to attain any distinction as a writer. His principal work is on surgery, and he was as famous as a surgeon as was Avicenna in medicine. He performs venesection, after the manner of the Arabians, upon the sound side and recommends the employment of the same with the view of prophylaxis, an idea from which subsequently originated a pernicious custom. Besides the surgical diseases already noticed from his treatise on operations, he recognzes a gangrenous epidemic erysipelas, warty excrescences, fractures, which, after the manner of his age, he rectifies by means of machines—a cruel procedure of which reminiscences still exist among the public. Plates of instruments adorn the work. He valued anatomy as an important aid in the practice of surgery. This was unusual and interesting in an Arabian. He was a bold operator and a man of keen insight. His work on surgery was the most complete of that time, and was used for years after his death as a text-book.

The celebrity of the Arabian school of medicine is based, not on its real merits, but on the fact that the surrounding countries were in a very much lower state of medical knowledge. From the eighth to the twelfth centuries was the period of Europe's most complete superstition in natural science. The principal remains of a taste for literature and science, or for the fine arts, were found among the Moors and Arabs; and it was from this source, by the intervention of the crusaders, and the intercourse which was thus effected between the Asiatics and Europeans, that the philosophical and medical writings of the Greeks were first made known to the inhabitants of Italy and France. For some time after their introduction into Europe, they were still translated from the Arabic, and it was not until much later that they were read in Greek. Inasmuch as the study of the Greek tongue was so completely suspended during the Dark Ages, it is possible that the writings of the ancient physicians might have been lost to posterity, if they had not been preserved in these Arabic translations.

There are two points in which the Arabians conferred a real obligation upon their successors—the introduction of various new articles into the materia medica, and the original description of certain diseases. The Arabian school is said to be the first to found a hospital in which medical students received clinical instruction. The menace of Saracenic power was real and terrifying to Southern Europe, its unchecked success might have been fraught with disastrous results to civilization, but at least the very nearness of the peril led to the acquisition from the Orient by the Occident of the elements of an almost forgotten learning.

After the extinction of the Sarecenic school in Spain, there is an interval of about three hundred years, from the twelfth to the fifteenth centuries, during which time Europe was enveloped in scientific darkness. Every department of natural investigation was neglected, and medicine, as a science, fell into its lowest state of degradation. What remained was in the possession of the monks, who regarded knowledge as being useless unless it had some theological bent, and who desired to keep mankind looking ever to a future world and not to this. The practice of medicine, if such it may be called, was chiefly in their hands, and they adhered closely to the principles and practices of Galen. But mixed with these was a large portion of superstition, magic and astrology. By means thus employed, they gradually came to possess a profound influence over the minds of the people, and operated so powerfully on the imagination of their patients that their doings seemed almost supernatural.

It is certain, however, that there were, besides the monkish physicians, laymen who practised medicine, but they held no such position as once they had. The lay physician was not looked upon as a learned man, for the latter was one who had been duly instructed in a monastic school, where the curriculum would not admit the art of medicine, wherefore the lay physician was considered as a mechanic or tradesman. Laws were enacted to restrain and govern these men, and they were made responsible for any want of skill, while the fee for any given piece of surgery or medical advice was stipulated.

In addition to the monks, there existed also many Jewish physicians, who had been educated at Alexandria, later in the Arabian school, and they were lay physicians of a high order. They attended princes and even popes, in spite of edicts of the Church prohibiting this very thing. The monks, however, held the highest place, which was low enough to be sure, until the solid foundation of Salerno and the European universities. Yet there were many of the clergy, especially among the Benedictines, who studied the ancient physicians and were more worthy of the name. Under the direction of the Church, many institutions and orders sprang up. These had in view the helping of diseased and maimed mankind, and houses were used especially for their care and maintenance. The monks were regulated in their cures by the orders of the Church. Their medical practices were theurgic to an extreme degree. Prayers, amulets and many superstitions were employed generally and openly for the cure of every-day diseases. Sickness was regarded as a direct evidence of personal sin, or as due to the incantation of a witch, or as a visitation from the devil. The monks held the principle of "similia similibus," and "treated the poisoning occasioned by swallowing a toad by directing the patient to eat another toad." The higher monks were first restrained in the twelfth century, and the practice of medicine forbidden them. Then, later, the lower monks were also restricted, and particularly all burning and cutting (surgery) were forbidden them on the principle: "The Church shuns bloodshed."

The Benedictines were the most scientific of the monks, and they cultivated medicine to a considerable extent. An excellent influence upon medieval medicine and its development was exercised by the monastic infirmary at Monte Cassino, and still more eminently and effectively by the school of Salerno. The former, founded by St. Benedict himself, was mainly for practice rather than instruction, and miracles were said to be performed here. The monks came from foreign lands to learn treatment and to study. The glory of Monte Cassino was displaced by Salerno, which attained its greatest position in the twelfth century. It held its prominence for more than a century.

Salerno was founded as early as 200 B.C. by the Romans, and because of its charming situation and climate, it enjoyed a wide reputation as a health resort. It is probable, therefore, that physicians were always located there. After the establishment of Christianity, it became the resort of pilgrims, as well as a kind of medical resort. The dissection of a body was allowed every five years. This was allowed by Salerno's patron, Frederick II. The importance of Salerno as regards medical culture depends not on any wonderful contributions to science, but rather because the principles of the great ancients were preserved in the Greek itself, and also through Arabians.

The school of Montpellier was equally important in the culture of the West, for here, too, they studied the ancients, especially Hippocrates, and also the Arabians and Galen. The reputation of the school was so great than to have studied there lent a halo of glory to the monkish physician. They were liberal in viewpoint and demonstrated their practical scientific tendency by allowing the annual dissection of a criminal corpse (1376). About this time, other universities sprang up at Bologna, Oxford and Paris. These helped to start that reformation of thought which came later. The number of students speedily became very great, and often formed whole communities. The course of instruction in medicine was carefully watched over by the Church and subsequently by the State.

The great Hohenstaufer Frederick II., enlightened by the wisdom of the Orient, was especially active in the promotion of education, and above all, in the elevation of the position of physicians. He paid no heed to the triple ban of Pope Gregory IX. (1227-1241), and by his promotion of medical studies and educational institutions he became a benefactor of mankind, and especially of Italy. Through his medical ordinance, published in 1224, he has secured for himself forever an honorable place in the history of medical culture. Some of his reforms were of the nature of restraint and government of the practice of medicine. The surgeon must bring evidence that he had attended the lectures of the professors, and pursued for one year the curriculum which surgeons held necessary, especially human anatomy. Surgeons of the first class were examined by three professors, of whom one teacher of surgery conducted the examination in the Latin language, and in the presence of the prosector of the nation of the candidate.

The foundation of the new universities did two things to further medicine; one was that medicine, its teaching and to a certain extent its practice, fell into the hands of men who were thinkers and learned, and the other was the introduction of the so-called scholastic philosophy. The teachings of the Greek physicians, and the elaborations of those teachings by the Arabs, were cherished as very gospel, and the physicians of the period made no effort to change or add to them. Aristotle's philosophy, combined with Arabian, extended up to the seventeenth century.

This period, better known as the Age of the Arabists, is characterized by the medical men, both clergy and laymen, following the Arabians in science and practice. There was one famous Peter Abano, who lived near Padua, who was a man of refined views, altho markedly superstitious. He wrote several books on science.

A circumstance which tended to shake the authority of Galen, and

BYZANTINE AND ARABIAN SCHOOLS

to diminish the veneration in which his opinions had been held for so many ages, was the rise of the sect of Chemical Physicians. After chemistry had been used with advantage for the purpose of improving pharmacy, it was applied to the explanation of the phenomena of vitality and of the operation of morbid processes upon the living organism. The theories of these chemists were false, but they served to divide the profession, and acted as a wedge in the downfall of Galen's long influence.

The revival of human anatomy in the fourteenth century was so great an epoch in the history of medicine that it marks the point of turning toward modern science. Commerce, business, manufactures and the higher arts were more and more cultivated, especially in Italy. In 1330, the invention of gunpowder by Berthold Schwartz, so important in the history of civilization, was later the means of reforming surgery. Anatomy, in its practical human aspect, became an openly recognized department of medical science.

After the period of the Alexandrian anatomist, human anatomy, especially the practical portion of it, again had almost disappeared from the list of medical studies, tho here and there probably a sort of dissection may still have been practised. Even Galen dissected only animals, and he considered it one of the great advantages of Alexandria that human skeletons could there be seen. In the early Middle Ages the monks would have tolerated such a process quite as little as the Koran, feeling it to be an impairment of the capacity for resurrection, a belief still supposed to be involved in anatomical dissection.

How early, and where human dissections in aid of anatomical studies were revived, is unknown. This much, however, is certain, that the Senate of Venice (in spite of the prohibition by Pope Boniface VIII., eight years before) decreed in the year 1308, that a human body should be dissected annually. From this express decree it would seem to follow that this had already been often done heretofore. At all events, William of Salicet and others in Bologna had performed dissections. But, as a matter of historical fact, the credit of the revival of dissection belongs to Mondino alone, who took hold of the subject at the psychological moment.

Mondino de Luzzi was one of the first of this period, the fourteenth century, to write a treatise on anatomy and dissection of the human body. His work is written entirely in the spirit of the Arabians, and he followed Galen in describing the abdominal walls as being constructed without bony supports, in order to stretch sufficiently in cases of flatulence and abdominal dropsy, if perchance these diseases should befall one.

Mondino, to escape burdening his soul with mortal sin, did not yet venture to open the skull, but others were less fearful, and investigations were soon so popular that bodies for dissection were stolen, if they could not be otherwise obtained. The description was read from the book, as the professor did not dream of soiling his fingers by actually handling the body. Mondino's work was designed to be such a text-book of anatomy, and it maintained general acceptance as such down to the close of the Middle Ages.

After Mondino, little further advance was made for two centuries in anatomy, but a general spirit of progress now manifested itself in the arts and other sciences; philosophy in all its branches was studied on a more correct plan, and medicine accordingly improved. One of the first symptoms of this improvement was the increasing relish for the writings of Hippocrates, and a revival of his method of studying and practicing medicine.

Probably as a result, first, of the influence of the Crusades, in which many wounds were inflicted and subsequently treated; second, of the revival of anatomy, many surgeons of this period were excellent anatomists. As a result of the invention of gunpowder and its application to instruments of war, the surgical wounds changed in character, requiring, in their threatment, a more thorough knowledge of anatomy. On account of these things, surgery advanced with great strides, and that in spite of the fact that it still remained in the hands of the lower surgeons who were originally assistants of the clergy.

In Italy, surgery remained united with the practice of medicine, and was practised by all physicians who professed to be general doctors. It was always held in high esteem, both by the profession and by laymen in general, and never fell into the disreputable position that once existed in France. The surgeons of Italy were particularly clever in developing plastic surgery by the construction of artificial noses and ears. In France, on the other hand, surgery became entirely separated from medicine in the second half of the Middle Ages.

A class arose called "Barber Surgeons," because they shaved, and performed menial jobs of all sorts. They developed surgery very largely, forming themselves into a distinct profession, possessing a college of their own. Later they divided into guilds of "superior" and "inferior" surgeons, the former being subordinate to the latter, while both were under control of the physicians of internal medicine, called the Faculty. These surgeons, who were called "surgeons of the long robe," later formed a college, and separated themselves from the barbers, called "surgeons of the short robe."

Guy de Chauliac (1300) was one of the distinguished surgeons of early France. He showed wonderful comprehensiveness and judgment in his work, and in its description. His own observations of diseases, and his knowledge of anatomy were considerable. He used the thermo-cautery in treatment of cancer, which he declared was allied to leprosy. Non-ulcerating cancer he operated on and cut out from the roots. Operations on diseases of eye, and treatment of fractures, were well performed. He trephined the skull, performed lithotomy, and operated on nose and throat. Hemorrhage he divided correctly into arterial, or spurting, and venous, and his hemostasis consisted in modern methods of styptics, suturing, division of half-severed vessels, actual cautery and ligation.

During the fourteenth and fifteenth centuries formidable diseases made their appearance in Europe. Some of the causes were in part prolonged to their effect from the last days of antiquity, but the origin of others is still obscure. Among these one of the most remarkable was the Sudor Anglicanus, which is first mentioned about the end of the fifteenth century, and which for about fifty years raged at intervals with extreme violence in England and Western Europe. This disease, "English sweating sickness," as its name implies, was characterized by a severe sweating which consumed the strength of the patient, followed by terrible headaches, irregular heart action, delirium, stupor and finally death, all in the short space of twenty-four hours.

Another terrible and very widespread disease was leprosy. Hospitals and pest-camps were founded for these afflicted persons, who, if in fairly good health, had to go about dressed in a marked manner—a black gown with two white bands sewed upon the breast, and a large hat with a white band upon the head. Whatever they wished to buy, they must point out with a long stick, and their approach must be with a rattle.

"Holy-fire," or ergotism as it is now understood, was, if anything, worse than leprosy, for it maimed horriby those who did not die, deprived them of a hand or foot. It is a gangrenous disease caused by eating a fungus of rye, in bread, and is very painful. Scurvy was another disease due to malnutrition and improper feeding. It was most marked and diffuse in the fifteenth century, when it sprang out among those who traveled at sea for any length of time, where they could get no fresh vegetables or fruits, but must needs eat salt pork and dry biscuits.

Epidemics of influenza appeared in the early ages, and from those times it has been the custom to say, after sneezing, "God help us," because those attacked with this disease often died too quickly to expect aid from human hands. "The Black Death" was a most terrible and destructive plague. It is computed that fully one-fourth of all mankind was swept away by this plague! Besides these awful diseases, there were many famines, brought on about every decade or so, because of the widespread lack of cultivation of the land, and the universal insecurity of property.

CHAPTER V

THE CLOSE OF MEDIEVALISM

At the beginning of the Modern Era, continuing of course from the Middle Ages, the influences of superstition and ignorance were not at once obliterated, nor are they even to the present day. Martin Luther himself, the central figure of the greatest political and religious movement of all modern centuries, believed absolutely in the devil incarnate, and in all diseases he regarded the influence of Satan as paramount. The physicians were likewise under this influence. Even Paré believed in the workings of demons and the devil. And if great minds like those of Luther and Paré are found to have been fettered to those old ideas and beliefs, how much more must the lower classes and the ignorant have been?

But the most powerful agents in bringing about a better era were the new philosophical and skeptical currents of thought which arose to subject all medievalism to the tests of proof and doubt. This spread of new thought was due mainly to universal schooling and mental culture. Another influence which soon brought about an improvement in thought and education was commerce, developing ocean travel and through it bringing men of different languages and customs into immediate contact with each other.

Medicine in the beginning of the Modern Era received its mightiest impulse from the same strongly Protestant and progressive spirit which in the department of religion broke the solidarity of the ancient Church. In medicine, however, this spirit was led not only against the Church but also against Galen, against the Arabians and against the superstition of the priests and monks. Thus was called into existence a national medicine which through the living spirit of the nations and through their language won fresh momentum. The new forms of disease which had arisen in the last years of the Middle Ages brought a more reliable differentiation of the species of disease. The etiology and treatment of those new diseases could not be found in the records of the ancients, for the latter had never seen them; so it was a matter of sheer necessity to investigate them and learn all that was possible. The allied sciences of chemistry and botany, supplied with new material from the Old World, also advanced in many positive ways into the sphere of Medicine. Anatomy, already started on its correct basis, and physiology, which is founded upon anatomy, both advanced more rapidly.

The sixteenth century is as important in the development of medicine and its allied branches as was the age of Hippocrates, for during this time his principles and precepts were developed to a most wonderful degree. It was the century of reformation, of struggle and of protest against all medicine which had abandoned the teachings of Hippocrates; it was the outcry against tradition and authority and for correct principles of observation of nature. The levers whereby this reform was accomplished were humanism, the new anatomy, new diseases and the rebellion of Paracelsus and Paré.

Altho there is found an earnest effort to advance, a retrograde impulse of equal strength made itself manifest. Besides the clearest discernment stood darkest superstition; beside poor dupes stood the grandest imposters. At this time are found the superstitious physicians preaching that astrology is necessary for the study and the treatment of disease, while the belief in witches and their trials were approved by a large majority of the medical profession. The advances in mathematics and astronomy under the influence of the Copernican system laid the foundation for the final disbelief in astrology. The physicians of the sixteenth century were very active in philology and in translating and commenting upon the works of the ancients and the influence of these works was immediate. The reform proceeded from no single individual nor even from any one nation. The reaction became universal against Galen and the Arabians and terminated with their almost complete demolition. The first combustible thrown into the stagnant air of blind faith in authority was in the form of a dispute concerning the proper place for venesection in pleurisy, meaning both pleuritis and pneumonia. Now it seems a trivial thing, but at that time was so important that the medical profession was divided into two camps. The site to be chosen for bleeding was the whole subject of contention.

Pierre Brissot, a Parisian (1478-1522), taught the Hippocratic method of venesection. Many came to his side, but he gained more adversaries. Both Vesalius and Paré followed Brissot.

Paracelsus (Theophrastus von Hohenheim) lived about the same time as Brissot. He was instructed first by his father, who taught him alchemy, astrology and medicine. He studied at the University of Basle and later traveled as an itinerant student and surgeon in the wars. He was the first to deliver lectures on medicine in anything but the Latin language; that is, in German. As a result he had a great many hearers. But Paracelsus was far from modest concerning his own ability and standing. He proclaimed himself the greatest medical genius of Germany and compared himself with Hippocrates, whom he revered. As an outward and popular sign, he burnt the works of Galen and Avicenna in his lecture rooms, thus showing his unbelief in and disdain for these ancient authorities. He believed that experience and observation made the physician, not the knowledge of Latin and Greek and the useless principles of the ancients. Altho not properly educated in his department, he was possessed of ingenious medical instincts and through his extensive travels was better fitted for the work of a reformer than were the literati of the profession, who trod universally the paths of Galen and the Arabians.

His humanity and charity, virtues of the genuine physician, were famous. If he was rough and unpolished, it was because the times developed such men, and he could be gentle and kind. The influence that Paracelsus exerted was mostly on the Germans, because he wrote and spoke only in that language. Furthermore, his influence was limited to the unlearned rather than the learned, for the very reason that he did not know Latin and Greek, in which languages medicine had always heretofore been taught. Paracelsus was both a surgeon and a physician, at that time a rare circumstance, and he points out with great clearness and comprehension the great value of the alliance of these two departments of the medical science. Altho he was himself no operator, he taught the principles of the treatment for wounds. He held very strongly to the cleanliness of wounds, almost too strongly in direct opposition to the customs of the day, recommended spare diet and regulation of drink. In the treatment of ulcers he was less clear, but he used to good advantage mineral remedies and compression with bandages.

The physiology of Paracelsus recognizes as the proper active and life-giving agent in man his "archeus," whose home is in the stomach, who separates the material useful for nutrition (the "essence") from the useless (the "poison") and becomes thus the "alchemist of the body." Moreover, he is the spirit of life, the "astral body." The poison is excreted by two routes—all excrements are therefore poisons—and the essence remains in the body. It nourishes and maintains the latter, while each part and each member (since all possess their own special archeus, alchemist or stomach) attracts, extracts and assimilates what is appropriate for it. Digestion is a kind of putrefaction by which, on the one hand the assimilation of the nutritive slime, on the other the formation of the excrement, is rendered possible. Health is recognized by the regular action of this archeus.

A striking similarity with the doctrines of Darwin is found in the view of Paracelsus that the origin of everything is simply the transformation of germs always existing (and therefore is a metamorphosis), as well as in the fact that he maintained that every object and being originated at the expense of and through the destruction of another, a doctrine in which is seen already developed the war of individual against individual and the struggle for existence so much talked about nowadays.

Upon anatomy in the modern sense of the term—he calls it local anatomy—Paracelsus laid weight so far as concerns internal disease. He opposes to it a universal anatomy which the physician must know in order to cure and to understand diseases. Under this universal (or general) anatomy he understands the separation into that triad of fundamental bodies—salt, sulphur, mercury—of which the body consists, as well as the knowledge of the nature and power of an object and of its celestial model. In attempting to explain the phenomenon of life he mixed philosophy, alchemy and physiology. He believed that sulphur represented combustible elements in things, salt the soluble and mercury the volatile elements. He thus supported the theories of Valentine, for he too was a skilled alchemist.

The parts of the body stand in reciprocal relation with the stars, and, in fact, the seven great organs—the brain, heart, lungs, gall, kidneys and spleen—correspond to the moon, the sun, Mercury, Mars, Jupiter, Venus and Saturn. Furthermore, he makes seven kinds of pulses as there are seven planets. Epilepsy resembles the earthquake; apoplexy the lightning; flatulence the wind-storm; dropsy, inundations; the chilliness of fever, the quaking at the origin of new worlds. Fever in itself, according to his views, is an effort of the healing power of nature to equalize the disturbances of the body; that is, to cure. Paracelsus divided diseases into material and spiritual, acute and chronic.

The doctrines which he taught with such zeal were in the main the doctrines of Valentine, but enlarged and developed by the new light which he had gained by his own researches and studies. He discovered many new chemical bodies and introduced many new remedies. To him is largely due the spread of that drug, which perhaps more than any one drug has influenced the fortunes of mankind —namely, laudanum, the use of which is said to have been due to him. He was emphatically not an anatomist, not a physiologist, but a pharmacologist. He paid little heed to the doctrines of Galen and cared little or nothing for anatomy. He was a chemist to the backbone and his pathology was based not on changes of structure and their attendant symptoms but on the relation of diseases to drugs. He insisted that diseases ought to be known by the names of the drugs which cured them—morbus helleborinus and the like. In this he was a forerunner of an errant school of the therapeutics in modern times.

He believed that the color and physical properties of drugs should correspond somewhat to the locality and nature of the disease. As in the case of diseases of the eye, one should use euphrasia, because he black spot on that flower points the pupil of the eye. Also gold must be used in diseases of the heart because gold, according to cabalistic assumption, harmonizes with the heart. He was cautious in the use of venesection, but performed it when his astrological ideas permitted it.

The reform in surgery and its practice during the sixteenth century was the result not only of the change in the instruments used in warfare, but also of the impulse that had been given to the direct study of human anatomy. Altho the old-fashioned weapons were still employed, fire-arms and cannon were fast taking their places, and the wounds were of a more complex nature, demanding of the physician and surgeon a more intimate knowledge of the structures which had been wounded. This transformation of surgical after-treatment was the work of a single man, who so changed the prevailing methods of technique that those following in succeeding years began at once the uplifting of surgery to the foremost position which it to-day occupies.

Ambroise Paré (1510-1590) was the son of a barber and followed in his father's footsteps by being first a barber. When he had become a barber-surgeon and there spent many years on the battlefields, the best school of surgery. Altho by no means learned, he was most gifted, being an essentially practical physician. His fame became so great that he was appointed as one of the twelve royal surgeons and he was made a member of the great exclusive Collége de St. Côme, whose professors even overlooked the fact that he knew no Latin. Truly a great honor. The chief work of Paré was not the result of any inspiration, but was more or less an accident. Gunshot wounds up to this time had always been considered poisoned and the treatment of such was to destroy dangerous poisons. This was considered to be best done by cauterizing the wound with boiling oil. After a rather heavy day's fighting, in which many men had been wounded and were lying in the hospital tents awaiting their time for the prescribed treatment (there were no anesthetics used in those days), Paré found that his supply of oil had run short and that he could get no more for some days.

The knowledge of this fact upset and alarmed him a great deal, for he saw nothing but death for the untreated soldiers. These he was compelled merely to dress with clean cloths. Paré retired to bed that night, a tired and anxious man. The next morning he sought out without delay the men expected to die shortly, but what was his amazement and delight to find that they were all in far better condition than their comrades who had been subjected to the routine treatment with boiling oil! They suffered less pain, had fewer general symptoms, hence were more comfortable and the wounds were in better shape, there being less inflammatory reaction in them. Paré at once introduced this new idea into his treatment of wounds and began immediately to obtain much better results. As soon as he was himself positive of the superiority of this new method of treating gunshot wounds he wrote a treatise on the results of his great discovery, thus promoting surgery not only in France but throughout the world.

Another great achievement of Paré was the recommendation and practice of ligation of arteries when divided and bleeding. Altho this had frequently been done by the ancients and the Arabians, it had been dropped and supplanted by the red-hot cautery. Paré discovered it quite independently and deserves more credit because he applied it in the practice of amputation. In regard to amputations he was also a pioneer, for he excised a limb not through gangrenous and diseased tissues but above those areas, through the sound and healthy tissues, thus favoring the chance for primary healing without the formation of pus and infection. It is interesting to note that when large blood-vessels were ligated the surgeons took great care to include the nerves in the ligature, thinking thus to prevent the escape of any vital spirits! Paré was the first surgeon to use to any extent trusses for the reduction of ruptures (or hernias). He introduced many new plastic operations for deformities and invented feeding-bottles for the artificial feeding of infants with cows' milk.

In England two physicians of high rank—Linacre and John Kaye—freed English medicine from the control of the clergy and at the same time laid the foundation for the self-government of the English physicians.

As the new varieties of wounds necessitated a more thorough investigation and knowledge of anatomy, that subject began to be developed extensively. As Baas points out in his complete "History of Medicine," serious errors, handed down from antiquity, proved genuine hindrances to a far grander advancement. Such was the Galenic doctrine that the arteries, since they were empty in the cadaver, contained only the vital spirits, and that the veins alone contained blood; that the blood flowed forward in the veins during inspiration and backward in expiration, without returning to the heart, and was entirely consumed in the processes of nutrition.

It was in this sixteenth century that Galen's long hold on anatomy was broken. In this work Vesalius took the lead, and it is due to him primarily that anatomy was completely reformed, thus laying the foundations for physiology and pathological anatomy, both to be built up very soon.

Andreas Vesalius (1514-1564) was the first to declare that Galen's anatomy was based not upon human, but upon animal dissection. He proved his statement positively by many careful dissections and demonstrations upon the human body. He was the first to employ wood-cuts, made after Nature, in the illustration of his anatomical books. At the age of twenty-three years he was made a professor of anatomy at Padua. He at once began to teach anatomy in his own new way. Not to unskilled, ignorant barbers would he entrust the task of laying bare before the students the secrets of the human frame; his own hand, and his own hand alone, was cunning enough to track out the pattern of structures which day by day were becoming more and more clear to him.

Following venerated customs, he began his academic labors by "reading" Galen, as others had done before him, using his dissections to illustrate what Galen had said. But time after time the body on the table said plainly something different from that which Galen had written. He tried to do what others had done before him; he tried to believe Galen rather than his own eyes, but his eyes were too strong for him, and in the end he cast Galen and his writings to the winds and taught only what he himself had seen and what he could make his students see too.

Vesalius' great work is a work of anatomy, not of physiology. Tho to almost every description of structure there are added observations on the use and functions of structures described, and tho at the end of the work there is a short special chapter on what is now called experimental physiology, the book is in the main a book of anatomy. The physiology is incidental, occasional and indeed halting. Nor is the reason far to seek. Vesalius had a great difficult task before him. He had to convince the world that the only true way to study the phenomena of the living body was, not to ask what Galen had said, but to see for one's self, with one's eyes, how things really were. And not only was a sound and accurate knowledge of the facts of structure a necessary prelude to any sound conclusions concerning function, but also the former was the only safe vantage ground from which to fight against error. When he asserted that such a structure was not as Galen had described it, but different, he could appeal to the direct visible proof laid bare by the scalpel.

Almost everywhere Vesalius placed himself in express opposition to Galen. Thus he denied the existence of the "os intermaxillare" in adults and the composition of the inferior maxilla of two bones. In like manner he reduced Galen's seven bones of the sternum to three and gave to the sacrum (and coccyx) five or six pieces, instead of the three of Galen. In opposition to the latter, Vesalius also established the existence of marrow in the bones of the hand and refuted his assumption of an imputrescible bone of the heart, as well as his assertion of the strong curvature of the bones of the upper arm and the thigh. He maintained that nerves and muscles stood in no relation of proportionate strength to each other, for that stout nerves were distributed to small muscles and conversely; that the tendons were similar in constitution to the ligaments and not to the muscles, that the latter were in some respects independent.

Vesalius denied that the existence of a general muscle of the skin, proved that the intercostal muscles merely separate the ribs from each other, without either expanding or contracting the thorax, and discarded the origin of the vena cava inferior from the liver, all in opposition to Galen. He first described the course of the vena azygos and the subclavian vein, the ductus venosus; gave a description of the ear, the sphenoid bone of the head, the mediastinum, the peritoneum and omentum and many of the abdominal organs. Of course Vesalius was no more exempt than any other man from individual errors and those of his own and the past age. Thus in his view the veins alone were blood-vessels, while the arteries were still carriers of the vital spirits and simply appendages of the veins.

Even in this, which he ventured to print, the sarcastic note of skepticism made itself heard, but what he really thought he did not dare to put forward. He tells us in a later writing that "he accommodated his statements to the dogmas of Galen," not because he thought that

> "These were in all cases consonant with truth but because in such a new, great work he hesitated to lay down his own opinions, and did not dare to swerve a nail's breadth from the doctrines of the Prince of Medicine."

That physiological problems were before his mind, that he had thought over and indeed had tried to solve them by experimental methods, is shown in the brief chapter, "Some Remarks on the Vivisection of Animals," which is the last chapter in his great work. In this he relates his experiments on muscle and nerve, showing that which passes along a nerve in order to bring about movement passes by the substance and not by the sheath of the nerves. He affirms that it is through the spinal cord that the brain acts on the trunk and limbs; that an animal can live after its spleen has been removed; that the lungs shrink when the chest is punctured; that the voice is lost when the recurrent laryngeal nerve is cut; that by artificial respiration an animal can be kept alive, tho its chest is laid wholly bare, and that under these circumstances a heart which has almost stopped beating may be revived by the timely use of the bellows.

Vesalius' results were impugned and indeed were corrected by his compeers and his followers, but they were impugned and corrected by the method which he had introduced. Inquirers asserted that in this or that point Galen was right and Vesalius was wrong, but they no longer appealed to the authority of Galen as deciding the question; they appealed now to the actual things as the judge between the two. And even those who were Vesalius' most devoted disciples never made of him a second Galen; they never appealed to him as an authority, for they were content to show on the actual body that what he had said was right.

Under a more special aspect he may be regarded as the founder of physiology as well as of anatomy, inasmuch as physiology is based upon anatomy, and he was the distinct forerunner of Harvey, for Harvey's great exposition of the circulation of the blood did, as will be seen, for physiology what Vesalius' "Fabrica" did for anatomy; it first rendered true progress possible. And Harvey's great work was the direct outcome of Vesalius' teaching, the direct outcome and yet one reached by successive steps, steps taken by men of the Italian school, of which Vesalius was the founder and father.

Pathological anatomy had its beginning, small as it was, in this century, and it grew naturally as a result of the great anatomical zeal. It began really as a search for curiosities and gross abnormalities. The horror and dread of dissecting and thus defiling the dead were fast being stamped out, especially in the minds of earnest medical students, who had profited by Vesalius' great rebellion against the anatomy of Galen. The human body was searched for stones and concretions, which were found in the kidneys, bladder, lungs, gall-bladder, brain and other places, thus further deciding against Galen, for he insisted that there could be stones only in the kidney and bladder.

Servetus, an anatomist of a few years later, was the first to teach that the septum between the chambers of the heart was not perforated, as had been advocated. In his "Restitutio" occurs this remarkable passage:

"In order, however, that we may understand how the blood is the very life, we must first learn the generation in substance of the vital spirit itself which is composed and nourished out of the inspired air and very subtle blood. The vital spirit has its origin in the left ventricle of the heart, the lungs especially helping toward its perfection; it is a thin spirit, elaborated by the powers of heat, of a yellow (light) color, of a fiery potency so that it is, as it were, a vapor shining out of the blood, containing the substance of water, of air, and of fire. It is generated through the commingling which is effected, in the lungs, of the inspired air, with the elaborated subtle blood communicated from the right ventricle to the left. That communication does not, however, as is generally believed, take place through the median wall (septum) of the heart, but by a signal artifice the subtle blood is driven by a long passage through the lungs. It is prepared by the lungs, is rendered yellow (light) and passes from the artery-like vein. In the vein-like artery it is mixed with the inspired air, and by the expiration is cleansed from its fumes. And so at length it is drawn in, a complete mixture, by the left ventricle through the diastole, stuff fit to become the vital spirit.

"That the communication and preparation does take place in this way through the lungs is shown by the manifold conjunction and communication of the artery-like vein with the vein-like artery. This view is confirmed by the conspicuous size of the artery-like vein which would not have been made so large and so stout, and would not discharge from the heart itself such a power of very pure blood into the lungs for the mere purpose of nourishing these organs. Nor would the heart serve the lungs in this manner, especially since at an earlier date in the embryo on account of the little membranes of the heart, the lungs themselves are up to the hour of birth nourished from other sources, as Galen teaches."

These words show beyond all possible doubt that Servetus rejected wholly and unreservedly the hypothetical passage of the blood through the septum; he went far beyond the merely hinted skepticism of Vesalius. They further show that he had grasped the true features of the pulmonary circulation, the passage of the blood from the right side through the lungs to the left side. He must have attained these results by his own unaided inquiry and thought; and had he given to science the labors which he gave to theology, he might have deserved the title of one of the great physiologists of the time.

Servetus' only obscure point in his theory of the lesser circulation, as the pulmonary circulation is called, is that the blood returning from the lungs to he heart, through the pulmonary veins, contained pneuma (air) and blood. A few years later, however, this idea was dispelled by Colombo, who demonstrated, by experiment, that the pulmonary veins contained blood only. Cesalpino, a pupil of Colombo, came nearest to Harvey in describing the lesser circulation perfectly, saying that the blood anastomosed from arteries to veins in the lungs; that the blood was cooled in the lungs, and that no air was in the blood. Yet he admitted the existence of pores in the wall of the heart. He also held some correct views concerning the greater circulation.

For the performance of all dissections in the universities (they were still prohibited by the Church) papal indulgences were necessary, and these, of course, cost money. Tübingen received such an indulgence as early as 1482, while in Strassburg, in spite of papal prohibition, permission to dissect an executed criminal was granted by the magistrates in 1517. Before and after each special dissection (which was, however, a relatively infrequent occurrence) religious ceremonies in many places were considered necessary. In order that those who came into contact with it might not become "disreputable," the corpse was first made "reputable," the professor beginning the proceedings by reading a decree to that effect from the lord of the land, and then, by order of the Senate or the medical faculty, stamping upon its breast the seal of the university.

The body was then carried (upon the cover of the box in which it had been brought in) by volunteers for this service into the anatomical hall, and the cover, upon which it rested during these ceremonies, was then taken back to the executioner, who had meanwhile remained at some distance with his vehicle. Afterward entertainments, graced with music by the guilds of city fifers, trumpeters, trombone players, etc., or by "itinerant actors," were given.

Gradually, however, this folly waned, and in the second half of the century public anatomical theaters were established. Such a theater was built by Fabricius ab Aquapendente in Padua (the most popular and famous medical institution of the sixteenth century), at his own expense, in 1549. The price of a skeleton in that day was very high. Thus Heidelberg in 1569 paid $72 for a single skeleton, an immense sum in ancient values.

The higher physicians, usually of the laity and not clergy, received their education in the universities. The Italian were the best, altho France and Germany had excellent schools. The students, especially in upper Italy, were so strong and large a community in themselves, that they controlled the university, both its curriculum and the appointment of its professors. The poorer students were known as "Traveling Students." They traveled from first one Latin school to another, gradually becoming more and more fitted, and thus advanced themselves to the best university. They traveled in bands or groups, and during their pilgrimages, the worst sort of atrocities and crimes were committed. They supported life in many ways, by singing, begging and stealing. The "traveling" began in early youth, and for many students never came to an end. Some few of them became great men, but most of them fell into dissolute and vicious lives.

The physicians of this century were quite as roving as the students and professors. Surgery was largely neglected, as unbecoming a gentleman, so that it was relegated to a lower class of practitioners. The self-satisfied literati considered it an important part of their business to consult the stars for proper time to bleed and purge a patient. In general, the physicians of the so-called "long-robes" enjoyed considerable respect, but they never treated the masses, not only because they did not want to, but also because the poor people were not advanced enough to go to them.

CHAPTER VI

THE CENTURY OF SCHOOLS

THE seventeenth was the "Century of Schools," the outgrowth of the adoption into medical science of accessory natural sciences such as physics and chemistry. Germany, involved in the great thirty years' religious war, was not able to advance in the sciences as she had done in the preceding century, so other countries took the lead, especially England and Italy. The sixteenth century had been idealistic, but in the seventeenth, modern realism in all departments of thought was developed, and in the adoption of the natural sciences, often to an extreme degree, medicine gave the first instance of the modern "exact" method. Hence this century is called the greatest in the devolopment of medicine. As the accessory sciences developed more and more, they acquired an influence over and control of medicine proper to an alarming extent. Physicists and chemists took control of medicine, not only in trying to theorize and explain life's phenomena, but even to the extent of dictating methods of treatment, the real purpose of medicine being lost sight of—that is, the cure of disease and alleviation of human suffering.

One of the greatest inventions ever made, and one of especial importance in the advance of the medical sciences, was that of the microscope by Jansen in 1620. Other inventions, such as the thermometer, besides many discoveries of natural laws in physics and astronomy, had no little influence on the advancement of medicine. The natural sciences became separated in this century from philosophy and religion, and became founded upon the correct basis of observation and experimentation. Zoology and botany, after the discovery of the microscope, made rapid advances, also having their influences on anatomy, both normal and pathological. The first classification of plants led to the effort to study diseases in a similar manner.

The influence of preceding centuries was still felt, but it had been so broken, that only in certain quarters could it wreak harm. Altho Galen and the Arabians, and even Hippocrates, made themselves felt here and there, Paracelsus possessed by far the largest number of disciples. The doctrines of this mystic and pietist were gathered by Van Helmont into a system based upon chemical principles. The latter was a true son of his century, a mystic and at the same time, a realist. He studied mathematics, astronomy, philosophy, medicine and chemistry, vacillating from one to the other. The system which he founded was not an enduring one, and he had only a few followers. In his doctrine of the elements, he differs from the ancients and from Paracelsus, in regarding air and water as elements, and held that from water, everything on earth takes its origin. Man has a soul, commanding a spirit called the "Archeus," which exists also in lower animals. Besides these, there is also "gas," which arises from the action of the Archeus on the water. The active principle of the Archeus, both in health and disease, is a ferment. The "ferment" is the chief agent in digestion, adheres to the acid of the stomach, and obeys the commands of the Archeus.

Deeply impressed with this idea of the action of ferments, Van Helmont makes it the basis of his system of physiology. Nearly all the writers before him had caught hold of the phenomena of the fermenting wine-vat, as being, though mysterious in themselves, illustrative of the still more mysterious phenomena of the living body; and the old idea of the physiological spirits of the body, natural, vital and animal, was connected in its origin with this same formation of alcohol, of spirits of wine by fermentation.

His exposition of physiology is based on the theory of fermentations. The ordinary vinous fermentation gives him his initial idea; following this up, he regards all the changes in the body (not digestion only, but also others, including nutrition, impregnation and even movements) as due to the action of ferments.

He assumes the current teaching of the day to be (1) that the food absorbed from the stomach and intestine is in the liver endued with natural spirits, (2) that in the heart the natural spirits are converted into vital spirits, and (3) that in the brain the vital spirits are converted into animal spirits. He claims there are six different grades of digestion, corresponding to the days of creation.

In accordance with these cosmogenetic and physiological views, Helmont in his general pathology considers disease something active, not simply an impairment or loss of health. The general cause of disease is the fall of man. As regards special pathology, disease depends upon a perverted action of the Archeus, upon morbid ideas, or upon errors of the Archeus, as the result of which it sends the ferment of the stomach to improper places. These morbid ideas of the Archeus arise, however, from its anxiety, dread, hate, terror, anger, or passion. Fever is an expression of the sensibility of the Archeus injured by the cause of the fever. The period of chill is the expression of its passion or terror; the stadium of heat, that of its fury. On the other hand, inflammation originates in a "spina" (irritation), which springs from excitation of the Archeus, or from external causes. Among the occasional causes of diseases Van Helmont ranks demons, witches, ghosts, necromancers, and similar weird forms.

Van Helmont's special etiology gives as the cause of dropsy, hindrance to the excretion of urine by the enraged Archeus. In inflammation of the chest, where, he says, the blood coagulates outside of the vessels, the Archeus sends the acid secretion of the stomach into the lungs; in gout, into the joints, etc. In catarrh the mucus is formed from the remnants of the food sticking to the palate; vesical calculi originate in a deposit of the urinary salts. "Putrefaction" in the closed lumen of the vessels he does not recognize as the cause of disease in fevers. Altho Van Helmont made local diseases so very prominent in his system, and therefore desired to improve the condition of pathological anatomy, still, like Paracelsus, he placed no value upon normal anatomy. Surgery he claimed to be inseparable from medicine.

Altho in therapeutics Van Helmont laid great weight on universal medicine, conjurations, charms and prayer, and in his pious style claimed God's mercy as the basis of the efficacy of medicines, yet he did not despise earthly remedies, whose active principles are contrasted with the chemical constituents. He gives opium (to the stimulant effect of which, for the first time he called attention), mercury, antimony and wine in fevers (alcoholic treatment of fevers), and makes frequent use of Arcana. The latter, in his view are to be considered specially active against the wrathful, or in any way excited Archeus, against whose discontent and ill-humor and morbid ideas in general, all therapeutics were to be directed; while the remedies first mentioned, especially those of metallic origin, act in a similar way, only not specifically.

In general he lays stress upon simple chemical remedies, and abhors bleeding because of its tendency to debilitate, a tendency to which he first called attention. In the colossal abuse of bleeding which prevailed at this time, his caution on this subject merits every commendation. In the calendars, bleeding, according to the rules of astrology, was preached as a general prophylactic until the opening of the present century.

The medical studies, in which Van Helmont first found something solid to rest upon, were not the vague Galenic teachings which were all that had been offered to Paracelsus, but teachings based on the exact anatomical knowledge provided by Vesalius and his school, and on all which that knowledge carried with it. By gas, he meant, and by the introduction of the new term indicates his appreciation of the discovery of, what is now called carbonic acid gas, or carbon dioxide; and the development of a great deal of chemistry, and especially of the chemistry of living beings, has turned on the nature and properties of gases.

It was in relation to this gas that Van Helmont parts company with Paracelsus. He argues that Paracelsus was wholly wrong in maintaining that sulphur, mercury and salt were the three elements. There are, he contends, two elements only, air—that is to say, the natural atmosphere—and water. He spends much time in proving that air and water can never be changed, the one into the other; that they are distinct and never convertible; that the vapor of water is something wholly different from real air. On the other hand, by what he called water, he meant everything which is not air; he insists that all things, plants and animals, can be reduced to water, that they are in fact water endued with certain properties.

The Chemical System, founded by Sylvius (1624-1672), was based upon the elements of chemistry, the new knowledge of the circulation and the improved anatomy. It absolutely neglected the vital forces of life. It was a system of "humors." Altho Van Helmont paid little heed to that part of physiology which is derived by deductions from anatomy, by experiments on animals or by the application of mechanical principles, Sylvius was well versed in all these things, and wrote well on the circulation of the blood and on the mechanics of respiration.

The humoral physiology of Sylvius, instead of the four cardinal fluids, adopts the "triumvirate" of the saliva, the pancreatic fluid and the bile. Instead of varieties of the pneuma, it accepts the collective idea of the "vital spirits," in contradistinction to the system of Van Helmont, and from this time forward played one of the most prominent parts, and occasioned the greatest confusion, in the theoretic views of medicine. The forces were compelled to give place to the chemical process of fermentation and effervescene, the qualities, to acid and alkali (origininating in the acid or alkaline salt). Saliva and pancreatic fluid are acid. The bile is alkaline; the first affects stomach-digestion, while the two latter accomplish the digestion of the chyme into chyle and feces. In this process, an effervescence occurs and produces a kind of gas, which, in the form of voltatile spirit, with a delicate oil and salt neutralized by weak acid, enters into the composition of the chyme. Such a spirit of fermentation is also transmitted from the spleen to the blood and perfects the latter. Hence the importance of the spleen (with which the glands are connected in importance and action) becomes perfectly clear.

The blood is the headquarters for the development of the processes of healthy and a morbid life. Normally, it contains the bile already performed. This is separated in the gall-bladder, but again partially mixed in the liver with the blood, whose fluidity it serves to maintain. The blood and bile then proceed to the right side of the heart, where both (together with the chyle) bring about a vital fermentation by means of the innate heat of the latter organ. In the lungs the blood of the right heart is again cooled, and passes to the left side of the heart which, on its part, is dilated by a new "effervescence" of the blood.

The contraction of this half of the heart is now excited by means of the vital spirits, and the blood is driven into the greater circulation. These vital spirits, comparable in their nature to alcohol, are distilled in the brain (still regarded as a glandular organ), and are carried by the nerves (which were supposed to be hollow) to the whole body, in order to facilitate sensation. The vital spirits which reach the glands, by means of an acid developed from the blood, undergo here their metamorphosis into lymph. Under the form of lymph they return once more to the blood, passing from the glands into the brain, thus forming a circulation distinct from that of the blood. The milk, however, which is related to lymph, originates from the blood, which, through the influence of a mild acid prepared in the mammary gland, changes its color in that organ, just as vegetable colors are changed by the action of acids.

According to the general pathology of Sylvius, health consists in the undisturbed performance in the body of the process of fermentation, without the appearance of the acid or alkaline salt. If, however, one of the two latter salts becomes prominent, it gives rise to an acridity and furnishes the cause of diseases. The individual diseases are divided into two groups: those depending upon an acid acridity, and those originating in an alkaline acridity. The two varieties of acridity, however, are subject to numerous modifications, and thus arise subordinate classes of the above groups of diseases. The bile is an example of the principal humors; if it is alkaline, it occasions ardent and continued fever; if acid, it is the cause of engorgements.

In regard to the semeiology, diagnostics and therapeutic principles of Sylvius, the following passage furnishes some clue: "As often as the whole blood appears black, it indicates that acidity predominates; if the blood is redder, it shows that the bile in it is superabundant. In the first case, that acid in the blood must be diminished; in the second, the bile must be lessened and its power broken. If the blood, which normally is free from odor and of a sweetish taste (especially the serum), tastes salty, the alkali in the body is too pure, and when brought into contact with the acid spiritus, engenders a humor of a saline taste and prejudicial to the body; for such a taste, tho milder, may pass into the urine, but not into the serum or its products, the lymph, the pancreatic juice and the saliva. This saline taste indicates a reduction and correction of the alkali." Fever is diagnosticated by the pulse, not by the heat of the body.

Accordingly, therapeutics has two extremely simple duties: to get rid of the acid or the alkali. The first is accomplished by the administration of alkalis, the latter, by the prescription of acids. The "effervescence of the bile" and the diseases flowing therefrom are removed by cathartics. Sylvius recommended diaphoretics, absorbents and emetics, but reprehended bleeding. Opium is of service against both acid and alkali, since it tempers equally both acridity and effervescence. The general objects of therapeutics (never, alas to be accomplished) are "to maintain the strength, to remove diseases, to mitigate symptoms and to remove their causes." The stereotyped theory, and especially the stereotyped therapeutics of Sylvius gained for him a large following; but they also procured him numerous opponents, especially in later times, when his therapeutics were reproached with having during their prevalence cost, on the whole, as many human lives as the Thirty Years' War. This, under any circumstances, is an exaggerated estimate, for nature, from the most remote ages down to the present day, has preserved the sick, at least in the majority of cases, from the worst consequences of the healing art of infatuated theorists and corrupt or incapable practitioners. But Sylvius must be given credit for having brought the chemical investigation of physiological problems into line with the mechanical and physical investigation of them.

In opposition to the Chemical School, Borelli (1608-1679) formed the Mechanical or Physical School. He sought to explain most, if not all, the phenomena of the living body as mere problems of the new mathematical, mechanical and physical science. For instance, he taught that digestion is a purely mechanical process. Concerning gastric digestion itself, Borelli, with his mind directed chiefly to mechanical effects, had pointed out the great grinding, crushing force which was provided for by the muscular coats of the stomach. He calls attention to the fact "that in birds, with few exceptions, the crushing, erosion and trituration of food is effected by the muscular stomach itself, compressing one part of its horny lining against another. Thus, with the help of small hard and sharp pebbles contained in it, which served instead of teeth, the stomach, by pounding the food swallowed and rubbing its inner surfaces on this way and that, like millstones, crushed the parts of the food until they are converted into a very fine powder."

He appears to think that in most birds the digestive action is wholly mechanical, and indeed he maintained that the pebbles in the stomach might not be only mere mechanical aids, but when crushed might serve for nutriment. He admits, however, in the case of some stomachs, there is a corrosive juice. In this point, as in others, the followers of Borelli went beyond their master, and the physical school after him were prepared to deny action in all cases, and to maintain that digestion was in reality a mere trituration of the food by the muscular mill of the stomach into the creamy mass known as chyle.

In pathology Borelli was an opponent of the Chemical School, on the ground that is was demonstrable neither by common experience nor by experiment, and he denies as well any evidence that fever originates in excessive action of the heart-muscle, due to irritation of the latter by an acrid nervous-fluid. There is no such thing as corruption of the blood, and, even if there were, a stoppage of the organs of secretion is rather to be assumed. In his therapeutics Borelli considers purgation and bleeding ineffective in removing the acidity of the nervous fluid, but he expects that strengthening the organs by means of chinchona and favoring the invisible perspiration will be the more effectual in fever. He alone, too, remains true to the mechanical theory in the therapeutics.

There was one man, however, in this century of unscientific systems or schools, who steered clear of the influences of his day. He was Thomas Sydenham (1624-1689), an Englishman. His model was Hippocrates, upon whom he seems to have formed himself almost exclusively, and whose principles, with some modifications resulting from the condition of knowledge in his day—on the whole, only a few—he made his own. In pathology he was, like Hippocrates, a humorist without being a theorist, and he defended himself against those who laid this to his reproach in almost the same words used by Hippocrates. Like the latter, too (Sydenham was called the "English Hippocrates"), he knew only one standard—observation and experience—tho he was somewhat skeptical as to the certainty of their results, and, like him, he recognized nature, or the healing power of nature, as the sole, ultimate, undefined and undefinable, but (fortunately for physicians) existing and powerful assistant.

In accordance with his disposition to practical objects, Sydenham laid little weight upon anatomy and physiology, a feeling which shared with almost all great practitioners. Yet he recognized their value when not employed in the production of hypotheses based upon pure theory. The latter he rejected, tho he admitted hypotheses borrowed from practice for the sake of elucidating disease, and especially for the determination of curative indications, or of a definite therapeutics (hypotheses based upon practice).

While Medicine was thus struggling through its systems and schools, Surgery worked slowly and surely into a scientific branch free from speculation and theories. The tourniquet was invented by Morel, and the first transfusion of blood from one person to another was performed by Denis. Obstetrics advanced even more than surgery, and began finally to pass out of the hands of women into the care of men, and these simple surgeons, not physicians, contributed not a little to its improvement. Scientifically it was greatly benefited by anatomy and physiology, but practically it did not make such marked progress at first. The invention of obstetric forceps was at first of no benefit to practical obstetrics, since it was kept secret by the Chamberlen family, who invented the instrument. Seventy-five years after the occurrence of this invention, De la Motte was driven to utter the following sentence, which, even if it be just, is not particularly merciful: "He who keeps secret so beneficent an instrument as the harmless obstetric forceps, deserves to have a worm devour his vitals for all eternity, for all human science, up to the present time, has not been able to find such an instrument!"

The circulation of the blood was first correctly and distinctly set forth by William Harvey (1578-1667). He was an Englishman, who studied first at Cambridge and then went to Padua, where he worked in the study of medicine for four years. It must be remembered that Harvey had not the exact sciences of physics or of chemistry on which to base his experiments. Harvey's must be ranked the foremost master-mind, for altho Vesalius, Servetus, and Fabricius all opened new fields in the physiology of the heart and circulation, it remained for Harvey to demonstrate the great truths which his predecessors had failed to grasp. Refuting the erroneous ideas of the ancients, and with an eye upon the teachings of Aristotle, Galen, Colombo and others—the work of Servetus was unknown to him, while Aristotle and Galen were cautiously opposed—but on all new points proceeding only upon purely experimental methods, Harvey set forth the doctrine of the circulation as it is held to-day. He first presented the ancient beliefs on the subject in his wonderful paper: "As we are about to discuss the motion, action and use of the heart and arteries," he says, "it is imperative to state what has been thought of these things by others in their writings, and what has been held by the vulgar and by tradition, in order that what is true may be confirmed, and what is false set right by dissection, multiplied experience and accurate observation.

"Almost all anatomists, physicians and philosophers up to the present time have supposed, with Galen, that the object of the pulse was the same as that of respiration, and only differed in one particular, this being conceived to depend on the animal, the respiration on the vital faculty; then too, in all other respects, whether with reference to purpose or to motion, comporting themselves alike. Whence it is affirmed, as by Hieronymus Fabricius of Acquapendente, in his book on 'Respiration,' which has lately appeared that as the pulsation of the heart and arteries does not suffice for the ventilation and refrigeration of the blood, therefore were the lungs fashioned to surround the heart. From this it appears that whatever has hitherto been said upon the systole and diastole, or on the motion of the heart and arteries, has been said with especial reference to the lungs.

"But as the structure and movements of the heart differ from those of the lungs, and the motions of the arteries from those of the chest, so it seems likely that other ends and offices will thence arise, and that the pulsations and uses of the heart, likewise of the arteries, will differ in many respects from the heavings and uses of the chest and lungs. For did the arterial pulse and the respiration serve the same ends; did the arteries in their diastole take air into their cavities, as is commonly stated, and in their systole emit fuliginous vapors by the same pores of the flesh and skin; and further, did they, in the time intermediate between the diastole and the systole, contain air, and at all times either air or spirits, or fuliginous vapors, what should then be said to Galen, who wrote a book on purpose to show that by nature the arteries contained blood, and nothing but blood, and consequently neither spirits nor air, as may readily be gathered from the experiments and reasonings contained in the same book?

"Now, if the arteries are filled in the diastole with air then taken into them (a larger quantity of air penetrating when the pulse is large and full), it must come to pass that if you plunge into a bath of water or of oil when the pulse is strong and full, it ought forthwith to become either smaller or much slower, since the circumambient bath will render it either difficult or impossible for the air to penetrate. In like manner, as all the arteries, those that are deep-seated as well as those that are superficial, are dilated at the same instant and with the same rapidity, how is it possible that air should penetrate to the deeper parts as freely and quickly through the skin, flesh and other structures, as through the cuticle alone? And how should the arteries of the fetus draw air into their cavities through the abdomen of the mother and the body of the womb?

"And how should seals, whales, dolphins, and other cetaceans, and fishes of every description, living in the depths of the sea take in and emit air by the diastole and systole of their arteries through the infinite mass of water? For to say that they absorb the air that is present in the water, and emit their fumes into this medium, were to utter something like a figment. And if the arteries in their systole expel fuliginous vapors from their cavities through the pores of the flesh and skin, why not the spirits, which are said to be contained in those vessels, at the same time, since spirits are much more subtile than fuliginous vapors or smoke?

"And if the arteries take in and cast out air in the systole and diastole, like the lungs in the process of respiration, why do they not do the same thing when a wound is made in one of them, as in the operation of arteriotomy? When the windpipe is divided, it is sufficiently obvious that the air enters and returns through the wound by two opposite movements; but when an artery is divided, it is equally manifest that blood escapes in one continuous stream, and that no air either enters or issues. If the pulsations of the arteries fan and refrigerate the several parts of the body, as the lungs do the heart, how comes it, as is commonly said, that the arteries carry the vital blood into the different parts, abundantly charged with vital spirits, which cherish the heat of these parts, sustain them when asleep, and recruit them when exhausted?

"How should it happen that, if you tie the arteries, immediately the parts not only become torpid and frigid, and look pale, but at length cease even to be nourished? This, according to Galen, is because they are deprived of the heat which flowed through all parts from the heart, as its source; whence it would appear that the arteries rather carry warmth to the parts than serve for any fanning or refrigeration. Besides, how can their diastole draw spirits from the heart to warm the body and its parts, and means of cooling them from without? Still further, altho some affirm that the lungs, arteries and heart have all the offices, they yet maintain that the heart is the workshop of the spirits, and that the arteries contain and transmit them; denying, however, in opposition to the opinion of Columbus, that the lungs can either make or contain spirits. They then assert, with Galen, against Erasistratus, that it is the blood, not spirits, which is contained in the arteries.

"Nor let any one imagine that the uses of the pulse and the respiration are the same, because, under the influences of the same causes, such as running, anger, the warm bath, or any other heating thing, as Galen says, they become more frequent and forcible together. For not only is experience in opposition to this idea, tho Galen endeavors to explain it away, when we see that with excessive repletion the pulse beats more forcibly, while the respiration is diminished in amount; but in young persons the pulse is quick, while respiration is slow. So it is also in alarm and amid care, and under anxiety of mind; sometimes, too, in fevers, the pulse is rapid, but the respiration is slower than usual.

"These and other objections of the same kind may be urged against the opinions mentioned. Nor are the views that are enertained of the offices and pulse of the heart, perhaps, less bound up with great and most inextricable difficulties. The heart, it is vulgarly said, is the fountain and workshop of the vital spirits, the center from which life is dispensed to the several parts of the body. Yet it is denied that the right ventricle makes spirits, which is rather held to supply nourishment to the lungs. For these reasons it is maintained that fishes are without any right ventricle (and indeed every animal wants a right ventricle which is unfurnished with lungs), and that the right ventricle is present solely for the sake of the lungs.

"Moreover, when they appoint the pulmonary artery, a vessel of great size, with the coverings of an artery, to none but a kind of private and single purpose (that, namely, of nourishing the lungs), why should the pulmonary vein, which is scarcely so large, which has the coats of a vein, and is soft and lax, be presumed to be made for many—three or four different—uses? For they will have it that air passes through this vessel from the lungs into the left ventricle; that fuliginous vapors escape by it from the heart into the lungs; and that a portion of the spirituous blood is distributed to the lungs for their refreshment.

"If they will have it that fumes and air—fumes flowing from, air proceeding toward, the heart—are transmitted by the same conduit, I reply, that nature is not wont to construct but one vessel, to contrive but one way for such contrary motions and purposes, nor is anything of the kind seen elsewhere.

"Since, therefore, from the foregoing considerations and many others, to the same effect, it is plain that what has heretofore been said concerning the motion and function of the heart and arteries must appear obscure, inconsistent, or even impossible to him who carefully considers the subject, it will be proper to look more narrowly into the matter to contemplate the motion of the heart and arteries, not only in man, but in all animals that have hearts; and also, by frequent appeals to vivisection, and much ocular inspection, to investigate and discern the truth."

Harvey divided the circulation into three sections: the lesser, the greater and that of the heart itself. In his prolonged investigations he made use of both warm and cold blooded animals, but differed from our "exact" investigators of the present day in not describing minutely each individual experiment, but contenting himself with adducing his results and leaving to deduction its just place. He computed the mass of the blood, and thus proved that there must be a circulation, for all the blood could not be employed in nutrition, nor could it all be newly supplied by the absorption of nutriment. Of "spiritus" he said that he had never found anything of the kind in his dissections. He still lacked, however, the intermediate bond of the capillary zone. In place of this he assumed larger porosites of the flesh and vessels, tho he also employed the term "capillaries." He still regards the heart as the place for the improvement of the blood and the renewal of its strength, and calls it "the sun of the microcosm, the beginning of life, the household-god of the body, the author of everything, the foundation of life."

He goes on to describe his experiments on animals and to prove his assertions. "In the first place, then, when the chest of a living animal is laid open and the capsule that immediately surrounds the heart is slit up or removed, the organ is seen now to move, now to be at rest; there is a time when it moves, and a time when it is motionless. These things are more obvious in the colder animals, such as toads, frogs, serpents, small fishes, crabs, shrimps, snails and shellfish. They also become more distinct in warm-blooded animals, such as the dog and hog, if they be attentively noted when the heart begins to flag, to move more slowly, and, as it were to die; the movements then become slower and rarer, the pauses longer, by which it is made much more easy to perceive and unravel what the motions really are, and how they are performed. In the pause, as in death, the heart is soft, flaccid, exhausted, lying, as it were at rest.

"In the motion, and interval in which this is accomplished, three principal circumstances are to be noted: 1. That the heart is erected, and rises upward to a point, so that at this time it strikes against the breast and the pulse is felt externally. 2. That it is everywhere contracted, but more especially toward the sides, so that it looks narrower, relatively longer, more drawn together. The heart of an eel, taken out of the body of the animal and placed upon the table or the hand, shows these particulars; but the same things are manifest in the hearts of all small fishes and of those colder animals where the organ is more conical or elongated. 3. The heart being grasped in the hand, is felt to become harder during its action. Now, this hardness proceeds from tensions, precisely as when the forearm is grasped, its tendons are perceived to become tense and resilient when the fingers are moved. 4. It may further be observed in fishes and the colder-blooded animals, such as frogs, serpents, etc., that the heart, when it moves, becomes of a paler color, when quiescent of a deeper blood-red color.

"From these particulars it appears evident to me that the motion of the heart consists in a certain universal tension—both contraction in the line of the fibers and constriction in every sense. It becomes erect, hard, and of diminished size during its action; the motion is plainly of the same nature as that of the muscles when they contract in the line of their sinews and fibers; for the muscles, when in action, acquire vigor and tenseness, and from soft become hard, prominent; and thickened; and in the same manner the heart.

"We are therefore authorized to conclude that the heart, at the moment of its action, is at once constricted on all sides, rendered thicker in its parietes and smaller in its ventricles, and so made apt to project or expel its charge of blood. This, indeed, is made sufficiently manifest by the preceding fourth observation, in which we have seen that the heart, by squeezing out the blood that it contains, becomes paler, and then when it sinks into repose and the ventricle is filled anew with blood, that the deeper crimson color returns. But no one need remain in doubt of the fact, for if the ventricle be pierced the blood will be seen to be forcibly projected outward upon each motion or pulsation when the heart is tense.

"These things, therefore, happen together or at the same instant: the tension of the heart, the pulse of its apex, which is felt externally by its striking against the chest, the thickening of its parietes, and the forcible expulsion of the blood it contains by the constriction of its ventricles.

"And now I may be allowed to give in brief my view of the circulation of the blood, and to propose it for general adoption. Since all things, both argument and ocular demonstration, show that the blood passes through the lungs and heart by the force of the ventricles, and is sent for distribution to all parts of the body, where it makes its way into the veins and porosities of the flesh, and then flows by the veins from the circumference on every side to the center, from the lesser to the greater veins, and is by them finally discharged into the vena cava and right auricle of the heart, and this in such a quantity or in such a flux and reflux thither by the arteries, hither by the veins, as cannot possibly be supplied by the ingesta, and is much greater than can be required for mere purposes of nutrition, it is absolutely necessary to conclude that the blood in the animal body is impelled in a circle, and is in a state of ceaseless motion; that this is the act or function which the heart performs by means of its pulse; and that it is the sole and only end of the motion and contraction of the heart.

"But the following matter seems worthy of consideration, the reason, namely, why veins when ligatured swell on the far side and not on the near side of the ligature. This is a fact well known by experience to those who let blood; for they place the ligature on the near side of the place of incision, not on the far side, because the veins swell on the far side, not on the near side of the ligature. But exactly the contrary ought to happen if the movement of the blood and the spirits took place in the direction from the viscera to all parts of the body. When a channel is interrupted, the flow beyond the interruption ceases; the swelling of the veins therefore ought to be on the near side of the ligature."

Harvey erred in subordinate points—*e.g.*, in respect to the quantity of blood driven into the arteries at each systole of the heart, which he assumed to be half an ounce—but even if his anatomical description of the structure of the heart was insufficient and, indeed, imperfect, he was certainly the first who introduced the heart into its right place in the circulation in accordance with its mechanical significance and action—an advance which cannot be disputed or denied him. The main facts of his exposition remained quite indisputable, altho in his own day they were heavily assailed, and these accessory matters were eagerly utilized as a means of attack. The previous doctrine of the importance of the liver, and of the "spirits" in the heart, was first overthrown by him, and with it fell the four immemorial fundamental humors and qualities.

That so important a discovery, which cleared up the ancient and time-honored obscurities and overturned the whole physiological and philosophical foundations of the medicine of the past, by certain results gained through the inductive method, necessarily created among medical men both opponents and partizans in great number, is self-evident. It is a fashion to speak of Harvey as "the immortal discoverer of the circulation"; but the real character of his work is put in a truer light when it is said he was the first to demonstrate the circulation of the blood.

His demonstration was the death-blow to the doctrine of the "spirits." The names, it is true, survived for long afterward, but the names were henceforward devoid of any really essential meaning. For the view of the natural and vital spirits was based on the supposed double supply of blood to all the tissues of the body, the supply by the veins carrying natural spirits and the supply by the arteries carrying vital spirits. The essential feature of Harvey's new view was that the blood through the body, passing from arteries to veins in the tissues, and from veins to arteries through the lungs and heart, suffering changes in the substance and pores of the tissues, changes in the substances and pores of the lungs.

The new theory of the circulation made for the first time possible true conceptions of the nutrition of the body, it cleared the way for the chemical appreciation of the uses of blood, it afforded a basis which had not existed before for an understanding of how the life of any part, its continued existence and its power to do what it has to do in the body, is carried on by the help of the blood. And in this, perhaps, more than its being a true explanation of the special problem of the heart and the blood-vessels, lies its vast importance.

The anatomists of the sixteenth century, and of the early part of the seventeenth century, were content, like their forefathers, to carry on their studies with the naked eye, unassisted by any optical instruments. Hence their statements as to the finer structure of the various organs and parts of the body were necessarily vague and incomplete. They could tease certain parts more or less completely into strands of greater or less thickness, and hence could speak of fibers and of fibrous structure. They recognized skins and membranes of various thickness. They could distinguish what is now called fatty or adipose tissue by means of its gross features. And they could follow out the blood-vessels and later on the lymphatic vessels until they were lost to view as minute channels.

Beyond this, they were content to speak of that part of the substance of an organ which could not be split into fibers, and into which the minute vessels seemed to disappear, as "parenchyma," using the word introduced in ancient times by Erasistratus, but no longer attaching to the word the original meaning of something poured out from the veins. By parenchyma they simply meant the parts which were not distinctly made up of fibers and which in most cases at least were porous. Thus Harvey speaks of the blood which flows along the pulmonary artery as being discharged into the porous parenchyma of the lungs and gathered up thence by the beginnings of the pulmonary veins. The histology, if the word may be so used, of these older writers was of a simple kind.

It was only a short while later that Marcello Malpighi (1628-1694), a professor in Bologna University, discovered what Harvey had failed to explain—namely, the transition of blood from arteries to veins by means of the capillary system. He was the first who, calling into his aid the newly invented microscope, opened up the way for a true grasp of the minute structure of the tissues and organs of the animal body, and in so doing opened up also a new branch of physiology. He was the first Histologist, and with the new histology came new ideas of the functions of many important parts of the body.

The microscope revealed to Malpighi features of structure transcending mere mechanical notions. He saw that the tissues in their minuter structure were governed by laws of their own, by laws different from those which determined the uses of machines; and thus there came to him the new conception of an animal morphology. In his brief epistles, Malpighi announced two discoveries of fundamental importance. In the first letter he described the vesicular nature of the lung and showed how the divisions of the windpipe ended in the dilated air vesicles. He thus for the first time supplied an anatomical basis for the true conception of the respiratory process.

A little later he turned his attention to the simpler lung of the frog, and in this he had the happiness, calling into his aid the microscope, to see that minute but definite channels, the channels which we now call capillaries, joined the endings of the minute arteries to the beginnings of the minute veins. This was the first observation of the capillaries. It made Harvey's work complete.

In another letter he says: "And I myself, in the omentum of the hedgehog, in a blood-vessel which ran from one collection of fat to another opposite it, saw globules of fat, of a definite outline, reddish in color. They presented a likeness to a chaplet of red coral." He mistook, however, the nature of what he saw. What evidently were blood corpuscles he thought to be fat cells passing from the fatty tissue into the current of the blood.

After this, the first real accurate description of the red corpuscles is ascribed to Leeuwenhoek, who in 1674, in the Philosophical Transactions, gave an account of the red blood corpuscles in man, and in various papers carefully described the blood corpuscles of different animals, showing that while circular in mammals, they are oval in birds, frogs and fishes, and proving that in all cases the redness of blood is due to these red bodies.

Malpighi was no mere professor. His time was not spent wholly in the laboratory and lecture room. He was actively engaged in healing the sick; he was as familiar with the phenomena of disease as with the phenomena of the healthy living being. He brought to bear on the former the same clear intellect which he turned toward the latter, seeking to find out the causes of the events which he witnessed. He was as busy in the post-mortem room as in the dissecting theater, and his writings on the character and causes of disease justify the claiming for him the merit of having laid the foundation of scientific pathology.

Malpighi may also be regarded as, almost in the same degree, the founder of that great and important branch of biological science which is known as embryology.

Within a few years of the publication of Harvey's book anatomists became aware of a new set of vessels, of whose existence no one before had dreamed, vessels neither arteries nor veins; vessels containing not blood, but either a milky or a clear limpid fluid, and carrying their contents not to but away from the tissues, carrying them, moreover, not to that great organ, the liver, which in the old view was the chief seat of all concoction, but directly into the venous blood stream and so to the heart, from thence to be distributed all over the body. That such a conception almost at once found general acceptance is, as we have just said, a striking proof of how rapidly and profoundly Harvey's work had influenced the views of physiologists. These were the vessels of the lymphatic system.

Aselli detected the presence of valves in these vessels and recognized that they hindered the backward flow. He saw clearly, indeed, that his newly discovered vessels were channels for conveying the chyle, the elaborated contents of the intestine, away from the intestine; but influenced, doubtless, by the accepted view that all the absorbed food must be carried to the liver, to be there elaborated into blood, he went wrong as to the ultimate course taken by these vessels; he thought he could trace them into the liver. It may here be noted in passing that Aselli in his treatise speaks of and indeed figures the cluster of lymphatic glands lying in the mesentery as "the pancreas"; and this cluster of glands was afterward often spoken of as "the pancreas of Aselli."

State medicine, altho much advanced in the sixteenth century, was even more in the seventeenth, by the physicians of all civilized countries. Medical police were organized for public hygiene, giving out plague ordinances, advice relative to clothing and food, inspection of provisions, etc. The epidemic diseases of this period were many and very destructive to human life. Plague was, perhaps, the worst, altho typhus fever raged fiercely, especially during the Thirty Years' War. Malarial disease, dysentery, ergotism, scarlet fever and smallpox were others which carried off many people.

The clerical element having entirely disappeared from the ranks of the public phycicians, there was more opportunity for improvement in the standing of the lay profession. A special characteristic of the seventeenth century physician, in addition to their great zeal for science, is found in their frequent and intimate occupation with chemistry, mathematics and natural philosophy.

One of the old state books of that century enumerates the following practitioners of medicine: I. The Medical Profession proper: a. Medici in general: commissioned court, field, hospital and plague medici. b. Surgeons, barbers, regimental surgeons, oculists, herniotomists, lithotomists, bath-keepers. c. Superior sworn midwives, nurses. d. Apothecaries, druggsits, confectioners and grocers.

II. Sundry Imposters and Pretended Physicians: Old women, village priests, hermits, quacks, executioners, calf-doctors, Jews, vagrants, musicians, rat-catchers, jugglers and gipsies.

Instruction in medicine assumed better conditions. Italy, which had for so long held first place in educational matters, lost hold, the lead being taken by France and the Netherlands. Clinical and bedside instruction were taken up and tried, but not with much success. Students still had some influence in the management of their curriculi, but not to the same extent of the preceding century. Anatomy was studied more frequently upon human bodies, so that dissections were performed in most universities. Occupation with practical anatomy was, of course, still regarded by the higher physicians as a business unworthy of them. They left it to the inferior surgeons, and merely pointed out and explained themselves with a staff what the surgeon had exposed. Thus the surgeons were the best anatomists and teachers of anatomy.

CHAPTER VII

THE PERIOD OF SYSTEMATIZATION

It has been said that the eighteenth century was a continuation of the idealistic tendency of the sixteenth, interrupted by the seventeenth, which was not idealistic. The masses were released from most of their bonds and fetters, and the principles of independence and free right of develpoment were established. The tendency was humanitarian rather than humanistic, revolutionary rather than reformative. The numerous wars had no great effect on the development of general medicine, except surgery. It is in Germany, France and England that works of real permanence are found, the revival of experimental physiology, developments of physical diagnosis and scientific study of statistics.

In the eighteenth century is found an age of systems and theories, the outgrowth of the vast amount of new material gathered from the new sciences. These systems lived a short life, and in that brief span contributed somewhat to the advancement of medical science. No system, even if it be wrong, can retard the progress of medicine, unless, like the Galenic, it be prolonged over a great space of time. The saving grace of the systems of the eighteenth century lies in the fact that they did not degenerate into pure theory, but the art of observation was cultivated in a prominent manner, and was practiced carefully and soberly, aided by reason and the use of the natural senses.

The Eclectic System was founded by Boerhaave (1668-1738), who was one of the greatest of modern scientists. He was a capable chemist, and so popular a lecturer in medical subjects that hearers came from all over the world. He was a splendid clinical instructor, and as a practitioner is considered by Bass the most famous man of his age. He was the first to give separate lectures on ophthalmology and to use the magnifying glass in examining the eye. His was a great character, free from vanity and selfishness.

The doctrines of Boerhaave do not form any really new system, but rather include many ideas of the earlier systems. According to Boerhaave, disease is that condition in which the bodily "actions" are disturbed or unsettled, and take place only with difficulty. The reverse of this condition furnishes his conception in health. Fever is the effort of nature to ward off death. Hence the nervous fluid flows too quickly into the muscles, and the heart contracts too rapidly, so that the blood flows too rapidly in the capillaries.

Digestion, like the circulation, is explained on mechanical principles. He says: "The antecedent causes of this acid acridity are: 1. Food consisting of farinaceous, acid and juicy, fresh, raw, fermenting or fermented portions of vegetables. 2. The want of good blood in the body which receives this nutriment. 3. Debility of the fibrous tissue, the vessels and intestines. 4. Lack of animal motion.

"Primarily, it has its seat chiefly in the localities of primary digestion, whence it slowly infects the blood and finally all the humors. It occasions acid eructations, hunger, pain in the stomach and bowels, flatulence, spasms, sluggishness of and various changes in the bile, and acid chyle. In the blood, it produces pallor, acid, chyle, and hence in women milk too prone to acidity, sour perspiration, acid saliva, and thus itching obstructions, pustules, ulcers; then excitement of the brain and nerves with resulting convulsions, disturbance of the circulation, and finally death. Hence its effects may be perfectly predicted and the mode of cure may be known. The cure is effected: 1. By animal and vegetable food opposed to acidity. 2. By the fluids of birds of prey, which fluids resemble good blood. 3. By strengthening remedies. 4. By active movement. 5. By medicines which absorb, dilute, weaken or change the acid. The selection, preparation, dose and timely employment of these remedies depend upon the judgment of the physician as to the disease, its seat, the condition of the patient, etc. Hence it is clear why some diseases are common in boys, the indolent young women and certain artizans." In forming his system, Boerhaave was not mindful of the doctrines of Hoffmann, and particularly of the influence which the brain and nerves exercise over the operations of the animal economy, altho he never fully appreciated their power.

In therapeutics, besides his efforts to sweeten the acid, to purify the stomach, and to get rid of the acridities, Boerhaave claimed Hippocrates and Sydenham as his models, but without being by any means exempt from hypotheses in his determination of the indications. He was, however, for this time, comparatively simple in his actual therapeutic prescriptions, altho the latter were often enough odd in their character, as the blood of birds of prey. His medicines were, at all events, less effective than his personal presence, which indeed is true, "mutatis mutandis," of all treatment. It was Boerhaave who first permanently established the clinical method of instruction, and its diffusion was due to his pupils, particularly Haller and Van Swieten. His influence in a medico-historical point of view is greater than his real scientific importance would warrent.

George Stahl (1660-1734), a profound thinker, founded a system distinctly independent. It is dynamico-organic, piestic and antagonistic. He makes the soul or "anima" the supreme principle. Stahl put forward and brilliantly maintained the view that all the chemical events of the living body, even tho they might superficially resemble, were at the bottom wholly different from the chemical changes taking place in the laboratory, since in the living body all chemical changes were directly governed by the sensitive soul, "anima sensitiva," which pervaded all parts and presided over all events. This resembles the "archeus" of Van Helmont. His fundamental position is that between living things, so long as they are alive, however simple, and non-living things, however composite, however complex in their phenomena, there is a great gulf fixed. The former, so long as they are alive, are actuated by an immaterial agent, the sensitive soul; the latter are not. Further, the living body is fitted for special ends and purposes; the living body does not exist for itself; it is constituted to be the true and continued minister of the soul. The body is made for the soul; the soul not made for and is not the product of the body. When the body is diseased, the symptoms are the manifestation of the soul trying to restore normal movements in the organism.

As Baas says: "With this object the soul is frequently compelled to make powerful exertions. As the soul ordinarily employs the circulation and the capacity of the parts of the body for contraction and relaxation (tonus) as the route and instrument of its influence upon the body, so also in disease, where, in consequence of the necessarily hastened and increased activity of the soul, either the pulse is accelerated, the temperature rises, etc., in a word, 'fever' makes its appearance, or spasmodic movements, 'convulsions,' are developed. In the false movements within the organism lies also the main cause of sickness, but not in the numerous external influences assumed by others. Were the latter the case, the frequency of sickness and the number of diseases would necessarily be much greater than they, in fact, are.

"Since, too, the soul governs the organisms chiefly by way of the circulation, disturbances and stagnation in the latter are also the main causes of disease. These disturbances arise most frequently from 'plethora,' which plays an important rôle in the system and the therapeutics of Stahl. To get rid of this plethora, the soul employs the means mentioned above; either fever, with its heat, by which the blood is imperceptibly driven out or dissolved, or convulsive movements, by which the blood is driven into certain parts and there visibly discharged.

"In childhood, plethora produces a pressure of blood toward the head, and the soul, as a compensation for this, provides a hemorrhage from the nose. During youth this blood-pressure is directed rather

THE PERIOD OF SYSTEMATIZATION

toward the chest, and is equalized by hemoptysis and pneumorrhagia and bleeding 'piles,' which Stahl considers a safety-valve of the utmost importance. From this time dates the very high estimation of 'hemorrhoids' and "hemorrhoidal impulses,' the 'hemorrhoidal flow' which prevailed among physicians until a very recent period, and is the rule among the laity even at the present day. When this hemorrhoidal flow stagnates, it is by all means to be again started up. In the stoppage of this flow lie the chief causes of hypochondria and melancholy, as well as of all chronic diseases."

"Fever, as we have seen, was for Stahl a salutary effort of the soul to preserve the body. This was true even of intermittent fever (seen in malaria), and accordingly he never suppressed this disease with cinchona. On the other hand, inflammation was, in his view, a stagnation of the blood (an iatro-mechanical idea—and such ideas are accepted by him also in other directions), under the forms of erysipelas, phlegmon and its suppuration."

Stahl scorned anatomy and physiology, thinking them beneath his dignity, and swore boldly by the maxim that good theorists (among whom he was one of the chief) may be bad practitioners. He says, in sarcasm: "The structure of the meandering passages in the ear, of the anvil, the hammer, and the stirrup and—what a noble discovery!—the round ossicle (all bones for the mechanism of hearing), if it were unknown, would render the physical knowledge of the body very defective. But medicine, that is, practical medicine, profits by this knowledge precisely as much as by the knowledge of the snow which fell ten years ago!"

In therapeutics, Stahl placed at the head the healing power of nature, which is identical with his "soul." "It is the simple truth that man has his physician in himself, that nature is the physician of diseases and offers a better prospect of curing diseases than the most successful apparatus of our art." For the rest, he follows his system here, too, with the utmost strictness. The soul, as it is the cause of all diseases, so it is that which cures them. Therapeutics can, or rather should, act upon this alone; that is, upon the "movements" occasioned by it. If too strong, they must be restrained; if too feeble or utterly wanting, we must endeavor to strengthen them or to call them forth.

Venesection, of which Stahl made excessive use in acute as well as in chronic cases, is to be considered the main check upon these movements. He even recommended venesection as a preventive or prophylactic measure twice a year, and by it the people have been served and injured down to modern times. Beside venesection he ranked care to reëstablish the hemorrhoidal flow by the use of irritating drugs, which Stahl in other circumstances discarded. To these measures were added his "balsamic pills" (aloes, hellebore, etc.), stomach-powder, etc., rostrums which brought him a lucrative business. In addition Stahl gave purgatives and emetics, diaphoretics and especially alternatives, including his favorite saltpeter. He discarded, however, many effective drugs (and particularly the poisons), above all the Cinchona (because by its astringent properties it suppressed the febrile state, which was in itself sanative), opium and ferruginous preparations and mineral waters, because Hoffmann recommended them.

Stahl's teaching, as summarized by Foster, was briefly this: "Learn as much as you can of chemical and physical processes, and in so far as the phenomena of the living body exactly resemble chemical and and physical events occurring in non-living bodies, you may explain them by chemical and physical laws. But do not conclude that that which you see taking place in a non-living body, will take place in a living body, for the chemical and physical phenomena of the latter are modified by the soul. The events of the body may be rough hewn by chemical and physical forces, but the soul will shape them to its own ends and will do that by its instrument, motion."

It was the reaction against the exclusively mechanical and chemical theories of the seventeenth century and has fulfilled its mission in the history of culture. As Spiess says in defense of Stahl's theories, "It was enough for Stahl, in contrast to his contemporaries, who were all too prone to utilize the laws of mechanics then alone known and the trifling chemical knowledge of that period, of which they were proud, and which they employed entirely too extensively in the explanation of the phenomena of life—it was sufficient, I say, for Stahl to have rescued life as a specific active force, at least for organized beings." He thus stands forth as the founder of "animism," which doctrine, tho his sensitive soul fell back later to the lower stage of "a vital principle," maintained itself in many minds through the two succeeding centuries and exists at the present day.

Friedrich Hoffmann (1660-1742) was the founder of the so-called Mechanico-dynamic System, which was held in high esteem by the most eminent physicians of that time. The train of thought in Hoffmann's system is as follows: "Our knowledge is finite, rooted in the senses and limited to what is perceptible by the senses; all final causes, however, are inscrutable. Forces and influences beyond the range of the senses, cognizable by metaphysical speculation, lie without its limits. Forces are inherent in matter and express themselves as mechanical movements, determinable by mass, number and weight. In the body also these forces express themselves by movement, as action and reaction, contraction and relaxation, "tonus." Life is movement, especially movement of the heart; death the cessation of the movements of this organ, as the result of which putrefaction begins. Death and life are mechanical phenomena. Health is synonymous with the regular occurrence of the movements; disease a disturbance of the same. The contraction of the heart, the blood-vessels and animated fibers set in motion the circulation of the blood and effect regular secretion and excretion, the chief phenomena of health. Digestion is the solution of food by means of the saliva and warmth, perspiration an effect of heat alone, and takes place not only through the pores, but also through the smallest vessels of the skin.

"The body is precisely like a hydraulic machine. Its movements are effected and maintained by that dynamico-material principle of fluid, but extremely volatile, constitution, 'the ether' (synonymous with nervous ether, nervous spirit, 'sensitive soul,' the pneuma of the ancient physicians). This acts in accordance with the laws, not of ordinary mechanics but of a higher and still uninvestigated science, and is in very small part derived from the atmosphere, but chiefly secreted from the blood in the brain. The 'movements' of the latter organ drive it, by way of the nerve tubules, throughout the whole body. This motor principle possesses conception and sensation and is the soul which alone perceives things. It forms and maintains the body in accordance with its idea, and each special particle of it has a conception of the composition and mechanism of the body. The chief reservoir and center of the ether is the medulla oblongata at the base of the brain."

Hoffmann's therapy was simple and designedly poor in drugs (according to the ideas of that time), but by no means free from theoretical views. The physician has, before all else, to regulate the disturbed movements, for nature is frequently not able to do this. But there are diseases which cure other diseases; that is, fever cures spasms. Hoffmann divided drugs (which he held worked under mechanical laws) into those which strengthen or weaken, alter or evacuate. He was especially partial to the use of his own remedies and wine, particularly Hochheimer, which he considered the best of all wines, as the English, at his instance, do at the present day. Camphor he strongly recommended; likewise mineral waters, cold water, Seidlitz salt, cinchona and iron. He often practiced venesection and laid great stress upon the observance of prescribed diet, as absolute diet, milk diet, wine diet, exercise, etc. Poisons in general he rejected; the preparations of lead he absolutely discarded for internal use and desired to limit the employment of opium.

William Cullen (1712-1790), a Scotchman, was at first a barber, then surgeon, and after years of hardship he finally got his education at the university. Then for years he was a professor of chemistry and medicine. He founded a system of nervous pathology. The main foundation of Cullen's system is formed by the living solid parts of the body, not the fluids; the chief agents are the nerves. An undefined dynamic something, which is different from Hoffmann's material ether and the supernatural soul of Stahl and which Cullen calls "the nervous force," "nervous activity," "the nervous principle," is the proper life-giving element. He also calls this principle "the animal force" or "energy of the brain," in which he also includes the spinal cord. He believed that the soul of man is inseparably united with his brain.

The nervous principle produces spasm and atony. The former is not, however, dependent upon increased nervous activity, but may also originate from feebleness of the brain, which is the center of nervous activity. The nerves are the conductors of the activity of the brain. Everything is effected through the brain and the nerves, and everything, including the causes of disease, works upon both of these. The causes of disease are chiefly of a debilitating character, but they awaken reaction and the healing power of nature. Fever is such a reparative effort of nature, even in its cold stage, and its cause is diminished energy of the brain, often united with a kind of delirium, due to a contemporaneous spasm of the extremities of the vessels, which produces a reflex acceleration of the heart and a stimulation of the arteries.

The blood plays no part in fever, which is excited by weakening influences, as fright, cold, intemperance, the emanations of marshes or human beings, etc. Besides the spasm of the vascular extremities and the feebleness of the brain, there is also an accessory atony, which is propagated by sympathy to the tunics of the stomach and occasions the loss of appetite associated with all fevers. Both spasm and atony continue until the brain has recovered its ordinary activity, a result due to the increased activity of the heart, and recognized by the establishment of perspiration.

Cullen's explanation of the gout was famous. According to his view, this disease depends upon an atony of the stomach or organs of digestion, against which is set up periodically a reparative effort in the form of an inflammation of the joints. Gout is a general disease, but there is no gouty material. His therapeutics were simple, and, from his renunciation of the previous abuse of venesection, they were very salutary.

Anton de Haën (1704-1776), of The Hague, a pupil of Boerhaave, was the founder of the old Vienna school, a union of Hippocrates, Sydenham and Boerhaave. Its chief merits are in its practical and diagnostic services and in its generally sober observations. He believed, like Hippocrates, in the simplest possible treatment, united with careful observation. Nature must not be disturbed by medicines of a powerful action. He warmly embraced hygiene and prophylactic views. He reintroduced the thermometer and demon-

THE PERIOD OF SYSTEMATIZATION

strated that in the cold stage of fever an elevation of temperature, often considerable, could occur.

The school of Montpellier, led by Borden, maintained the existence of a general life of the body, which resulted from the harmonious working of the individual lives and powers of all its organs. These organs are associated one with the other, but each has a different function. The most important organs are the heart, stomach and brain. These regulate the life of the other organs. From them proceed sensibility and motion, the two chief phenomena of life. The nerves are the chief organs which, with the brain as their center, distribute and regulate motion and sensation throughout the body, but do not act in conformity with chemical and physical laws. The stomach presides over nutrition, the heart propels the blood and chyle through the body. Health is the undisturbed circulation of motion and sensation from and to the three centers of the body. There is no such thing as perfect health, for it fluctuates from moment to moment. Secretions and excretions, sleep and waking, muscular activity, the employment of the external and internal senses, all are subordinated to these three chief organs.

Animal magnetism was a theory advanced by Franz Mesmer (1734-1815), later called mesmerism. He claimed that there was some "magnetic fluid" existing everywhere throughout the world, and, of course, in man also, and this overflowed from the hand with a healing influence upon others, and that the sick were particularly susceptible. He erected a private institution, where he treated simpletons and credulous old ladies. He later went to Paris, where he was "the rage" for a long while and to the betterment of his pocketbook. Mesmerism is merely the application of hypnotism, such as may be practiced by any one. It is the result of a play on the imagination of the patient, who thereby renders himself more susceptible to suggestions which the hypnotist may offer. It has lately been applied to certain forms of hysteria and nervousness with great success.

Galvanism was considered the genuine "vital force," the positive pole being identified with irritability, the negative sensibility, and the theory was carried so far as to declare man the irritating and active pole and woman the sensitive and passive! Galvani himself had located the seat of electricity in the brain and he held that by means of the nerve-tubes it reached the whole body and especially the muscles, producing in them contractions analogous to the accidentally discovered twitchings of the frog. Disease was the disturbance of this electricity in the body.

Chemical and physical theories arose as the result of the advances made in chemistry and physics. The Phlogistic Theory is the theory of animal heat. According to this the free heat existing in the inspired air is incorporated with the body by means of respiration, and at the same time "phlogiston" is removed from the blood. Disease is the result of too much or too little heat. Against this arose the Antiphlogistic Theory, in which the newly discovered oxygen was accepted as the "vital force." Disease depended upon the appropriation of too much or too little oxygen.

The Brunonian System, founded by John Brown (1735-1788), was the most brilliant of the eighteenth century. According to Brown, life is not a natural condition, but an artificial and necessary result of irritations constantly in action. All living beings, therefore, tend constantly toward death. That irritations can compel life is their characteristic. Living beings, too, are capable of excitability, which is, indeed, inscrutable in its nature, but its seat in the muscles and the medulla of the nerves may be demonstrated. The latter is the cause of the processes which take place in the body, whether sound or diseased, and consequently of life itself.

Irritations are of two kinds, external and internal. To the external belong food, blood, the fluids in general, warmth, air, etc.; the functions of thought, feeling, muscular activity, etc., are to be considered internal irritations, which have the same action as the external. Moreover, irritations are general or local. General irritations arouse excitement in the whole body; the local act first of all upon an individual part and subsequently upon the whole body. Health is an intermediate grade of excitement, diseases too high or too low a grade. The two are not conditions substantially different, but simple gradations of one and the same action upon the excitability.

Excitement is divided into different grades according to the degree of action of the irritation. The extreme grades of this scale are like the exhaustion and accumulation of irritability as the result of too great or too little power of the irritants and are death. The intermediate result is ordinary weakness (asthenia), either direct or indirect. Direct asthenia depends upon the presence of an excess of excitability, accordingly upon too great an accumulation of excitability the result of a deficiency of irritation. It is to be removed by new irritations, which reduce that excess to the normal proportion of health. Indirect asthenia is to be referred to an excess of irritation, by which excitability becomes exhausted. It is to be relieved by opposing a weaker irritation to the too strong causative irritation. The grades of excitability are always in inverse proportion to the excitement. Most diseases are dependent upon asthenia. Sthenia is more rarely a cause of disease and is the result of a less powerful irritation.

Brown's diagnosis requires no special symptomatology, but simply a consideration of the antecedent injuries and the earlier condition of the health, without any distinction between local and general diseases. It demands only the determination of the grade of diseases in accordance with the strength or weakness of the acting irritation. For this purpose some pupils of Brown drew up a kind of barometer of disease.

Like the system of Asclepiades, with those views (Methodism) Brown's doctrine, setting aside its change of terms, has the greatest similarity, the Brunonian system held substantially the position that it is not nature which cures diseases but the physician. The latter must continue to irritate or weaken until the medium height of the barometer of irritation is again reached. Of all the therapeutic methods, that of Brown is the one most deeply sunken in theory, from which even the nearly allied system of Asclepiades was more exempt. It was a fatal principle when applied to practice. For how could one recognize, and by what means could he bring about, the medium height of the barometer of irritation? One should always aim at general effects and not desire those of a local character, and with this object in view, he should not limit himself to a single remedy, but rather employ several that "the excitability may be attacked generally and uniformly." The "materies morbi" furnishes no indications for the treatment. The physician need not work for its expulsion, but merely allow it time to leave the body.

The pure Brunonian system, in comparison with other far less logical and ingenious theories, won immediately after its announcement only a few partisans and opponents, however great was the attention which it aroused on its publication. Perhaps the important occurrences of the period may have been partially responsible for this— an explanation which applies with particular force to France—but the disagreeable characteristics of its founder and the countermining of his enemies (especially the highly esteemed Cullen) contributed their share.

Philippe Pinel (1745-1826) founded a theory called Realism. He is famous for the efforts he made to improve the conditions of the insane and for his study and treatment of mental diseases. Pinel became of great importance in the development of general medicine by his principle of substituting exclusively the analytic, or so-called natural-scientific, method for the synthetic method heretofore in vogue. He sought to determine diseases by a diagnosis carefully constructed from the symptoms, a thing which he considered easy. He desired further to classify them in accordance with their pure symptoms, a matter which he regarded as practicable, inasmuch as he considered "disease" a simple, indivisible whole, composed of chief symptoms, following each other with perfect regularity, and varying only in unessential collateral phenomena, and capable of classification like the objects of the natural sciences. Perhaps the artificial classifications of Linneus and others may have supplied him with models. Pathological anatomy he subordinated to the symptoms. Pinel, accordingly, regarded even fever as something essential. His classes, in the second place, are arranged according to the tissues. He divides diseases into fevers, inflammations, active congestions, neuroses, diseases of the lymphatics and the skin, and undetermined diseases.

It is interesting to notice that altho the eighteenth century was replete with systems and theories, they were not new ones and did not materially advance medicine or save human life. The systems were almost invariably based upon the theories of the preceding centuries, but the great error of these men lies in the fact that they did not appreciate that medicine, as the science of both healthy and morbid life, like life itself, cannot be compressed into a system.

CHAPTER VIII

THE CONTRIBUTIONS OF THE PRACTITIONER

The steady advance of medicine and its allied sciences depended not so much on the great number of systems and theories that were springing up here and there, but upon the many physicians who shunned the ostentation of creating new systems. These were the men working along steadily, either in the laboratories on anatomy, physiology and chemistry, or at the clinics and besides, seeking always a way to alleviate pain and to cure disease. One of the latter was Auenbrugger (1722-1809), who in his own words can best describe his services to practical medicine:

"I here present the reader with a new sign which I have discovered for detecting diseases of the chest. This consists in the percussion of the human thorax, whereby, according to the character of the particular sounds thence elicited, an opinion is formed of the internal state of that cavity. In making public my discoveries respecting this matter I have been actuated neither by an itch for writing, nor a fondness for speculation, but by the desire of submitting to my brethren the fruits of seven years' observation and reflection. In doing so, I have not been unconscious of the dangers I must encounter; since it has been the fate of those who have illustrated or improved the arts and sciences by their discoveries to be beset by envy, malice, hatred, detraction and calumny. This, the common lot, I have chosen to undergo; but with the determination of refusing to every one who is actuated by such motives as these all explanation of my doctrines. What I have written I have proved again and again, by the testimony of my own senses, and amid laborious and tedious exertions; still guarding, on all occasions, against the seductive influence of self-love."

His invention was of great diagnostic importance in diseases of the chest, but its significance was not grasped until many years later. Altho the ear had been employed in auscultation and in the percussion of tympanites and ascites as far back as the ancients, no diagnosis of the diseases of the great viscera had been attempted in this way.

Diseases of the intestines were not much described, as the hemorrhoids and portal stagnation of Stahl were still strongly accepted. Diseases of the peritoneum were first studied by Morgagni and Walter. Diseases of the lungs were studied, but not successfully, being long obscure. "Dropsy of the chest" included many diseases which could not be separated from one another, as emphysema, hydrothorax, etc. Catarrh of the lungs and the bronchi were not differentiated, nor pleurisy and pneumonia, both being called peripneumonia, as in the days of Hippocrates. Morgagni was the first to clear these up.

Tuberculosis of the lungs was only fairly understood. Some of the English thought consumption due to an excess of oxygen in the lungs, and proposed to offset it with inhalations of carbonic acid gas. Diseases of the heart, pericardium and aneurisms were studied by Morgagni, but not much advance made. Diseases of the nervous system were carefully studied. Neuralgia of the face was known (also by the Arabians) and treated with electricity.

Diseases of the brain were developed a little. Morgagni first wrote of "meningitis." Robert Whytte told of "water on the brain." Hoffmann demonstrated the bloodclot in the brain of a person who died from apoplexy. Epilepsy was studied by Tissot. St. Vitus' dance and hysteria were examined. The diseases of children received much attention. The anemias were described and better understood. Scurvy and gout were written about. Haller, by the injection of putrefying matter into the veins, proved the existence of "septic" poisoning, and prepared the way for the doctrine of septicemia. Pole and Dobson found sugar in the urine of diabetics.

Surgery attained, in this century, the rank of equality with so-called internal medicine, not only from the scientific, but also from the practical standpoint. Its higher representatives received the same social rank. The impulse to all this advance again proceeded from France, the headquarters of modern surgery. The surgeons of this time took up ophthalmology very extensively and cultivated it to such a degree that it soon became a specialty of high rank, practiced by eminent men. It had up to this point been in the hands of the charlatans. The English surgeons were famous for skill and daring and much of the advance is due to their good work.

The surgeons helped advance not only operative technique, but also anatomy and physiology. Cheselden, White, the Hunters and Bell were among those who made the English famous for surgery. Obstetrics was even more thoroly cultivated than surgery. It was separated from surgery and assumed the dignity of a specialty, due mainly to the excellent work of the French.

There had been such an upheaval in the study of anatomy in the preceding century, that there was not very much more to investigate. But it was studied constantly and thoroughly, there being frequent additions to anatomical knowledge, of the more minute and less striking parts. The relation of anatomy to physiology was better appreciated, and anatomy began to be studied from that standpoint. Miscopic anatomy, also, was quiet as compared with the preceding century. Pathological and general anatomy were newly created.

A still more important acquisition of the eighteenth century in the fundamental sciences of medicine was the revival and study of experimental physiology. This revival, which marks an epoch in the history of medicine, was effected by Albert von Haller (1708-1777), of Berne, a distinguished scholar and thinker, a poet, botanist and statesman. His anatomical discoveries were made while working out his chief doctrines. He enriched the anatomy of the heart, while studying his doctrine of irritability in reference to that organ. He showed that the dura mater or covering of the brain formed the venous sinuses, and he thought the dura had no nerves in it; he studied the structure of the uterus and showed it was a muscular organ.

Of the highest importance were his researches on the mechanics of respiration, on the formation of bone, and on the development of the embryo; the latter indeed stands out as the most conspicuous piece of work on this subject being Malpighi and Von Baer, tho marred by the theoretical speculations attached to it. What is, perhaps, his greatest work, was the establishment of the doctrine of muscular irritability. In dealing with each division of physiology he carefully describes the anatomical basis, including the data of minute structure, physical properties, and chemical composition so far as these were then known.

In the physiology of the circulation, he studied the mechanism of cardiac motion. He believed that the internal mechanism was due to irritation, and on this based his Doctrine of Irritability.

In his physiology of digestion, he departed from his predecessors. According to him, saliva is neither acid nor alkaline; and so far from attributing to it the great virtues claimed for it by Sylvius and Stahl, he seems to regard its great use as being that of softening the food and helping deglutition.

Dwelling on the difficulty of obtaining gastric juice in the pure condition, noting that acidity is often a token of the onset, and alkalinity of the advance of putrefaction, he concludes that pure gastric juice is neither acid nor alkaline; and while speaking of it as a macerating liquor which softens and dissolves the food, he refuses to regard it as a ferment. It is not a corrosive liquid, as are many acids, and tho it may be at times acid, the acidity is a token of the degeneration of the digested food, not of digestion itself, which "imparts to the food a wholesome animal nature"—*i.e.*, gives it the beginning of vitality; and the characteristic of living animal tissues is, he urges, alkalinity rather than acidity.

Trituration he regards as a useful aid, especially where hard grains form a part of food, as in that of birds, but only an aid. "They have done well who have brought back to its proper mediocrity the power of trituration so immensely exaggerated." Bile he insists is not, as some have thought, a mere excrement. Retained for a while, and slightly altered during its stay in, but not formed by the gall-bladder, secreted, on the contrary, by the substance of the liver, partly perhaps from the blood supplied by the hepatic artery but mainly from that of the vena porta, bile is a fluid viscid and bitter, but not acid, and indeed not alkaline, a fluid which, as all know, has the power of dissolving fat and so acts on a mixture of oil and water as to form out of them an emulsion; it thus dissolves all the food into chyle. This view is almost entirely correct.

The old idea, handed down from the ancients, that the mechanism of respiration was due to the lungs contracting independently, he fought against, as he did not believe that air existed in the pleural sac, which would be necessary if the equilibrium be maintained in and outside the lungs. The most brilliant contribution of Von Haller to the physiology of the nervous system was his refutation of the doctrine of oscillatory motion of the nerves, and his administration of the death-blow to the doctrine of vital spirits. Haller proved that sensation takes place in the nerves, or in organs which contain nerves.

Glisson taught "irritability of the fiber" as well as of the fluids, under the influence of external and internal irritation—a doctrine which he discovered by the deductive method. But Haller proceeded to follow up this principle by the inductive method, proving its existence by experiment. But in contrast to Glisson, he demonstrated that this irritability was something entirely special, a simple peculiarity of muscular substance, and differing from sensation. He showed that muscle tissue will contract (being irritable) even when no nerves go to it, and set up a long dispute as to whether nerve or muscle involved the contraction. It must not be forgotten that in all his researches, Von Haller did not have the aids and accessories of modern physiologists, so that he deserves more credit for his great work.

Pathological Anatomy was established by Morgagni, of Italy (1682-1772). He was the first to devote attention extensively and thoroly to the anatomical products of common diseases. Prior to him, only the rare and very evident lesions of disease were noted and discussed. He studied the clinical pictures, the history of the symptoms, and the course of the disease as well, thus making his observations complete. He erred, however, in regarding the products of diseases as their cause. He showed how important it is to know the steps in the pathological conditions of any organs in a disease, how it aids in diagnosis of the affection, and how it helps in the treatment. He was the first to appreciate a nervous reflex, especially that of sneezing, although he knew nothing of the sympathetic nervous system.

Morgagni studied the action of alcohol on the human system. He pointed out that the excitation of the heart was due to reflex action, following overdistention of the arteries. The overdistention, or increased tension, led to degenerations in the arterial walls. Thus he investigated aneurism and showed the changes that take place in an artery thus diseased, and he recommended special and careful diet as a treatment for early aneurism. In the study of tuberculosis, he was most penetrating. He insisted that it was contagious, and he believed in it to the extent of refusing to do autopsies on that disease. He taught and believed in the early operation for the treatment of cancer. He was a strong opponent to venesection.

General Anatomy was founded by Marie Bichat (1771-1802). He was a great teacher of anatomy. Through his wonderful mental fertility and power, and in spite of his early death, he wrote, in the few years of his life, a great number of works—they include nine volumes. As an evidence of Bichat's enormous activity it may be stated that in a single winter he examined 700 bodies. His chief works were the "Traité des membranes" (1800), "Anatomie générale" (1801) and "Anatomie pathologique."

From Bichat's general and pathological anatomy a new tendency in medicine—that tendency which it manifests to-day—took its origin, as Baas points out. Bichat's genius, masterly mental power and charming gracefulness of exposition, founded chiefly the realistic and pathologico-anatomical epoch. He uttered the famous apothegm, "Take away some fevers and nervous troubles and all else belongs to the kingdom of pathological anatomy."

Bichat established the tendency of similar tissues to similar anatomical forms of disease. This last division is connected with Bichat's creation of general anatomy. He distinguished general tissue-systems, found everywhere in the body, as cellular tissue, the nervous system of animal and organic life, the arterial system, the venous system, the system of exhalant vessels and lymphatics; and special tissue-systems, peculiar to certain parts exclusively, as the osseous, medullary, cartilaginous, fibrous and fibro-cartilaginous systems, the animal and vegetative muscular system, system of serous and mucous membranes, system of synovial membranes, glandular system, dermoid system, epidermoid system and the hairy system. These twenty-one tissues, selected without the aid of the microscope (which Bichat did not employ), were distinguished as simple and similar elements of the body, like the elements of chemistry, and like the cells which Virchow chose for his elements. They were assigned to general anatomy, while, on the other hand, descriptive anatomy had to do with their different combinations. Thus, according to Bichat, the stomach, as the subject of descriptive anatomy, is composed of a are the mucous, serous and fibrous; the compound membranes are serous, mucous and organic muscular coat. The simple membranes formed by juxtaposition of these, and are called fibro-serous, seromucous and fibro-mucous, uniting in themselves one or more of the properties of the simple membranes.

Bichat overthrew the ontological and speculative tendency of medicine, placed "facts" in the front rank and banished ideas and "ideologists" from the science. "If I have gone forward so rapidly, the result has been that I have read little. Books are merely the memoranda of facts. But are such memoranda necessary in a science whose material is ever near us, where we have, so to speak, living books in the sick and dead?" "Let us halt when we have arrived at the limits of the most careful and thoro observation, and let us not strive to press forward where experience cannot show us the way"—a sentiment which certainly does not accord with his earlier vitalistic views. Bichat was the first who claimed for medicine the rank of an "exact" science. "Medicine was long thrust forth from the bosom of the exact sciences. It will have the right to be associated with them, at least as regards the diagnosis of diseases, as soon as we shall everywhere have united with the most thoro and rigorous observation, the investigation of those changes which our organs suffer."

In the course of the further development of such views, and in consequence of the great sympathy extended to them everywhere, a new one-sidedness seized upon the medicine of the last century—a one-sidedness quite as great as the by-gone and partial idealism of the eighteenth century. This was the thoroly realistic method, which gives to medicine the rank of one of the natural sciences, and finally goes so far as to desire to interpret and explain by pure realism even the mental characteristics.

Inoculation was no new thing when introduced during the eighteenth century. The communication of natural smallpox to the healthy, in order to protect them from the natural disease, reaches back into hoary intiquity. The custom is mentioned among the Indians in the Atharva Veda. The operation was always performed by the Brahmins, who employed pus produced by those who had been inoculated with natural smallpox one year before, and also the pus of these secondary inoculations. They rubbed the place selected for operation—in girls the outside of the arm, in boys the outside of the forearm—with wool until red, scratched these places several times with knives for a space about an inch long, and laid upon them cotton soaked in variolous pus and moistened with water from the Ganges.

Before inoculation a preparatory course of diet lasting for four weeks was considered necessary. The inoculation was performed in the open air, and the inoculated were required to remain out of bed to sprinkle themselves morning and evening with cold water. If fever made its appearance the sprinkling was discontinued and the inoculated might at most stretch themselves before the threshold, and must eat sparingly. The Brahmins traveled about the country to perform inoculation, and the operation was practiced in the beginning of spring. Under the influence of such excellent hygienic regulations the results were for the most part favorable.

Among the Chinese the so-called "pock-sowing" was practiced as early as 1000 B.C. by introducing into the nasal cavities of children, aged three to six years, a pledget of cotton saturated with variolous pus. The Arabians had a "pox-sale." Pus from a patient suffering with small-pox was purchased for raisins and inoculated with needles.

The Circassians, too, by means of needles, inoculated handsome girls upon the cheek, right wrist, left ankle, and over the heart, in order to preserve their beauty.

In the states of North Africa incisions were made between the thumb and index-finger; among the negroes inoculation was performed in the nose, and in Denmark, Scotland, the Auvergne and other places, this operation was performed at an early period. The employment of the inoculation of natural smallpox by the Greeks of Constantinople, where the custom had been long naturalized and practiced by old women instructed in the art, exercized a most important influence upon the West.

But it remained for Edward Jenner to solve the problem. He demonstrated that a simple attack of mild, never fatal cowpox, deliberately acquired, would serve as a protection against the fatal smallpox. His discovery was the result of his genius for original investigation. On the 14th of May, 1796, vaccine matter was taken from the hand of a dairy maid and inserted into the arms of a healthy boy of eight. He went through an attack of cowpox in regular fashion; then, two months later, Jenner inoculated him with real smallpox pus, but with no deleterious result. In his very complete and explicit report, he says:

"The deviation of man from the state in which he was originally placed by nature seems to have proved to him a urolific source of diseases. From the love of splendor, from the indulgence of luxury, and from his fondness for amusement he has familiarized himself with a great number of animals, which may not originally have been intended for his associates. The wolf, disarmed of ferocity, is now pillowed in the lady's lap. The cat, the little tiger of our island, whose natural home is the forest, is equally domesticated, and caressed. The cow, the hog, the sheep, and the horse, are all, for a variety of purposes, brought under his care and dominion.

"There is a disease to which the horse, from his state of domestication, is frequently subject. The farriers have called it the 'grease.' It is an inflammation and swelling in the heel, from which issues matter possessing properties of a very peculiar kind, which seems capable of generating a disease in the human body (after it has undergone the modification which I shall presently speak of), which bears so strong a resemblance to the smallpox that I think it highly probable it may be the source of the disease.

"In this dairy country a great number of cows are kept, and the office of milking is performed indiscriminately by men and maid servants. One of the former having been appointed to apply dressings to the heels of a horse affected with the 'grease,' and not paying due attention to cleanliness, incautiously bears his part in milking the cows, with some particles of the infectious matter adhering to his fingers. When this is the case, it commonly happens that a disease is communicated to the cows, and from the cows to the dairymaids, which spreads through the farm until the most of the cattle and domestics feel its unpleasant consequences. This disease has obtained the name of 'cowpox.'

"Inflamed spots now begin to appear on different parts of the hands of the domestics employed in milking, and sometimes on the wrists, which quickly run on to suppuration, first assuming the appearance of the small vesications produced by a burn. Absorption takes place, and tumors (enlarged lymphatic glands) appear in each axilla.

"The system becomes affected—the pulse is quickened: and shiverings, succeeded by heat, with general lassitude and pains about the loins and limbs, with vomiting, come on. The head is painful, and the patient is now and then even affected by delirium. These symptoms, varying in their degrees of violence, generally continue from one day to three or four, leaving ulcerated sores about the hands, which, from the sensibility of the parts, are very troublesome, and commonly heal slowly, frequently becoming phagedenic, like those from whence they sprang. The lips, nostrils, eyelids, and other parts of the body are sometimes affected with sores; but these evidently arise from their being heedlessly rubbed or scratched with the patient's infected fingers.

"Thus the disease makes its progress from the horse to the nipple of the cow, and from the cow to the human subject. Morbid matter of various kinds, when absorbed into the system, may produce effects in some degree similar; but what renders the cowpox virus so extremely singular is that the person who has been thus affected is forever after secure from the infection of the smallpox; neither exposure to the variolous effluvia, nor the insertion of the matter into the skin, producing this distemper.

"I have often been foiled in my endeavors to communicate the cowpox by inoculation. An inflammation will sometimes succeed the scratch or puncture, and in a few days disappear without producing any further effect. Sometimes it will even produce an ichorous fluid, and yet the system will not be affected. The same thing we know happens with the smallpox virus.

"The very general investigation that is now taking place, chiefly through inoculation (and I again repeat my earnest hope that it may be conducted with the calmness and moderation which should ever accompany a philosophical research), must soon place the vaccine disease in its just point of view. The result of all my trials with the virus on the human subject has been uniform. In every instance the patient who has felt its influence has completely lost the susceptibility for the variolous contagion; and as these instances are now become numerous, I conceive that, joined to the observations in the former part of this paper, they sufficiently precluded me from the necessity of entering into controversies with those who have circulated reports adverse to my assertions, on no other evidence than what has been casually collected."

It was not long before the opposition to the practice of vaccination took definite form, and it has continued down to this very day. Statistics are advanced by those who favor its use to show that the ravages of smallpox have decreased, and those who oppose it show that there have been many fatal results from the vaccination itself. Medical opinion is almost uniformly favorable.

Another great advance in the prevention of human suffering was begun by Philippe Pinel in 1792. While in charge of the Bicêtre Hôpital he removed chains from the insane patients, and instituted a rational and humane treatment, such as is adopted to-day.

Throughout the eighteenth century an incredible number of strange and useless remedies were regarded as efficacious, such as mummy, millepeds, wood-lice; and even amulets were found in shops. Instead of simplifying the materia medica, a great many new drugs were added.

It has already been stated that the ancients, from the days of the Asclepiadæ, employed the waters of healing springs, mineral waters, often too frequently—Archigenes had the patient drink as much as fifteen pints for the relief of stone. Indeed, waters were even classified according to their constituents as alum-waters, sulphur-waters, chalybeate waters, bituminous waters, etc. The Italian physicians of the last half of the Middle Ages prescribed these waters. At a later period mineral waters were drunk still more frequently, indeed in considerable quantities, for at that time, even more than to-day, the excellence and efficacy of the water was judged by its strength, particularly its cathartic effects. Paracelsus exercised a great influence upon the theory and employment of mineral springs (particularly those of Pfeffers, Gastein, etc.), and it is one of his chief services that he subjected the learned medicine of his day (which thought itself safe only in guilds and study-rooms) to the test of living observations and actual life, and employed chemistry in medicine, particularly also as it related to the question of mineral springs. As the science of chemistry itself was improved, the subject of mineral waters likewise enjoyed increasing attention.

The use of ordinary water as a remedial drink and in the form of (cold and tepid) lavations and baths for the cure of diseases, especially those of a febrile character, first made its way into German practice in the eighteenth century, tho it had been in use among other nations at an earlier period.

Even Hippocrates permitted baths in febrile diseases, tho rather tepid baths than cold. He was particularly fond of these in pneumonia, to mitigate the pain and facilitate expectoration and respiration. It is remembered that Musa cured the Emperor Augustus by means of cold baths, after warm baths had failed to produce any benefit. Asclepiades, Charmis of Marseilles, Agathinus, Herodotus, Celsus, Aretæus, Aëtius and others likewise employed cold water, most frequently in the form of affusions in the case of eliptics and lethargic patients, and as lavations and cold dressings upon the head in typhus. Galen, like Hippocrates, was no great friend of cold lavations and baths, tho he employed the former in the fevers of young people, excluding hectic fever. Among the Arabians, Rhazes recomended cold lavation and dipping in cold water in cases of smallpox and measles. Avicenna followed Galen, and regulated his employment of cold in accordance with the age, constitution and season of the year. The American Indians also practiced hydrotheraphy in the treatment of yellow fever.

The epidemics of the eighteenth century, while not so severe as those of the preceding centuries(were frequent and extensive enough to create new problems for investigation and treatment. Plague was still seen in northern Europe; typhus fever was prevalent mostly after the wars; typhoid fever was first described in this century; malaria gave rise to great epidemics; dysentery, ergotism and diphtheria were very common. Diphtheria was particularly prevalent and deadly. Smallpox has diffused generally over all the world. In 1770, smallpox carried off 3,000,000 in the East Indies. Yellow fever was mostly confined to America. Hospitals during the whole eighteenth century were undesirably managed. "Hospital fever" never left them, as there was no hospital hygiene. Many hospitals contained large beds, occupied often by from four to six patients, and the mortality was rarely less than 20 per cent. Almost all who underwent operations, especially amputations, died. However, with the introduction of clinical instruction for students, conditions became improved.

The physician of the eighteenth century was even in externals distinct professionally, at least on festive occasions, from other men, and was distinguished, as are many modern "precise followers" of

Æsculapius, by the fashionable cut of his clothing, his universal greetings, rapid gait, and amiability. Usually a thermometer, stethoscope, or percussion-hammer is described as peeping out of his pockets. The English physician had become a man of standing and took his rank with the parson and the squire.

CHAPTER IX

NINETEENTH-CENTURY THEORIES

THE beginning of the nineteenth century marks one of the most important movements in the history of all sciences, especially medicine. There was a great upheaval in all things, intellectual and otherwise, due mostly to the terrible revolution in France. After the peace, scientific study of all the branches began to assume wonderful proportions, especially in chemistry, histology, pathology and clinical instruction. The physicians and scientists of other countries flocked to Paris and there learned the new method of investigation and research—that is, experimentation. These new ideas and methods were carried to other countries and stimulated the development of science.

The eighteenth century regarded as its chief task, the rescue of the people from the medieval restrictions and limitations, particularly the spiritual side of life. On the other hand, the nineteenth century struggled almost extravagantly for the accomplishment of the economical or material demands for existence. This was seen in the many revolutions and wars for that purpose, abolishing slavery and placing in the foreground the individual, exposing him to the test of freedom.

Over the medicine of the present day the natural sciences have attained a control which is even more absolute than that seen in the seventeenth century. Buckle says regarding the cultivation of the natural sciences: "It cannot, however, be concealed that we manifest an inordinate respect for experiments, an undue love of minute detail and a disposition to over-estimate the inventors of new instruments and the discoverers of new but often insignificant facts." In another place he says, "In vain do we demand that the details be more generalized, and reduced into order. We want ideas, and we get more facts. We hear constantly of what Nature is doing, but we rarely hear of what man is thinking. We are in the predicament that our facts have outstripped our knowledge and are now encumbering its march."

The theory of excitement was a modification of Brunonianism and was one of solidism. According to this theory, life depends upon irritability, which is inherent in the organism as an independent capacity. Thus two things, irritability and organization, are taken into consideration, while Brown recognized only the former. The grade of irritability determines the condition and behavior of the body, and health consists in moderate irritation and moderate excitability. Another offshoot of the Brunonian theory, far worse, was the "New Italian Theory." Its author was Rasori, of Milan. Its bad effects were the more evident and deplorable because when applied to the treatment of diseases, humanity must needs suffer. He taught that the diagnosis of diseases cannot be made from the symptoms, but solely from the remedies which benefit them or make them worse. Venesection is regarded as the most reliable diagnostic means. If it be beneficial, a certain condition exists which calls for certain medicines. If, after twice performing venesection, there is no benefit, the disease must be treated on other lines. Enormous doses of medicine were given, often interfering to an alarming extent with the process of healing.

In direct opposition to this system of medicine was early homeopathy. The action of drugs on healthy persons becomes the guide for a selection of remedies with which to treat disease. Accordingly, for the removal of a given group of symptoms, that remedy must be selected which when given to a healthy person has produced the same, or at least a similar, group of symptoms. The homeopathic physician thus is required to know thoroly and accurately the effect of every drug on the human system; must know every symptom group, so as to apply the correct remedies, working thus on the theory "similia similibus curantur," and thus works with a complete knowledge of what he is doing. Samuel Hahnemann (1755-1843), of Meissen, was the founder of this school. By long study he came to the conclusion that all diseases were general, none local. He discovered four hundred and twelve symptoms of the "psora," or itch, which had its chief symptoms in the skin, and occasioned "so many secondary symptoms, that at least seven-eighths of all chronic complaints arose from this single source." He claims that lycopodium in extremely minute doses sets up a wonderful group of symptoms —falling of the hair, confusion of thought, eruptions, etc. In therapeutics, there are specifics only, and their efficacy is added to by dilution.

A single dose of a properly chosen specific frequently cures immediately. In the administration of homeopathic medicines the strictest diet must always be maintained. An offshoot of this early school of homeopathy was a doctrine called Isopathy. According to this, like was to be cured by like, no matter how nauseous or abhorrent to the taste. It occasioned attacks on its parent system and lived only a short life. Modern Homeopathy, however, has developed to no inconsiderable magnitude, and possesses many followers to-day whose reputation is often not less than the allopath. But even more important is the beneficial effect Hahnemann's work had in modifying the giving of large doses of potent drugs.

François Broussais (1772-1838) advanced a theory which he called Physiological Medicine. According to him, life depends upon external irritation, especially that of heat. The latter sets up in the body peculiar chemical reactions, which maintain regeneration and assimilation, as well as contractility and sensibility. When these functions, which are supported by heat, cease, death comes on at once. Health depends upon the moderate action of the external irritants; disease upon their weakness or on their exceptional strength. Diseases originate from local irritations, proceeding from a certain diseased organ, or part of an organ, particularly from the heart, and often from the mucous membrane of the stomach and intestines, and these irritations diffuse themselves throughout the rest of the body through sympathy and by way of the nervous system. Every irritation which through sympathetic irritation of the heart produces fever, has become an inflammation, and the judge of this is hyperemia. The famous "gastroenteritis" is the most usual result of irritations of the brain. Through complications, it causes typhus and all other so-called infectious diseases. He denied the existence of specific morbid poisons. This "gastroenteritis" or "basis of pathology," he divided into two classes: If gastroenteritis predominates, it is accompanied with pains in the gastric region, and sudden vomiting of food and drink. If, however, the enteritis (not the stomach, but the intestine) is the chief lesion, great thirst, a sensation of internal heat, a sensitive abdomen, a rapid hard pulse, and a coated tongue are the chief phenomena.

In therapeutics Broussais believed that the physician is the lord of Nature. He must anticipate disease, particularly the gastroenteritis, against which all his efforts must be exerted. For this purpose, the antiphlogistic or weakening method is best. Febrile and inflammatory diseases he treated by the withdrawal of nourishment, carried to the extreme. He preferred, as the most efficient, antiphlogistic treatment, in place of venesection, which he strongly approves of, the employment of leeches, applying them to the gastric region. In robust individuals, thirty to fifty might be applied at once. In rheumatism and gout, they were applied to the joints, and to the pit of the stomach.

The French School of Pathological Anatomy helped to advance medicine. It taught that pathology was pathological anatomy, while aiming to elevate the latter science into a "clinical anatomy," requiring the physician to search his patient for the changes of pathological anatomy. It required him to remove the products of the disease, rather than try to cure or remove the cause of the disease. The living patient became a mere subject for diagnosis and local therapeutic investigation. Many diseases were therefore considered incurable, and the desire and ability to cure disease were weakened.

Functional or dynamic disturbances were disregarded, while diseases of the fluids of the body were at first almost entirely forgotten, these errors being due to the fact that on autopsy no lesions were discovered. The patient was treated rather as a living cadaver, not as a being endowed with vital forces. But if the practice of medicine lost by these methods, on the other hand, knowledge of the changes produced in the body by disease was greatly increased.

The School of Natural Philosophy was founded in Germany. It was a purely speculative system, full of scholastic phrases. The school brought forth mainly a philosophy of medicine, rather than philosophical medicine. The School of Natural History followed. Baas claims that this was the expression of the turn which medicine was compelled to take to escape from the after-effects of the one-sided, ideal or systematizing tendency of the eighteenth century (of which natural philosophy was the final product), and to enter upon the realistic or positive tendency of science and culture in the nineteenth century in both medicine and the other science. It shows everywhere its mediatorial position between the old traditions and the most recent times. Thus, for the purpose of careful observations, it fostered, indeed, the ancient Hippocratic diagnosis and method, by which it preserved its connection with the earlier medicine, and which the later school of natural science almost entirely set aside. In addition, however, it cultivated considerably the physical, and particularly the microscopic, diagnosis adopted from France. Indeed this school gave a decisive impulse to microscopic investigation in general, so that Virchow, one of its scions, subsequently founded upon it his cellular pathology, and thus elevated the microscope to the fundamental instrument in pathology and pathological anatomy.

The attempt was made by this school to classify diseases "naturally," into classes, families, species or kinds, such as in botany. There were some physicians in this school who later considered diseases to be genuine second organisms in the diseased body.

The new Vienna school was a continuation of the pathologico-anatomical school of Paris, greatly elaborated upon and added to. The leaders of the school had at their disposal over a thousand bodies annually to dissect, so that, as a matter of course, pathological anatomy was utilized from the standpoint of statistics. The microscope and chemistry were added for further study. Later the introduction of the laws of sound into the interpretation and conception of physico-diagnostic phenomena was made by Joseph Skoda, by his views on physical diagnosis, showed himself an independent spirit who got his impulse from France, but far outstripped the French diagnosticians. On the other hand, practical medicine in his hands degenerated again into simple diagnosis. Not long after this physiology was utilized to explain pathology.

Henle defines the duty of the physician to be the prevention and cure of diseases. Here two methods of proceeding are to be distinguished, the empirical and the rational (theoretic, physiological). The latter is likewise the method of physiology; it is the method of all experimental sciences and particularly of the natural sciences. Moreover, the genuine scientific spirit is said to consist not in ignoring or scorning philosophy, but "in the conscious and provisional renunciation of the knowledge of the first cause of things, because the time of proofs is not yet past." "Accordingly if the collection of experiences is the chief thing, yet hypotheses must form a balance to its instability."

"In experimenting we fix arbitrarily the cause, so far as possible, and by observing the results we assure ourselves of the correctness of our conclusions. In this process the so-called localization of symptoms—that is, the search for the organ from which the symptoms proceed—is aimed at, but in addition, too, a knowledge of the quality of pathological changes, by a comparison of the altered form and composition with the normal. Pathology owes its weightiest facts to the employment of the microscope and to organic chemistry. Moreover, the hypothesis of a vital force is admissible and is just as good or as weak as that of electric attraction or of gravitation.

Disease is "a deviation from the normal, typical—*i.e.*, healthy—process of life, a modification of health, a removal from the relative norm. The essence of disease, however, is an expression of typical force under unwonted conditions." Disease, too, like itself, is a process. Diseases are anomalies of this process. Any alternation which completely abolishes this process occasions not disease but death. Death is the cessation of the interchange of material. The termination in health follows spontaneously or through artificial or accidental influences. The transition to health ensues gradually in most chronic and in many acute diseases; in others, especially in acute diseases, the symptoms disappear suddenly. The first and slower method is called lysis, the last method crisis—the latter term a relic handed down from the mythical beginnings of medicine. A critical secretion is, in the main, nothing more than a secretion belonging to the stadium of the crisis. "The belief in crises, according to Henle, stands upon the same footing as belief in the devil. That the exorcist had expelled a devil was demonstrated by the foul odor left behind by the evil spirit. The odor was a fact; that it could be diffused in no way except by the devil was perfectly self-evident." The same was the case with critical perspiration and such matters.

The modern chemical system, in opposition to the chemical system of the eighteenth century which was founded on inorganic chemistry,

NINETEENTH-CENTURY THEORIES

was the result of the active researches and discoveries in organic chemistry, and upon it the present theory of metabolism is based. According to this theory the physical changes in the body, so far as they cannot be classified as mechanical processes, are nothing more than oxidation or combustion of the elements of the body, effected by the oxygen in the blood, from inspired air the body is a living retort or test-tube. The parts of the body were supposed to be destroyed and then regenerated. This process of oxidation is twofold, depending upon the two great classes of food-stuffs which compose the body or are taken into it. The respiratory foods (hydrocarbons, fats) are burned in the lungs during respiration and chiefly excreted there as carbonic acid. The so-called nutritive materials (nitrogenous, blood-forming foods), which compose the tissues proper, are consumed in the tissues themselves and are discharged as urea in the renal secretion.

Animal heat, they claimed, was the result of the processes of oxidation going on constantly within the body. The one class of foods, albuminous or nitrogenus, serves for the formation of the blood and construction of the large parts of the body, the other class is similar to ordinary fuel and serves mainly for the production of heat.

Fever was regarded as an abnormal increase in the process of combustion, disease a defect in this process. If one group of these materials is missing, therapeutic measures are indicated to increase the food of this sort and thus supply the deficiency. The theory regards the living body from the viewpoint of a chemist, to the chemical laboratory and chemical analysis, and does not pay sufficient attention to the adaptable side of physical life nor to the ever-changing and powerful influences in which the body is always placed. Yet the theory was of great importance in that it placed dietetics once more in the foreground.

Modern cellular vitalism was the result of the researches of Rudolph Virchow, born 1821. Then later, through the works of Beale, Louis Agassiz, Sharpey, Hassall, Bastian, Tyndall, Huxley and others, every organized structure of the living body was subjected to microscopic analyses and found to be composed of individual cells, varying in size and shape, and performing a great variety of functions, but all composed essentially of an organizable substance recognized as the physical basis of life and called by some investigators protoplasm and by others bioplasm. Its most distinctive attribute is its vital capacity to grow and multiply or propagate itself. Thus they found all living bodies, both animal and vegetable, composed of protoplasm aggregated in minute forms called cells and united in various ways to constitute all the organized matter in the fluids and solids of living bodies.

The theory is merely a modified employment of the old idea of the "vital force," referring the latter to the concrete, minutest parts, the so-called "corporeal" elements. "Every animal appears as a sum of vital unities," this school declared, "each of which bears all the characteristics of life. The characteristics and unity of life cannot be found in any determinate point of a higher organization—*e.g.*, in the brain of man—but only in the definite, ever-recurring arrangement which each element presents. Hence it results that the composition of a large body amounts to a kind of social arrangement, an arrangement of a social kind in which each of a mass of individual existences is dependent upon the others, but in such a way that each element has a special activity of its own, and that each, altho it receives the impulse to its own activity from other parts, still itself performs its own functions."

The cell is thus the actual, ultimate, proper morphological element of every vital manifestation—"omnis cellula e cellua"—and the action takes place within the cell itself. The most constant part of the cell is the nucleus or central spot of the cell. Next to the cell is the membrane. The development or increase of cells is continuous; it takes place by continual growth of cells, and a new growth of cells presupposes existing cells.

The reception of nutritive materials is effected through the activity of the tissue elements in the form of an attraction of this material by the tissues themselves in proportion to their needs. Virchow taught that certain tissue elements have the power to extract certain materials, thus possessing specific affinity; thus the liver extracts sugar and bile from the blood. He also held that the vascular system was completely closed by membranes.

In the doctrine of inflammation Virchow, in addition to the four well-known phenomena of inflammation—redness, heat, swelling, pain—took up the disturbance of the function of the diseased part. In fact, he laid most stress on this as the most effective symptom.

Many important points of the vitalistic cellular theory have already been disproven in the light of more recent microscopic interpretations. It is the one great theory on which its author did not try to build a system of therapeutics. One of the results of this theory was the formation of the school of natural sciences, which seeks chiefly by the aid of pathological anatomy and microscopy to render medicine an "exact" science. The hygiene school also advanced to the front. The tendency of this latter school was to split up medicine into specialties and increase the number of subordinate branches.

CHAPTER X

MODERN TREATMENT OF DISEASE

The Modern Parasitic, or Germ Theory, had its origin shortly after the invention of the microscope, when a former school maintained that diseases were due to microscopic organisms and animals. In the present day, however, the lowest order of plants is believed to be the infecting material in certain infectious diseases. Haller, some years ago, injected putrid matter into the veins of an animal and caused pyemia and then became the creator of experimental pathology. Parasites were discovered causing diseases in animals and plants; in skin and scalp diseases the modern theory of the production of diseases through infection found further support in the investigations relative to the processes of fermentation and putrefaction, with which the processes of disease were at once compared.

Pasteur demonstrated that fermentation and putrefaction were caused not by chemical ferments, as Liebig thought, but were merely the vital processes of lower organisms. These he divided into two great classes—aérobes, which work only in the presence of oxygen, and anaérobes, which work without oxygen but do not survive after action. Wound infections were for the first time considered infected from the outside. Robert Koch demonstrated the development of bacteria from spores. At the present day no consistent theory exists which fully explains parasitic action in disease. Certain of the lower fungi, as parasites within or upon the body, cause diseases of the infectious type. There are two theories concerning the modus operandi of these parasites. One is that by the development and growth of these germs in the system the body is deprived of its nutriment and life endangered by the lack of oxygen. According to the other theory, these parasites give off in their own metabolism poisonous products (toxines), which interfere with the action of normal cells.

Elie Metchnikoff, of Odessa, observed that the wandering cells—the white blood corpuscles—after the manner of amœbæ, surround and attack and then devour ("phagocyte") the germs which enter the body, thus rendering them harmless. He considered inoculation as a sort of preliminary training of these wandering white cells, so that if the disease against which the patient had been inoculated should befall him the "phagocytes" would be prepared and the more readily destroy the offending bacteria. When a person dies of an infectious disease, he explains it by claiming that the number of bacteria was too large for the wandering cells to overcome and devour. His theory has many opponents, who declare that diseases are cured by the cessation of the process of development of the bacteria in consequence of their death.

The practical medicine of the modern age has gained many important and permanent advantages through the improvements in diagnosis of the phenomena and pictures of disease. These aids to practical knowledge are derived from the natural sciences, which have been so wonderfully developed in modern days. The physical diagnosis of the present time took its origin in the eighteenth century, when Auenbrugger announced his method of percussion. Not long after that René Laennec presented his method of auscultation, a method of listening to the sounds produced in the chest when air is inspired and expired in health and disease, and also to the sound produced by the heart and its valves in health and disease. It was quite by accident that he came upon his great invention.

He says: "I was consulted by a young person who was laboring under the general symptoms of a diseased heart. In her case percussion and the application of the hand (what modern doctors call palpation) were of little service because of a considerable degree of stoutness. The other method, that namely of listening to the sound within the chest by the direct application of the ear to the chest wall, being rendered inadmissible by the age and sex of the patient, I happened to recollect a simple and well-known fact in acoustics and fancied it might be turned to some use on the present occasion. The fact I allude to is the great distinctness with which we hear the scratch of a pin at one end of a piece of wood on applying our ear to the other.

"Immediately on the occurence of this idea I rolled a quire of paper into a kind of cylinder and applied one end of it to the region of the heart and the other to my ear. I was not a little surprised and pleased to find that I could thereby perceive the action of the heart in a manner much more clear and distinct than I had ever been able to do by the immediate application of the ear.

"From this moment I imagined that the circumstance might furnish means for enabling us to ascertain the character not only of the action of the heart, but of every species of sound produced by the motion of all the thoracic viscera, and consequently for the exploration of the respiration, the voice, the râles and perhaps even the fluctuation of fluid effused in the pleura or pericardium. With this conviction I forthwith commenced at the Necker Hospital a series of observations from which I have been able to deduce a set of new signs of the diseases of the chest. These are for the most part certain, simple and prominent, and calculated perhaps to render the diagnosis of the dis-

MODERN TREATMENT OF DISEASE

eases of the lungs, heart and pleura as decided and circumstantial as the indications furnished to the surgeons by the finger or sound in the complaints wherein these are of use."

He worked out the practical and mechanical aspect, making a stethoscope about ten inches long with a diameter of four inches, and contained in its lower end an obturator, upon which he laid great stress. Laennec's interpretation of the sounds heard was based upon perfectly definite morbid conditions existing in the thoracic viscera, while Skoda formed his physical rules upon the basis of the principles of acoustics. Piorry improved the stethoscope and invented the pleximeter, an instrument used for the aid of mediate percussion. The percussion hammer was next invented, designed to take the place of the fingers for tapping.

One of the greatest inventions of all ages is that of the ophthalmoscope by Helmholtz. By means of this instrument the oculist can inspect the interior of the eye and easily decide whether it is in healthy or diseased condition. The laryngoscope is second in importance only to the ophthalmoscope. A few of the other diagnostic instruments that have since been in use are the aural and nasal specula, rectal and vaginal specula, the endoscope for examining the interior of the bladder and the spectroscope for the detection of sugar and blood-stains.

The laboratory for chemical and bacteriological examinations of excreta and secretions has since been of such aid in diagnosis that it is hard to appreciate the fact that the profession has had its benefit only for a few years past. The progress of physical diagnosis has been of incalculable benefit to humanity; the physician has been more accurate in finding the disease or its cause, and once having established this, has been able to treat the disease with more confidence and surety.

The progress of surgery in modern days has been described by Baas: "Surgery has always presented in its development a much pleasanter picture of steady progress than that offered by medicine proper, for its objects and its practice do not necessitate the illumination of the dark paths by the torch of theory, which diffuses far more soot than light. Accordingly Chamisso calls surgery the "seeing portion of the healing art." Thus, too, the surgery of our century, in accordance with the character of the people who have shared in its development, but unaltered by the opinions of schools and their often varying methods, has striven vigorously and steadily after a perfection based upon the foundation of experience and for principles which the past, and particularly the eighteenth century, had taught. If the sixteenth century opened the way for the checking of hemorrhage and established this art in its scientific position, and if the seventeenth century accomplished the same results in the simplification and improvement of the art of dressing wounds; if too the eighteenth century gave a scientific elevation, so far as its means would permit, to both these methods, so in our own century surgery stands upon a scientific level with medicine proper, tho its objects are far more accessible, direct and comprehensible than those of the latter science and its position more favorable, so that its progress has been almost constant and uninterrupted.

"In full possession of the results of a normal surgical and topographical anatomy, almost perfect in its development (a position which admits of both boldness and certainty in treatment), it has likewise been able to utilize in an eminently practical way the acquisitions of pathological anatomy, applying them as well to diagnosis as to operative and therapeutic aims. Microscopic pathological anatomy in particular has become of extended importance in surgical knowledge and practice. By it, above all, our knowledge of secondary wound-diseases, of the fate of the secretions of wounds and their effects upon the organism, of the character of the different forms of tumors and their methods of growth and diffusion, etc., has been rendered clearer, and thus many fruitful facts and views have been contributed to surgical treatment.

"Above all the external conditions of the healing process have been observed more attentively than in the entire past, and consequently the after-treatment of wounds, both local and hygienic, has been brought more into the foreground. Above all, amputations, so frequent at an earlier date, have largely disappeared, and military surgery, as well as hospital and civil surgery, has inclined rather to the preservation of wounded parts and members than their removal. Thus has grown up the scientific and rational, so-called conservative surgery of our century.

"A characteristic stamp has been impressed upon the surgery of our century by the bold and somewhat unexpectedly successful practice of visceral surgery, or the surgery of the cavities of the body, from the ligation of the great internal vessels to the extirpation of ovarian tumors, the spleen, kidneys, larynx, etc., a practice which contrasts strongly with that of earlier surgery, which was, on the whole, rather a surgery of the outer members, if such an expression is permissible."

Also should be mentioned the improvement in plastic operations, among which should be counted the operation of osteoplasty, introduced by B. Langenbeck in 1859. The operations mentioned and other operative methods, some of them tedious and difficult, were certainly greatly facilitated, in fact almost conditioned, by the discovery of the anesthetic effects of ether and chloroform, one of the most beneficent discoveries ever made. The rapid operations of an earlier date now disappeared, and instead of rapidity of method, the security of the patient and the certainty of success were now demanded. Pain was no longer the occasion for an avoidance of more tedious, but safer methods of procedure. Another advance in surgery, not so beneficent, however, in its results, was the rubber bandage of Esmarch, introduced in 1873 for the production of artificial anemia.

The use of animal fibers for sutures was suggested first by Sir Astley Cooper. In 1852 plaster bandages were used first and have been constantly employed since then for fractures.

The discovery of anesthesia by Dr. William T. G. Morton in 1846 was one of the greatest boons to mankind that the history of the world records. For many centuries and in many climes there had been constant search for the abolishment of pain during operations. The Chinese have been able, or made claims to that effect, to produce anesthesia by means of a preparation they call Mago. Herodotus says that the Scythians were accustomed to intoxicate themselves by the inhalation of the fumes of hemp-seed. Pliny tells of the anesthetic qualities of the mandragora and its use preparatory to surgical operations. Opium and hyoscyamus were used in the Middle Ages, and this was continued down to the time of Morton's discovery of pure sulphuric ether as a perfect narcotic and anesthetic. He was a dentist and experimented on himself in Boston. His description follows: "I shut myself up in my room, seated myself in the operating chair and commenced inhaling. It partially suffocated me, but produced no decided effect. I then saturated my handkerchief and inhaled it from that. I looked at my watch and soon lost consciousness. As I recovered, I felt a numbness in my limbs with a sensation like a nightmare and would have given the world for some one to come and arouse me. I thought for a moment I should die. At length I felt a slight tingling of the blood in the end of my third finger and made an effort to touch it with my thumb, but without success. At a second effort I touched it, but there seemed to be no sensation. I pinched my thigh, but sensation was imperfect. I immediately looked at my watch. I had been insensible between seven and eight minutes."

Shortly after Morton's discovery of ether, which was not fully appreciated at the time except in Boston, Professor Simpson, of Edinburgh, introduced chloroform to be used for destroying pains in obstetrics.

To Lord Lister, of England, is due the introduction of the antiseptic method in the surgical treatment of wounds, from which was later developed the aseptic technique now employed in every hospital and in all surgical operations. In the Lancet for March 16, 1867, Lister published the first of a series of articles entitled "On a New Method of Treating Compound Fracture, Abscess, etc., with Observation on the Condition of Suppuration." In the first article of this series the following statements appear:

"Turning now to the question how the atmosphere produces decomposition of organic substances, we find that a flood of light has been thrown upon this most important subject by the philosophic researches of M. Pasteur, who has demonstrated by thoroly convincing evidence that it is not to its oxygen or to any of its gaseous constituents that the air owes this property, but to minute particles suspended in it, which are the germs of various low forms of life, long since revealed by the microscope and regarded as merely accidental concomitants of putrescence, but now shown by Pasteur to be its essential cause, resolving the complex organic compounds into substances of simpler chemical constitution, just as the yeast plant converts sugar into alcohol and carbonic acid.

"Applying these principles to the treatment of compound fracture, bearing in mind that it is from the vitality of the atmospheric particles that all the mischief arises, it appears that all that is requisite is to dress the wound with some material capable of killing these septic germs, provided that any substance can be found reliable for this purpose, yet not too potent as a caustic.

"My attention having for several years been directed to the subject of suppuration, more especially in its relation to decomposition, I saw that such a powerful antiseptic was peculiarly adapted for experiments with a view to elucidating that subject, and while I was engaged in the investigation the applicability of carbolic acid for the treatment of compound fracture naturally occurred to me.

"My first attempt of this kind was made in Glasgow Royal Infirmary in March, 1865, in a case of compound fracture of the leg. It proved unsuccessful, in consequence, as I now believe, of improper management; but subsequent trials have more than realized my most sanguine anticipations.

"There is, however, one point more that I cannot but advert to, viz., the influence of this mode of treatment upon the general healthiness of a hospital. Previously to its introduction the two large wards in which most of my cases of accident and of operation were treated were among the unhealthiest in the whole surgical division of the Glasgow Royal Infirmary, in consequence apparently of those wards being unfavorably placed with reference to the supply of fresh air, and I have felt ashamed when recording the results of my practice to have so often to allude to hospital gangrene of pyemia. It was interesting, though melancholy, to observe that whenever all or nearly all the beds contained cases with open sores, these grievious complications were pretty sure to show themselves; so that I came to welcome simple fractures, though in themselves of little interest either for myself or the students, because their presence diminished the proportion of open sores upon the patients. But since the antiseptic treatment has been brought into full operation, and wounds and abscesses no longer poison the atmosphere with putrid exhalations, my wards have completely changed their character; so that during the last nine months not a single instance of pyemia, hospital gangrene or erysipelas has occurred in them. As there appears to be no doubt regarding the cause of this change, the importance of the fact can hardly be exaggerated."

After the development of surgery through anesthesia and the antiseptic treatment of wounds, came the turn of medicine in the twentieth century. The science of immunity has come to bulk more and more largely in medical importance, and in its two great branches of serum therapy and vaccine therapy has appeared the most hopeful method yet devised by man for dispelling disease. In a word, immunity may be said to be the privilege which enables an animal to be exempt from harm by a particular micro-organism or a particular toxin which is harmful for other animals of its own or different species.

Natural immunity is possessed normally by certain individuals or certain species. For example, there are certain individuals who can work in the very midst of an epidemic of infectious disease and never contract the infection. Again, Man is immune to certain diseases which are destructive to all cattle, such as the rinder-pest; while, on the other hand, nearly all animals are immune to Man's greatest scourge—syphilis.

Acquired immunity or artificial immunity is a state that is obtained as the result of having successfully passed through and overcome infection. As is well known, one attack of scarlet fever, measles, whooping cough, etc., confers a more or less enduring immunity against further attack. Vaccination and serum therapy can rudely be considered as technical procedures to provide this acquired immunity by giving the equivalent to an attack of the infection.

It was in 1883 that Elie Metchnikoff, in his famous address given in Odessa, revealed to the world the then new theory of phagocytosis. He showed that there are in the blood of the human being certain unicellular organisms (of two kinds, large "macrophages" and small "leucocytes"), amoeba-like in character, which devour invading bacteria in the blood. He showed, moreover, that when an infection occurs—which is another way of saying when there is an invasion of hostile microbes—there is a sudden increase in the number of these defenders of the body, and, in addition, these leucocytes are "free" and can hasten to the infection.

The next important step in the development of the science of immunity was the discovery of anti-toxins in the blood of patients suffering from diphtheria and tetanus. In 1890, Von Behring and Kitasato showed that certain bacteria, especially those of diphtheria, tetanus, a form of dysentery and a form of meat poisoning, produce a poisonous secretion or toxin in the medium in which they are growing. The fluids of the body produce a defender, an antibody which neutralizes the toxin or poison and is therefore called an antitoxin.

By injecting into an animal small, and later large, doses of the toxin, the animal's blood becomes well loaded with antitoxin. This antitoxin can then be injected into a person in whose blood is the toxin—in other words, who is ill—and the antitoxin from the animal will neutralize the poison and cure the patient.

The third great step was a discovery in 1903 by Wright and Douglas of a new substance in the blood serum which has the power of acting upon the hostile bacteria in such a way as to make them more easily digested, by the defensive phagocytes. This substance has been given the name of opsonin. The blood of some patients—such as those afflicted with boils—has been found to be low in the possession of these substances, and consequently they are said to have a low opsonic index. By certain injections to raise this opsonic index, the invading bacteria are rendered digestible to the phagocytes and the patient is on the recovery from that infection.

So far, then, there has been presented the double ring of defenses in the body of every man or woman: First, the ring of body cells—the phagocytes; secondly, the allied forces in the body fluids—the opsonins, which weaken the invading hosts.

But the matter is not so simple as this mere statement would suggest. The invading micro-organism does not tamely submit to being devoured by a phagocyte or weakened by an opsonin, nor to have his toxic product neutralized by an antitoxin. No two bacteria act the same way. Of the hosts of different varieties that exist, only a few give forth true toxins; only a few are easily conquered by the phagocyte; only a few are susceptible to the effect of the opsonin.

Most of them have an unfortunate and baneful power of developing resistant races. An injection of the trypanosomes of Nagana into an animal will cause the organisms to appear on the second day; they then multiply enormously; five days later the animal has a "crisis" and the trypanosomes disappear. After a few days, however, the micro-organisms again appear in the blood-stream, but these are a new race, and they have acquired properties which enable them to resist being killed off by processes to which the first had no resistance. This is the case in Relapsing Fever. It is also the case in Syphilis, and it is generally believed that there is a series of resistant races in Tuberculosis. The "typhoid carrier" possesses a resistant organism. In 1909, Bail advanced a theory which has secured considerable support, that certain micro-organisms secrete substances called "agressins," which paralyze the phagocytes, so that the infection proceeds without any resistance from the defending army.

Serum-therapy has been marvellously successful in two diseases—diphtheria and tetanus. It is fairly successful with one of the dysenteries (Shiga-Kruse), but its value is yet to be made absolutely unquestioned in other fields.

Antibacterial sera, as contrasted with antitoxic, are distinctly dangerous. Only in cerebro-spinal meningitis is the record mainly one of success. The typhoid serum of Chantemesse is rather a vaccine than a true antibacterial serum. Others have given good results experimentally in Plague, Cholera and Anthrax, but not sufficiently to justify a wide use on human beings.

Vaccine-therapy is the immunization of a patient by attenuated virus to produce protection against the fully virulent virus. It is not without its dangers, as indeed is true of all similar modes of treatment; but in Smallpox, Typhoid Fever, Cholera and Plague it undoubtedly has caused great reductions in the mortality.

A development that has given rise to much experiment was made by Marie and Leri in 1914, when in a case of cerebral hemorrhage they noticed that the serum was fluorescent, and based upon this observation a system of chromo-sero diagnosis, which has been shown to be of considerable value in internal hemorrhages.

The use of auto-sero-therapy, which consists of withdrawing and reinjecting sera from the patient's own body, has been used experimentally. Spiethoff reported a large number of chronic skin diseases with favorable results. Injection of an autolysate of cancer cells produced a recovery which only medical caution prevented from being declared a cure.

Chemo-therapy—which is the imitation of Nature's method of overcoming an infection by the aid of substances which destroy the microorganisms, while leaving the cells of the body of the host uninjured—has been the significant development of the second decade of the twentieth century. Of the chemicals used, the arsenic derivatives have been most prominent, and "606" (salvarsan) and "914" (neo-salvarsan) became widely known to the public for their therapeutic value against Syphilis, Relapsing Fever and Framboesia. The value of eosin and selenium salts has been shown in arresting certain types of malignant tumors closely resembling cancer. This is one of the most fruitful fields of research, and compounds of value are being added to progressive therapeutics constantly.

CHAPTER XI

MODERN PHYSIOLOGY

The views concerning the working of the human body and its structure, while very complete, are not infallible even at the present day. To understand the functions of the several parts of the human mechanism, it is absolutely essential that one should be acquainted with the structure of all its parts, even to the smallest details, so that in reviewing the modern physiological beliefs one also sees modern anatomy. Thomas Huxley summed up the workings and structure of the human organism and the following description is based upon his statements, these having been brought up to the latest word in physiological and anatomical research.

A man in health and "neither gaining nor losing flesh" is incessantly oxidating and wasting away and periodically making good the loss. So that if, in his average condition, he could be confined in the scale-pan of a delicate spring balance, like that used for weighing letters, the scale-pan would descend at every meal and ascend in the intervals, oscillating to equal distances on each side of the average position, which would never be maintained for longer than a few minutes. There is, therefore, no such thing as a stationary condition of the weight of the body, and what we call such is simply a condition of variation within narrow limits. The gains and losses of the daily bodily economy balance each other.

Suppose this diurnally balanced physiological state to be reached, it can be maintained only so long as the quantity of the mechanical work done and of heat or other force evolved remains absolutely unchanged.

Let such a physiologically balanced man lift a heavy body from the ground and the loss of weight which he would have undergone without that exertion will be increased by a definite amount, which cannot be made good unless a proportionate amount of extra food be supplied to him. Let the temperature of the surrounding air fall, and the same result will occur if his body remains as warm as before.

On the other hand, diminish his exertion and lower his production of heat, and either he will gain weight or some of his food will remain unused.

Thus, in a properly nourished man, a stream of food is constantly entering the body in the shape of complex compounds containing comparatively little oxygen, as constantly the elements of the food (whether before or after they have formed part of the living substance) are leaving the body combined with more oxygen. And the incessant breaking down and oxidation of the complex compounds which enter the body are definitely proportioned to the amount of energy the body gives out, whether in the shape of heat or otherwise, just in the same way as the amount of work to be got out of a steam engine and the amount of heat it and its furnace give off bear a strict proportion to its consumption of fuel.

The condition to which the name of fever is given is characterized essentially by the temperature of the body being higher than is usual in health. Thus it may rise to as much as 41° C. (105.8° F.) or occasionally even above this point, and there has been much dispute as to how high temperature arises. A common cause is a disturbance of the mechanism by which heat is lost to the body, some diminution in loss of heat leading naturally to a rise of temperature. On the other hand, direct measurement shows that a fevered person often gives off more heat than usual and at the same time uses up more oxygen and produces more carbonic acid and urea than usual. In such cases there is no doubt that the abnormally high temperature is largely due to an over-production of heat.

From these general considerations regarding the nature of life, considered as physiological work, one may turn for the purpose of taking a like broad survey of the apparatus which does the work.

The human body is obviously separable into head, trunk and limbs. In the head, the brain-case or skull is distinguishable from the face. The trunk is naturally divided into the chest or thorax and the belly or abdomen. Of the limbs there are two pairs—the upper, or arms, and lower, or legs, and legs and arms again are subdivided by their joints into parts which obviously exhibit a rough correspondence— thigh and upper arm, leg and forearm, ankle and wrist, toes and fingers, plainly answering to one another. And the two last, in fact, are so similar that they receive the same name of digits, while the several joints of the fingers and toes have the common denomination of phalanges.

The whole body thus composed (without the viscera or organs which fill the cavities of the trunk) is seen to be bilaterally symmetrical; that is to say, if it were split lengthwise by a great knife, which should be made to pass along the middle line of both the dorsal and ventral (of back and front) aspects, the two halves would almost exactly resemble one another.

One-half of the body, divided in the manner described, would exhibit in the trunk the cut faces of thirty-three bones, joined together by a very strong and tough substance into a long column, which lies much nearer the dorsal (or back) than the ventral (or front) aspect of the body. The bones thus cut through are called the bodies of the vertebræ. They separate a long, narrow canal called the spinal canal, which is placed upon their dorsal side, from the spacious chamber of the chest and abdomen, which lies upon their ventral side. There is no direct communication between the dorsal canal and the ventral cavity.

The spinal canal contains a long white cord—the spinal cord—which is an important part of the nervous system. The ventral chamber is divided into the two subordinate cavities of the thorax and abdomen by a remarkable, partly fleshy and partly membranous partition, the diaphragm, which is concave toward the abdomen and convex toward the thorax. The alimentary canal traverses these cavities from one end to the other, piercing the diaphragm. So does a long double series of distinct masses of nervous substance, which are called ganglia. These are connected together by nervous cords and constitute the so-called sympathetic system. The abdomen contains, in addition to these parts, the two kidneys, one placed against each side of the vertebral column and connected each by a tube, the ureter, to a muscular bag, the bladder, lying at the bottom of the abdomen; the liver, the pancreas or "sweetbread," and the spleen. The thorax encloses, besides its segment of the alimentary canal and of the sympathetic system, the heart and the two lungs. The latter are placed one on each side of the heart, which lies nearly in the middle of the thorax.

Where the body is succeeded by the head the uppermost of the thirty-three vertebral bodies is followed by a continuous mass of bone, which extends through the whole length of the head, and, like the spinal column, separates a dorsal chamber from a ventral one. The dorsal chamber, or cavity of the skull, opens into the spinal canal. It contains a mass of nervous matter called the brain, which is continuous with the spinal cord, the brain and the spinal cord together constituting what is termed the cerebro-spinal system. The ventral chamber, or cavity of the face, is almost entirely occupied by the mouth and pharynx, into which last the upper end of the alimentary canal (called gullet or oesophagus) opens.

Thus the study of a longitudinal section shows that the human body is a double tube, the two tubes being completely separated by the spinal column and the bony axis of the skull, which form the floor of the one tube and the roof of the other. The dorsal tube contains the cerebro-spinal axis; the ventral tube contains the alimentary canal, the sympathetic nervous system, the heart and the lungs, besides other organs.

Transverse sections taken perpendicularly to the axis of the vertebral column or to that of the skull show still more clearly that this is the fundamental structure of the human body and that the great apparent difference between the head and the trunk is due to the different size of the dorsal cavity relatively to the ventral. In the head the former cavity is very large in proportion to the size of the latter; in the thorax or abdomen it is very small.

The limbs contain no such chambers as are found in the body and the head, but with the exception of certain branching tubes filled with fluid, which are called blood-vessels and lymphatics, are solid or semi-solid throughout.

Such being the general character and arrangement of the parts of the human body, it will next be well to consider into what constituents it may be separated by the aid of no better means of discrimination than the eye and the anatomist's knife.

With no more elaborate aids than these, it becomes easy to separate that tough membrane which invests the whole body and is called the skin, or integument, from the parts which lie beneath it. Furthermore, it is readily enough ascertained that this integument consists of two portions: a superficial layer, which is constantly being shed in the form of powder or scales, composed of minute particles of horny matter, and is called the epidermis, and the deeper part, the dermis, which is dense and fibrous. The epidermis, if wounded, neither gives rise to pain nor bleeds. The dermis, under like circumstances, is very tender and bleeds freely. A practical distinction is drawn between the two in shaving, in the course of which operation the razor ought to cut only epidermal structures, for if it go a shade deeper it gives rise to pain and bleeding.

The skin can be readily enough removed from all parts of the exterior, but at the margins of the apertures of the body it seems to stop, and to be replaced by a layer which is much redder, more sensitive, bleeds more readily and which keeps itself continually moist by giving out a more or less tenacious fluid called mucus. Hence at these apertures the skin is said to stop and to be replaced by mucous membrane, which lines all those interior cavities, such as the alimentary canal, into which the apertures open. But, in truth, the skin does not really come to an end at these points, but is directly continued into the mucous membrane, which last is simply an integument of greater delicacy, but consisting fundamentally of the same two layers—a deep, fibrous layer, called also dermis, and containing blood-vessels, and a superficial, bloodless one, now called the epitheium. Thus every part of the body might be said to be contained between the walls of a double bag, formed by the epidermis, which invests the outside of the body, and the epithelium, its continuation, which lines the alimentary canal.

The dermis of the skin and that of the mucous membranes are chiefly made up of a filamentous substance, which yields abundant gelatine on being boiled and is the matter which tans when hide is made into leather. This is called connective tissue, because it is the great connecting medium by which the different parts of the body are held together. Thus it passes from the dermis between all the other organs, ensheathing the muscles, coating the bones and cartilages and eventually reaching and entering into the mucous membranes. And so completely and thoroly does the connective tissue permeate almost all parts of the body that if every other tissue could be dissected away a complete model of all the organs would be left composed of this tissue. Connective tissue varies very much in character; in some places being very soft and tender, at others—as in the tendons and ligaments, which are almost wholly composed of it—attaining great strength and density.

Among the most important of the tissues embedded in and ensheathed by the connective tissue are some of the presence and action of which can be readily determined during life.

If the upper arm of a man whose arm is stretched out be tightly grasped by another person, the latter, as the former bends up his forearm, will feel a great soft mass, which lies at the fore part of the upper arm, swell, harden and become prominent. As the arm is extended again the swelling and hardness vanish.

On removing the skin, the body which thus changes its configuration is found to be a mass of red flesh, sheathed in connective tissue. The sheath is continued at each end into a tendon, by which the muscle is attached, on the one hand, to the shoulder-bone and on the other to one of the bones of the forearm. This mass of flesh is the muscle called biceps, and it has the peculiar property of changing its dimensions—shortening and becoming thick in proportion to its decrease in length—when influenced by the will as well as by some other causes, called stimuli, and of returning to its original form when let alone. This temporary change in the dimensions of a muscle, this shortening and thickening, is spoken of as its contraction. It is by reason of this property that muscular tissue becomes the great motor agent of the body; the muscles being so disposed between the system of levers which support the body that their contraction necessitates the motion of one lever upon another.

These levers form part of the system of hard tissues which constitute the skeleton. The less hard of these are the cartilage, composed of a dense, firm substance, ordinarily known as "gristle." The latter are the bones, which are masses of tissue, hardened by being impregnated with phosphate and carbonate of lime. They are animal tissues which have become, in a manner, naturally petrified; and when the salts of lime are extracted, as they may be by the action of acids, a model of the bone in soft and flexible animal matter remains.

More than 200 separate bones are ordinarily reckoned in the human body, though the actual number of distinct bones varies at different periods of life, many bones which are separate in youth becoming united in old age. Thus there are originally, as we have seen, thirty-three separate bodies of vertebræ in the spinal column, and the upper twenty-four of these commonly remain distinct throughout life. But the twenty-fifth, twenty-sixth, twenty-seventh, twenty-eighth and twenty-ninth early unite into one great bone, called the sacrum, and the four remaining vertebræ often run into one bony mass called the coccyx.

In early adult life the skull contains twenty-two naturally separate bones, but in youth the number is much greater and in old age far less.

Twenty-four ribs bound the chest laterally, twelve on each side, and most of them are connected by cartilages with the breast-bone or sternum. In the girdle which supports the shoulder two bones are always distinguishable as the scapula, or shoulder-blade, and the clavicle, or collar-bone. The pelvis, to which the legs are attached, consists of two separate bones called the ossa innominata, or hip-bones, in the adult; but each os innominatum is separable into three (called publis, ischium and ilium) in the young.

There are thirty bones in each of the arms and the same number in each of the legs, counting the patella, or knee-pan.

All these bones are fastened together by ligaments, or by cartilages, and where they play freely over one another a coat of cartilage furnishes the surfaces which come into contact. The cartilages which thus form part of a joint are called articular cartilages and their free surfaces, by which they rub against each other, are lined by a delicate synovial membrane, which secretes a lubricating fluid—the synovia.

Tho the bones of the skeleton are all strongly enough connected together by ligaments and cartilages, the joints play so freely and the center of gravity of the body, when erect, is so high up, that it is impossible to make a skeleton or a dead body support itself in the upright position. That position, easy as it seems, is the result of the contraction of a multitude of muscles which oppose and balance one another. Thus the foot affording the surface of support, the muscles of the calf must contract or the legs and body would fall forward. But this action tends to bend the legs, and to neutralize this and keep the leg straight, the great muscles in front of the thigh must come into play. But these, by the same action, tend to bend the body forward on the legs, and if the body is to be kept straight, they must be neutralized by the action of the muscles of the buttocks and of the back.

The erect position, then, which we assume so easily and without thinking about it, is the result of the combined and accurately proportioned action of a vast number of muscles. What is it that makes them work together in this way?

Let any person in the erect position receive a violent blow on the head, and the effect is rapid. On the instant he drops prostrate, in a heap, with his limbs relaxed and powerless. What has happened to him? The blow may have been so inflicted as not to touch a single muscle of the body; it may not cause the loss of a drop of blood; and, indeed, if the "concussion," as it is called, has not been too severe, the sufferer, after a few moments of unconsciousness, will come to himself and be as well as ever again. Clearly, therefore, no permanent injury has been done to any part of the body, least of all to the muscles, but an influence has been exerted upon a something which governs the muscles. And a similar influence may be the effect of very subtle causes. A strong mental emotion, and even a very bad smell, will, in some people, produce the same effect as a blow.

These observations might lead to the conclusion that it is the mind which directly governs the muscles, but a little further inquiry will show that such is not the case. For people have been so stabbed or shot in the back as to cut the spinal cord without any considerable injury to other parts, and then they have lost the power of standing upright as much as before, tho their minds may have remained perfectly clear. And not only have they lost the power of standing upright under these circumstances, but they no longer retain any power of either feeling what is going on in their legs, or, by an act of their own will, causing motion in them.

And yet, tho the mind is thus cut off from the lower limbs, a controlling and governing power over them still remains in the body. For if the soles of the disabled feet be tickled, though the mind does not feel the tickling, the legs will be jerked up, just as would be the case in an uninjured person. Again, if a series of galvanic shocks be sent into the spinal cord, the legs will perform movements even more powerful than those which the will could produce in an uninjured person. And, finally, if the injury is of such a nature as not simply to divide or injure the spinal cord in one place only, but to crush or profoundly disorganize it, all these phenomena cease; tickling the soles, or sending galvanic shocks along the spine, will produce no effect upon the legs.

By examinations of this kind carried still further, the remarkable result is reached that, while the brain is the seat of all sensation and mental action and the primary source of all voluntary muscular contractions, the spinal cord is by itself capable of receiving an impression from the exterior and converting it, not only into a simple muscular contraction, but into a combination of such actions.

Thus, in general terms, it may be said of the cerebro-spinal nervous centers, that they have the power, when they receive certain impressions from without, of giving rise to simple or combined muscular contractions.

But these impressions from without are of very different characters.

Any part of the surface of the body may be so affected as to give rise to the sensations of contact or of heat or cold, and any or every substance is able, under certain circumstances, to produce these sensations. But only very few and comparatively small portions of the bodily framework are competent to be affected in such a manner as to cause the sensations of taste or of smell, of sight or of hearing, and only a few substances or particular kinds of vibrations are able so to affect those regions. These very limited parts of the body, which induce relation with particular kinds of substances or forms of force, are what are termed sensory organs. There are two such organs for sight, two for hearing, two for smell and one, or more strictly speaking two, for taste.

With this brief view of the structure of the body, of the organs which support it, of the organs which move it and of the organs which put it in relation with the surrounding world, or, in other words, enable it to move in harmony with influences from without, next must be considered the means by which all this wonderful apparatus is kept in working order.

All work implies waste. The work of the nervous system and that of the muscles, therefore, implies consumption either of their own substance or of something else. And as the organism can make nothing, it must possess the means of obtaining from without that which it wants, and of throwing off from itself that which it wastes; and we have seen that, in the gross, it does these things. The body feeds, and it excretes. Now passing from the broad fact to the mechanism by which the fact is brought about, it is seen that the organs which convert food into nutriment are the organs of alimentation; those which distribute nutriment all over the body are organs of circulation; those which get rid of the waste products are organs of excretion.

The circulatory organs consist of a system of minute tubes, with very thin walls, termed capillaries, which are distributed through the whole organism except the epidermis and its products, the epithelium, the cartilages and the substance of the teeth. On all sides, these tubes pass into others, which are called arteries and veins; while these, becoming larger and larger, at length open into the heart, an organ which, as has been seen, is placed in the thorax. During life, these tubes and the chambers of the heart, with which they are connected, are all full of liquid, which is, for the most part, that red fluid with which all are familiar as blood.

A simple statement of the circulatory system, made recently by Albert M. Polon, runs as follows: "There are two sets of tubes connected with the heart, viz., arteries and veins, in which are valves permitting the flow of the blood in one direction only. The terminations of the arteries are connected with the veins by means of minute vessels, called capillaries. The principles upon which the blood is caused to circulate in these tubes is well represented by a hollow closed ring, with an enlargement at one point (corresponding to the heart), in which there is a valve opening only one way. It is clear that if such a ring be filled with water and placed upon the table there will be no movement in the tube, but if pressure be applied, the water within the tube will flow in the direction of least pressure and toward the point where the valve opens. Just as the difference of pressure thus is the causative factor of the flow in this ring, so in the heart, arteries, capillaries and veins the contraction of the heart muscle performs the same office. The heart contracting propels the blood into the arteries. From these the blood passes into the capillaries, where the pressure is lower, and thence it proceeds into the veins, where the pressure is still lower, until it finally reaches the heart.

"To appreciate clearly the working of the circulatory system, it is necessary briefly to consider the anatomy of the heart. The heart is a hollow muscular organ, the cavity of which is separated into right and left halves by a longitudinal section, and each half is divided into an upper receiving chamber, the 'auricle,' and the lower ejecting chamber, the 'ventricle.' But each ventricle is not completely separated from the corresponding auricle; the two communicate by means of an opening, called the 'auricular ventricular aperture,' which is provided with a valve, allowing the passage of blood from the auricle to the ventricle, but effectually preventing its return.

"Let a given quantity of blood be traced through this system, starting with one of the larger arteries. As said before, the blood will pass into the smaller arteries, thence into the 'arterioles' and finally into the capillaries. From here it is drained into 'venules,' which grow larger and larger to become veins and terminate at the upper half of the right side of the heart, viz., the right auricle. From the right auricle the blood is sent along into the right ventricle. This in its turn ejects it into the pulmonary arteries, which carries blood to the lungs. From the lungs the blood returns by the pulmonary veins to the left auricle, from where it enters into the left ventricle, to be finally ejected into the arteries. Thus the circulation of the blood has two phases: (1) When the blood is ejected from the right ventricle into the lungs, and back into the left ventricle, and (2) when the blood ejected from the left ventricle passes through the system and is returned to the right side of the heart. This first phase is known as 'pulmonary' and the second as 'systemic.'"

The organs of alimentation are the mouth, pharynx, gullet, stomach and intestines, with their appendages, the pancreas and the liver. What they do is, first, to receive and grind the food. They then act upon it with chemical agents, of which they possess a store which is renewed as fast as it is used; and in this way convert the food by processes of digestion into a fluid containing nutritious matters in solution or suspension, and innutritious dregs or feces.

Now the fluid containing the dissolved or suspended nutritive matters which are the result of the process of digestion, traverses the very thin layer of soft and permeable tissue which separates the cavity of the alimentary canal from the cavities of the innumerable capillary vessels which lie in the walls of that canal, and so enters the blood, with which those capillaries are filled. Whirled away by the torrent of the circulation, the blood, thus charged with nutritive matter, enters the heart, and is thence propelled into the organs of the body. To these organs it supplies the nutriment with which it is charged; from them it takes their waste products, and, finally, returns by the veins to the heart, loaded with useless and injurious excretions, which sooner or later take the form of water, carbonic acid, and urea.

These excretionary matters are separated from the blood by the excretory organs, of which there are three—the skin, the lungs and the kidneys.

Different as these organs may be in appearance, they are constructed upon one and the same principle. Each, in ultimate analysis, consists of a very thin sheet of tissue, like so much delicate blotting-paper, the one face of which is free, or lines a cavity in communication with the exterior of the body, while the other is in contact with the blood which has to be purified.

The excreted matters are, as it were, strained from the blood, through this delicate layer of tissue, and on to its free surface, whence they make their escape.

Each of these organs is especially concerned in the elimination of one of the chief waste products—water, carbonic acid and urea—tho it may at the same time be a means of escape for the others. Thus, the lungs are especially busied in getting rid of carbonic acid, but at the same time they give off a good deal of water. The duty of the kidneys is to excrete urea (together with other substances, chiefly salts), but at the same time they pass away a large quantity of water and a trifling amount of carbonic acid; while the skin gives off much water, some carbonic acid, and a certain quantity of saline matter, with a trace of urea.

Finally, the lungs play a double part, being not merely eliminators of waste, or excretionary products, but importers into the economy of a substance which is not exactly either food or drink, but something as important as either—to wit, oxygen.

As the carbonic acid (and water) is passing from the blood through the lungs into the external air, oxygen is passing from the air through the lungs into the blood, and is immediately carried by the blood to all parts of the body. The waste which leaves the body contains more oxygen than the food which enters the body. Indeed oxidation, the oxygen being supplied by the blood, is going on all over the body. All parts of the body are thus continually being oxidized, or, in other words, are continually burning, some more rapidly and fiercely than others. And this burning, tho it is carried on in a peculiar manner, so as never to give rise to a flame, yet nevertheless produces an amount of heat which is as efficient as a fire to raise the blood to a temperature of about 37° C. (98.6° F.); and this hot fluid, incessantly renewed in all parts of the body by the torrent of the circulation, warms the body, as a house is warmed by hot-water apparatus. Nor is it alone the heat of the body which is provided by this oxidation; the energy which appears in the muscular work done by the body has the same source. Just as the burning of the coal in a steam-engine supplies the motive power which drives the wheels, so, tho in a peculiar way, the oxidation of the muscles (and thus ultimately of the food) supplies the motive power of those muscular contractions which carry out the movements of the body. The food, like coal combustible or capable of oxidation, is built up into the living body, which, in like manner combustible, is continually being oxidized by the oxygen from the blood, thus doing work and giving out heat.

These alimentary, circulatory or distributive, excretory, and respiratory (oxidational) processes would, however, be worse than useless if they were not kept in strict proportion one to another. If the state of physiological balance is to be maintained, not only must the quantity of food taken be at least equivalent to the quantity of matter excreted; but that food must be distributed with due rapidity to the seat of each local waste. The circulatory system is the commissariat of the physiological army.

Again, if the body is to be maintained at a tolerably even temperature, while that of the air is constantly varying, the condition of the hot-water apparatus must be most carefully regulated.

"In other words," says Huxley, "a coördinating organ must be added to the organs mentioned, and this is found in the nervous system, which not only possesses the function already described of enabling us to move our bodies and to know what is going on in the external world; but makes us aware of the need of food, enables us to discriminate nutritious from innutritious matters, and to exert the muscular actions needful for seizing, killing and cooking; guides the hand to the mouth, governs all the movements of the jaws and of the alimentary canal, and determines the due supply of the juices necessary for digestion.

"The various functions which have been thus briefly indicated constitute the greater part of what are called the vital actions of the human body, and so long as they are performed, the body is said to possess life. The cessation of the performance of these functions is what is ordinarily called death."

But there are really several kinds of death, which may, in the first place, be distinguished from one another under the two heads of local and of general death.

(i) Local death is going on at every moment, and in most, if not in all, parts of the living body. Individual cells of the epidermis and of the epithelium are incessantly dying and being cast off, to be replaced by others which are, as constantly, coming into separate existence. The like is true of blood-corpuscles, and probably of many other elements of the tissues.

This form of local death is usually insensible and is essential to the due maintenance of life. But, occasionally, local death occurs on a larger scale, as the result of injury, or as the consequence of disease. A burn, for example, may suddenly kill more or less of the skin; or part of the tissues of the skin may die, as in the case of the slough which lies in the midst of a boil; or a whole limb may die, and exhibit the strange phenomena of mortification.

The local death of some tissues is followed by their regeneration. Not only all the forms of epidermis and epithelium, but nerves, connective tissue, bone, and at any rate, some muscles, may be thus reproduced, even on a large scale.

(ii) General death is of two kinds, death of the body as a whole, and death of the tissues. By the former term is implied the absolute cessation of the functions of the brain, of the circulatory, and of the respiratory organs; by the latter, the entire disappearance of the vital actions of the ultimate structural constituents of the body. When death takes place, the body, as a whole, dies first, the death of the tissues not occurring until after an interval, which is sometimes considerable.

Hence it is that, for some little time after what is ordinarily called death, the muscles of an executed criminal may be made to contract by the application of proper stimuli. The muscles are not dead, though the man is.

The modes in which death is brought about appear at first sight to be extremely varied. One speaks of natural death by old age, or by some of the endless forms of diseases; of violent death by starvation, or by the innumerable varieties of injury, or poison. But, in reality, the immediate cause of death is always the stoppage of the functions of one of three organs: the cerebro-spinal nervous system, the lungs, or the heart. Thus, a man may be instantly killed by such an injury to a part of the brain which is called the spinal bulb or medulla oblongata as may be produced by hanging, or the breaking of the neck. Or death may be the immediate result of suffocation by strangulation, smothering or drowning—or, in other words, of stoppage of the respiratory functions. Or, finally, death ensues at once when the heart ceases to propel blood. These three organs—the brain, the lungs, and the heart—have been fancifully termed the tripod of life.

In ultimate analysis, however, life has but two legs to stand upon, the lungs and the heart, for death through the brain is always the effect of the secondary action of the injury to that organ upon the lungs or the heart. The functions of the brain cease when either respiration or circulation is at an end. But if circulation and respiration be kept up artificially, the brain may be removed without causing death. On the other hand, if the blood be not aerated, its circulation by the heart cannot preserve life; and, if the circulation be at an end, mere aeration of the blood in the lungs is equally ineffectual for the prevention of death.

With the cessation of life, the everyday forces of the inorganic world no longer remain the servants of the bodily frame, as they were during life, but becomes its masters. Oxygen, the slave of the being organism, becomes the lord of the dead body. Atom by atom, the complex molecules of the tissues are taken to pieces and reduced to simpler and more oxidized substances, until the soft parts are dissipated chiefly in the form of carbonic acid, ammonia, water and soluble salts, and the bones and teeth alone remain. But not even these dense and earthy structures are competent to offer a permanent resistance to water and air. Sooner or later the animal basis which holds together the earthy salts decomposes and dissolves—the solid structures become friable, and break down into powder. Finally, they dissolve and are diffused among the waters of the surface of the globe, just as the gaseous products of decomposition are dissipated through its atmosphere.

It is impossible to follow, with any degree of certainty, wanderings more varied and more extensive than those imagined by the ancient sages who held the doctrines of transmigration; but the chances are, that, sooner or later, some, if not all, of the scattered atoms will be gathered into new forms of life.

The sun's rays, acting through the vegetable world, build up some of the wandering molecules of carbonic acid, of water, of ammonia and of salts, into the fabrics of plants. The plants are devoured by animals, animals devour one another, man devours both plants and other animals. Thus there is constant change of these elements from one living organism to another through all time and ages.

MATHEMATICS

INTRODUCTION

THE general reader, for whom this writing is primarily designed, though he be college-bred, and may thus have had a mathematical discipline extending possibly through an elementary course in the calculus, probably entertains very erroneous or very inadequate notions respecting the proper character of mathematics, and especially respecting alike its marvelous growth in modern times and the great range and variety of doctrines that the term has come to signify. With a view to correcting such errors, at least in some measure, if they exist, and in order to enhance the reader's interest and to enlighten his appreciation, it seems worth while to preface the exposition proper with some general indications—albeit they must needs be mainly of an exterior kind—of the nature and extent of the science whose foundations are to be subsequently explained.

Let it be understood, then, that, while mathematics is the most ancient of the sciences, it is not surpassed by any of them in point of modernity, but is flourishing even to-day as never before, and at a rate unsurpassed by any rival. To compare it to a deep-rooted giant tree of manifold high and far-branching arms is not an adequate simile. Rather is the science like a mighty forest of such oaks. These, however, literally grow into and through each other, so that by the junction and intercrescence of limb with limb and root with root and trunk with trunk the manifold wood becomes a single living, organic, growing whole. The mathematical achievements of antiquity were great achievements. The works of Euclid and Archimedes, of Apollonius and Diophantus, will endure forever among the most glorious monuments of the human intellect. And just now, owing to Dr. Heath's superb English edition of Euclid's "Elements"—a beautiful translation of the thirteen books from the definitive text of Heiberg, with rich bibliography and extensive commentary setting the whole matter in the composite light of ancient and modern geometric research—one sees even better than ever before how great, mathematically, was the age that produced the immortal Alexandrine classic. Yet the "Elements" of Euclid is as small a part of Mathematics as the "Iliad" is of Literature; as the "Pandects" of Justinian is of human Jurisprudence; or as the sculpture of Phidias is of the world's total Art.

Not the age of Euclid, but our own, is the golden age of mathematics. Ours is the age in which no less than six international congresses of mathematics have been held in the course of ten years. Today there exists more than a dozen mathematical societies, containing a growing membership of over two thousand men and women representing the centers of scientific light throughout the great culture nations of the world. In our time more than five hundred scientific journals are each devoted in part, while more than two score others are devoted exclusively, to the publication of mathematics. It is in our time that the "Jahrbuch über die Fortschritte der Mathematik" ("Yearbook for the Progress of Mathematics"), tho it admits only condensed abstracts with titles and does not report upon all the journals, has, nevertheless, grown into nearly forty huge volumes in as many years. It requires no less than the seven ponderous tomes of the forthcoming "Enkyclopädie der Mathematischen Wissenschaften" ("Encyclopedia of the Mathematical Sciences") to contain, not expositions, not demonstrations, but merely compact reports and bibliographic notices sketching developments that have taken place since the beginning of the nineteenth century. This great work is being supplemented and translated into the French language. Finally, to adduce yet another evidence of like kind, the three immense volumes of Moritz Cantor's "Geschichte der Mathematik" ("History of Mathematics"), tho they do not aspire to the higher forms of elaborate exposition, and tho they are far from exhausting the period traversed by them, yet conduct the narrative down only to 1758. (A fourth volume in continuation of Cantor's work has recently appeared. It was composed mainly by other hands.) That date, however, but marks the time when mathematics, then schooled for over a hundred eventful years in the fast unfolding wonders of Analytic Geometry and the Calculus, and rejoicing in these the two most powerful instruments of human thought, had but fairly entered upon her modern career. And so fruitful have been the intervening years, so swift the march along the myriad tracks of modern Analysis and Geometry, so abounding and bold and fertile withal has been the creative genius of the time, that to record, even briefly, the discoveries and the creations since the closing date of Cantor's work would require an addition to his great volumes of a score of volumes more.

It is little wonder that so vital a spirit as that of Mathesis, increasing in tensity and more and more abounding as the ages have passed—it is small wonder that since pre-Aristotelian times it has challenged the mathematician and the philosopher alike to tell what it is—to define mathematics; and it is now not surprising that they should try in vain for many hundreds of years; for, naturally, conception of the science has had to grow with the growth of the science itself.

INTRODUCTION

The most striking modern measurements, as of the volume of a planet, the weight of a sunbeam, the growth of cells, the valency of atoms, rates of chemical change, the penetrative power of radium emanations, are none of them done by direct repeated application of a unit or by any direct method whatever. They are all of them accomplished by one form or another of indirection. It was perception of this fact that led the famous philosopher and respectable mathematician, Auguste Comte, to define mathematics as "the science of indirect measurement." But the thought is not yet sufficiently deep or comprehensive. For there is an immense range of admittedly mathematical activity that is not in the least concerned with measurement, whether direct or indirect. Consider, for example, that splendid creation of the nineteenth century, known as Projective Geometry. Here is a boundless domain of countless fields, where reals and imaginaries, finites and infinites, enter on equal terms, where the spirit delights in the artistic balance and symmetric interplay of a kind of conceptual and logical counterpoint—an enchanted realm where thought is double and flows throughout in curiously winding but parallel streams. In this domain there is no concern with number or quantity or magnitude, and metric considerations are entirely absent or completely subordinate. The fact, to take a simplest example, that two points determine a line uniquely, or that the intersection of a plane and a sphere is a circle, or that any configuration whatever—the reference is here to ordinary space—presents two reciprocal aspects according as it is viewed as an ensemble of points or as a manifold of planes, is not a metric fact at all: it is not a fact about size or quantity or magnitude of any kind. In this region of thought it was position, rather than size, that seemed to some the central matter, and so it was proposed to call mathematics the science of measurement and position.

The conception, thus mightily expanded, yet excludes many a mathematical realm of vast extent. Consider, for example, that limitless class of things known as operations—limitless alike in number and in kind. Now it so happens that there are many systems of operations such that any two operations of a given system, if they be thought as following one another, together thus produce the same effect as some single operation of the system. Such systems are infinitely numerous, and present themselves on every hand. For a simple illustration, think of the totality of possible straight motions in space. The operation of going from point A to point B, followed by the operation of going from B to point C, is equivalent to the single operation of going straight from A to C. Thus it is seen that the system of such operations is a closed system: that is, combination of any two of the operations yields a third one, not without, but within the system. The great notion of Group, thus simply exemplified, tho it had barely emerged into consciousness a hundred years ago, has meanwhile become a concept of fundamental importance and prodigious fertility. It not only affords the basis of an imposing mathematical doctrine—the Theory of Groups—but therewith serves also as a bond of union, a kind of connective tissue, uniting together a large number of widely dissimilar doctrines as organs of a single body. But—and this is the point to be noted here—the abstract operations of a group of operations, tho they are very real things, are neither magnitudes nor positions.

This way of trying to come at an adequate conception of what mathematics is, namely, by attempting to characterize in succession its distinct domains, or its varieties of subject matter, or its modes of activity, in the hope of finding a common definite mark, is not likely to prove successful. For it demands an exhaustive enumeration, not only of the fields now occupied by the science, but also of those destined to be conquered by it in the future, and such an achievement would require a prevision that none may claim.

Fortunately, there are other paths of approach that seem more promising. Every one has observed that mathematics, whatever it may be, possesses a certain mark, namely, a degree of certainty not found elsewhere. So it is proverbially, the exact science par excellence. Exact, no doubt, but in what sense? An excellent answer is found in a definition given about one generation ago by a distinguished American mathematician, Professor Benjamin Peirce: "Mathematics is the science which draws necessary conclusions." This formulation is of like significance with the following, yet finer, mot, by that scholar of Leibnitzian attainment and brilliance, Professor William Benjamin Smith: "Mathematics is the universal art apodictic." These statements, tho neither of them is adequate nor final, are both of telling approximations, wondrously penetrating insights, at once foreshadowing and neatly summarizing for popular use, the epoch-making thesis established mainly by the creators of modern logistic, namely, that mathematics is included in, and in a profound sense may be said to be identical with, Symbolic Logic. Observe that the emphasis falls on the quality of being "necessary"; that is, correct logically, or valid formally.

But why are mathematical conclusions correct? Is it that the mathematician has a reasoning faculty different in kind from that of other men? By no means. What, then, is the secret? Reflect that conclusion implies premises, that premises involve terms, that terms stand for ideas, concepts or notions, and these latter are the ultimate material with which the spiritual architect, called the Reason, designs and builds. Here, then, one may expect to find some light. The apodictic quality of mathematical thought is not due to any special kind of faculty peculiar to the mathematician, nor to any peculiar mode of ratiocination, but is rather due to the character of the concepts with which he deals. What is that distinctive characteristic? The answer is: precision and completeness of determination. But how comes the mathematician by such precision and completeness? There is no mystery or trick involved: some concepts admit of such precision and completeness, others do not—at least not yet; the mathematecian is one who deals with those that do. The matter, however, is not so simple as it may now seem, and the attentive consideration of the reader is invited to what is yet to follow.

The Two Movements of Logico-mathematical Thought.—The foregoing thesis is the joint result of two modern movements of thought, which have had separate origins, have followed separate paths, and, having been carried on by two distinct and even alien groups of investigators, have recently converged, to the astonishment of both groups, upon the thesis in question. One of these movements originated at the very center of mathematics itself, and may be appropriately designated as the critico-mathematical movement. The other, which may be called the logistical movement, took its rise in other interests and in what seemed to logicians and mathematicians alike to be a very different and even a scientifically alien field—the interests and the field of what is known as Logistic or Symbolic Logic.

The Critico-mathematical Movement.—For more than a century after the inventions (*i.e.*, the discoveries) of Analytical Geometry by Descartes and Fermat, and the Infinitesimal Calculus by Leibnitz and Newton, mathematicians devoted themselves almost riotously to application of these powerful instruments to problems of physics, mechanics and geometry, without much concerning themselves about the nicer questions of fundamental principle, logical cogency and precision of concept and argumentation. In the latter part of the eighteenth century the efforts of "the incomparable Euler," of Lacroix, and others, to systematize results, served to reveal in a startling way the necessity of improving foundations. Constructive work was not, indeed, arrested by that disclosure. On the contrary, new doctrines continued to rise and old ones to expand and flourish. But a new spirit had begun to manifest itself. The science became increasingly critical as its towering edifices more and more challenged attention to their foundations. Manifest already in the work of Gauss and Lagrange, the new tendency, under the powerful impulse and leadership of Cauchy, rapidly developed into a momentous movement. The Calculus, while its instrumental efficacy was meanwhile marvelously improved, was itself advanced from the level of a tool to the rank and dignity of a science. The doctrines of the real and of the complex variable were grounded with infinite patience and care, so that, owing chiefly to the critical constructive genius of Weierstrass and his school, that stateliest of all the pure creations of the human intellect—the Modern Theory of Functions, with its manifold branches

—came to rest on a basis not less certain and not less enduring than the very integers with which we count and tell the number of coins in the coffer or cattle in the field. The movement still sweeps on, not only extending to all the cardinal divisions of Analysis, but, through the agency of such as Lobachevski and Bolyai, Grassmann and Riemann, Cayley and Klein, Hilbert and Lie, Peano, Pieri and Pasch, recasting the foundations of Geometry also.

In the light of all this criticism of mathematics by mathematicians themselves, the science assumed the appearance of a great ensemble of theories, competent no doubt, interpenetrating each other in a wondrous way, yet all of them distinct, each built up by logical processes on its own appropriate basis of pure hypothesis, or assumptions, or postulates. As all the theories were thus seen to rest equally on hypothetical foundations, all were seen to be equally legitimate; and doctrines like those of Quaternions, non-Euclidean Geometry and Hyperspace, for a time suspected because based on postulates not all of them traditional, speedily overcame their heretical reputations and were admitted to the circle of the lawful and orthodox.

The Logistical Movement.—It is one thing, however, to deal with the principal divisions of mathematics severally, underpinning each with a foundation of its own; as, for example, the theory of the cardinal numbers (the positive integers) was assumed as the basis for the upbuilding of function theory. That, broadly speaking, was the plan and the effect of the critical movement above sketched. But it is a very different and a profounder thing to underlay all the divisions at once—both those that are and those that are yet to be—with a simple foundation, with a foundation that shall be such, not merely for the divisions, but for something else, distinct from each and from the sum of all, namely, for the organic whole, the science itself, which they constitute. It is nothing less than that achievement—the founding, not of mathematical branches, but of mathematics—which, unconsciously at first, consciously at last, has been the aim and destined goal of the logistical movement—research in symbolic logic.

The advantage of employing symbols in the investigation and exposition of the formal laws of thought is not a recent discovery. As every one knows, symbols were thus employed to a small extent by the Stagirite himself. The advantage, however, was not pursued; because for two thousand years the eyes of logicians were blinded by the blazing genius of the "master of those that know." With the single exception of the reign of Euclid, the annals of science afford no match for the tyranny that has been exercised by the logic of Aristotle. Even the important logical researches of Leibnitz and Lambart, and their daring use of symbolical methods, were powerless to break the spell. It was not till 1854, when George Boole, having invented an algebra to trace and illuminate the subtle ways of reason, published his symbolical "Investigation of the Laws of Thought," that the yet advancing revolution in logic really began. Altho it was neglected for a time by logicians and mathematicians, it was this work of Boole, who was both logician and mathematician, that inspired and inaugurated the scientific movement now known and honored throughout the world under the name of Symbolic Logic. Under the leadership of C. S. Peirce in America, of Bertrand Russell in England, of Schröder in Germany, of Couturat in France, and of Peano and his disciples and peers in Italy—supreme histologist of the human intellect—the deeps of logical reality have been explored in the present generation as never before in the history of the world. Not only have the foundations of the Aristotelian logic—the Calculus of Classes —been recast, but side by side with that everlasting monument of Greek genius there rise to-day two other structures, fit companions of the ancient edifice, namely, the Logic of Relations and the Logic of Propositions.

And now the base of this triune organon—the Calculus of Classes, the Calculus of propositions, the Calculus of Relations—is surprising in its seeming meagerness, for it consists of a score or so of primitive propositions—the principles of logic—and less than a dozen primitive notions called logical constants. Yet more surprising, however, is the fact—justly described as "one of the greatest discoveries of our age" —that this foundation of logic is the foundation of mathematics also. So one may say: Symbolic logic is mathematics, mathematics is symbolic logic; the twain are one.

CASSIUS T. KEYSER.

MATHEMATICS

CHAPTER I

NUMBER

The notion of number is extremely slow to develop, both in the individual and in the race, yet it has its origin at such a remote period in the evolution of man that only a possible reconstruction of its history may be given. Such an account may be built up mainly from three sources, a study of the knowledge and use of number among peoples lowest in the scale of civilization at the present time, the genesis of the number concept in the mind of the child and a comparison of root words of the various languages, past and present.

Number is coeval with spoken language, and probably antedates by a long period any written language or symbolism. Primitive man recorded the results of hunting or fishing excursions, the number of warriors in the opposing camp, or the number of days' journey from home by the use of pebbles, shells, knots in cords, nicks in woods, scores on stone, and, most important for the present study, by the fingers and toes.

The mode of recording numbers by knots on cord gave rise to the term "quipu" reckoning, from the Peruvian language, quipu meaning knot. Edward Clodd, in "The Story of the Alphabet," has this reference: "The quipu has a long history, and is with us in the rosary upon which prayers are counted, in the knot tied in a handkerchief to help a weak memory, and in the sailor's log line." Herodotus tells that when Darius bade the Ionians remain to guard the floating bridge which spanned the Ister, he "tied sixty knots in a thong, saying: 'Men of Ionia, do keep this thong and do as I shall say: so soon as ye shall have seen me go forward against the Scythians, from that time begin and untie a knot each day; and if within this time I am not here, and ye find that the days marked by the knots have passed by, then sail away to your own lands.'"

The quipu reached its more elaborate form among the ancient Peruvians. It consisted of a main cord, to which were fastened at given distances thinner cords of different colors, each cord being knotted in divers ways and each color having its own significance. Red strands stood for soldiers, yellow for gold, white for silver, green for corn, and so forth, while a single knot meant ten, two single knots meant twenty, double knots one hundred, two double knots two hundred. Each town had its officer whose special function was to tie and interpret the quipus. They were called Quipucamayocuna, or knot-officers (compare "harpedonaptæ," or rope-stretchers, in connection with the Geometry of the Egyptians).

The knot-reckoning is in use among the Puna herdsmen of the Peruvian plateau. On the first strand of the quipu they register the bulls, on the second the cows, these again they divide into milch-cows and those that are dry; the next strand register the calves, the next the sheep, and so forth, while other strands record the produce; the different colors of the cords and the twisting of the knots giving the key to the several purposes. The Paloni Indians of California have a similar practice, concerning whom Dr. Hoffman reports that each year a certain number are chosen to visit the settlement at San Gabriel to sell native blankets. "Every Indian sending goods provided the salesman with two cords made of twisted hair or wool, on one of which was tied a knot for every real received, and on another for each blanket sold. When the sum reached ten reals, or one dollar, a double knot was made. Upon the return of the salesman each person selected from the lot his own goods, by which he would at once perceive the amount due, and also the number of blankets for which the salesman was responsible. Hawaiian tax-gatherers kept accounts of the assessable property throughout the island on lines of cordage from four to five hundred fathoms long.

A method of keeping the account of the British exchequer before the use of writing paper was by means of tally sticks. These were of willow about 8 or 10 inches long. Notches were cut, a deep one for a pound, a small one for a shilling. The stick was then sawed half in two near one end and split down to this cut, each half bearing a record of the notches. The shorter piece was given to the depositor and the bank retained the longer.

A great mass of these sticks was still in the basement of the Parliament houses when it was decided to burn them in 1834. Samuel S. Dale describes the bonfire. He says, "A pile of little notched sticks bearing strange-looking inscriptions in abbreviated Latin and old English script, the evidence of thrift for a thousand years, tokens of all the motives that prompt men and women to save, love, hate, greed and sacrifice, hope and fear, frugality and fraud, the proceeds of honest toil and of crime, held for ages that the missing pieces carried away by successive generations might be redeemed, their presence a mute evidence of the blasted hopes of depositors for a thousand years. They were fed steadily to the flames from early morning until a few

NUMBER

minutes before seven o'clock in the evening of Thursday, October 16, 1834, when suddenly a furnace flue, overheated by the unusual fire, started a blaze in the room above, and in a few hours the House of Lords and the House of Commons were in ashes, along with nearly all wooden tally sticks and all the basic standards of weight and measure for the British Empire." A few of the old tally sticks were saved.

When the savage in his first dim gropings for truth recognizes that two objects are more than one, the first step is taken toward the formation of the number concept. That a long pause ensued before the next step was taken is evidenced by the number of cases, cited by various writers, of tribes whose only number words are for "one" and "many" or "one," "two" and "many." This word for "many" plays the same rôle in the language of the savage as "infinity" in ordinary parlance, a number inexpressibly or inconceivably great. The growth of expressibility of number may be compared with the ever-widening ripples when a pebble is dropped into still water, the outer ripple representing the upper bound of conceivable number. All the region beyond would be, in the language of the savage, "many."

The Hindu number system is the first ever devised which has no outer bounds. This fact has led to a more precise use of the word "infinity" in modern mathematical terminology.

The possibilities of the Hindu system are well illustrated by the answers to the celebrated Archimedean "cattle problems." These answers, ten in number, were composed of 206,545 figures each. Such a number if printed in small pica type would be nearly a quarter of a mile in length.

The ability to form a definite conception of a number grows with intelligence, but in the presence of numbers of such magnitude it is opportune to ask what relation exists between the power to conceive the number and the ability to represent it. There seems to have been a curious crossing over of the two. The poverty of the aboriginal language should not be taken as evidence of inability to use larger numbers. It simply means that the verbal expression paused for a longer time after the number "two" than did the number sense. Instances are given of peoples whose number names do not go beyond ten, but who reckon as far as one hundred. The number sense grows along with other mental development, but has not kept step with the verbal and symbolic expression of large numbers. It is questionable if the number 10,000 stands for a distinct conception if it is measured by units. One obtains an idea of such a number only by grouping it, say, into a hundred hundreds.

There are several distinct steps in the formation of a number system: The recognition of increase by adding, in succession, single objects to a group, counting, attaching a number name to the group counted, as "three" sticks (such a number in which the object or unit is named is called a concrete number), the final separation of the number notion from the objects counted or abstraction (one asks how many sticks in the group and the answer is "three," an abstract number), the indicating of the number name by a symbol, the choosing of a method of grouping and finally the perfection of the system by arrangements and combinations of the number words and symbols. It is a long way from the "mokenam," "one"; "uruhu," "many," of the Bococudos to the modern notion of number of the mathematician, "the class of all similar classes."

Number in its primitive sense answers the question, "How many?" It is a pure abstraction which results from counting. Cardinal number tells how many of the group, as "seven" trees, while the ordinal number of any one of the objects indicates the position of the particular object in the series, as the "sixth" tree. These two ideas are equally fundamental, each being derivable from the other. Counting is simply pairing off, or, in mathematical language, establishing a one-to-one correspondence between the individuals of a group of objects counted, as pebbles, the fingers, marks or scores, number names or the symbols for these number names.

In the first stages it would be comparatively easy to invent a word and a symbol for each number, but as the need for larger numbers grew some method of grouping became necessary. In "Problemata," attributed to Aristotle, the following discussion takes place: "Why do all men, barbarians as well as Greeks, numerate up to ten, and not to any other number, as two, three, four or five, and then repeating one and five, two and five, as they do one and ten, two and ten, not counting beyond the tens, from which they again begin to repeat? For each of the numbers which precedes is one or two and then some other, but they enumerate, however, still making the number ten their limit. For they manifestly do it not by chance, but always. The truth is, what men do upon all occasions and always they do not from chance, but from some law of nature. Whether is it, because ten is a perfect number? For it contains all the species of number, the even, the odd, the square, the cube, the linear, the plane, the prime, the composite. Or is it because the number ten is a principle? For the numbers one, two, three, and four when added together produce the number ten. Or is it because the bodies which are in constant motion are nine? Or is it because of the ten numbers in continued proportion, four cubic numbers are consummated (Euclid viii, 10), out of which numbers the Pythagoreans say that the universe is constituted? Or is it because all men from the first have ten fingers? As therefore men have counters of their own by nature, by this set, they numerate all other things."

Dr. Conant gives an illustration which typifies the beginnings of this grouping in "The Number Concept." "More than a century

NUMBER

ago," he says, "travelers in Madagascar observed a curious but simple mode of ascertaining the number of soldiers in an army. Each soldier was made to go through a passage in the presence of the principal chiefs; and as he went through a pebble was dropped on the ground. This continued until a heap of ten was obtained, when one was set aside and a new heap begun. Upon the completion of ten heaps, a pebble was set aside to indicate one hundred, and so on until the entire army had been numbered."

That man carries in the fingers the natural counting machine is shown by the fact that the great majority of number systems have been based on five, ten or twenty. A typical case of such a number system is that of the Zuni scale:

1—töpinte..............taken to start with.
2—kwilli...............put down together with.
3—ha'ï.................the equally dividing finger.
4—awite...............all the fingers all but one done with.
5—öpte................the notched off.
6—topalĭk'ya..........another brought to add to the done with.
7—kwillilĭk'ya.........two brought to and held up with the rest.
8—hailĭk'ye............three brought to and held up with the rest.
9—tenalĭk'ya..........all but all are held up with the rest.
10—ästem'thla..........all the fingers.
11—ästem'thla topayä'thl'-tona...all the fingers and another over above held.
And so forth to 20.
20—kwillik'yënästem'thlan . two times all the fingers.
100—ässiästem'thlak'ya....the fingers all the fingers.
1,000—ässiästem'thlanak'yënästem'thla........the fingers all the fingers times all the fingers.

Arithmetic has been defined as the science of number and the art of computation. This twofold nature of the subject is due to the fact that the Greeks divided the subject into "Arithmetic" proper, which is the science of numbers, a subject for the philosopher, and "Logistic," or computation, which was to be taught to the slave.

Notation and numeration are respectively the writing and reading of numbers. A theory of the building up of a number system is given by Dean Peacock in his article on arithmetic in the "Encyclopedia Metropolitana": "The discovery of the mode of breaking up numbers into classes, the units in each class increasing in decuple proportion, would lead, very naturally, to the invention of a nomenclature for numbers thus resolved, which is simple and comprehensive. By giving names to the first natural numbers, or digits—*i.e.*, the first nine numbers, called digits, from counting on the fingers—and also to the units of each class in the ascending series by ten, we shall be enabled, by combining the names of the digits with those of the units possessing local or representtive value, to express in words any number whatsoever. Thus the number, resolved by means of counters in the manner indicated by Fig. 2, would be expressed (supposing seven, six, five, and four denote the numbers of the counters, in A, B, C, D, and ten, hundred, and thousand, the value of each unit in B, C, and D) by seven, six tens, five hundreds, four thousands; or inverting the order, and making slight changes required by the existing form of the language, by four thousand, five hundred, and sixty-seven."

The successive columns A, B, C, D are called orders. The number of ones in any order required to make one of the next higher order, in this case ten, is called the radix, scale or base of the system. In the above formation when nine have been put in the column A, the

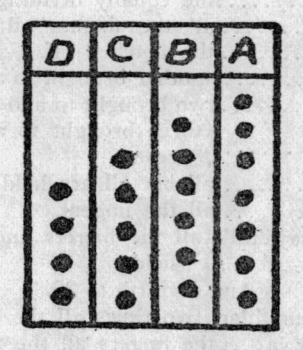

Fig. 2 — OLD METHOD OF COMPUTATION WITH COUNTERS.

tenth would be placed in column B and the nine removed from column A. Such a system is called a decimal or "ten times" system.

One of the earliest devices for reckoning consisted of a board strewn with sand on which parallel lines were drawn with the finger. These lines fulfill the same office as the compartments above marked A, B, C, D. Upon the lines the counters were laid. This reckoning board was called an abacus from an old Semitic word abaq, meaning sand. The development of the abacus from the sand-board to the swan pan of the Chinese and the counting frame of the kindergarten is to be considered in connection with reckoning.

It was the custom of the Romans to drive a nail in the temple of Minerva for each year. When, as with counters, the number of marks exceeded the power of the eye to grasp at a glance, grouping was used.

The simplest method of writing a number is by a mark or stroke for each unit, or one in the number, as | | | | | | | for seven. The stroke was universally used by primitive peoples as a symbol for one. The drawing of the tomb-board of Wabojeeg, a celebrated war chief who died on Lake Superior about 1793, shows this clearly. His totem, the reindeer, is reversed. The seven strokes number the war parties

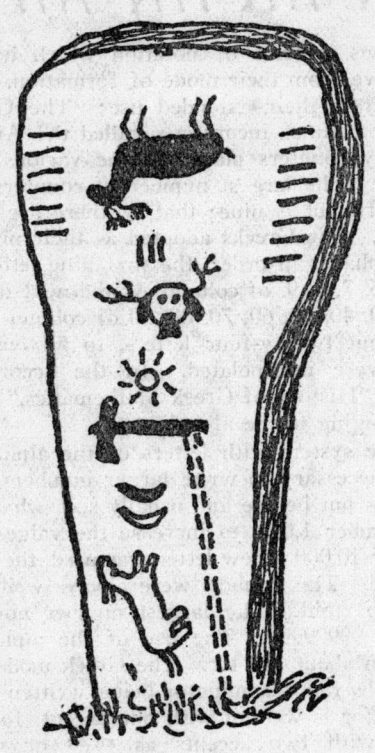

Fig. 3.—TOMB-BOARD OF WABOJEEG.

he led, the three upright strokes symbolize wounds received in battle. The horned head tells of a desperate fight with a moose.

The scoring of each fifth one counted may be regarded as a second step in the development of a satisfactory number symbolism. Such a method of recording succeeding events is not uncommon to-day. The thresher often so marks each sack of grain as it leaves the machine, and in loading and unloading vessels it is frequently the mode used by the tallyman. Thus twenty-two would be written

/// /// /// /// //

Of the numerous systems of notation which have been devised, three are distinctive from their mode of formation, from their logical completion, and from their extended use: The Greek, the Roman, and the Hindu, sometimes incorrectly called the Arabic. Consider a number formed by counters placed in the various compartments A, B, C, D (Fig. 2). The largest number of counters that may be put in any one compartment is nine; that is, there are nine numbers for each compartment. The Greeks adopted as their number symbols the letters of their alphabet in order, the first nine letters for nine numbers 1, 2, 3, 4, 5, 6, 7, 8, 9, of column A; the next nine letters for the numbers 10, 20, 30, 40, 50, 60, 70, 80, 90 of column B. As the alphabet consisted of but twenty-four letters, to fill out column C three obsolete letters were interpolated. In the accompanying scheme, taken from Gow's "History of Greek Mathematics," the starred letters are those not belonging to the alphabet.

The limit of the system with letters of the alphabet alone is 999. When it became necessary to write larger numbers, a stroke like an inverted prime was put before and usually somewhat below the letter, as seen in the number 1,000, to increase the value of the letter one thousandfold. For 10,000 a new letter was used, the M, the first letter of μυριοι or myriad. The symbols were always written in descending order from left to right. The largest number now possible in the Greek notation is 99999999. The use of the alphabet as numerals seems to date from about 500 B.C. The Greek mode of writing fractions is quite simple, the denominator being written over the numerator, or the numerator is written with one accent, followed by the denominator twice with two accents as $κα/ις$ or $ις'κα''κα''$. If the numerator is unity it is omitted. 1/32 would be written $λβ'$ or $λβ''$. Special signs were sometimes used for ½, ⅔, addition and subtraction.

Archimedes devised a plan by which the Greek number system might be prolonged indefinitely and which has been thought by some to contain the germ of the modern notion of logarithm. "In a pamphlet entitled ψαμμιτης (in Latin Arenarius, the sand-reckoner), addressed to Gelon, king of Syracuse," says Gow, "Archimedes begins by saying that some people think the sand cannot be counted, while others maintain that, if it can, still no arithmetical expression can be found for the number. 'Now I will endeavor,' he goes on, 'to show

NUMBER

you, by geometrical proofs which you can follow, that the numbers which have been named by us and are included in my letter addressed to Zeuxippus, are sufficient to exceed not only the number of a sandbox as large as the whole earth, but of one which is as large as the universe. You understand, of course, that most astronomers mean by "the universe" the sphere of which the center is the center of the earth and the radius is a line drawn from the center of the earth to the center of the sun.' Assume the perimeter of the earth to be 3,000,000 stadia (a stadium was nearly 200 yards), and in all the following cases take extreme measurements. The diameter of the earth is larger than that of the moon and that of the sun is larger than that of the earth. The diameter of the sun is thirty times that of the moon and is larger than the side of a chiliagon (a polygon of 1,000 sides) inscribed in a great circle of the sphere of the universe. It follows from these measurements that the diameter of the universe is less than 10,000 times that of the earth and is less than 10,000,000,000 stadia.

"Now suppose that 10,000 grains of sand not $<$ 1 poppy-seed, and the breadth of a poppy-seed $<$ 1/40 of a finger-breadth. Further using the ordinary nomenclature, we have numbers up to a myriad myriads (100,000,000). Let these be called the first order and let a myriad myriads be a unit of the second order and let us reckon units, tens, etc., of the second order up to a myriad myriads; and let a myriad myriads of the second order be a unit of the third order and so on ad lib. If numbers be arranged in a geometrical series, of which 1 is the first term and 10 is the radix, the first eight terms of such a series will belong to the first order, the next eight to the second order and so on. Calling these orders octads and using these numbers, following the rule that spheres are to one another in the triplicate ratio of their diameters, Archimedes ultimately finds that the number of grains of sands which the sphere of the universe would hold is less than a thousand myriads or ten millions of the eighth octad. This number would be expressed in our notation as 1 with sixty-three ciphers annexed." There seems to have been no attempt to apply this method further, the ordinary system being sufficient for the needs of the time.

The main principle underlying the Roman system was to provide a symbol for each column or order, the symbol being repeated for each unit in the order. The following reconstruction of the Roman process is made for the purpose of comparison with the other two systems and is not offered as a probable historical course.

For each unit of column A a Roman I was used, it being the nearest to the primitive stroke or score |; X was used for the second order, C for the order of hundreds and M for thousands. These are called unit letters. So far the gap from 1 to 10 is too great, it being necessary to write I nine times for 9. A half-way symbol was then provided for each interval: V for 5, L for 50, and D for 500. These are called half-unit letters. It is altogether probable that the half-unit letter is a relic of the pause in finger reckoning when the first hand was completed. Many of the decimal systems still preserve this trace of a quinary base.

The half-unit symbol may have arisen in connection with the use of the reckoning board, placing counters on the spaces as well as upon the lines as the notes of the musical staff. Fig. 5 indicates the method of writing 7,868 on the sand-board. It is very probable that the use of the spaces was derived from the half-unit letter rather than in the reverse order.

So far the system is built upon an additive basis, the value of a

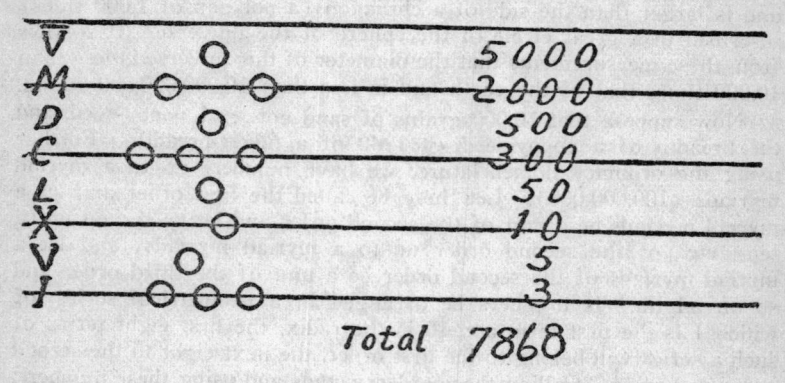

```
V̄           O              5000
M̄       O       O          2000
D        O                  500
C    O   O   O              300
L        O                  50
X        O                  10
V        O                  5
I    O   O   O              3
              Total 7868
```

Fig. 5 — ROMAN UNITS AND HALF-UNITS.

symbol of equal or less value written at the right of a given symbol being added to the value of the given symbol; thus if 20 is to be written, another is written at the right of the X for 1, as XX, while 16 would be written XVI. At this stage four would be written IIII, a form still to be seen on a clock face. A still further improvement, lessening the number of symbols, was the adoption of a subtractive principle. This means that a symbol of lesser value written at the left of a given symbol has its value taken from the value of the greater symbol. In this way 4 would be written IV. Two facts are here noticeable. The subtractive principle need be used but twice in each column; in the column A, for example, in writing 4 and 9, 3 might be written IIV with no advantage over III. A half-unit letter is never used in the subtractive sense; that is, L is used for 50 rather than LC.

The third and final step was the adoption of the multiplicative principle (also seen in the Greek notation). In the Roman scheme it appeared as a dash of vinculum drawn over a letter to increase its value a thousandfold; as in Fig. 5, a V with a stroke across the top indicates 5,000. The Roman mind was not of a scientific cast and one would scarcely expect to find the number system worked out to logical perfection. In fact, there is a decided lack of uniformity in the manner of writing numbers used by various Roman authors.

The following set of rules compiled by Dr. French seems to be the logical working out of the system: "Affirmative Rules: (1) The value of a unit letter is repeated with every repetition of the letter; (2) the value of a letter written at the right of a letter of equal or greater value is added to that value; (3) the value of a unit letter written at the left of the next higher unit or half-unit letter is subtracted from the value of that letter; (4) a vinculum placed over a letter increases its value a thousandfold. Negative Rules: (1) A half-unit letter is never repeated; (2) a half-unit letter is never written before a letter of greater value; (3) a unit letter is never written before a letter of greater value except the next higher half-unit and unit letters—*i.e.*, 99 is never written IC; (4) the vinculum is never placed over I; (5) a letter is not used more than three times in any order."

Little may be said of the origin of the Roman Numerals. It is generally supposed that the system was inherited from the Etruscans. Various and interesting have been the theories advanced to explain the choice of the symbols. One is that the I is a sort of hieroglyphic form of the extended finger, V for the hand, and X for the double hand. Another theory is that decem is related to decussare, to cut across, and that the cutting across of a symbol multiplies its value by 10; thus I cut across is X. C is the initial letter of centum, one hundred.

Traces of the subtractive principle have been found on brick tablets from the Temple Library of Nippur, recently deciphered by Professor Hilprecht of the Babylonian Expedition of the University of Pennsylvania. These bricks probably date from about the twentieth century B.C.).

Each of the wide symbols indicated a ten, the final straight wedge a one, the twenty and one being combined in a subtractive sense to give nineteen.

The fundamental principle of assigning a symbol to each column destined the Roman system of notation to ultimate disuse. By this principle an indefinitely large number would mean an indefinitely large number of columns, and hence an indefinitely large number of symbols. No difference how many symbols were in use, it would be easy to specify a number which could not be written. Such a system must finally give way to another with no such limitations.

The Babylonian number system was based on 60, both for whole numbers and fractions. The possible explanation of this sexigesimal system is that the year was reckoned as 360 days, thus dividing the circle into 360 parts, and they were probably aware of the division of the circle into 6 parts by stepping off the radius 6 times on the circumference, and by so doing arriving at 60 parts of the circle in each part stepped off. 60 proved to be a particularly favorable base, being divisible by 2, 3, 4, 5, 6, 10, and 12. A large mass of information

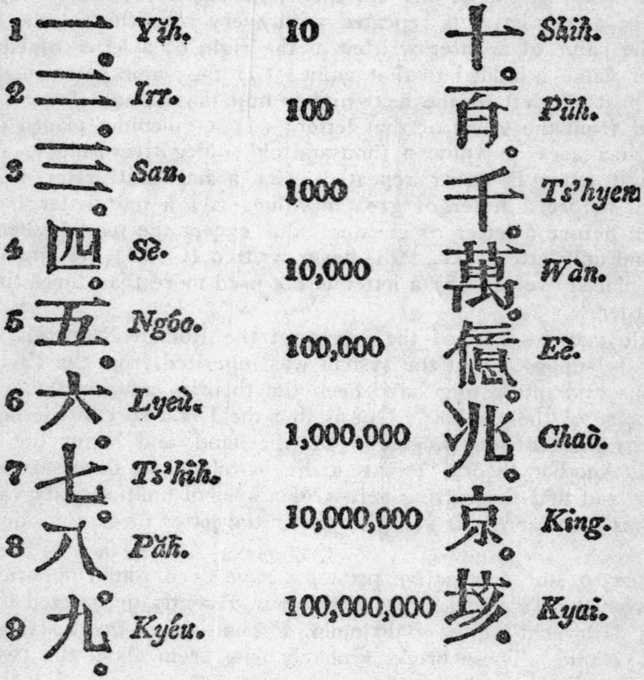

1 一	Yih.	10 十	Shih.
2 二	Irr.	100 百	Pŭh.
3 三	San.	1000 千	Ts'hyen
4 四	Sè.	10,000 萬	Wàn.
5 五	Ngôo.	100,000 億	Eĕ.
6 六	Lyeŭ.	1,000,000 兆	Chaò.
7 七	Ts'hih.	10,000,000 京	King.
8 八	Pŭh.	100,000,000 垓	Kyai.
9 九	Kyéu.		

Fig. 6 —Chinese Number System.

as to the mathematical accomplishments has recently been revealed by Professor Hilprecht, who has examined more than 50,000 cuneiform inscriptions from the Temple Library of Nippur.

The Babylonians had a strange custom of deriving their numbers from a large number which may be called a basal number. This basal number is 12,960,000 or 60^4. This number is, according to the theory of Professor Hilprecht, the famous "Number of Plato," Republic, Book VIII. "This number is constructed from 216, the minimal number of days of gestation in the human kind, and is called the lord of better and worse births." If the 216 be interpreted as days, together with 12,960,000, the latter number gives 36,000 years, the "great Platonic year," which was the length of the Babylonian cycle. Thus is implied that Plato's famous number and the idea of its influence upon the destiny of man originated in Babylonia.

The Aztec system of numeration had the score for its basis. There were special signs for the first five numerals: for twenty, for its square, four hundred, and for the cube, eight thousand. Certain combinations of signs symbolized the other numerals.

The Chinese had, from earliest times, constructed a system of numerals, similar in many respects to what the Romans probably inherited from their Pelasgic ancestors. It is only to be observed that the Chinese mode of writing is the reverse of the Arabic, and that beginning at the top of the leaf it descends in parallel columns to the bottom, proceeding, however, from right to left, as practised by most of the Oriental nations. Instead of the vertical lines used by the Romans, therefore, horizontal ones are found in the Chinese notation. Thus "one" is represented by a horizontal stroke with a barbed termination, "two" by a pair of such strokes. The mark for "four" has four strokes with a flourish. Three horizontal strokes and two vertical ones form the mark for "five," and other symbols exhibit the successive strokes abbreviated as far as "nine." "Ten" is figured by a horizontal stroke, crossed with a vertical score, to show that the first rank is completed, while a hundred has two vertical scores connected by three short horizontal ones.

The Hindu system was based on the principle of assigning a symbol to each of the nine numbers of the first column, 1 for one, 2 for two, 3 for three, 4 for four, 5 for five, 6 for six, 7 for seven, 8 for eight, and 9 for nine. The Hindu notation may be reconstructed as follows: It is required to write the number pictured in the accompanying cut. There are four in the A column, or four ones, three in the B column, or three tens, five in the C column, or five hundreds, one in the D column, or one thousand, and four in the E column, or four ten thousands. Using the symbols above, 4 is written in the A compartment, 3 in the B compartment, etc. So long as a box arrangement is used with the compartments named, the method would be considered complete. In fact, the above number could be written just as well without the cells, as 41534, and the order for which any symbol stands would be determined by its position with reference to the others. This is called the place-value property, and is the important feature of the system.

But one thing is lacking: the method fails when any column is empty. Suppose columns A and C above to be vacant; there would be then 4 E's, 1 D, 3 B's, and no A's nor C's. This could be written in cells, but could not be written without some scheme of labeling the columns. To avoid this difficulty a new symbol, O, was invented. It was called cipher from an Arabic word meaning empty. The above number may now be written 41,030.

In the Hindu notation each symbol has in addition to its intrinsic value an acquired value resulting from its position. Thus the 3, standing in the second place, has the value thirty; 3 being its intrinsic value and the ten being its acquired or place value. Thus both the multiplicative and additive principles are involved in place-value 325 is $3 \times 100 + 2 \times 10 + 5$. Writing two symbols, now called figures, side by side adds then after the left-hand figure has been multiplied by ten.

It is readily seen that there is no limit to the number of columns that may be used without increasing the number of symbols; that is,

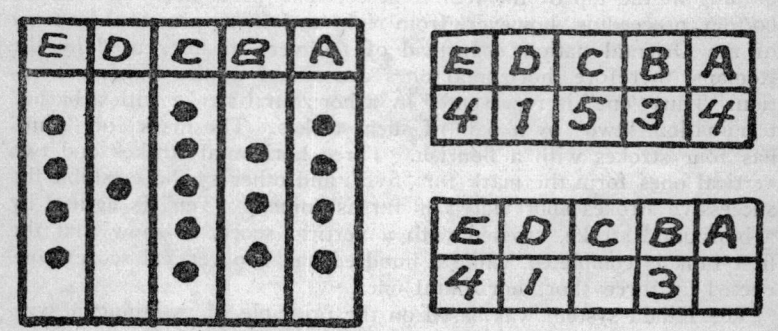

Fig. 7 —Hindu Notation Arrangement.

the Hindu notation begins at units' column and may be carried indefinitely to the left. The smallest number that may be written, so far, is Unity, or one. The two final steps in the perfecting of the system, the invention of the decimal point, which permits of the writing of numbers indefinitely small, striking off the right-hand barrier, and the discovery of the exponential notation and logarithms, which facilitate computations, will be considered later, together with the long struggle between the Roman and Hindu systems for supremacy.

The origin of the Hindu notation is shrouded in mystery. It is customary for Orientals to attribute any great discovery or invention to the direct revelation of the gods. Professor Hilprecht gives an illustration of this trait. "According to Berosus, a Babylonian priest who lived some time between 330 and 250 B.C., the origin of all human knowledge goes back to divine revelation in primeval times. 'In the first year there made its appearance from a part of the Erythraean Sea, which bordered upon Babylonia, a living being endowed with reason, who was called Oannes. According to this tradition, confirmed by Apollodorus, the whole body of this creature was like that of a fish, and it had under a fish's head another or human head, and feet similar to those of a man subjoined to the fish's tail, and it also had a human voice; and a representation of him is preserved even to this day. This being, it is said, in the day time used to converse with men, without, however, taking any food; he instructed men in the knowledge of writing, of sciences and every kind of art; he taught them how to settle towns, to construct temples, to introduce laws and to apply the principles of geometrical knowledge, he showed them how to sow and how to gather fruit; in short, he instructed men in everything pertaining to the culture of life. From that time [so universal were his instructions] nothing else has been added by way of improvement. But when the sun set, this being Oannes used to plunge again into the sea and abide all night in the deep; for he was amphibious.'"

Professor Florian Cajori thus sums up the leading conclusions due to Woepcke as to the historical development of the Hindu numeral system: "The Hindus possessed the nine numerals, without the zero or cipher, as early as the second century after Christ. It is known that about that time a lively commercial intercourse was carried on between India and Rome, by way of Alexandria. There arose an interchange of ideas as well as of merchandise. The Hindus caught glimpses of Greek thought, and the Alexandrians received ideas on philosophy and science from the east. The nine numerals, without the zero, thus found their way to Alexandria, where they may have attracted the attention of the Neo-Pythagoreans. From Alexandria they spread to Rome, thence to Spain and the western part of Africa.

"Between the second and eighth centuries the nine characters in India underwent changes in shape. A prominent Arabic writer, Albirûni (died 1038), who was in India during many years, remarks that the shape of Hindu numerals and letters differed in different localities, and that when (in the eighth century) the Hindu notation was transmitted to the Arabs the latter selected from the various forms the most suitable. But before the East Arabs thus received the notation it had been perfected by the invention of the zero and the application of the principle of position.

"Perceiving the great utility of the Columbus-egg, the zero, the West Arabs borrowed this epoch-making symbol from those in the East, but retained the old forms of the nine numerals which they had previously received from Rome. The reason for this retention may have been a disinclination to unnecessary change, coupled, perhaps, with a desire to be contrary to their political enemies in the East. The West Arabs remembered the Hindu origin of the old

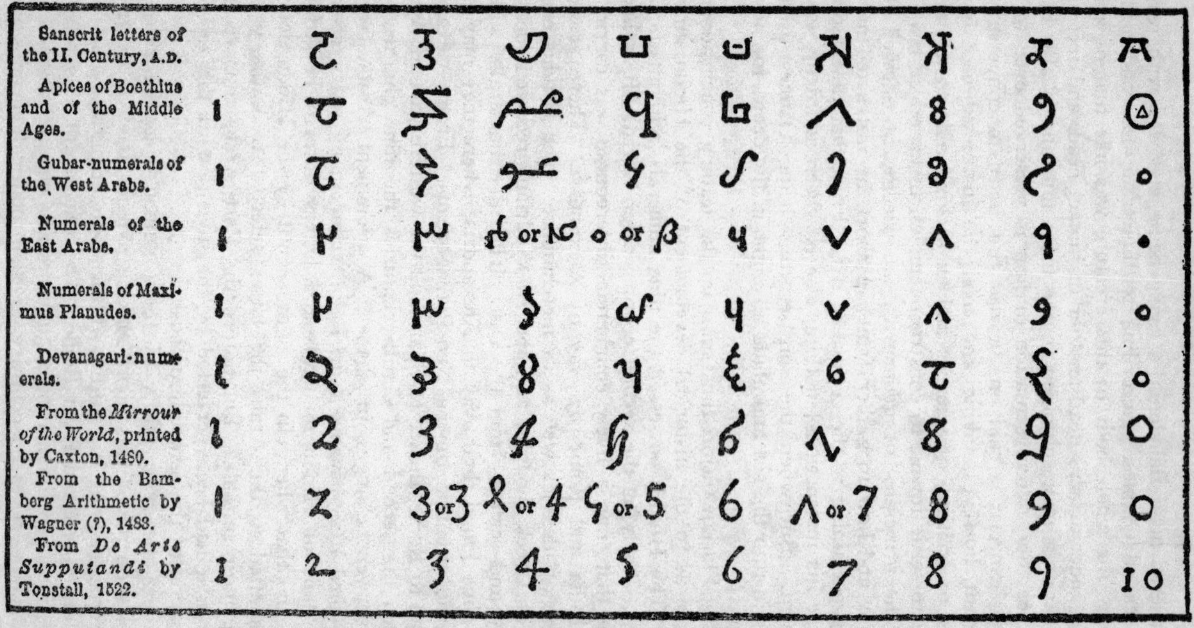

Fig. 9 —Showing the Development of the Hindu Numerals.
(Cajori.)

NUMBER

forms, the so-called Gubar or "dust" numerals. After the eighth century the numerals in India underwent further changes, and assumed the greatly modified forms of the modern Devanagari numerals." Professor Moritz Cantor recently expressed the opinion that the use of the zero was probably due to the Babylonians, 1700 B.C.

There are two methods of reading numbers in general use, in both of which the orders are grouped, beginning with the first order, or the order of units. In the French method each group consists of three orders, such a group being called a period. The names of the first three orders, beginning with the lowest, are units, tens and hundreds. These names are applied also to the three orders in each period followed by the name of the period. The names of the first 12 periods follow:

1. Units.
2. Thousands.
3. Millions.
4. Billions.
5. Trillions.
6. Quadrillons.
7. Quintillions.
8. Sextillions.
9. Septillions.
10. Octillions.
11. Nonillions.
12. Decillions.

In the English method each period consists of six orders, named units, tens, hundreds, thousands, ten thousands, and hundred thousands. The names of the periods follow:

1. Units.
2. Millions.
3. Billions.
4. Trillions.
5. Quadrillions.
6. Quintillions.

In both systems the number names are read in descending order from left to right, and in all cases compounds are formed in the same way, except in the interval from 10 to 20. Professor Brooks, in "Philosophy of Arithmetic," gives the following account of number naming: "A single thing is called 'one'; one and one more are 'two'; two and one are 'three'; and in the same manner we obtain 'four,' 'five,' 'six,' 'seven,' 'eight,' and 'nine,' and then adding one more and collecting in a group we have 'ten.' Now regarding the 'ten' as a single thing, and proceeding according to the principle stated, we have one and ten, two and ten, three and ten, and so on up to ten and ten, which we call two tens. When we arrive at ten tens, we call this a new group, a 'hundred.' This is the actual method by which numbers were originally named; but unfortunately, perhaps, for the learner and for science, some of these names have been so modified and abbreviated by the changes incident to use, that, with several of the smaller numbers at least, the principle has been so far disguised as not to be generally perceived. If, however, the ordinary language of arithmetic be carefully examined, it will be seen that the principle has been preserved, even if disguised so as not always to be immediately apparent. Instead of one and ten we have substituted 'eleven,' derived from an expression formerly supposed to mean one left after ten, but now believed to be a contraction of the Saxon 'endlefen,' or Gothic 'ainlif' (ain, one, and lif, ten); and instead of two and ten, we use the expression meaning, two left after ten, but now regarded as arising from the Saxon twelif, or Gothic tvalif (tva, two, and lif, ten). In the numbers following twelve, the stream of speech 'running day by day' has worn away a part of the primary form, and left the words that now exist. Thus, supposing the original expression to be three and ten, if we drop the conjunction we have three ten; changing the ten to teen and the three to thir, we have thirteen." In a similar manner twenty is a contraction of two tens. It is to be noticed that Professor Brooks has always used to form two and ten rather than ten and two. That such use leading to the forms from 10 to 20 is the exception rather than the rule is seen when it is recalled that from 20 on the larger number is always read first.

The word million seems to have been used first by Marco Polo (1254-1324). During the next 300 years it was used by writers in several senses, and not until the sixteenth century did it succeed in finally securing its place in the number system. Billion in the English system is equivalent to one thousand French billions, or a trillion.

An example will suffice to show the two methods of reading a number. Thus, 436,792,543,896,578, according to the French method, is read four hundred thirty-six trillion, seven hundred ninety-two billion, five hundred forty-three million, eight hundred ninety-six thousand, five hundred seventy-eight; while the English method would be four hundred thirty-six billion, seven hundred ninety-two thousand, five hundred forty-three million, eight hundred ninety-six thousand, five hundred seventy-eight.

The primitive form of the abacus was a board strewn with sand, upon which lines were drawn and pebbles were used as counters. On the Egyptian abacus the lines were at right angles to the operator, and Herodotus states that they "calculate with pebbles by moving the hand from right to left, while the Greeks move it from left to right," thus indicating that the units' column was taken with the Egyptians on the extreme left. The varying values of the counters when changed from one column to another is referred to in the comparison of Diogenes Laertius, "A person friendly with tyrants is like a stone in computation, which signifies now much, now little," which recalls Carlyle's ranking of men with the pieces on a chessboard. A single example of a Greek abacus is extant in the form of a marble table discovered on the island of Salamis in 1846, and now preserved in Athens. This table is 5 feet long and 2½ feet wide, and the lines, which are parallel to the operator, are in a good state of preservation.

Difficulty of calculation with Roman numerals rendered necessary the use of the abacus, inherited from the Greeks, and in turn, the ease with which the ordinary computations were performed with its aid prevented the perfecting or inventing of a usable system of notation.

Horace (Sat. I, 6, 75) alludes to the practice of boys marching to school with the abacus and box of pebbles suspended from the left arm: "Quo puero magnis ex centurionibus orti, Lævo suspensi loculos tabulamque lacerto." In the time of greatest Roman luxury (Juvenal, Sat. II, 131) the counters were of ivory, silver, and gold.

A more serviceable form was developed under Roman usage, in which the table or board was replaced by a thin metal plate with grooves cut entirely through, in which were metal buttons which could be slid from one end of the groove to the other. If at one end, a button registered one in that groove; if at the other, it was valueless. In place of a long groove containing 9 buttons, a shorter groove registered 4 and a still shorter one, immediately above, had a value of 5. At the right of units' column were two short columns in which could be registered twelfths, the Roman fraction, still preserved in name, in ounce and inch. Several of these metal abaci are to be found in museums.

Another form of abacus still in general use in the Orient is that of a frame across which wires are strung, upon which are movable beads. This is the "swanpan" of the Chinese and the "tchotu" of the Russians. In 1812 the abacus was carried from Russia to France, in the form of the counting frame, as a device for teaching number in primary work, and is now found in all kindergartens, a slight evidence of belief in the "culture-epoch" theory that the training of the child mind should follow the steps in the mental development of the race.

At the decadence of Rome the Roman notation and abacus reckoning remained as an inheritance to central Europe. The Arabs being in possession of the Hindu numerals carried them to Spain, and they were used in the commercial towns bordering the eastern end of the Mediterranean Sea. Some of the more aspiring youths of England and France journey to Spain to acquire the learning of the Greeks and Hindus which had been preserved and cultivated assiduously by the Moors. Others, merchantmen of Italy, perceived the advantage gained in the use of these numerals in the Phoenician towns, and they in turn carried the knowledge home.

Of the former who visited Spain was Gerbert (d. 1003), afterward Pope Sylvester II. Gerbert's abacus was of leather, and contained 27 columns. In place of the old counters new ones of horn were used, upon each of which one of the first nine numerals was written. Thus the first step in the use of Hindu numerals was taken. Of the latter, merchantmen of Italy, was Leonardo of Pisa, who in 1202 wrote a treatise on mathematics called "Liber Abaci." It begins thus: "The nine figures of the Hindus are 9, 8, 7, 6, 5, 4, 3, 2, 1. With these nine figures and this sign, 0, which in Arabic is called sifr, any number may be written."

The long struggle of 500 years for supremacy between the line-reckoning, or abacus, and the Hindu numerals, began. In one of the cuts is seen a page of line-reckoning from an early English textbook, "The Ground of Artes," by Robert Recorde, 1558. This work, which ran through at least 28 editions, is in the form of a dialogue between master and pupil. The following extract concerns the diffi-

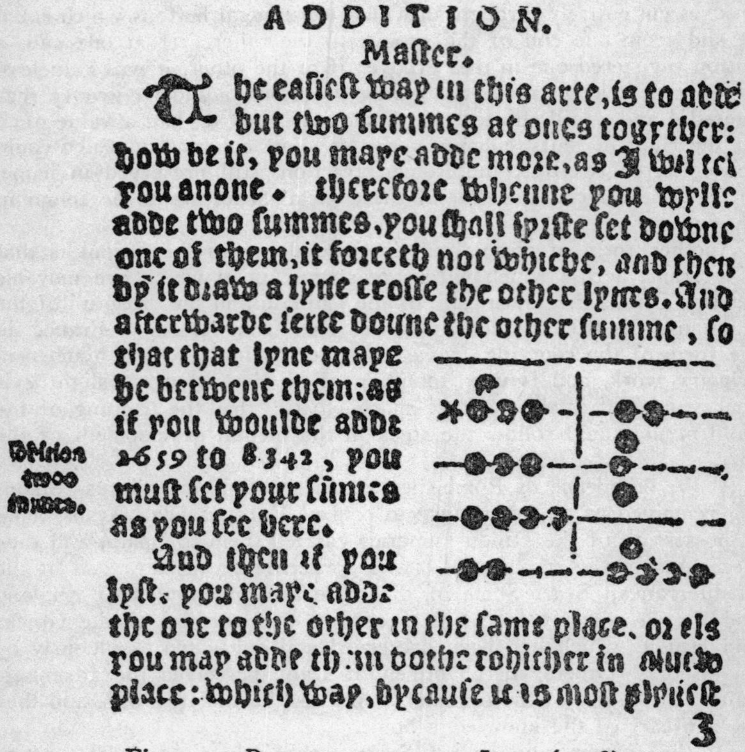

ADDITION.
Master.

The easiest way in this arte, is to adde but two summes at ones togyther: how be it, you maye adde more, as I wyl tel you anone. therefore whenne you wylle adde two summes, you shall fyrste set downe one of them, it forceth not whiche, and then by it drawe a lyne crosse the other lynes. And afterwarde sette downe the other summe, so that that lyne maye be betwene them: as if you woulde adde 2659 to 8342, you must set your summes as you see here.

Addition of two summes.

And then if you lyst, you maye adde the one to the other in the same place, or els you may adde them bothe togither in muche place: which way, bycause it is most spyicke

3

Fig. 12 —Reckoning on the Line (1558).

culty the pupil has in multiplying by a fraction as to why the product should be less than the number multiplied. The master explains the definition of multiplication, but the scholar is not satisfied, and the master says:

"*Master.*—If I multiply by more than one, the thing is increased; if I take it but once, it is not changed; and if I take it less than once, it cannot be as much as before. Then, seeing that a fraction is less than one, if I multiply by a fraction, it follows that I do take it less than once."

"*Pupil.*—Sir, I do thank you much for this reason; and I trust that I do perceive the thing."

The use of counters had not disappeared in England and Germany before the middle of the seventeenth century.

Various methods of finger reckoning have been developed, and are commonly found in the older arithmetics.

According to Pliny the image of Janus or the Sun was cast with the fingers so bent as to indicate 365 days. Some have thought that Proverbs iii, 16, "Length of days in her right hand," alludes to such a form of expressing numbers.

An interesting illustration is given by Leslie: "The Chinese have contrived a very neat and simple kind of digital signs for denoting numbers, greatly superior to that of the Romans. Since each finger has three joints, let the thumbnail of the other hand touch these joints in succession, passing up one side of the finger, down the middle, and again up the other side, thus giving nine marks applicable to the decimal notation. On the little finger these signify units, on the next tens, on the next hundreds, etc. The merchants of China are accustomed, it is said, to conclude bargains with each other by help of these signs, and to conceal the pantomime from the knowledge of bystanders.

The Korean schoolboy carries to school a bag of counting-bones, each about 5 inches long, and somewhat thinner than the ordinary leadpencil. A box of square sticks, 4 inches in length and about ½ inch square, called sangi, is used in a very ingenious fashion by the Chinese for the solution of algebraic equations.

The form of reckoning board adopted in the Middle Ages has left some words and customs. Fitz-Nigel, writing about the middle of the twelfth century, describes the board as a table about ten feet long and five feet wide, with a ledge or border, and was surrounded by a bench, or "bank," for the officers. From this "bank" comes the modern word bank as a place of money changing. The table was covered after the term of Easter each year with a new black cloth divided by a set of white lines about a foot apart, and across these another set which divided the table into squares. This table was called "scaccarium," which formerly meant chessboard, from which is the term exchequer, the Court of Revenue.

CHAPTER II

CALCULATION

Under the term "logistic" the Greeks treated what is now ordinarily termed computation or calculation, the latter word coming from a Latin word meaning "pebble," inasmuch as the reckoning was done with counters or pebbles. Calculation is the process of subjecting numbers to certain operations now to be defined. There are six fundamental operations in arithmetic, all growing out of the first. Formerly these were differently classified, sometimes as high as nine being considered, the other three being special cases or complications of the fundamental six.

These six operations are divided into two groups, the direct operations, of which there are three, and the inverses, each of which has the direct of undoing one of the former three.

DIRECT	INVERSE
1. Addition.	4. Subtraction.
2. Multiplication.	5. Division.
3. Involution.	6. Evolution.

When one object is put with a group of like objects, forming thus a new group having one more object than the original group, the process is said to be that of addition, and is indicated by $+$. (This sign appears in a work by Grammateus in 1514, and in 1517 in a book by Gillis vander Hoecke. Thus, 1 apple added to 2 apples gives 3 apples, or with abstract numbers, $2+1=3$. The objects or numbers added are called "addends" or "summands," and the resulting group or number is the "sum." The ending -end or -and, so common in mathematical terminology, is Latin present passive participle; in this case addends is to be translated literally the "being added" numbers.

Addition is, in its simplest form, the putting together or uniting of two numbers; and all additions of this nature may be broken up into a series of repetitions of the fundamental process of increasing a number by unity. Thus, if it be desired to add 3 apples to 5 apples,

CALCULATION

it may be done at a single step, or at three partial steps, which may be indicated thus:

$$5 \text{ apples} + 1 \text{ apple} = 6 \text{ apples};$$
$$6 \text{ apples} + 1 \text{ apple} = 7 \text{ apples};$$
$$7 \text{ apples} + 1 \text{ apple} = 8 \text{ apples};$$
$$\text{or } 5 \text{ apples} + 3 \text{ apples} = 8 \text{ apples};$$

the three steps resulting the same as the single step given last, which justifies the statement above that addition rests upon the fundamental process of increasing a number by unity.

Like numbers are those in which the same unit is used; 7 apples and 3 apples are like numbers, as also 7 and 3; 4 trees and 9 stones are unlike numbers, as are 5 ones and 7 tens; that is, in a number 435, written in the Hindu notation, 4 in hundreds' order is not like 3 in tens' order, nor like 5 in units' order. It is fundamental that only like numbers may be added; before 3 tens is added to 5 ones, the 3 tens must be changed into 30 ones. This is a very simple matter, only being, as it were, a shift in thought, and it accounts in a great measure for the simplicity of the operations with Hindu numerals. In 435, the 4 may be thought of, in turn, as 4 hundred or as 40 tens or as 400 ones. The place-value feature permits of numbers being immediately broken up into parts, and these parts treated one at a time. Thus, in addition, like orders are written in the same column and the columns are added separately. This process is illustrated in the following example:

$$432 = 4 \text{ hundred} + 3 \text{ tens} + 2 \text{ ones};$$
$$265 = 2 \text{ hundred} + 6 \text{ tens} + 5 \text{ ones};$$
$$697 = 6 \text{ hundred} + 9 \text{ tens} + 7 \text{ ones};$$

The sum of the ones, $5 + 2 = 7$, is first found, and written below the column of ones, and the other orders are added in succession.

A difficulty arises when the sum of a column is greater than 9, the largest number that may be written in a column. An example will make this clear:

$$387 = 3 \text{ hundred} + 8 \text{ tens} + 7 \text{ ones};$$
$$256 = 2 \text{ hundred} + 5 \text{ tens} + 6 \text{ ones};$$

$$643 = 5 \text{ hundred} + 13 \text{ tens} + 13 \text{ ones};$$
$$\text{or } 5 \text{ hundred} + 14 \text{ tens} + 3 \text{ ones};$$
$$\text{or } 6 \text{ hundred} + 4 \text{ tens} + 3 \text{ ones}.$$

The 13 ones is changed to 1 ten and 3 ones; the 3 is written in ones' column and the 1 ten is added in ("carried to") the tens' column. The 14 tens' is treated in a similar way.

Addition obeys the commutative law; that is, the addition may be performed in any order. $5 + 3 = 3 + 5$. It is immaterial whether the 3 is added to the 5 or the 5 is added to the 3.

The associative law is also valid for addition. If 5 and 7 are to be added to 4, it does not matter whether the 5 be added and then the 7, or the 5 and 7 first united and then added to the 4. This is expressed by means of parentheses. The parentheses mean that the numbers within are first united: $4 + 5 + 7 = 4 + (5 + 7)$. If two numbers are added, the sum is a number. This statement seems like mere verbiage, but will take on meaning when considered in the light of the other operations.

Subtraction is the inverse operation of addition. Addition is putting one number with another to form a third, and subtraction is taking one number from another to form a third. If addition has been stated in the form: given two numbers, to find their sum, subtraction would be stated: given the sum of two numbers and one of them, to find the other. The sum of two numbers is 8, and one of them is 5, what is the other? would be solved by taking 5 from 8, leaving 3. Subtraction is indicated by —. The number taken away is called the "subtrahend," and the number from which the subtrahend is taken is named "minuend." The resulting number is called "remainder," or "difference," depending upon which of the two phases of subtraction is considered. These two points of view may be brought out by concrete examples.

If A has $10 and pays out $7, how many dollars has he remaining? In this example, the $7, or subtrahend, was originally a part of the minuend $10, and is taken away. The $3 is then called "remainder." Again: If A has $10 and B has $7, how many dollars must B earn to have as many dollars as A? Here the $10 of A and the $7 of B are distinct numbers, and the resulting number is called the "difference."

In subtraction, the subtrahend is written below the minuend, with like orders in the same column. Each column is subtracted separately:

$$476 = 4 \text{ hundred} + 7 \text{ tens} + 6 \text{ ones};$$
$$263 = 2 \text{ hundred} + 6 \text{ tens} + 3 \text{ ones};$$
$$213 = 2 \text{ hundred} + 1 \text{ ten } + 3 \text{ ones}.$$

Two methods are in general use in the case that the number in an order of the subtrahend is too large to be taken from the number in the same order of the minuend. Both methods are inherited from the Hindus, having come down from the earliest printed textbooks, and seem to be of about equal difficulty.

The method of Decomposition, or Borrowing, consists of taking 1 unit from the next higher order, changing it to the order in question,

CALCULATION

adding to the number in that order, which makes the subtraction possible. 7 hundred $+ 2$ tens $+ 4$ units $= 7$ hundred $+ 1$ ten $+ 14$

$$\begin{array}{r} 724 \\ -\ 269 \\ \hline 455 \end{array}$$

$$\begin{array}{r} 6\text{ hundred} + 11\text{ tens} + 14\text{ units} \\ -\ 2\text{ hundred} + \ \ 6\text{ tens} + \ \ 9\text{ units} \\ \hline = 4\text{ hundred} + \ \ 5\text{ tens} + \ \ 5\text{ units.} \end{array}$$

The method of Equal Additions is based on the fact that the same number may be added to both minuend and subtrahend without changing the value of the difference; that is, $724 - 269 = (724 + 100 + 10) - (269 + 100 + 10)$. The 10 in the minuend is thought of as 10 ones, while in the subtrahend it is necessary to think of it as 1 ten. Similarly for the 100. The example used above is worked by means of equal additions, and will show the transformations involved:

$$\begin{array}{cc} 724 & 724 + 100 + 10 \\ \quad\text{is replaced by} & \\ -\ 269 & -\ 269 + 100 + 10 \end{array}$$

	hundreds	tens	ones	hundreds	tens	ones
$724 + 10$ tens $+ 10$ ones $=$	7	$+ (2+10) +$	$(4+10) =$	7	12	14
$269 + 1$ hundred $+ 1$ ten $=$	$(2+1) +$	$(6+1) +$	9 $=$	3	7	9
				4	5	5

In use with the first method it may be said

$$\begin{array}{r} 724 \\ -\ 269 \end{array}$$

9 from 14, 5;
6 from 11, 5;
2 from 6, 4.

With the second method,

9 from 14, 5;
7 from 12, 5;
3 from 7, 4.

Another mode of thinking of subtraction is called the Austrian method, or the method of "making change." That the greater portion of subtractions in the business world is concerning with making change has led to a wide use of the method in the school-room. It consists in building to the subtrahend until the minuend is reached. That it is the natural method is evidenced by the fact that it is almost invariably used by those who have never had the benefit of, or have forgotten, school training:

$$987$$
$$-236$$

One says 6 and 1 are 7; writes 1;
3 and 5 are 8; writes 5;
2 and 7 are 9; writes 7.

Its introduction as a distinct method is due to Augustus de Morgan, England's foremost writer on arithmetic.

It is readily seen that subtraction does not obey the commutative law. One may subtract 5 from 8, but not 8 from 5. This leads to the query, If one number is subtracted from another, is the result always a number? The answer is "yes," if the minuend is larger than the subtrahend. Otherwise, that the result is not a number, such as those heretofore considered. These will be called natural numbers. If 5 is to be subtracted from 8 no difficulty arises; but if attempt be made to take 8 from 5, the fact arises that no such operation is possible. Such a condition brings the arithmetician face to face with one of the most important considerations in mathematics, one without which the complete structure, modern mathematics, would not be possible. It is the principle of continuity, or principle of no exception, due to Hankel. It may be stated in this form: There shall be no exception to the applicability of any operation. If the result is not found in such numbers as already belong to the system, call this result a number of a new kind and determine its properties.

Suppose a man has $50 and spends $40, he has left $10. This operation is subtraction. Suppose he spends $60 instead of $40. This seems very much the same kind of operation. It is agreed to call this subtraction also, and say that he has a debt of $10, which is a new kind of number. The natural numbers may be represented by dots with any chosen interval between them:

1 2 3 4 5 6 7 8 9 10
· · · · · · · · · ·

If one goes 4 dots to the right from the third dot, he is at dot 7, or $3+4=7$. If one goes 5 dots to the left from dot 9 he is at dot 4. This going to the left is expressed by — or subtraction, $9-5=4$. But if one starts at dot 5 and attempts to go 8 dots to the left, no dot is found to mark the stopping point. The fiat of mathematician says, let there be a dot there. In this manner a series of dots is obtained extending to the opposite direction,

$-6\ -5\ -4\ -3\ -2\ -1\quad 0\ \ 1\ \ 2\ \ 3\ \ 4\ \ 5\ \ 6\ \ 7$
· · · · · ·   · · · · · · · ·

CALCULATION

These may be named or marked at pleasure. Call the first one, at the left of 1, 0, the second — 1, the third — 2, etc. The reason for the choice of these names is apparent. If a man has $1 and spends $1, he has no dollar remaining, and the symbol for an empty place is 0. If he now spends $1 he is $1 in debt. As this is the opposite of $1 credit, it is appropriate to mark it — 1, giving it a sign — to distinguish it from 1. If it is desired to mark the 1, a plus sign, $+$, is put before it, calling all numbers to the right of 0 positive numbers and those to the left negative numbers. Then $5 - 8 = -3$, while $8 - 5 = +3$. All the numbers, as now represented, are called whole numbers, or "integers." If it is agreed always to mark the ones at the left of 0, one may mark the ones at the right, or not, at will, and no confusion will arise. 0 is now a number dividing the positives from the negatives. It is called zero.

The properties of a negative number which are most important are two: (1) A negative number may be represented by a dot as far to the left of 0 as the corresponding positive number is to the right. (2) A negative number destroys the effect of, or annuls, a positive number of the same value when added to it; thus, $+8 + (-5) = +3$, the -5 destroying $+5$ of the $+8$, leaving $+3$.

If in an addition example, all the addends are the same, as in $2 + 2 + 2 + 2 = 8$, the form is shortened into $4 \times 2 = 8$, the first number, or the "multiplier," indicating how many addends were taken. The second number, showing the addend, is called the "multiplicand." The St. Andrew's cross, indicating that the operation of multiplication is to be performed, was introduced by William Oughtred in 1631. Robert Recorde, about 1557, introduced $=$ as the sign of equality, which he says is

"A paire of parallels or Gemowe lines of one length, thus $=$ becaufe noe 2 thyngs can be moare equalle."

Multiplication is, then, in essence, repeated addition.

The Commutative Law is seen to be valid in this operation: 7 rows of 3 dots is the same as 3 rows of 7 dots; or $3 \times 7 = 7 \times 3$.

Multiplication also obeys the associate law; that is, in a multiplication example where more than two numbers, or factors as they are called when used in multiplication, are involved, these factors may be grouped in any manner.

$$3 \times 7 \times 5 = 3 \times (7 \times 5) = (3 \times 5) \times 7.$$

The 3 may be multiplied by the 7, and this result, called a product, may then be multiplied by 5; or the 7 and 5 may first be multiplied and then the 3 used, etc.

A negative number multiplied by a positive gives a negative product. If in the line of dots one goes 5 dots to the left, 3 times, one arrives at dot -15, or $-5 \times 3 = -15$. But if one attempts to

474 MATHEMATICS

multiply 3 by —5, no meaning is attached. One may perform a certain act 3 times, or 1 time, or 0 times (which means that the act is not performed), but to attempt to perform an act —5 times is meaningless. In keeping with the Principle of No Exception, such an operation must be given a meaning, and it is done by widening the definition of multiplication; but in doing so the old multiplication (repeated addition) must be kept as a special case.

It should be noted that this application of the Principle of Continuity is a purely arbitrary process. It may be said since the multiplication by a negative has no meaning, simply reject it and say it cannot be performed. Such was the usage for a long time, and had it continued so the whole system of mathematics would have been like

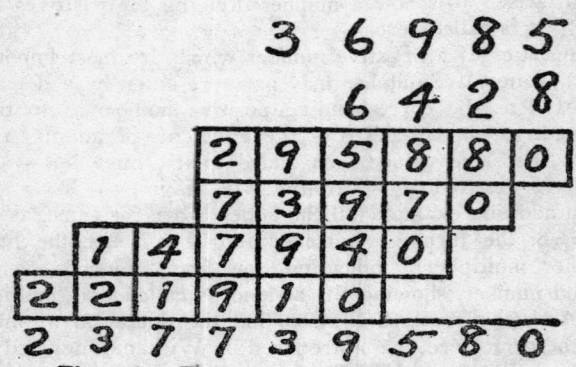

Fig. 16 —TESSELLATED MULTIPLICATION.

an unsymmetrical tree, simply allowed to develop and branch in any manner. The filling out or completing the meaningless cases is like a process of grafting which rounds out and gives a symmetrical growth.

One method of procedure here would be as follows: $—5 \times 3 = —15$, and knowing that with positive numbers the commutative law holds, it is agreed to still let it be valid, from which, $—5 \times 3 = 3 \times —5$, but $—5 \times 3 = —15$; therefore, $3 \times —5 = —15$, and the conclusion is multiplication by a negative number changes the sign of the multiplicand and then multiplies it. Another and better method is to define the operation of multiplication in such a way that it will be applicable in all cases. Such a definition is the following: Multiplication is the performing that operation on the multiplicand which, if performed on unity (or one), produces the multiplier. To multiply 3 by —5.

The operation upon 1 which produces —5 is to change the sign of 1 and repeat it 5 times. Do the same with 3, —3, —3, —3, —3, —3, the sum of which is —15, as before. It will be seen that this definition of multiplication includes repeated addition as a special case. In the same manner it is seen that $-3 \times (-5) = +15$. Considering the four cases,

$$+3 \times (+5) = +15, \qquad +3 \times (-5) = -15,$$
$$-3 \times (-5) = +15, \qquad -3 \times (+5) = -15,$$

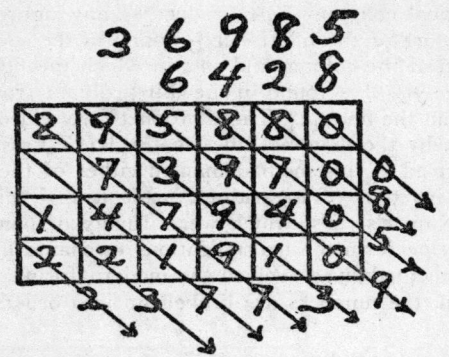

Fig. 17 —Quadrilateral Multiplication.

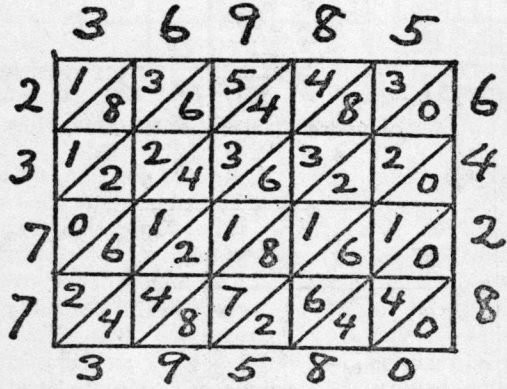

Fig. 18 —Latticed Multiplication.

it is clear that when the two signs are both $+$ or both $-$, that is, alike, the product is $+$; when they are unlike, the product is $-$. The conclusion is, then, in multiplication, two like signs produce $+$, and two unlike signs produce $-$. The sign $+$ is read plus, and $-$ is read minus.

One of the commonest forms of the early methods for multiplication is the Tessellated Multiplication, very much akin to the usage of to-day.

476 MATHEMATICS

Another was the Quadrilateral Multiplication. In this form the partial products do not progress to the left, as in the Tesselated style, and are added obliquely, as shown by the arrows. These were not drawn in the work.

Lucas de Burgo called the third form Latticed Multiplication. The multiplicand is the outside top horizontal row, the multiplier the outside right vertical column. The product of any figure of the multiplicand by a figure of the multiplier is found in the square formed by the intersection of the column and row in which the figures multiplied are found; thus 9×2 is found in the third column from the left, and second row from the bottom. These products are added in the oblique column cut out by the diagonal lines to the left. Less purely mental work is performed in this method than in either of the other two.

Napier, the inventor of logarithms, made use of this method in a device called Napier's rods, which were usually of bone, and enabled the operator to perform the multiplications mechanically.

From these methods was evolved the modern form. As in addition and subtraction, the numbers are broken up into orders:

$$\begin{array}{r} 437 \\ 56 \\ \hline 2622 \\ 2185 \\ \hline 24472 \end{array}$$

	Hundreds.	Tens.	Ones.
	4	3	7
		5	6
	24	18	42
20	15	35	

or,

42 ones = 4 tens + 2 ones;

18 tens + 4 tens = 22 tens = 2 hundred + 2 tens;

24 hundred + 2 hundred = 26 hundred = 2 thousand + 6 hundred.

In the second row of partial products,

35 tens = 3 hundred + 5 tens;

15 hundred + 3 hundred = 18 hundred = 1 thousand + 8 hundred.

20 thousand + 1 thousand = 21 thousand = 2 ten thousands + 1 thousand.

The two partial products then appear thus, and are added:

CALCULATION

$$\begin{array}{r} 2622 \\ 2185 \\ \hline 24472 \end{array}$$

The product of any two whole numbers is a whole number. The product of 0 and any whole number is 0.

The inverse operation of multiplication is called division. In its simplest form it is repeated subtraction. If it is asked how many 2's in 8? the answer would be determined by subtracting 2 from 8 in succession as many times as possible, noting the number of times, 4, as the answer. Division has two phases. One may think of finding how many times one number is contained in another. which is "Division," proper, a species of measurement, or one may wish to divide a number into equal parts, the number of such parts being given. This form is called "Partition." With abstract numbers no such distinction need be made, but with concrete numbers it is important.

The name of the number to be divided is "Dividend," of the dividing number "Divisor," and of the resulting number "Quotient." If any part of the Dividend is left undivided it is called "Remainder."

There are various signs used to indicate division; $\frac{8}{2}$ or 8/2 may be regarded as indicating that 8 is to be divided by 2, as also 8 : 2. The sign in general use, ÷, was used by Dr. John Pell (1610-1685), altho this sign had been in use with other meaning by earlier German writers.

Three methods or algorithms for what is now termed long division deserve to be mentioned. One of the epoch-making works on arithmetic was written by Luca Paciuolo, a Franciscan monk. This book, published in Venice in 1494, gives the first of these methods, the galley or scratch method, a dividing upward. It is a relic of the old method of reckoning on sand, where the figure is scratched out as soon as used.

Thus to divide 59078 by 74. In the first step, 7 is divided into 59, and the quotient 7 is written, 7 7's are 49; 49 from 59 is 10, which is written above 59. The dividend is now /078. 7 4's are 28; 28 from 100 is 72, which is written still above the last dividend. The new dividend is now /78, and the division continues, each figure being scratched out as soon as used.

The first downward division, the present Italian method, appears in a printed arithmetic by Calandri (1491), altho it is found occasionally in manuscript form during the fifteenth century.

Consider the example following.

I

```
74)59078(798 26/74
   518
   ———
   727
   666
   ———
   618
   592
   ———
   26 Rem.
```

I shows the completed form of solution, and II the successive steps, obtained by separating the number into orders.

II

	Tens.	Units.		Ten thousands.	Thousands.	Hundreds.	Tens.	Units.		Hundreds.	Tens.	Units.
	7	4	)	5	9	0	7	8	(	7	9	8
					49	28						
					51	8						
				5	1	8						
						7	2	7				
						63	36					
						66	6					
					6	6	6					
							6	1	8			
							56	32				
							59	2				
						5	9	2				
							2	6	Remainder			

The three lines show the partial product in the three stages of its reduction.

CALCULATION 479

The third, or Austrian, method consists in omitting the partial products and performing the subtraction at once:

```
74) 59078 (798 24/74
    727
    618
     26
```

Comparing the three methods as to two points, (1) beginning on the left to subtract the partial product, (2) writing the partial product, the following scheme will show their relations:

	Galley.	Italian.	Austrian.
(1)	Yes	No	No
(2)	No	Yes	No

The Galley method is so called on account of the final form, which resembles a boat under full sail. The Austrian method, which probably will ultimately replace the Italian, is constructed from a combination of the best features of both the older methods (2) of the galley and (1) of the Italian.

As in the inverse process of subtraction it was found that the operation did not always result in a natural number, and it was necessary to create a new kind of number, the negative, thus widening the number system to form the class of whole numbers, or integers, it is to be expected that a like condition exists in the case of division.

If 2 be divided by 1 the quotient is 2; but if one attempts to divide 1 by 2 no corresponding whole number is found. Considering the second phase of division, the separating of a number into 2 equal parts, it is agreed to let this quotient be a number such that it requires two of them to make 1, or unity. This new number is named one-half, and written by putting the number divided above a short horizontal line, and the divisor below the line, as ½. The class of such numbers is called "Fractions," from the Latin, frangere, to break. The number below the line is called the "denominator," or namer, telling what the part is; the number above the line tells how many parts are taken, and is called the "numerator," or numberer. This function of the numerator will be apparent later.

The first widening of the number system, which arose in the case of the inverse operation, subtraction, created exactly as many new numbers as there were already in the system before the new numbers entered. Every combination of two numbers with a minus sign between them gives a positive or natural number, when the larger number appears before the sign; and a negative—that is, a new—number when the smaller number comes first. In division, the case is the exception rather than the rule where either order of the numbers results in a whole number, as 3/2 and 2/3, and if one order does so result the other does not, as 8/2 and 2/8. It is apparent, then, that the new numbers taken in under the name fraction are infinitely greater in number, when compared with the number already in.

A fraction may be interpreted in any one of three ways: the fraction 3/2 may be thought of as (1) 3 units divided into 2 equal parts, (2) 1 unit divided into 2 equal parts, and 3 of these parts taken, as 3 times ½; (3) an indicated division not yet performed. The distinction between (1) and (2) may be seen from a figure, where unity or 1 is represented by a line 1 centimeter in length.

If the numerator of a fraction is 1, it is called a unit fraction, as 1/2, 1/7, 1/8. A "proper" fraction has a numerator less than its denominator, as 1/7, 2/3, 3/12. All other fractions are "improper," as 8/3, 5/2, 4/2. Such a fraction can always be changed to either a whole number, as $4/2 = 2$, or a whole number and a unit fraction, as $3/2 = 1½$.

The whole numbers were represented by dots arranged on a line at equal intervals, extending to the right and left indefinitely from a chosen dot, marked 0, or zero.

$-6 -5 -4 -3 -2 -1 \quad\quad 0 \quad 1 \quad 2 \quad 3 \quad 4$

. . . .
½ 1½ 2½

The creation of the number ½ introduces a point midway between 0 and 1, and by combination with each of the whole numbers in the manner $3/2 = 1½$ also places a point midway in each interval. The fraction ¼ places a point half way from 0 to ½. By continuing this process it is seen that distance between the dots representing fractions is made smaller and smaller, as the various fractions take their places on the line. When all of the fractions have been represented, if one chooses a particular dot, say 3/7, one can always find another dot among those placed whose distance from the given dot, 3/7, is less than any assigned length of line. The proof of this may be put in the form of conversation between A and B. If the dot 1 is 1 inch from the dot 0, A is to show that a dot may be found in the collection of dots which represent fractions which shall be nearer to the dot 3/7 than any fractional part of an inch which B may name.

B says, "Is there a dot nearer to 3/7 than 1/10 of an inch?"

A's reply is, "Choose the dot 31/70, whose distance from 3/7 is 1/70."

B then says, "Find me a dot nearer than 1/100 of an inch."

A's answer is, "The dot 301/700 is only 1/100 of an inch from 3/7"; and so forth for any value B may name.

The dots are said to be "dense," and it might be thought that the whole line is filled up, that it has become a continuous line rather than a collection of discrete dots. But such is not the case; there are infinitely more dots on the line that do not represent fractions than

CALCULATION 481

there are dots that do represent them. The third of the inverse processes, evolution, will reveal the existence of the missing dots, and by its aid they, as a new type of number, will be included in the number system, which will then be represented by a continuous line.

Fractions are treated in the most ancient mathematical handbook known, written by an Egyptian scribe, Ahmes, or Moon-born, some time before 1700 B.C. This papyrus, now preserved in the British Museum, is entitled "Directions for obtaining the knowledge of all dark things," and covers practically the whole extent of Egyptian mathematics, no substantial advances being made until the time of Greek influence. Another papyrus, that found at Akhmim, written perhaps after 500 A.D., gives the same treatment of fractions as is found in the work of Ahmes. Thus Egyptian Mathematics was in its most flourishing condition when Abram left Ur of the Chaldees, and remained stationary for a thousand years.

The writer gives, in most cases, no general rule for obtaining results, simply a succession of like problems, the easy step of generalizing by induction seemingly being beyond his power. Whole numbers receive no treatment, the work beginning with fractions, which subject was evidently very difficult, as the author confines his attention solely to unit fractions and fractions with numerator 2. Fractions of the latter type are changed into the sum of two or more unit fractions. Thus Ahmes changed 2/9 into 1/6 and 1/18, and gives a table of such changes of fractions between 2/3 and 2/99. By the aid of this table any fraction of odd denominator could be broken up.

In this way Ahmes could solve such a problem as "Divide 5 by 21." The 5 is first broken into 2 and 2 and 1; from the table is found $2/21 = 1/14$ and $1/42$; $5/21 = 1/21$ and ($1/14$ and $1/42$) and ($1/14$ and $1/42$) $= 1/21$ and ($2/14$ and $1/42$) $= 1/21$ and $1/7$ and $1/21$ $= 1/7$ and $2/21 = 1/7$ and $1/4$ and $1/42$. The fractions were written side by side, with no sign for addition between them.

While the Egyptians met the difficulties of fractions by reducing them to fractions having a constant numerator, 1, the Babylonians avoided the same difficulties by treating only fractions with a fixed denominator, 60, and the Romans also used a single denominator, 12.

The usual rule for the division of fractions by inverting the divisor and then multiplying is not common in the textbooks of the sixteenth century. It is given as follows by Thierfeldern (1578):

"When the denominators are different invert the divisor (which you are to place at the right) and multiply the numbers above together and the numbers below together; then you have the correct result. As to divide ¾ by ⅝, invert thus: $3/4 \times 8/5 = 24/20 = 1\frac{1}{5}$.

The close of the eighth century found the Hindu decimal notation practically perfect as a means of writing whole numbers. The final perfection of the method by applying it to fractions, is the form of

Simon Stevin (1548-1620). In seven pages of his work, published in decimals, did not occur until the time of 1585, Steven leaped what had been an impassable gap for 900 years. The reason for this pause is not difficult to determine.

In decimal fractions, or decimals, unity, or 1, is divided into ten equal parts, each part called a "tenth"; a tenth is divided into ten equal parts and each part called a "hundredth"; thus the orders on the right of units' column are symmetrically named, adding the suffix -th, with those on the right. As the number of orders on the left is unlimited, so the numbers of orders on the right is unbounded, and one is enabled to write numbers of unlimitedly small value; the smaller the value of the number (less than 1), the larger the number of orders required to express it. The units' column is marked by placing a period after it (sometimes the period is midway between the top and bottom lines of the type, as 3·8, but ordinarily it is written on the base line, as 3.8 for 3 and 8 tenths). In reading decimals the decimal point is always read "and."

In the first grouping of units there was no reason for putting ten in a group rather than any other number, the use of ten simply growing out of the use of the hands as a counting machine. In fact, it would have greatly simplified some applications of the number system if primitive mathematicians had been born with six fingers on each hand. A duodecimal, or 12 scale, would enable the writing of such common fractions, $\frac{1}{3}$, $\frac{2}{3}$, $\frac{1}{6}$, duodecimally, in the form .4, .8, .2; whereas decimally they have a continually recurring set of figures, $\frac{1}{3} = .3333$, etc.; $\frac{1}{6} = .1666$, etc. Charles XII. of Sweden, a short time before his death, while lying in the trenches before a Norwegian fortress, seriously debated introducing the duodecimal system of numeration into his dominions.

On the other hand, there is a very decisive predetermining feature in the case of the division of the unit. Necessity arose for halving or dividing objects into two equal parts long before the separation into ten parts was even thought of; while the difficulty of dividing into ten equal parts is apparent. The use of the period (or comma) to mark the unit order began with Pitiscus, 1612. With all the advantages of the decimal notation carried to the right of the units' column, it was not until the nineteenth century that decimals came into ordinary arithmetic.

CHAPTER III

ANALYTIC GEOMETRY

The final union of algebra and geometry by means of the analytic geometry is usually attributed to Des Cartes. Algebra has been used at various times in connection with geometry by Apollonius and Vieta in particular, but in their works the idea of motion is wanting. Des Cartes, by introducing variables and constants, was enabled to represent curves by algebraic equations. A point in a plane is determined by its distances from two intersecting lines, which, for convenience, may be taken as perpendicular to each other. By allowing these two distances to vary, the point moves and generates a curve. By expressing the relation between these two variable distances in the form of an equation, the curve becomes subject to investigation following the laws of algebra. This is the great contribution by Des Cartes, and by it "the entire conic sections of Apollonius is wrapped up and contained in a single equation of the second degree." (Cajori.)

The plotting of an equation of the first degree which results in a straight line was spoken of in connection with algebra, as was also an equation of the second degree. The general equation of the second degree is written in the form
$$Ax^2 + Bxy + Cy^2 + Dx + Ey + F = 0.$$
Two processes are applied to change the form of an equation, which evidently depends upon the axes chosen. One of these is to translate (or move parallel to themselves) the axes, and the other is to rotate them about the point of intersection, which is called the origin. If the general constants, A, B, C, D, E, F, are such that the equation can be reduced by one or both of these operations to the form $b^2x^2 \mp a^2y^2 = a^2b^2$, the curve is an ellipse; if to the form $x^2 + y^2 = r^2$, the circle, $b^2x^2 - a^2y^2 = a^2b^2$, is the equation of the hyperbola, and $y_2 = 2\,px$ is the parabola. If the left number of the equation can be factored, it is a degenerate conic. The equation of the third degree gives a curve which is called the cubic. Newton gave a classification of the cubic curves, the general form of which is a closed loop and an open branch. The curves of higher degree comprise some of the historic curves.

In addition to the algebraic curves there is a great class of curves called transcendentals. To this class belong the curves of the trigonometric functions. The most famous of the transcendentals is the cycloid, the path of a point on the rim of a carriage wheel as the wheel rolls on the ground. If the wheel rolls on the circumference of a circle, instead of on a line, the curve generated is called an epicycloid, and is one of the curves used in laying out gear wheels.

Some idea of the number of curves that have been investigated may be gathered from the fact that an Italian writer listed these

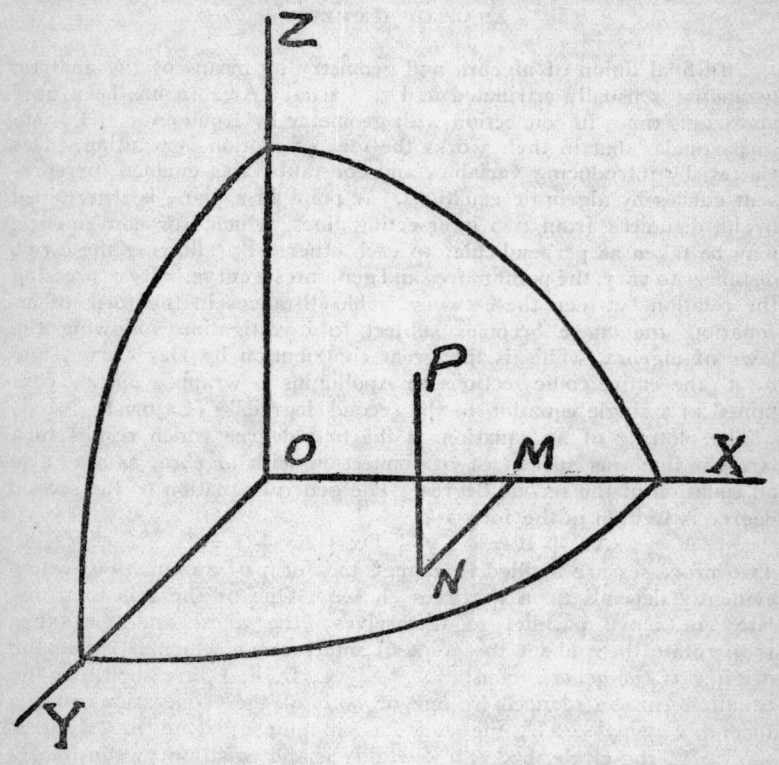

curves, with a short description of each, filling a large book of about 700 pages.

The method of Des Cartes is easily carried to three variables. An equation of this form might be $z = f(xy)$. The plane determined by the two perpendicular lines OY and OX is the old XY plane; perpendicular to it the new Z-axis, OZ. Since x and y are independent of each other, any value, as OM, may be laid off for x on the X-axis; perpendicular to this axis a value of y, say MN, is plotted. Putting these values in the equation, z is determined, which is laid off at right angles to the plane XOY, or NP; that is, P is one point of the surface represented by the equation. If a corresponding point is found for every point in the XY plane, the entire surface will be plotted.

An equation of the second degree in three variables, x, y, and z, represents one of what are called quadric surfaces. Such surfaces are of two classes; on a surface of the first class, such as the ellipsoid, no straight lines may be drawn and the geodesics are all curved lines. The ellipsoid is generated by a variable ellipse moving parallel to itself. In the second class of surfaces, called the ruled surfaces, the geodesics are straight lines. The hyperboloid of one sheet may be generated by a line moving parallel to itself while constantly touching two circles in parallel planes, the planes being oblique to the moving line. Such a surface has two sets of line generators, one set inclined to the right, and the other to the left.

The cubic surface, or surface of the third degree, contains 27 straight lines, a fact discovered by Dr. Cayley in 1849.

The principal advances in analytic geometry have been along three lines:

1. Changes in the system of coördinates.
2. Changes in the element used.
3. The introduction of the imaginary element.

In 1857 President Hill, of Harvard, gave a list of 22 systems of coördinates then in use, and since that time many more have been added. One of the most useful systems is known by the term polar coördinates, in which a point P is located by the distance $r = OP$ from the origin and the angle θ between OP and the initial line through O.

This system greatly simplifies some of the equations of the Cartesian system; for example, $r = $ a constant is the equation of a circle in polar coördinates. The general equation of the straight line in Cartesian coördinates is $Ax + By + C = 0$. This equation is seen to lack homogeneity, or likeness, two of the terms containing variables and the third term being a constant. This unlikeness is removed if, in place of choosing as determining coördinates the distances from two intersecting lines, three lines are taken which intersect in pairs; that is, do not pass through the same point. Instead of using the three distances the three ratios of these distances are taken as the trilinear coördinates of a point.

In Euclid's choice of elements, the primary element is the point, with the circle and line as secondary, each of these being an aggregate of points. A point in motion generates a line or curve; the curve in motion, not along itself, generates a surface, which if moved outside of itself gives a solid. And the whole geometry is a point geometry, made up problems in which a certain point is to be found, the intersection of two lines, a line and a circle, or of two circles.

Looking at these elements from another viewpoint, they are but the circle which Euclid could draw and its two limiting cases, as the radius becomes indefinitely small, and becomes indefinitely great. The latter Euclid could not draw, whence he assumes straight-edge as one of his instruments. The symmetry of the three suggests that the line might just as well be taken as the point. A line is made up of an infinite number of points arranged in a certain way, and a point is made up of an infinite number of lines arranged in a definite manner.

A theorem which is thought of as a relation between points, it is evident, may be by simply interchanging the words "point" and "line" becomes the expression of a relation between lines. This principle of Duality was first worked out in its entirety by Jean Victor Poncelet, a brilliant young French lieutenant of engineers, who was made prisoner in the French retreat from Moscow in 1812. Finding himself in prison, without books or any means of enjoyment, he occupied himself with investigations in geometry, and wrote his classic work on "The Projective Properties of Figures," in which the principle of Duality is completely worked out.

The analytical or algebraic investigations of geometry very often result in giving values which involve the imaginary element i. Every equation of the second degree represents a conic, and if two such equations are solved simultaneously for the points of intersection, four such points result. If the equations are those of circles, it is seen that two circles at most intersect in two real points. The other solutions result in imaginary solutions. The coördinates of these two points are conjugate imaginaries; one is of the form $a + ib$ and the other of the form $a - ib$. These two points are indicated by I and J and are called the two circular points at infinity, for it is found that every two circles, besides intersecting in two real or two imaginary points in the finite region of the plane, also intersect in I and J. Again, it requires five points to determine or pick out a conic section, and it is known that three points determine a circle. What about the two missing points? They are I and J, which lie on every circle in the plane. In this conception, a circle is the aggregate of all of the points in its circumference and the two points I and J.

If a circle has its radius indefinitely diminished it approaches as a limit a point, a degenerate conic which was its center. The equation of a circle with the center at the origin of coördinates is $x^2 + y^2 = r^2$. If r be made zero the equation is $x^2 + y^2 = 0$, which may be factored, giving $x = iy$ and $x = -iy$. These are the equations of two imaginary lines called isotropic lines, which have some interesting properties.

Through every point of the plane pass two isotropic lines.

These isotropic lines make the same angle with every real line through the point.

The distance between any two points on an isotropic line is zero, from which property they are called minimal lines.

The isotropic lines join the real point through which they pass with I and J respectively.

Perpendicularly between two real lines through the real point is a relation between the two lines and the two isotropic lines through the point.

The algebraic treatment of geometry permits the investigation of imaginary elements with exactly the same rigor as that of the real elements, and the only distinction between real and imaginary elements is not one of existence but of adaptability to the picturing processes of the mind. The term imaginary originally implied non-existence, but the development of algebraic processes has entirely swept away that meaning. The whole question of existence with the geometer is not one of material existence; points, lines and planes are but creations of thought without materiality. That which exists is that which is consistent in thought, coherent and non-contradictory. A real element is one which may be represented, as a line by a mark or string, a surface by a sheet of paper, and the imaginary is one of which no such picture or image may be formed.

The disposition to seek decision upon matters which do not come within the domain of present knowledge, that intuitive desire of mankind to rely upon the doctrine of chance, seems to be a universal trait with humanity. That such an instinct should arise and be cultivated in every branch of the human race is but a corollary of the fact that the future is hidden. Probability is more or less a factor in the life of every individual. It may be said that in no contingency which arises is there more than probable evidence upon which to proceed. Voltaire puts the case more strongly. "All life," says he, "rests on probability." As a moral guide it is said that the following theory was taught by 159 authors of the Church before 1667: "If each of two opposite opinions in matters of moral conduct be supported by a solid probability, in which one is admittedly stronger than the other, we may follow our natural liberty of choice by acting upon the less probable."

This gaming instinct has left as a heritage a number of games of great antiquity, varying from those in which skill and mental acuteness is the predominant factor down to those in which no element enters except that of pure chance. The best type of the first class is the game of chess, while perhaps midway comes cards and finally dice. Games akin to chess and checkers are represented in Egyptian drawings as early as 2000 B.C.

Professor Forbes puts the origin of chess "between three and four thousand years before the sixth century of our era. "Altho this antiquity is to be doubted, it must be considered as extremely old. The game of chaturanga is said to have been invented by the wife of Ravana, King of Ceylon, when his capital, Lanka, was besieged by Rama. That the game was in some way connected with war seems evident. The Chinese name for chess is literally "the play of the sciences of war." The word chaturanga means the four divisions of the army, elephants, horses, chariots and foot soldiers.

The intricacies of the game are seen when it is known that there are as many as 197,299 ways of playing the first four moves, and nearly 72,000 different positions at the end of these moves.

The move of the knight is one move forward and one diagonally, and from this has been framed a famous problem: So to move the knight that it occupies but once each of the 64 squares of the board. This problem gives rise to some very odd geometrical designs on the board, if a straight line is drawn between each two successive positions. The number of possible solutions has been shown to be over 31,054,144.

The origin of cards is as uncertain as that of chess. They appeared in Europe about 1200. If one seeks to go back from this, one trail leads through Spain to Africa and Egypt, another over the Caucasus to Persia and India, and perhaps another is picked up in China. In the Chinese dictionary (1678) it is said that cards were invented in the reign of Sèun-ho, 1120 A.D., for the amusement of his various concubines. Tradition says that cards have existed in India from time immemorial and that they were invented by the Brahmans.

One form of cards, the Tarot card, was brought into Europe from the East by gipsies, who used them for divination purposes. They undoubtedly have been connected with witchery from the very beginning.

A number of famous problems have been devised with cards. The first to be spoken of is Gergonne's, or the three-pile problem. In this trick 27 cards are dealt face upward in three piles, dealing from the top of the pack, one card at a time to each pile. A spectator is requested to note a card and remember in which pile it is. Taking this pile between the other two the operation is repeated, and the third time is noted the middle card of each pack. Ask now for the pile and it is the card noted in this pack. Now if the three piles are taken up face down in the same order and dealt from the top it is the fourteenth card. Gergonne generalized the problem to a pack containing m^m cards.

The mouse-trap is another noted game with cards. A set of cards marked with consecutive numbers from 1 to n are dealt in any order face upward in the form of a circle. The player begins with

ANALYTIC GEOMETRY

any card and counts round the circle. If the kth card has the number k on it, a hit is scored and the player takes up the card and begins afresh. The player wins if he takes up all the cards. If he counts up to n without taking up a card, the cards win. In Tartaglia's work occurs a similar problem: A ship, carrying as passengers fifteen Turks and fifteen Christians, encounters a storm; and the pilot declares that in order to save the ship and crew one-half of the passengers must be thrown into the sea. To choose the victims, the passengers are arranged in a circle, and it is agreed to throw overboard every ninth man, reckoning from a certain point. In what manner must they be arranged that the lot will fall exclusively upon the Turks?

The number of combinations possible in various card games is enormous. With the whist deal this number is 53,644,737,765,488,792,-839,237,440,000.

Dice and dolasses go back in history at least 3,000 years. Apollo taught their use to Hermes. These Greek gods probably got their knowledge from Egypt, where dice, and it is even said loaded ones, have been found in the tombs. Gaming with dice was common with the Romans, who had two forms, one like those of the present and the other oblong and numbered on but four sides. On these the deuce and the five were omitted. The convulsion of nature which overwhelmed Pompeii found a party of gentlemen at the gaming table, and they have been uncovered two thousand years after, with the dice firmly clenched in their fists. Seneca brings the gambling Emperor Claudius finally to Hades, where he is compelled to play constantly with a bottomless dice-box.

The two theories of choice and chance are very closely bound up together. Choice is made up of two branches, those problems which deal with arrangements and those with combinations alone. A problem of the first type is to find the number of ways in which 10 men may be seated at a round table. The first man has manifestly no choice; he may be seated anywhere; after he is seated the second man has 9 choices, and the third 8 and so on until the tenth man, who has but one choice. It is a principle that if a thing may be done in a ways and another in b ways, the two together may be done in $a \times b$ ways. Therefore the 10 men may be seated in $9 \times 8 \times 7 \times 6 \times 5 \times 4 \times 3 \times 2 \times 1$ ways, which is denoted by 9! or 9 factorial. The general expression for n things taken r at a time is $n!/(n-r)!$

If there is no distinction between the objects—that is, the order is immaterial—a choice is called a combination; as to find in how many ways a committee of 4 men may be chosen from 25 men. The mode of solution is to find in how many ways 25 men may be arranged if chosen 4 at a time, and divide by the number of arrangements possible with the 4 men.

MATHEMATICS

If an event happens a times and fails b times, the probability of the event happening is $\frac{a}{a+b}$ and the probability of it failing is $\frac{b}{a+b}$. $\frac{a}{b}$ are the odds in favor and $\frac{b}{a}$ are the odds against the event happening. This may be illustrated in finding the probability of throwing at least 4 with 2 dice. The number of favorable cases is the number of cases in which 4, 5, 6, 7, 8, 9, 10, 11, 12 may be thrown. The number of unfavorable cases is the number of ways in which 2 and 3 can be thrown. 2 can be thrown in one way by throwing 1 and 1. 3 can be thrown in two ways, 2 and 1 and 1 and 2. The number of unfavorable cases is 3. The total number of cases is 6×6 or 36. The number of favorable cases is then $36 - 3$ or 33, and the probability of throwing at least 4 is $\frac{33}{36}$ or $\frac{11}{12}$.

If 52 cards be dealt to 4 players, the probability that a particular player will hold 4 aces is $\frac{11}{4165}$.

An application of the theory of probability may be given in determining the expectancy of a player in the ordinary "crap" game; A and B play with two dice, A throwing, and B being the "banker." If A throws 7 or 11 he wins; if he throws 3, or 2 aces, or 2 sixes, B wins. But if he throws 4, 5, 6, 8, 9 or 10 he continues throwing to duplicate his first throw, in which event he wins; if in throwing a 7 comes up, B wins. To determine the chances of the two players.

The chance of throwing 7 or 11 is $\frac{2}{9}$; of 2, 3 or 12 is $\frac{1}{9}$; of 4, 5, 6, 8, 9, or 10 is $\frac{2}{3}$. If A throws 4 his chance of winning the second throw is $\frac{1}{12} \cdot \frac{2}{3}$; of the third throw is 1/12 of 2/3 of [1 — (1/12 + 1/6)] of 1/12 of 2/3 of 3/4.

A's chance of winning on 4 is $2/9 + 1/12$ of $2/3$ $[1 + 3/4 + (3/4)^2 + (3/4)^3 + \ldots] = 4/9$.

A's chance of winning on 5 is $2/9 + 1/9$ of $2/3$ $[1 + 13/18 + (13/18)^2 + (13/18)^3 + \ldots] = 22/45$.

A's chance of winning on 6 is $2/9 + 5/36$ of $2/3 \,[1 + 25/36 + (25/36)^2 + (25/36)^3 + \ldots] = 52/99$.

A's chance of winning on 8, 9 or 10 is the same as for 6, 5, or 4.

A's chance is then $1/3 \,(4/9 + 22/45 + 52/99) = 722/1485$.

B's chance is $1 - \dfrac{722}{1485} = \dfrac{763}{1485}$.

The odds in favor of B are $\dfrac{763}{722}$. (Zerr's solution).

One very important application of probability is to determine the probable error in a number of observations. In 1805 Legendre gave his Law of Least Squares, which may be simply stated as follows: The most probable value of a measured quantity is that in which the sum of the squares of the differences between this quantity and the observed values, provided they are equally good, is a minimum.

Probability finds its greatest function, however, in determining the probable death-rate upon which are based insurance premiums. When it is recalled that at the present time the greatest amount of money that is involved in any single business is that in insurance, the words of Augustus de Morgan, penned in 1838, seem more than prophetic:

"The theory of insurance, with its kindred science of annuities, deserves the attention of the academic bodies. Stripped of its technical terms and its commercial associations, it may be presented from a point of view which will give it strong moral claims to notice. Tho based on self-interest, yet it is the most enlightened and benevolent form which the projects of self-interest ever took. It is, in fact, in a limited sense and a practicable method, the agreement of a community to consider the goods of its individual members as common. It is an agreement that those whose fortune it shall be to have more than the average success shall resign the overplus in favor of those who have less. And tho, as yet, it has only been applied to the reparation of the evils arising from storm, fire, premature death, disease, and old age, yet there is no placing a limit to the extensions which its application might receive, if the public were fully aware of its principles and of the safety with which they may be put in practice."

The science of probability had its origin in a problem proposed in 1654 to Blaisé Pascal by Chevalier de Méré, a professional gambler. It is now known as the problem of points. Two players want each a given number of points in order to win: if they separate, how should the stakes be divided? Pascal's solution is as follows: Two players play a game of 3 points and each player has staked 32 pistoles.

Suppose that the first player has gained 2 points and the second player 1 point; they have now to play for a point on this condition, that if the first player wins he takes all the money at stake, namely, 64 pistoles, and if the second player gains each player has two points, so that if they leave off playing each ought to take 32 pistoles. Thus, if the first player gains 64 pistoles belong to him, and if he loses 32 pistoles belong to him. If, then, the players do not wish to play this game, the first player would say to the second: "I am certain of 32 pistoles if I lose this game, and as for the 32 pistoles, perhaps I shall have them and perhaps you will have them: the chances are equal. Let us then divide these pistoles equally and give me also the 32 pistoles of which I am certain." Then the first player would have 48 pistoles and the second 16 pistoles.

Next, suppose that the first player has gained two points and the second player none, and that they are about to play for a point; the condition then is that if the first player wins this point he secures the game and the 64 pistoles, and if the second player gains this point they will be in the position just examined, in which the first player is entitled to 48 pistoles and the second to 16 pistoles. Thus, if they do not wish to play the first player would say to the second, "If I gain the point I gain 64 pistoles; if I lose I am entitled to 48 pistoles. Give me the 48 pistoles of which I am certain, and divide the other 16 equally, since our chances of gaining the point are equal." Thus the first player gets 56 pistoles and the second 8 pistoles.

Finally, suppose that the first player has gained one point and the second player none. If they proceed to play for the point the condition is that if the first player gains it the players will be in the position first examined, in which the first player is entitled to 56 pistoles; if the first player loses the point each player is then entitled to 32 pistoles. Thus if they do not wish to play, the first player would say to the second, "Give me the 32 pistoles of which I am certain and divide the remainder of the 56 pistoles equally—that is, divide 24 pistoles equally." Thus the first player will have the sum of 32 and 12 pistoles—that is, 44 pistoles—and consequently the second player will have 20 pistoles.

Thus the science which underlies the greatest business of the twentieth century had its origin at the gaming table. Pascal corresponded with his friend Fermat regarding the problem, and the subject continued to be developed to such an extent that Professor Todhunter's "History of Probability," from which the above problem is taken, covers 624 pages.

The theorem at the base of Probability is thus stated by James Bernoulli: "If a sufficiently large number of trials is made, the ratio of the favorable to the unfavorable events will not differ from the ratio of their respective probabilities beyond a certain limit in excess or defect, and the probability of keeping within these limits, however small, can be made as near certainty as we please by taking a sufficiently large number of trials." The inverse problem of reasoning from known events to probable causes is much more complicated. De Morgan thus states the principle of the inverse probability: "When an event has happened and may have happened in two or three different ways, that way which is most likely to bring about the event is most likely to have been the cause."

Another principle, due to Bayes, is thus stated: Knowing the probability of a compound event and that of one of its components, we find the probability of the other by dividing the first by the second.

Michell more than a century ago gave a classic attempt to apply the inverse theorem when he strove to find the probability that there is some cause for the fact that the stars are not uniformly distributed over the heavens.

The following witty dictum is from Poinsot:

"After having calculated the probability of an error, it is necessary to calculate the probability of an error in the calculations."

One thus gets in an endless regression by in turn calculating the probability of the correctness of the next preceding calculation.

Poincare closed his lectures on the calculus of probabilities with this skeptical statement: The calculus of probabilities offers a contradiction in the terms itself which serve to designate it, and if I would not fear to recall here a word too often repeated, I would say that it teaches us chiefly one thing—*i.e.*, to know that we know nothing.

An idea floating about in the minds of mathematicians for centuries, most nearly approached in the method of exhaustions used by Archimedes and in the method of indivisibilities of Cavaleri, pupil of Galileo, was, by aid of the introduction of the notion of variable into geometry, finally evolved almost simultaneously and independently by the two greatest mathematicians of the period, Sir Isaac Newton and Gootfried Wilhelm Leibnitz, and has become the mighty engine of analysis, the first and only mathematical subject to be dignified by the article "The," The Calculus.

This subject is based upon two fundamental and comparatively easily understood operations: the direct operation, Differentiation, and its inverse, Integration. A few preliminary ideas are necessary.

A variable quantity is said to have a limit when it approaches a constant quantity in such a way that the difference between the variable and the constant quantity can be made to become and remain less than any previously assigned value. The constant quantity is called the limit of the variable. The condition is very often added that the variable never actually reaches its limit, but this is not necessary and very much narrows the application of the notion. Starting with the number 1, add to it its one-half, and continue the process indefinitely, each time adding one-half of the next preceding addition, thus: $1 + 1/2 + 1/4 + 1/8 + 1/16 + \ldots$

It is evident that this sum never reaches 2, but may, by proceeding far enough, be made to differ by 2 by as small a number as we please.

Inscribe in a circle a regular polygon; take the mid-point of each arc and join it with straight lines to the two adjacent vertices of the polygon. A new polygon is formed with double the number of sides of the original. Continuing indefinitely, a polygon may be formed which in area and perimeter differs from the circle by as little as we please, but the circle is never actually reached.

A quantity which approaches zero as a limit is called an infinitesimal. An infinitesimal is not necessarily an exceedingly small quantity; the smallness is not the important matter, but the fact that it can be made small.

Zeno's paradox of Achilles and the tortoise rested upon the consideration of infinitesimals. Achilles was a certain distance behind the tortoise and attempting to overtake it. Zeno argues that he can never do so, for, says he, while Achilles travels half the distance between them the tortoise has traveled a certain distance; while Achilles is traveling half the remaining distance the tortoise has moved forward, etc. If these half distances were traveled in finite intervals of time Zeno's argument would be correct. But the intervals of time are approaching zero as well as the distances.

The differential calculus is based on finding the limit of the ratio of two infinitesimals. Suppose a train travels without stop from A to B, a distance of 100 miles, in 100 minutes, and it is required to find its speed. One says a mile a minute, but the train started from rest at A and comes to rest at B, whence there are points at which the speed is less than that given and at other points greater, so that the speed assigned is not the speed at every point, but what might be called an average speed. Suppose it is required to find the speed at a particular point, C; one would proceed in this manner: Measure a distance of say 1,000 feet along the track of which C is the middle point; time the train over this distance. The ratio of the distance to the time is the speed or rate, but it cannot be said that this is the rate at C; it is an average rate over the 1,000 feet. Take a shorter distance, say 500 feet; the ratio of this shorter distance to the shorter time is more nearly the rate at C than the former. Continue this process, and the ratio of the distance to the time as each becomes indefinitely small comes nearer and nearer to the exact rate at C. If the motion of the train was subjected to a law by which the limit of this ratio could be found, that limit would be the rate of C. Differentiation is this process of finding the limit of the ratio of two infinitesimals that are mutually dependent.

A geometric example will be given.

It is required to find the direction in which the point moves which generates the curve in the figure as it passes through the particular position, P. This direction will be along a tangent line, PR, since if the point were to continue in the direction in which it is moving at P, it would move in a straight line tangent to the curve at P. Take a second point, P', on the curve and pass a line through P and P'.

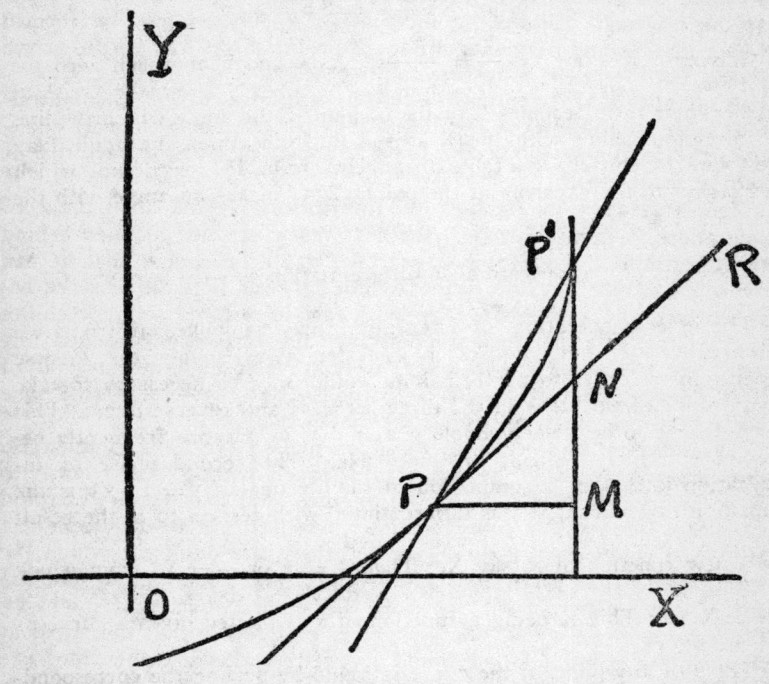

Now if P' moves along the curve toward P this line swings around toward the limiting position PR. The direction of PP' is fixed by the angle MPP', of which the tangent is MP'/PM. As P' approaches P, both MP' and PM approach zero, but they have a limiting ratio which is equal to MN/PM, or the tangent of the angle MPN.

The mode of applying this operation algebraically is quite simple. The coördinates of P are given, say $(x_1\ y_1)$. A second point, P', is chosen with coördinates $(x_1 + h,\ y_1 + k)$ and subjected to the condition that P' lies on the curve. This is done by finding the relation of h and k by substituting $x_1 + h$ and $y_1 + k$ in the equation of the curve in place of x_1 and y_1. The limit of the ratio of $h = PM$ and $k = MP'$ is then found as h and k approach zero.

In the parabola $y^2 = 8x$, find the direction or slope of the tangent at point P whose coördinates are 2 and 4. Take P' $(2+h, 4+k)$, a point on the curve. Since it lies on the curve these coördinates must satisfy the equation of the curve. Putting $2+h$ for x and $4+k$ for y one has

$$(4+k)^2 = 8(2+h)$$
$$\text{or } 16 + 8k + k^2 = 16 + 8h$$
$$\text{or } 8k + k^2 = 8h$$

Solving for $\dfrac{k}{h}$ one has $\dfrac{k}{h} = \dfrac{8}{8+k}$. As k and h approach zero together their ratio becomes 1, or the tangent of the angle which the line of direction makes with the X-axis is 1, from which the angle may be found, by consulting a table of tangents, to be 45°, or the line which is tangent to the parabola at the point (2, 4) makes an angle with the X-axis of 45°.

The sign of the operation of differentiation is $\dfrac{d}{dx}$.

The inverse operation, or integration, may be looked at from two viewpoints. If one chooses to consider it as simply the inverse operation, in order to perform it it would only be necessary to take cognizance of the steps in the direct process and reverse them. This would seem to be a very simple matter, but in practice frequently becomes extremely difficult or impossible. The second phase of integration is that of a summation of infinitesimals. $y = f(x)$ is the equation of a curve; if y is differentiated with respect to x, the result is a new function of x, say X. Then $\dfrac{d}{dx} = y$ or $\dfrac{dy}{dx} = X$, from which $dy = X\,dx$. This X being a function of x if plotted gives a curve as in the figure.

The y of any point of the curve is found by putting the corresponding value of x in the equation $y = X(x)$, as x gives y, x_2 gives y_2, etc.

In $dy = X\,dx$, take $dx_1 =$ the interval $(x_1\,x_2)$ and let $(x_1\,x_2) = (x_2\,x_3) = (x_3\,x_4)$, etc.

Then for $x = x_1$, $dy_1 = y_1 \times dx_1 = y_2 \times (x_1\,x_2) =$ area of rectangle x_1 R.

For $x = x_2$, $dy_2 = y_2 \times dx = y_2 \times (x_2\,x_3) =$ area of rectangle x_2 S.

For $x = x_3$, $dy_3 = y_3 \times dx = y_3 \times (x_3\,x_4) =$ area of rectangle x_3 T.

ANALYTIC GEOMETRY

Now if dx and dy each be made to approach zero and the sum of the dy's be taken to find y, this sum will be equal to the sum of the areas of these rectangles, as each rectangle has its base diminished toward zero. When this occurs the small shaded triangles approach zero and the sum of the rectangles approaches the area bounded by the curve, the X-axis, y_1, and y_4.

This is written $y = \sum X \, dx =$ area APQB.

Where $\sum$ means the sum of all terms of the form x, dx as dx approaches zero.

If X be placed equal to Y and the curve plotted as above, and also

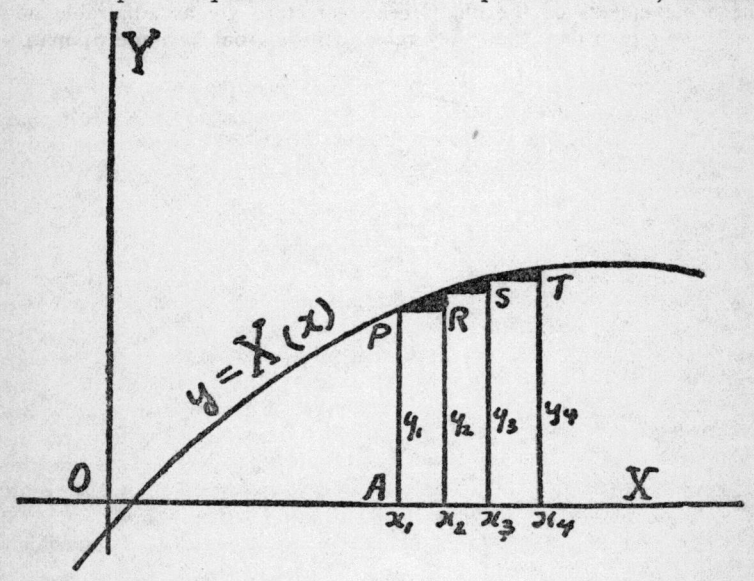

$y = f(x)$, the relations of the two curves is that the ordinate of any point of the second curve indicates the area under the first curve from a chosen point on the curve to the point for which the ordinate is taken.

When integration is regarded as above as a summation the sign $\sum$ is sometimes used, altho it is customary to write the usual sign of integration S.

With the invention of the Analytic Geometry and the Calculus, modern mathematics begins. Speaking of its development from the date 1758, which closes the period covered by the third volume of Moritz Cantor's "Geschichte der Mathematik," Professor Keyser says: "That date, however, but marks the time when mathematics, then schooled for over a hundred eventful years in the unfolding wonders of Analytic Geometry and the Calculus and rejoicing in the possession of these the two most powerful among instruments of human thought, had but fairly entered upon her modern career. And so fruitful have been the intervening years, so swift the march along the myriad tracks of modern analysis and geometry, so abounding and bold and fertile withal has been the creative genius of the time, that to record even briefly the discoveries and the creations since the closing date of Cantor's work would require an addition to his great volumes of a score of volumes more."

And throughout all this wonderful growth nothing is lost or wasted, the achievements of the old Greek geometers are as admirable now as in their own days, and they remain the eternal heritage of man.